QUANTITATIVE AQUATIC
BIOLOGICAL INDICATORS

Their Use to Monitor Trace Metal
and Organochlorine Pollution

POLLUTION MONITORING SERIES

Advisory Editor: Professor Kenneth Mellanby

Monks Wood Experimental Station,
Abbots Ripton, Huntingdon

QUANTITATIVE AQUATIC
BIOLOGICAL INDICATORS

Their Use to Monitor Trace Metal and Organochlorine Pollution

DAVID J. H. PHILLIPS
Fisheries Research Station, Aberdeen, Hong Kong

APPLIED SCIENCE PUBLISHERS LTD
LONDON

APPLIED SCIENCE PUBLISHERS LTD
RIPPLE ROAD, BARKING, ESSEX, ENGLAND

British Library Cataloguing in Publication Data

Phillips, David J H
    Quantitative aquatic biological indicators.
    1. Aquatic ecology 2. Trace elements in
    water 3. Organochlorine compounds—
    Environmental aspects 4. Water quality
    bioassay
    I. Title
    574.5′263   QH541.4.W3

    ISBN 0-85334-884-7

WITH 103 TABLES AND 99 ILLUSTRATIONS

© APPLIED SCIENCE PUBLISHERS LTD 1980

Printed in Great Britain by Galliard (Printers) Ltd, Great Yarmouth

For Charlie Boyden

Acknowledgements

I am grateful to several members of the Department of Agriculture and Fisheries, Hong Kong, for their help in the completion of this book. Dr Geoffrey Thompson has been a source of encouragement throughout the protracted writing phase and has offered his knowledge on gastropods (especially their sex lives) as well as several other subjects. Both the aforementioned and Dr Rudolph Wu have expended effort in the field to allow the earliest possible completion of the work. Miss Lulu Loh and several others of the technical staff have contributed time and talent, especially in the preparation of figures; Mr K. S. Tong and his staff have also contributed to the figures. In the final phase of figure preparation, and in indexing and proof-reading, I am particularly grateful to Miss Yuk-lin Sin, who has endured the tedious phase of each process, contributing talent and much effort. Miss Nancy Lui typed much of the original manuscript. The Director, the Hon. E. H. Nichols, is also owed thanks for his permission for me to work on the manuscript whilst undertaking research duties in the Department.

Many of the ideas dealt with have been developed in concert with members of the international research community; most of these were discussed and began to take serious form during the International Mussel Watch Conference in Barcelona between 4 and 7 December, 1978. I owe particular thanks to the members of that conference, especially to Professor Ed Goldberg, Dr Charles Boyden and Dr Scott Fowler, all of whom have been instrumental in the rapid rise of monitoring studies in the aquatic environment. In a sense, a review of this kind requires the acknowledgement by the author of all researchers who have contributed to the field reviewed; I hope the book meets some of their requirements.

I also wish to express my appreciation to Professor Kenneth Mellanby and to Applied Science Publishers Ltd for their original suggestion that such a book may be of interest to researchers at this time, and for their help in the production of the book itself.

I am grateful to the following publishers for the use of cited material from previously published papers: Academic Press Inc., London; American Fisheries Society, Maryland; American Society of Limnology and Oceanography Inc., Michigan; American Society for the Advancement of Science, Washington; Applied Science Publishers Ltd, London; Cambridge University Press, Cambridge; Charles C. Thomas, Illinois; Chesapeake Science, Maryland; Commonwealth Scientific and Industrial Research Organisation, Australia; HMSO, United Kingdom; Department of Scientific and Industrial Research, New Zealand; Elsevier/North Holland Biomedical Press, the Netherlands; Elsevier Scientific Publishing Company, the Netherlands; Institute of Freshwater Research, Drottningholm, Sweden; John Wiley and Sons Inc., New York; Macmillan Journals Ltd, London; Munksgaard International Booksellers and Publishers, Copenhagen; National Marine Fisheries Service, NOAA, Seattle; Pergamon Press Ltd, Oxford; Scientific Information and Publications Branch, Government of Canada; Springer-Verlag, Berlin; Springer-Verlag, New York. Where quotations or my redrawn figures are based on previous publications, the authors of these publications are cited.

Lastly, I have dedicated the book to Dr Charles Boyden; those readers who knew him will understand my reasons.

Preface

The quantitation of pollutants in aquatic ecosystems is a relatively new research field. Much of the impetus for such research has been derived from tragedies such as at Minamata, and the minimisation of the detrimental effects of pollutants on humans is sufficient justification for such studies. However, there is little or no evidence to suggest that man is particularly susceptible to most pollutants compared to other organisms. I therefore envisage the monitoring of pollutants in aquatic ecosystems as a first step in the protection of the ecology of those ecosystems rather than as an inexpensive safeguard to man, although these aims are not mutually exclusive.

The use of biological indicator organisms to quantitate pollutants has essentially developed only during the last decade. It is undeniable that the technique is a powerful tool in our understanding of pollutant abundance and bio-availability in aquatic ecosystems. Most or all water bodies can be studied by this method, employing either indigenous or introduced species. Such monitoring will define the general abundance of specific pollutants in the study area, and may also be used to elucidate point sources of pollutants. There is no doubt that these techniques will eventually extend beyond the study of trace metals and organochlorines to petroleum hydrocarbons and other groups of major pollutants. However, the pitfalls in the use of biological indicator organisms to quantitate pollutant availability or abundance in water bodies are many; I have attempted to define most of these in this book, in an effort to aid researchers who wish to use such methods.

My reviews of the use of biological indicator organisms to quantitate trace metals and organochlorines, published in the journal '*Environmental Pollution*' in 1977 and 1978, served as a 'springboard' for the completion of this work. Professor Kenneth Mellanby first suggested to me in late 1978

ix

that such a book might be a worthwhile project, as it became clear that the field was so broad that no journal review could cover all aspects completely. I have attempted to include all the aspects of major importance in this book, although I cannot pretend that the literature coverage is necessarily exhaustive throughout. Wherever possible, I have extended presently available data with cautious speculation and hypothesis. Further research is needed in almost every aspect of the use of biological indicators; if such speculation encourages further study, one aim of the book will have been satisfied.

The major intention of the book is, however, as an aid to refinement of the use of indicator organisms. If the correct sampling, analytical and interpretive techniques are employed, this method of monitoring provides rapid and inexpensive data which cannot be produced by any other type of study. I suggest that we need such data now, on a global scale, such that the process of improving water quality throughout the coastal and open ocean waters of the world may begin at once.

DAVID J. H. PHILLIPS

Contents

CHAPTER 1

Introduction: the Sources of Pollution

A. GENERAL

Pollution may be defined as a man-induced detrimental alteration to the ecosphere. In a sense, all organisms pollute their immediate environment, at least by the excretion of waste products. However, most organisms are rarely present at sufficient density to endanger their own viability by the excretion of wastes. By contrast, man excretes not only wastes derived from the breakdown of natural food products, but also expels toxic materials from his body, his factories and his cities. Whether the present global concern about man-induced pollution indicates a growing awareness that man is endangering his own viability and whether such an effect is due to the density of *Homo sapiens* or to the unusual ability of this organism to elicit massive and enduring alteration of the environment, are matters for conjecture.

This book is concerned with pollution of the aquatic environment by trace metals and organochlorines; areas of the greatest concern are dominated by anthropogenic inputs. Most of the published data considered herein for trace metals involve such elements as silver, arsenic, cadmium, cobalt, chromium, copper, iron, mercury, nickel, lead, selenium, tin and zinc. Occasionally, other elements (including radionuclides and trans-uranics) will be referred to, although the present work does not in any way pretend to cover these more esoteric elements completely. All such elements will be referred to collectively as trace metals, although this may be considered a misnomer in some cases. The organochlorines considered include the pesticide DDT and its metabolites DDE and DDD, methoxychlor, aldrin, dieldrin, endrin, heptachlor and its epoxide, and BHC (including γ-BHC, also known as lindane). In addition to these pesticides, the non-pesticide polychlorinated biphenyls (PCBs) will also be

TABLE 1

CHEMICAL IDENTITIES OF ORGANOCHLORINES AND OTHER PESTICIDES REFERRED TO IN
THE PRESENT REVIEW

Common name	Chemical name
Aldrin	1,4:5,8-Dimethanonaphthalene, 1,2,3,4,10,10-hexachloro-1,4,4a,5,8,8a-hexahydro-, *endo-exo* isomer
BHC	Cyclohexane, 1,2,3,4,5,6,-hexachloro-
Chlordane	4:7-Methanoindan, 1,2,4,5,6,7,8,8a-octachloro-3a,4,7,7a-tetrahydro-, *endo*-isomer
DDD	Ethane, 1,1-dichloro-2,2-bis (*p*-chlorophenyl)-
DDE	Ethylene, 1,1-dichloro-2,2-bis (*p*-chlorophenyl)-
DDT	Ethane, 1,1,1-trichloro-2,2-bis (*p*-chlorophenyl)-
Dieldrin	1,4:5,8-Dimethanonaphthalene, 1,2,3,4,10,10-hexachloro-6,7-epoxy-1,4,4a,5,6,7,8,8a-octahydro-, *endo-exo* isomer
Endosulfan	5-Norbornene-2,3-dimethanol-, 1,4,5,6,7,7-hexachloro-, cyclic sulphite
Endrin	1,4:5,8-Dimethanonaphthalene, 1,2,3,4,10,10-hexachloro-6,7-epoxy-1,4,4a,5,6,7,8,8a-octahydro-, *endo-endo* isomer
Heptachlor	4:7-Methanoindene, 1,4,5,6,7,8,8a-heptachloro-3a,4,7,7a-tetrahydro-, *endo*-isomer
Heptachlor expoxide	4:7-Methanoindan, 1,4,5,6,7,8,8a-heptachloro-2,3-epoxy-3a,4,7,7a-tetrahydro-, *endo*-isomer
Lindane	*Gamma* isomer of BHC (see BHC above)
Methoxychlor	Ethane, 1,1,1-trichloro-2,2-bis (*p*-methoxyphenyl)-
Mirex	1,3,4-Metheno-2*H*-cyclobuta (*cd*)pentalene, dodecachloro-octahydro-
Parathion	Phosphorothioic acid, *O,O*-diethyl *O-p*-nitrophenyl ester
Propanil	Propionanilide, 3′,4′-dichloro-
Sevin	Carbamic acid, methyl-, 1-naphthyl ester
Solan	*p*-Valerotoluidide, 3′-chloro-2-methyl-
Temefos (Abate)	*O,O,O′,O′*-Tetramethyl, *O,O*-thiodi-*p*-phenylene phosphor-othioate
Toxaphene	Chlorinated camphene containing 67–69 per cent chlorine

referred to; these compounds are used exclusively in industrial processes
and exhibit remarkably similar ecosystem cycling (and pollution potential)
to DDT and its metabolites (Peakall and Lincer, 1970).

All organochlorines referred to will be given their most common names
throughout the text, some of which are trade names. The chemical names of
each of these compounds are listed in Table 1 and structures of the most
important compounds are shown in Fig. 1. The principal primary
metabolites of DDT (1,1-dichloro-2,2-bis (*p*-chlorophenyl)ethylene and
1,1-dichloro-2,2-bis (*p*-chlorophenyl)ethane) will be termed DDE and

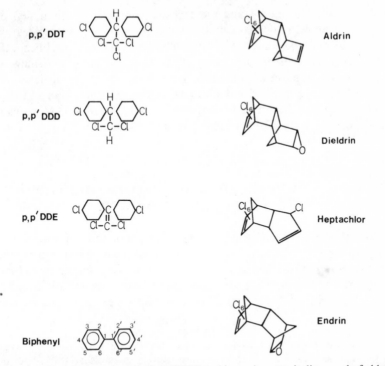

FIG. 1. Chemical structures of *p*,*p′* DDT and its major metabolites, and of aldrin, dieldrin, heptachlor and endrin. Also shown is the structure of the biphenyl ring on which PCBs are based.

DDD throughout and where any of these notations are used they refer to the *p*,*p′* isomers unless specifically stated otherwise. Some authors have reported data concerning the total concentration of DDT and its metabolites (DDT + DDE + DDD), without discriminating between the different compounds; the notation ΣDDT will be used throughout to refer to this combination. By contrast, the total amount of DDT in an organism will be referred to as whole-body DDT (where DDT alone is concerned) or whole-body ΣDDT (where the total concentration of DDT and its metabolites was measured). The annotation PCB will be used where authors have considered all polychlorinated biphenyls as a single group of compounds (adding peak heights to produce a total PCB concentration); if individual component PCBs were quantitated by authors, these will be referred to by use of their chemical names.

The emphasis of this review on the quantitation of trace metals and organochlorines in biota—and the corresponding lack of discussion of other environmentally hazardous chemicals such as herbicides or organophosphates—is a result of the greater threat of the former chemicals to the well-being of aquatic ecosystems. Thus, whilst not wishing to diminish the importance of other pollutants, the trace metals and organochlorines are considered, by virtue of their extremely high toxicities and persistence in aquatic biota, as those contaminants most likely to elicit serious perturbation of the delicately balanced structure of aquatic food webs.

B. INPUTS OF TRACE METALS AND ORGANOCHLORINES TO AQUATIC ENVIRONMENTS

Table 2 shows the effects of man on the mobilisation rates of trace metals from the crust of the earth. The mining of metals by man is increasing the mobilisation of most elements enormously over that achieved by natural geological weathering. Thus, zinc and copper (both of which are extremely toxic in marine and freshwater environments) are being mined and

TABLE 2

THE EFFECTS OF MAN ON THE MOBILISATION RATES OF TRACE METALS. GEOLOGICAL RATES OF METAL MOBILISATION ARE COMPUTED FROM ANNUAL RIVER DISCHARGES TO OCEANS

Element	Geological rate[a] (10^3 metric tons/year)	Man-induced rate (mining) (10^3 metric tons/year)		Total in oceans[c] (10^6 metric tons)
Iron	25 000	319 000[a]	395 000[b]	4 110
Manganese	440	1 600	8 150	2 740
Copper	375	4 460	6 000	4 110
Zinc	370	3 930	5 320	6 850
Nickel	300	358	481	2 740
Lead	180	2 330	3 200	41
Molybdenum	13	57	74	13 700
Silver	5	7	9	137
Mercury	3	7	10·5	68
Tin	1·5	166	227	14
Antimony	1·3	40	65	274
Cadmium	No data	No data	17	68

[a] Study of Critical Environmental Problems, MIT, 1970.
[b] US Bureau of Mines, Minerals Yearbook for 1970.
[c] From Bryan (1976); volume of oceans taken as $1·37 \times 10^{21}$ litres.

mobilised at rates over ten times those expected from simple geological processes of weathering. Other highly toxic metals such as mercury and silver are being produced at a slower rate, but their mobilisation rates by mining nevertheless exceed those achieved by natural forces. Obviously, not all the metals mined represent an immediate hazard to the aquatic environment, but the potential for change in the pollution of aquatic areas by metals is nevertheless extremely high in some cases. Table 2 also includes estimates of the amounts of metals in the world's oceans. The hazard caused by man's mobilisation of metals can be estimated by comparing the mining rate (presumably directly proportional to the industrial need for metals, which itself will vary approximately with the metal discharge to the oceans) with this metal content of the oceans. On this basis, metals such as lead, iron and tin appear to possess high pollution potential; zinc and copper present less of a threat, mercury and cadmium still less and nickel and molybdenum least of all. Such a ranking of metals on the basis of man's ability to alter the concentrations in the world's oceans does not, however, include consideration of the relative toxicities of metals. If these are included in the computation, the metals of greatest overall hazard would probably be considered as mercury, lead, zinc, cadmium and copper (see Dryssen *et al.*, 1971). It will be noted that, in general, the trace metal content of the oceans is much greater than the annual rate of metal mobilisation by man. At first sight these data suggest that the possibility of man significantly altering the oceanic content of trace metals is remote. However, the data for trace metals in the oceans include the entire marine waters of the world (volume taken as 1.37×10^{21} litres). Of this, only a small fraction may be considered to be highly productive and it is these surface—or near-surface—waters which man is preferentially polluting. Thus, all pollutants reach the marine environment via rivers or freshwater run-off or via the atmosphere; in all cases, the pollutant is introduced at, or near, the surface, where most of the active primary and secondary production occurs. If pollutants exhibit long residence times in surface waters they may accumulate in this portion of the water column and may thus affect the entire ecosphere.

By contrast to the situation described here for trace metals, where man is increasing the rate of pollutant inflow to the aquatic environment, the synthetic organochlorines would be entirely absent from these environments without the presence of man. Thus, the mere existence of organochlorines such as DDT in the aquatic ecosphere is an indictment of man's polluting nature.

Several developed countries in the northern hemisphere have banned the use of DDT for agricultural purposes (e.g. the USA, the USSR and

Sweden). This might be expected to lead to decreases in world usage of DDT. However, this is not so, due to a greatly increased usage of DDT in the tropical belt and southern hemisphere. Hence DDT has undergone a 'southward tilt' (Goldberg, 1975a). Estimates of world usage are rather uncertain, but Whittemore (1973) has suggested a current utilisation of 45–50 000 metric tons of DDT annually for agricultural purposes (Table 3)

TABLE 3

ESTIMATES OF ANNUAL UTILISATION OF DDT IN AGRICULTURAL ACTIVITIES, LATIN AMERICA, AFRICA AND ASIA. DATA ARE FOR 1973 AFTER F. W. WHITTEMORE, CITED IN GOLDBERG (1975a). TOTAL FUTURE ANNUAL REQUIREMENTS UP TO 1981 WERE ESTIMATED BY THE SAME AUTHOR AS APPROXIMATELY 69 000 METRIC TONS FOR THE SAME AREAS

| Region | DDT utilisation (metric tons per year) | | | |
| | Cotton-producing countries | | Other countries | Total |
	Cotton	Other crops	All crops	All crops
Central America	7 580	2 550	383	10 513
South America	18 800	6 200	1 180	26 180
Africa	2 186	729	605	3 520
Asia	5 568	1 523	410	7 501
Total, all regions	34 134	11 002	2 578	47 714

and Rafatjah and Stiles (1972) predict a similar figure of 47 000 metric tons annually (between 1971 and 1981) for anti-malarial programmes. These estimates agree well with the suggested world production of DDT of 100 000 metric tons per year, about 65 per cent of this being produced by the USA (N.A.S., 1971). The integrated world production of DDT (that produced since its introduction as a pesticide) has been estimated as 2 million metric tons. Of this, 25 per cent has been transferred to the sea by run-off and via the atmosphere, according to estimates by an expert panel (N.A.S., 1971).

Because of the enormous success of DDT in controlling mosquitoes and as a pesticide for agricultural use (especially for cotton), the production of this compound has probably far outstripped that of any other organochlorine. Production estimates are, however, difficult to ascertain for any of the organochlorines (see, for example, Peakall and Lincer, 1970). Certainly DDT is generally found far more frequently (and in greater amounts) in biota than are other organochlorines although, in certain areas, such as the Baltic Sea, PCBs are found in similar amounts in seals (Helle *et al.*, 1976a, b).

As previously discussed for trace metals, the organochlorines are introduced to the marine environment at, or near, the sea surface. In the case of organochlorines, however, introduction via the atmosphere is probably by far the most important route. Calculations by Lloyd-Jones (1971) indicate that the vapour pressure of DDT is sufficient to account for the complete vaporisation of the quantity of DDT used annually worldwide. Hartley (1969) has suggested two mechanisms, termed 'wick evaporation' and 'adsorption displacement', by which DDT may be lost from soils after its application. Other authors also have emphasised the importance of the atmospheric transport of DDT (Woodwell *et al.*, 1971; Bidleman and Olney, 1974), and calculations by Galley (1974) suggested that up to 10 per cent of the annual production of DDT may be present in the atmosphere between the earth's surface and a height of 1·6 km at any one time. The most important method of removal of this compound from the atmosphere is probably via rainfall (N.A.S., 1971).

The dissipation of organochlorines via the atmosphere tends to lead to a more diffuse input of these compounds into marine waters than is evident for trace metals, which are generally introduced to the sea via rivers. However, this distinction is a matter of degree only, as both groups of pollutants are introduced via both rivers and the atmosphere to the oceans; indeed, some authors believe the atmospheric input of trace metals to be highly significant (Topping, 1974; Young and Jan, 1976, 1977). Regardless of the major entry route for organochlorines, the spraying of areas with these compounds for either agriculture or anti-malarial purposes may elicit acute localised pollution of adjacent watercourses, which may, in turn, lead to 'hot-spots' of contamination in estuarine areas. Such estuarine regions receiving run-off from agricultural catchments were considered by Butler (1966) to be the areas at greatest risk from organochlorine pollution; they may also be considered as particularly high-risk areas as regards trace metal pollution.

C. THE PARTITIONING OF TRACE METALS AND ORGANOCHLORINES IN NATURAL WATERS

The above discussion has shown that man is mobilising or synthesising appreciable quantities of trace metals and organochlorines. These compounds (or a significant proportion of them) must eventually reach the aquatic environment, which may be envisaged as a final sink for most pollutants. The effects elicited by such contamination of rivers or marine

TABLE 4

CONCENTRATIONS OF METALS IN SATURATED SOLUTION IN AERATED SEAWATER OF
pH 7·8–8·2 AND TEMPERATURE 18–23 °C (KRAUSKOPF, 1956) AND THEIR COMPARISON
WITH PUBLISHED DATA FOR THE ACTUAL CONCENTRATIONS OF METALS FOUND IN
SEAWATER. (FROM THE REVIEW OF PYTKOWICZ AND KESTER (1971).)

| Metal | Compound added | Concentration in saturated solution (mg/litre) | | Concentration in seawater (μg/litre) |
		Minimum	Maximum	
Ag	$AgNO_3$	2·2	2·5	0·04–1·50
Cd	$CdCl_2$	4·0	1 000	0·02–0·25
Co	$CoCl_2$	30	200	0·005–4·10
Cr	K_2CrO_4	'very high'		0·04–0·43
Cu	$CuSO_4$	0·6	0·8	0·20–27·0
Hg	$HgSO_4$	118	700	0·03
Fe	$FeCl_3$	$0·005^a$		0·03–62·0
Mo	$(NH_4)_2MoO_4$	25	750	0·24–12·2
Ni	$NiCl_2$	23	455	0·13–43·0
Pb	$Pb(NO_3)_2$	0·3	0·7	0·02–0·40
V	$VOSO_4$	4·0	150	2·0–3·0
W	Na_2WO_4	2·0	280	0·10
Zn	$ZnCl_2$	1·2	2·5	1·0–50·0

[a] Fukai and Huynh-Ngoc (1968).

waters depend on several factors, but the most important of these factors is
dosage. It is thus vital for man to be able to quantitate the abundance of
trace metals and organochlorines in aquatic ecosystems.

Krauskopf (1956) concluded from his studies of the solubilities of trace
metals in seawater that, under normal conditions, aerated seawater in open
oceans is very considerably undersaturated with trace elements. The
minimum concentrations attainable in solution thus varied from
0·3 mg/litre for lead to 118 mg/litre for mercury (Table 4). As the actual
levels of elements in solution in seawater (even in the more highly
contaminated coastal waters) are in the μg/litre range (Table 4), the above
conclusion is clearly upheld. Most trace metals will thus rarely, if ever,
exceed their solubilities in seawater, and all the metal could be maintained
in solution under normal conditions. The only exception of any real
importance is iron, which exhibits very low solubility in seawater and is
maintained in the water column almost entirely by adsorption to suspended
particulates.

Studies of trace metals in seawater, however, have shown that no metal
exists entirely in solution. That which is in solution is in the form of simple

or complex ions. In addition, some metal is associated with inorganic or organic particulates of varying size and composition. Lastly, a certain percentage of the total metal present exists as chelates or colloids; these compounds are difficult to assign to either soluble or particulate phases and are generally poorly understood. The percentage of the total metal in each of these phases varies not only with the water body (e.g. significant differences exist in metal partitioning between the phases in fresh water and in salt water), but also with the particular metal considered. For example, in marine waters, iron is present almost completely in association with inorganic or organic particulates (Head, 1971; Preston *et al.*, 1972), whereas cadmium favours the soluble fraction to a great extent (Preston *et al.*, 1972), but may also associate with microplankton (Bruland *et al.*, 1978). The tendency of each metal to form chelates also varies widely; for example, copper is probably the only element to exhibit significant chelate formation with humic materials in salt waters whereas both copper and mercury are thought to form chelates with humic substances in fresh waters (Mantoura *et al.*, 1978). The effects of chelation of metals on their toxicity and biological availability are certainly more pronounced in fresh waters than in marine areas, and this factor may, in certain cases, be paramount in determining species viability in the former ecosystems.

It is interesting to compare the probable partitioning of organochlorines between the soluble and particulate fractions of either freshwater or seawater with that of trace metals. Organochlorines exhibit low solubilities in water (Table 5), although it should be noted that authors rarely agree on the absolute solubilities of any one of these compounds, as considerable differences are found with differences in research methodologies and with particle size and temperature (Gunther *et al.*, 1968).

This low solubility of organochlorines in water must be seen in perspective. It is clear that if concentrations of any organochlorine exceed the solubility of that compound in a water body, the excess must be present in a phase other than the solution phase; in reality, the excess would be associated with organic and inorganic particulate material by surface adsorption. However, although the solubility of these compounds in water is low, their usual concentrations are still lower. Thus, the lowest estimate of the solubility of DDT in water is 1·2 μg/litre (Bowman *et al.*, 1960). Reports of the Southern California Coastal Water Research Project indicate that even at the extremely highly polluted Los Angeles sewage outfall, average DDT concentrations ranged from 7·5 μg/litre in 1973 to 2·6 μg/litre in 1976. Other Californian municipal wastewaters generally contained much less DDT than did the Los Angeles outfall. Even the Los Angeles outfall

TABLE 5

REPORTED SOLUBILITIES OF ORGANOCHLORINES IN WATER, WITH COMPARATIVE DATA
FOR THREE COMMONLY USED ORGANOPHOSPHATES. DATA REFER TO A TEMPERATURE OF
15 °C. TWO FIGURES ARE QUOTED FOR DDT SIMPLY TO EMPHASISE THAT AUTHORS
RARELY AGREE

Compound	Type	Solubility in water (μg/litre)	Author
DDT	Organochlorine	1	Bowman *et al.* (1960)
DDT	Organochlorine	17	Biggar *et al.* (1966)
PCB[a]	Organochlorine	12	Courtney and Langston (1978)
PCB[b]	Organochlorine	25	Wiese and Griffin (1978)
Dieldrin	Organochlorine	90	Biggar *et al.* (1966)
Aldrin	Organochlorine	105	Biggar *et al.* (1966)
Endrin	Organochlorine	130	Biggar *et al.* (1966)
Lindane	Organochlorine	2 150	Biggar *et al.* (1966)
Parathion	Organophosphate	20 000	Martin (1963)
Malathion	Organophosphate	145 000	Martin (1963)
Dichlorvos	Organophosphate	10 000 000	Martin (1963)

[a] Refers to Aroclor 1254 and seawater; produced by air-lift pump system. Other
mixtures likely to differ considerably; few precise data appear to be available.
[b] Equilibrium concentration for Aroclor 1254 in membrane-filtered, charcoal-
filtered seawater at 16·5 °C. Solubilities of different components shown to differ,
components of lower chlorination dissolving more rapidly.

wastewaters, known to be unusually highly contaminated, therefore
contained DDT at only slightly higher concentrations than the lowest
estimate of its water solubility; certainly, after nearshore mixing of the
discharge with the receiving waters, all the DDT present could have been
maintained in solution. Organochlorines other than DDT generally exhibit
greater solubilities than that of DDT in seawater (Table 5) and, as a result,
these compounds would exceed their water solubilities only under very
extreme conditions of contamination.

This theoretical demonstration that organochlorines could—in most or
all cases—be maintained in solution does not imply that these compounds
do not associate significantly with particulates. The existence of solubility
maxima for organochlorines in the part per billion (μg/litre) range merely
establishes a ceiling above which particulate association would have to
occur; a direct parallel may be made to trace metals here. Very little
information is, in fact, available to indicate the precise nature of
organochlorines in fresh or marine waters, although these compounds
certainly exhibit a high lipid affinity and may be expected to associate

significantly with biota. Probably, organochlorines partition between the phases in a similar fashion to the trace metals; however, the difficulties of measuring such partitioning at ng/litre levels (parts per 10^{12}) or below have led to severe deficiencies in our understanding of such processes. Those studies which have reported data on organochlorine partitioning mostly deal with DDT. For example, Cox (1971) found very little DDT in solution in seawater samples from the west coast of the USA. The DDT present in these samples was thus virtually all associated with particulates; however, phytoplankton-bound DDT represented only about 10 per cent of the total, the remaining 90 per cent apparently being bound to very small particles and unavailable to phytoplankton. Other authors' results generally support these conclusions; if DDT is available to biota, it is taken up rapidly and very little remains in solution. Organochlorines other than DDT are probably distributed between the different components of seawater in a similar fashion to that described above, at least if their water solubilities are low. However, lindane (γ-BHC) exhibits a greater solubility in water compared with most other organochlorines (Gunther *et al.*, 1968) and probably favours the solution phase somewhat more as a result. The relative water solubilities of organochlorines may have a great influence on their persistence in biota, as will be discussed later.

D. QUANTITATION OF POLLUTANT ABUNDANCE: WATER ANALYSIS OR BIOLOGICAL INDICATORS?

Phillips (1977*b*, 1978*b*) has observed that three basic methods can be used to quantitate pollutants in aquatic ecosystems. These methods involve the study of pollutant levels in water itself, in sediments or in a member of the indigenous biota. Each method has its own particular advantages and disadvantages. For example, the analysis of pollutant levels in water samples is frequently costly and laborious, entailing sophisticated sampling and preconcentration of samples prior to analysis. The low levels of many pollutants in salt or fresh waters give rise to problems of analytical sensitivity as well as increasing the possibility for sample contamination. Even if the sampling and analytical difficulties can be overcome, two outstanding problems remain with the definition of polluted areas by analysis of water samples. The first of these is the extreme variation in pollutant levels present in natural waters with time. Such temporal variations have been particularly well discussed for trace metals (see Fig. 2 and authors such as Abdullah and Royle, 1974; Boyden, 1975; Fukai *et al.*,

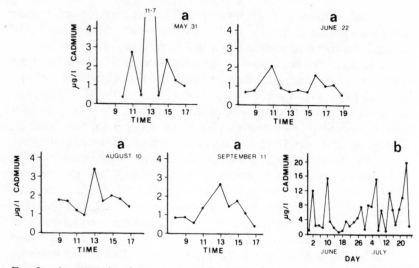

FIG. 2. An example of short-term and medium-term variation in the ambient concentration of a pollutant in an estuarine ecosystem. The four figures labelled (a) concern the fluctuation in cadmium concentrations in filtered water samples collected every one or two hours at a single site, in Poole Harbour, Dorset, UK. The figure labelled (b) shows similar fluctuations at the same site and is based on single samples taken every two days during June and July. Year of study was 1973. Produced from tabulated data in Boyden (1975), as shown in Phillips (1979b).

1975; Grimshaw *et al.*, 1976), and may depend on factors such as season, the extent of freshwater run-off, exact sampling depth, the intermittent flow of industrial effluents and hydrological parameters such as tides and currents. The accurate elucidation of mean or time-averaged concentrations of a pollutant at any one point in space therefore entails the analysis of large numbers of samples, which effectively decreases the number of sites covered per unit effort.

The second problem concerning the use of water analysis to elucidate the degree of contamination of aquatic ecosystems is by far the most important, although it has received little attention to date by researchers. This problem involves the estimation of the biological availability of a pollutant present in water. It should be understood that some pollutants present in a water sample may be sequestered in complexes or associations which render them totally unavailable to biota. Where this is so, the pollutant is of no consequence whatsoever to either the health of the aquatic ecosystem or to man. A contaminant may only be considered as a threat to the environment if it can be taken up by biota, through whatever route. It is not possible to equate a given empirically defined fraction of a water sample with the biological availability of a contaminant. Thus both 'soluble' and 'particulate' fractions of a water sample after filtration contain some components which are highly available to organisms and some which are unavailable, or available to a certain portion of the biota only. In the 'soluble' fraction, trace metal ions generally exhibit high biological availability, as do organochlorines in solution (due to their highly lipophilic nature). By contrast, some chelates or complexes present in solution may be unavailable. Pagenkopf *et al.* (1974) cited an example of this effect for copper in freshwaters, and the effects of chelation may be responsible for the observed variation in the toxicity of most trace metals in hard and soft natural waters. Similarly, the 'particulate' fraction of a natural water sample contains pollutants adsorbed and absorbed by microorganisms, which may be passed through the trophic levels of the food web (with or without amplification of contaminant levels) and which are generally considered highly available to secondary and higher consumers. However, inorganic particulates are also present in this fraction and may contain pollutants adsorbed to their surface (organochlorines or trace metals) or within their matrix (trace metals). Pollutants associated with inorganic particulates are probably unavailable to most organisms although suspension feeders may accumulate contaminants from this fraction. In addition, if a dynamic equilibrium exists between pollutants in solution and suspension, organisms which respond to pollutants in solution directly may also be able to accumulate such compounds from suspension via solution, although this must depend on the rate of pollutant exchange between the two fractions. The low biological availability of metals and organochlorines associated with inorganic particulates is evidenced by the high concentrations of these contaminants in estuarine sediments; these polluted sediments are a result of river-borne particulates settling out in the less turbulent estuarine area. Unless physical or biological mobilisation of these pollutants from sediments occurs rapidly, the overlaying of new particulates will bury the contaminants to remove them from the biological ecosphere.

Having emphasised the disadvantages of the use of water analysis, in particular the difficulty of producing a time-integrated value of pollutant bio-availability at each study site, some system must be found to replace this as a means of quantitating pollutant levels in the aquatic environment. Certain organisms have long been known to accumulate pollutants from the ambient water. For example, Boyce and Herdman (1898) found, more than 80 years ago, that the wandering leucocytes of oysters contained high concentrations of copper. Henze (1911) showed that ascidians accumulated vanadium to levels many times greater than those in seawater. The first report of cadmium in marine organisms involved the scallop *Pecten maximus* (Fox and Ramage, 1930; 1931). Since these reports, ascidians and many bivalves have been shown to accumulate a wide range of metals, with concentration factors (ratio of the metal concentration in the animal, $\mu g/kg$, to that in the ambient water, $\mu g/litre$) frequently ranging between 10^3 and 10^6. With respect to organochlorines, Cottam and Higgins (1946) suggested that DDT may elicit widespread effects on aquatic biota; it may be noted that this report, produced soon after the large-scale introduction of DDT as a pesticide, was almost completely ignored at the time. More recently, Gunther (1966) claimed that any qualified pesticide chemist should be able to detect DDT in any non-fossil sample; certainly, positive reports of this compound in biota from the Arctic and Antarctic regions appear to substantiate this claim. Roburn (1965) found, by comparing two methods of analysis for chlorine, some unknown chlorine-containing compounds in the tissues and eggs of wild birds in the United Kingdom. These compounds were identified by Jensen (1966) as polychlorinated biphenyls (PCBs) and were found to occur in feathers of white-tailed eagles from 1942, before the widespread use of DDT. PCBs have since been found in a wide range of terrestrial and aquatic organisms.

Thus, both trace metals and organochlorines may be accumulated by aquatic biota to levels far above those found in the surrounding environment. This phenomenon leads to the possibility of using selected organisms to monitor the levels of pollutants in water bodies. This use of so-called indicator—or sentinel—organisms to quantitate pollution has several advantages over the classical methods of water or sediment analysis. The greatest advantage is that the biological availability of the pollutants is measured directly and need not, therefore, be inferred from studies of metal speciation. In addition, an ideal indicator organism would produce a time-averaged index of pollutant availability, the degree of this time-integration depending on the rates of uptake and excretion of each particular pollutant. Practical advantages are also incurred by the much higher concentrations of pollutants present in biota compared with those in the surrounding water, leading to cheaper analysis with less sample preparation.

However, the use of indicator organisms to quantitate pollutants and their availability to biota in different regions is also subject to disadvantages compared with the analysis of water samples. The greatest of these is the possible interference of extraneous parameters with the uptake of pollutants by biota. These parameters include those pertaining to the organism itself (species, body lipid, age/size/weight, sex and the sexual cycle, growth and diet, and pollutant interactions at uptake, storage and/or excretion) as well as those concerned with the areas from which the organisms are sampled (salinity, water temperature and others). The effect of these parameters may be to eliminate, accentuate, or otherwise obscure, the differences in pollutant abundance at the study locations. In some cases, these effects may be consistent and severe enough to lead to complete misinterpretation of the results of indicator surveys with respect to the elucidation of areas subject to pollutant input. Any advantages of the use of indicator organisms to quantitate pollutants in different areas would obviously be nullified in these cases. It is therefore most important, when considering the use of biota to monitor any pollutant in any area, to take great care in both the selection of an indicator organism and the testing of that organism under field and laboratory conditions. Only after certain pre-requisites have been satisfied with respect to the effects of environmental, sampling and biological variables can the results of indicator surveys be fully relied upon to quantitate pollutant abundance at different study sites. The first stage in preparing for an indicator survey is the selection of an organism; this is subject to several practical and theoretical constraints, which will be considered in the following chapter.

(General conclusions again!)

CHAPTER 2

The Preliminary Selection of an Indicator Organism

A. BASIC PRE-REQUISITES

The selection of a suitable organism is one of the first tasks in the preparation of a monitoring survey for pollutants, once the decision to use a biological indicator has been made. The importance of this step cannot be overemphasised; an incorrect decision at this stage may render useless much of the ensuing research. Several attributes of both the organism and the study area must be considered. The basic pre-requisites for the organism were suggested by Butler *et al.* (1971) as follows:

(a) The organism should accumulate the pollutant without being killed by the levels encountered in the environment.

(b) The organism should be sedentary in order to be representative of the study area.

(c) The organism should be abundant throughout the study area.

(d) The organism should be sufficiently long-lived to allow the sampling of more than one year-class, if desired.

(e) The organism should be of reasonable size, giving adequate tissue for analysis.

(f) The organism should be easy to sample and hardy enough to survive in the laboratory, allowing defecation before analysis (if desired) and laboratory studies of pollutant uptake.

To these requirements, Haug *et al.* (1974) added the following:

(g) The organism should tolerate brackish water.

(h) A simple correlation should exist between the pollutant content of the organism and the average pollutant concentration in the surrounding water.

16

Phillips (1976*a*, 1977*b*) amended the final requirement as follows:

(h) All organisms of a given species used in a survey should exhibit the same correlation between their pollutant content and the average pollutant concentration in the surrounding water, at all locations studied, under all conditions.

B. RESPONSE TO DIFFERENT POLLUTANT LOADS

In addition to these basic requirements, the preliminary selection of an indicator species should take account of the differences in the response of different indicator species to particular routes of trace metal or organochlorine uptake. Thus, different species respond to different portions of the total pollutant load on an ecosystem. For organochlorines, which may be mainly particulate-associated in water (above), the selection of a filter-feeder might be advantageous as these organisms ingest large quantities of particulates. By contrast, some trace metals which exist primarily in solution (for example, cadmium) should be monitored adequately by organisms such as macroalgae, which respond primarily (and perhaps, exclusively) to metals in solution (see Morris and Bale, 1975, amongst others). The selection as indicators of organisms which are not primary producers should be considered in relation to their basic food source, as this will define the uptake routes for pollutants.

It can therefore be seen that there is no correct or incorrect organism which may be used as an indicator; rather, the selection of such species should be made with reference to the particular pollutant loads which the researcher wishes to monitor. Some examples should clarify this situation.

Bryan and Hummerstone (1977) reported detailed profiles concerning the concentrations of silver in organisms from the Looe Estuary, UK. Samples of macroalgae exhibited little difference in silver concentrations with distance upriver towards known sources of the element. In this case, the authors concluded that the silver in the estuary was particulate-associated and was not available to an organism such as *Fucus vesiculosus*, which primarily monitors pollutants in solution. Levels of silver in the herbivorous limpet, *Patella vulgata*, agreed well with the pattern derived from the alga; this species responds to silver in food (algae, which in turn respond to metals in solution only), as well as absorbing some metals from solution in its own right. By contrast, profiles from samples of filter-feeders such as the cockle, *Cerastoderma edule*, indicated higher concentrations of silver in upriver locations. The differences between these profiles and those of *F. vesiculosus* and *P. vulgata* must have been due to a significant effect of particulate-associated silver on the whole-body content of this element in the filter-feeder. As might be expected, concentrations of silver in deposit-feeders such as the bivalve, *Scrobicularia plana*, were similar to those found in the sediments of the estuarine area which, in turn, were derived by settling of particulate material containing silver. These studies thus present an elegant picture of the differences in indication ability of the three species groups, depending entirely on the diet of the species and the partitioning of the metal in question between these dietary components. The importance of this last parameter was demonstrated in the same study by the profiles noted for lead contamination. By contrast to the data for silver, the profiles for lead in each of the three groups of indicators (macroalgae and herbivores responding to metals in solution, filter-feeders and deposit-feeders) were very similar throughout the study area. This similarity must reflect the presence of a significant proportion of the total lead in solution as well as in particulates; in addition, the amount of lead in each phase apparently decreases in a similar fashion downstream towards the estuary, i.e. the ratio of lead in solution to that in particulates is similar at all study sites, notwithstanding the decrease in total lead with distance downriver.

Ireland and Wootton (1977) reported similar conclusions with respect to the indicator ability of different species during a study of the trace metal contents of the gastropod molluscs *Thais* (= *Nucella*) *lapillus* and *Littorina littorea*, taken from nine study locations around the coast of Wales. The profiles observed for copper, lead, manganese and zinc in the two species are shown in Fig. 3. Although both species exhibited the highest levels of metals at station 9 (Penarth), agreement between the profiles at the other study locations was often poor. The authors suggested that this was a result of the difference in diet of the two species; *T. lapillus* is a carnivore, feeding mainly on barnacles such as *Balanus balanoides*, and *L. littorea* is a herbivore, feeding mainly on species of *Fucus*. The latter species must therefore respond to solution-derived metals, both by direct uptake and via *Fucus*; by contrast, the filter-feeding habit of barnacles apparently introduces a significant effect of particulate-associated metals (in addition to those in solution) on the metal content of its predator *T. lapillus*. Differences in the ratios of metals in solution to those associated with particulates at the nine stations could then produce the variations between the two profiles, as seen in Fig. 3.

Phillips (1977c, 1978a, 1979a) also noted differences between the trace metal profiles exhibited by two indicator species, in this case the mussel, *Mytilus edulis*, and the alga, *Fucus vesiculosus*. Mussels from low salinity

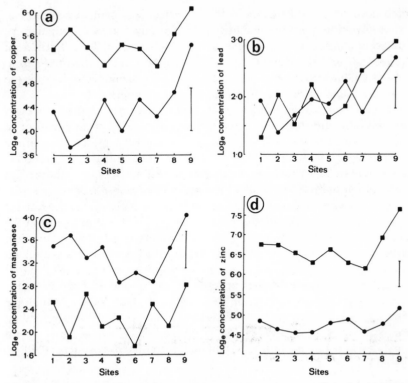

FIG. 3. Concentrations of (a) copper, (b) lead, (c) manganese and (d) zinc, in *Thais lapillus* (squares) and *Littorina littorea* (circles) from nine sites around Wales. Concentrations are expressed as the natural logarithm of the concentration in $\mu g/g$ dry weight. The vertical line on each figure represents the minimum value by which two points must differ in order to be judged significantly different. (After Ireland and Wootton (1977).)

waters in the Baltic exhibited higher concentrations of four metals than did those from waters of higher salinity (Kattegat and Skagerrak). The decrease in levels of these metals occurred in the mixing areas of the Sound and Great Belt. However, *Fucus vesiculosus* exhibited no such location dependence of metal concentrations. In this case, two possible routes might have lead to the differences between the pollution profiles of the two species. The first possibility was that the mussels might have been responding to metals from inorganic particulates, which were unavailable to the alga. However, the available evidence from direct studies on water samples did not support this hypothesis. Phillips (1979*a*) therefore concluded that the mussel profile depended on the differences in the concentrations of metals present in phytoplankton from the two areas, the two phytoplankton populations differing considerably in species composition due to the differences in salinity of the water masses involved. It will be noted that this mechnaism, involving differences because of the derivation of metals from food by the mussel, differs somewhat from the previous examples.

In such cases as those cited above, where two or more indicator species exhibit different profiles of contamination, it would appear pertinent to enquire which of the profiles produced is a correct representation of the pollution situation. However, it must be understood that this question is meaningless: both profiles are essentially correct. Furthermore, the profiles are not mutually exclusive and the conclusions reached from the profiles should likewise leave room for agreement. Hence, in the case of the data for the Looe Estuary (Bryan and Hummerstone, 1977), the profile from the alga indicates little difference in the availability of silver *from solution*, whereas those from the filter-feeders and deposit-feeders show an increased availability of silver *from particulates* in upriver locations. With strict interpretation of the profiles in terms of the response of the indicator species, therefore, no confusion should arise. In fact, the use of multiple indicators in any one study should lead to a more complete understanding of the pollution of the area considered, especially if the species used respond to different portions of the total pollutant load on the ecosystem (Phillips, 1979a).

C. TIME-INTEGRATION CAPACITY

One additional factor is important with respect to the preliminary selection of an indicator organism for monitoring trace metal or organochlorine contaminants. Just as it is important to consider the ability of any given species to respond to a pollutant which is found predominantly in a given phase (solution, particulate-adsorbed, etc.), so it is vital to examine the kinetics of pollutants in an organism which is being considered as a candidate for an indicator survey. The rates of uptake and excretion of a pollutant in an organism determine, to a great extent, the degree of time-integration of ambient pollutant levels exhibited by that organism. Different species exhibit widely divergent rates of uptake and excretion for any one contaminant, and this variation depends little on taxonomy; thus, closely related species may not be assumed to exhibit similar pollutant kinetics. In addition, any one species will exhibit unique kinetics for each pollutant, excreting one compound relatively rapidly (leading to a low time-integration capacity) and another very slowly (integrating ambient levels over long periods). Once again, these differences are often noted for pollutants of very similar chemical structure such as DDT or DDE, or different isomers of PCBs.

Thus, each species–pollutant pairing is unique in terms of pollutant kinetics or flux. This means that a given species–pollutant pairing will lead to a given degree of time-integration (although external factors may lead to variation here), which is a function of each component of the pair. If a researcher desires a continuous record of pollutant availability at any study site, the frequency of sampling must be adjusted to account for the time-integration capacity of the species used with respect to the particular pollutant measured. Evidently, where a single indicator species is used for multiple contaminants (each with its own kinetics), a decision must be made as to the sampling frequency by considering the range of time-integration capacities afforded by the chosen species. Reference to the published literature on laboratory studies of pollutant kinetics allows some general conclusions.

Macroalgae are frequently used as indicators of trace metal pollution, although they are rarely used to monitor organochlorines. The reason for this difference appears to be that these organisms respond mainly to pollutants in solution and the organochlorines probably exhibit higher association with particulates than do most trace metals. The time-integration of macroalgae for trace metals appears to be very great. Thus, once metals are bound to the plant they are lost very slowly—so slowly, in fact, that concentrations increase with increased age of the plant. Thus, several authors have reported higher concentrations of metals in stipes than in the thallus of such species as *Fucus vesiculosus, Laminaria digitata* and *Ascophyllum nodosum* (Bryan, 1969, 1971; Bryan and Hummerstone, 1973a; Fuge and James, 1973, 1974; Haug *et al.*, 1974; Whyte and Englar, 1974). The occasional estimates of biological half-life of metals in these species reflects this strong binding; however, measurable differences between the metals nevertheless exist. Thus, ^{65}Zn is lost extremely slowly from most species of *Fucus* (Gutknecht, 1965; Bryan, 1969). Young (1975) confirmed the slow loss of ^{65}Zn from *Fucus serratus* and contrasted this with the relatively rapid loss of ^{59}Fe (Fig. 4). This species therefore exhibits a much greater time-integration capacity for ^{65}Zn than for ^{59}Fe, although even the latter isotope has a rather long half-life in the alga. In *Fucus vesiculosus*, iron concentrations are known to increase with age of the plant

(Bryan and Hummerstone, 1973*a*); thus, iron may have a longer half-life in this related species than that recorded for ^{59}Fe in *F. serratus*.

The time-integration capacity of bivalve molluscs for trace metals is generally somewhat less than that of macroalgae (Phillips, 1977*b*). As a direct comparison with the above data, biological half-lives of ^{65}Zn have been reported for several bivalves. Seymour (1966) transplanted oysters *Crassostrea gigas* from Willapa Bay (polluted with ^{65}Zn) to Puget Sound

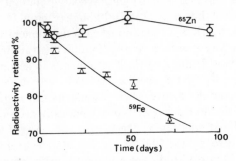

FIG. 4.   The loss of ^{65}Zn and ^{59}Fe from *Fucus serratus* exposed to these isotopes in the laboratory and subsequently placed in unlabelled seawater. The results have been corrected for physical decay; means and 95 per cent confidence limits are shown for each isotope. (After Young (1975).)

(where ^{65}Zn was virtually absent). The loss of ^{65}Zn was relatively constant with differences in season or year of study, averaging 0·55 per cent per day. The effective and biological half-lives (not corrected for decay of the isotope and decay-corrected, respectively), were estimated to be 125 and 255 days, respectively. Transplantation techniques were also used by Young and Folsom (1967) to investigate the kinetics of ^{65}Zn in mussels, *Mytilus californianus*. When transplanted from the Columbia River estuary to La Jolla, this species exhibited a biological half-life of 76 ± 3·5 days for ^{65}Zn in whole soft parts, corresponding to an effective half-life of 58 ± 2·7 days. Seymour and Nelson (1973) followed the decline in ^{65}Zn in both *M. edulis* and *M. californianus* from the Columbia River estuary following shutdown of the plutonium production reactors at Hanford in February, 1971. In *M. edulis*, effective and biological half-lives for ^{65}Zn were estimated to be 130 and 277 days; in *M. californianus*, 149 and 380 days, respectively were quoted. The cause of the large discrepancy between these latter values and those of Young and Folsom (1967) cited above for *M. californianus* is not clear, but the mussels studied by Seymour and Nelson (1973) were almost certainly exposed to significant amounts of ^{65}Zn, even after the Hanford shutdown, by solubilisation of the nuclide from Columbia River sediments. The authors acknowledged this fact by quoting the apparent biological half-life as an 'ecological half-life'—a term introduced by Held (1960) for use when concomitant (usually minor) uptake of the isotope studied may occur. Wolfe (1970a) also quoted results for ^{65}Zn loss by oysters *Crassostrea virginica* in terms of an ecological half-life, estimated to be 347 days for absolute activity and 276 days for specific activity (the difference being due to increased concentrations of stable element) in oysters from Beaufort, North Carolina. These data suggest that, in general, the loss of zinc by bivalves, although slow, is measurable and apparently faster than that by macroalgae. In addition, variation between bivalve species in the time-integration of zinc may also be expected on the basis of these data.

The only metal other than zinc for which sufficient data exists to extend these observations is mercury. Cunningham and Tripp (1973, 1975a, 1975b) have reported the results of extensive studies on mercury kinetics in the American oyster *Crassostrea virginica*. Exposure of this species to 10 or 100 mg/litre mercuric acetate in solution for 19 to 45 days was followed by studies of mercury excretion from whole soft parts at either a constant (25 °C) temperature or in declining temperatures (25 °C to 5 °C, to mimic autumn conditions in the study area). The biological half-life of the accumulated mercury was 16·8 and 9·3 days at 25 °C, and 35·4 and 19·9 days in the declining temperature regime, for oysters exposed to 10 and 100 μg/litre concentrations, respectively. These relatively short half-lives reflect the effect of total concentration on half-life (see also Keckes *et al.*, 1968), as well as the effects of ambient temperature. By comparison, Ünlü *et al.* (1972) and Miettinen *et al.* (1972) have reported half-lives of methyl mercury of 481 days for the bivalve *Tapes decussatus* and 1000 days for the mussel *Mytilus galloprovincialis*. Laboratory studies of the latter species by Fowler *et al.* (1978a) also indicated an extremely long half-life for methylmercury, although inorganic mercury was lost more quickly, with a half-life of perhaps 100 days. However, it must be emphasised that laboratory studies designed to estimate the biological half-lives of trace elements can produce only order-of-magnitude approximations. The estimates produced from laboratory studies thus depend very greatly on the route and length of the exposure period, as well as on the conditions of organism maintenance during depuration (Fowler *et al.* 1975a). Studies in the field are of greatest value and often produce results which are quite distinct from those of laboratory-based experiments (Fowler *et al.*, 1978a).

Consideration of the above examples suggests the existence of inter-species differences in the retention of single metals and also of intra-species variation in the retention of different elements. For example, the biological half-life of mercury in *Crassostrea virginica* of 9 to 36 days is much less than that reported for ^{65}Zn in the same species (347 days). Other reports are also known on this aspect. For example, Pentreath (1973a) found differences between the kinetics of zinc, manganese and iron in the mussel *Mytilus edulis*. Table 6 shows data from this study concerning the loss of stable

TABLE 6

THE LOSS OF STABLE ELEMENTS FROM TISSUES OF THE COMMON MUSSEL, *Mytilus edulis*, AFTER 42 DAYS' STARVATION IN THE LABORATORY, AND $t_{1/2}$ VALUES (DAYS) FOR NUCLIDE ACCUMULATION BY TISSUES OF THE SAME SPECIES.(AFTER PENTREATH(1973a).)

Tissue	Per cent loss, Zn Wet	Dry	$t_{1/2}$, ^{65}Zn	Per cent loss, Mn Wet	Dry	$t_{1/2}$, ^{54}Mn	Per cent loss, Fe Wet	Dry	$t_{1/2}$, ^{59}Fe
Foot	7·7	15·1	7·3	0·0	0·0	25·7	89·2	90·0	12·7
Mantle	27·8	23·1	5·4	0·0	0·0	11·9	32·9	28·6	10·6
Gonad	15·5	5·0	8·9	22·2	11·1	7·9	49·7	42·9	13·5
Adductor muscle	0·0	0·0	20·7	0·0	0·0	7·4	0·0	0·0	13·5
Stomach plus digestive gland	32·4	23·1	5·1	24·5	14·3	15·4	58·0	52·2	10·0
Gill	30·8	19·4	4·3	10·2	0·0	16·9	7·4	0·0	20·7

elements over a 42-day starvation period and the rate of accumulation of the corresponding nuclide. Although no data for whole soft parts were quoted, it is evident that the rates of nuclide accumulation were similar for each isotope, ^{65}Zn accumulation perhaps being slightly faster than that of ^{54}Mn or ^{59}Fe. However, excretion of the stable elements varied much more considerably, iron being lost much faster than either of the other metals. This faster loss of iron may be due to its unusual excretion route via the byssus (George *et al.* 1976; George and Coombs, 1977a). Certainly, the time-integration capacity of *M. edulis*, at least, for iron is much less than that for most other metals. It is interesting in this connection that Frazier (1975, 1976) suggested that both iron and manganese exhibited high turnover rates in the American oyster *Crassostrea virginica*, particularly during periods of shell deposition. The turnover of manganese was enormous in some parts of the seasonal cycle, peaking at up to twice the total body burden of this element per day. This organism would therefore appear to be a most unlikely candidate for the indication of iron and manganese in the environment, although the dynamics of zinc, cadmium and copper were independent of shell deposition and appeared consistent with those required from indicator species.

In addition to the differences noted in the excretion rates of different metals in any one species, different forms of any one metal may be excreted at widely varying rates. The most common examples here concern the kinetics of different forms of mercury in biota. Thus, Miettinen *et al.* (1969) showed that the excretion rates of mercury by brackish water mussels *Pseudanodonta complanata* exposed to different forms of mercury (as ^{203}Hg) by injection into the foot muscle varied considerably. Thus, the slow component of mercury excretion exhibited a biological half-life of 23 days for inorganic mercury, 43 days for phenylmercury and 86–435 days for methylmercury. The wide range quoted for methylmercury was a function of different ages or sizes of the test animals as well as of test temperature. This difference between the retention of different mercuric compounds by biota has been noted frequently in studies on finfish (see below), which generally agree with the data of Miettinen *et al.* (1969) cited above. By contrast to this pattern, Cunningham and Tripp (1975*b*) found little difference in the percentage retention of ^{203}Hg-labelled mercuric chloride or methylmercuric chloride by the tissues of oysters (*Crassostrea virginica*) previously exposed to these compounds in either water or food (the marine diatom *Phaeodactylum tricornutum*). This finding is somewhat unexpected, as the uptake rates of these two components into *C. virginica* differ quite significantly, methylmercury occurring at four times the concentration of inorganic mercury after a 74-day exposure period to 1 μg/litre of each compound (Kopfler, 1974).

George and Coombs (1977*a, b*) have reported interesting data on the effects of the complexation of iron and cadmium on their uptake and retention by the mussel *Mytilus edulis*. In the study of iron uptake, each of the seven compounds studied exhibited its own unique uptake kinetics, Fe(III) complexes of citrate, EDTA and 1, 10-phenanthroline being taken up faster than particulate ferric hydroxide, whereas ferrichrome *b* and the Fe(III) complexes of aceto- and benzo-hydroxamic acids were taken up slower. However, the excretion of each of these compounds compensated for the differences in uptake, leading to an almost constant residence time for the metal, regardless of form (George and Coombs, 1977*a*). Later studies on the uptake of cadmium by the same species indicated that complexation of the cadmium with EDTA, humic or alginic acids or pectin doubled the uptake rate and final tissue concentrations over those noted using cadmium chloride. The authors suggested that this was due to the need for complexation of cadmium to a carrier ligand prior to its transport into *M. edulis*. Unfortunately, no data for excretion rates of cadmium after exposure to these different complexes were given (George and Coombs, 1977*b*). It might be noted, in addition, that the final tissue distribution of cadmium was unaffected by differences in the exposure compound whereas that of iron differed according to the complex used. This difference between the two metals may reflect the different uptake mechanisms involved, iron apparently being taken up by endocytosis, whereas cadmium is probably taken up by a carrier mechanism, as described above; the essential difference here is the presence or absence of the complex subsequent to uptake.

Data for the kinetics of trace metals in finfish also support the concept of each species–metal pair exhibiting a unique time-integration, i.e. differences exist in the uptake and excretion rates of any one metal by different species and of different metals by any one species. Pentreath (1973*b, c,* 1976*a*) reported extensive data for the kinetics of ^{65}Zn, ^{54}Mn, ^{59}Fe and ^{58}Co in plaice, *Pleuronectes platessa*. The biological half-lives of ^{65}Zn and ^{54}Mn were similar after exposure of the fish to these nuclides in water (278–348 and 242–498 days, respectively) but the loss of both nuclides was more rapid after their ingestion in food and differences were observed between the two isotopes. Thus, mean biological half-lives were 103 days for ^{65}Zn and 39 days for ^{54}Mn after ingestion of labelled *Nereis diversicolor;* as the food route of ingestion appears predominant in the field, the latter figures probably more closely approximate natural values. The tissue retention of ^{59}Fe and ^{58}Co by plaice after their accumulation from water suggested that the biological half-lives of these nuclides resembled that of ^{54}Mn more closely than that of ^{65}Zn, but here again differences were noted in the kinetics of each of the nuclides studied. These differences no doubt depend on the distribution of the nuclide in the fish, as well as on the exchangeability of the nuclides present in each tissue. A further study of the uptake of these same four radionuclides from water by the thornback ray *Raja clavata* (Pentreath, 1973*d*) indicated slower accumulation of nuclides by this species compared with *P. platessa*. This difference may be related to the lack of drinking in elasmobranchs; however, the relevance of this observation in the field is doubtful as the food route of uptake presumably predominates, as noted for the plaice. In a later study, the uptake and excretion of ^{115m}Cd by both plaice and the thornback ray was studied, using both food and water routes of exposure (Pentreath, 1977*a*). The accumulation of this nuclide from water was faster by plaice than by rays at similar exposure concentrations (Fig. 5(A) and 5(B)); however, rays retained more ^{115m}Cd from food than did plaice (Fig. 5(C)). The species difference in time-integration of ambient levels of this nuclide therefore depended on the exposure route. The same conclusion was reached in later studies in which plaice were found to accumulate very little ^{110m}Ag or ^{237}Pu from either water or food, although rays accumulated both nuclides from food quite efficiently (Pentreath, 1977b, 1978a, 1978b). The dependence of time-integration of metals on the exposure route is an important

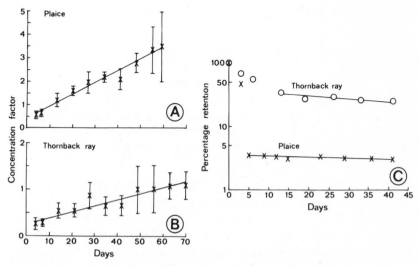

FIG. 5. The accumulation of ^{115m}Cd from water by whole plaice, *Pleuronectes platessa* (A), and thornback rays, *Raja clavata* (B); means ± 1 standard deviation are shown. The retention of ^{115m}Cd by single individuals of each species after ingestion of the nuclide in labelled *Nereis* is shown in Fig. 5(C) (After Pentreath (1977a).)

consideration in laboratory studies designed to investigate pollutant kinetics in organisms in their natural environments. As noted by several authors, the uptake and excretion rates of pollutants in laboratory animals may vary with the dosage, route and length of the exposure period (see for example, Fowler *et al.*, 1975a and Amiard, 1978b). More reliable data are produced by transplantation of biota from clean to polluted areas, or vice versa, as natural routes of uptake are then guaranteed. Data from authors other than Pentreath in general confirm the conclusions of his extensive studies, however (e.g. see Hoss, 1964, 1967; Jefferies and Hewett, 1971; Kimura and Ichikawa, 1972).

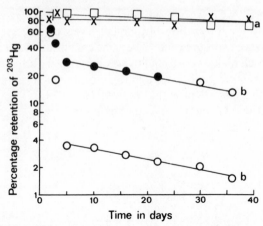

Fig. 6. The excretion of ^{203}Hg by the plaice, *Pleuronectes platessa*, after accumulation from food. (a) Plaice fed *Nereis* which had accumulated CH$_3$ ^{203}Hg Cl from seawater. (b) Plaice fed *Nereis* which had accumulated ^{203}Hg Cl$_2$ from seawater. The two lines in each case represent maximum and minimum values observed. (After Pentreath (1976d).)

Data for mercury kinetics in finfish from both salt and fresh waters are more extensive than are those for other stable metals or radionuclides. Pentreath (1976b, 1976c) has again studied accumulation of ^{203}Hg-labelled mercury and methylmercury from water by the plaice *P. platessa*. Tissue distributions of the mercury accumulated from water were widely different according to the form to which the fish were exposed. In addition, the biological half-life of methylmercury was more than double that of inorganic mercury after similar labelling periods ($t_{\frac{1}{2}}$ values of 231–347 days and 103–162 days, respectively). Later studies (Pentreath 1976d) on the same species were concerned with accumulation of both forms of mercury from labelled food. The greater rate of methylmercury accumulation and its greater retention than those of inorganic mercury were again demonstrated clearly (Fig. 6). Studies on the accumulation and retention of these mercury forms by the ray *Raja clavata* produced similar conclusions with respect to the time-integration of each form of the metal. In addition, the ray apparently accumulated more inorganic mercury from food than did plaice of a similar size at similar exposure concentrations (Pentreath, 1976e); this result is reminiscent of that for cadmium uptake by each species from food (Fig. 5(C) and see above). By contrast, the uptake of methylmercury from labelled food was similar for each species.

Information on the kinetics of different mercury compounds in

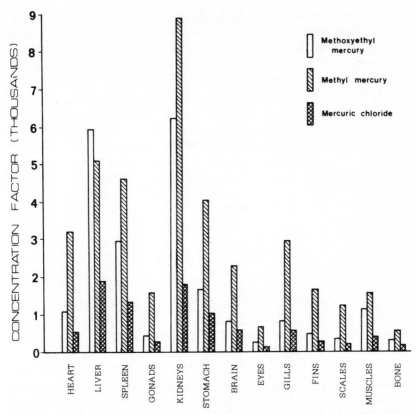

FIG. 7. Concentration factors for ^{203}Hg in tissues of pike, *Esox lucius*, exposed in ponds to inorganic mercury, methoxyethylmercury and methylmercury. (After Hannerz (1968).)

freshwater or brackish water fish confirms the general observation noted above for marine fish. Hannerz (1968) reported very extensive data on the accumulation of mercury by freshwater algae, molluscs and finfish. The relative uptake rates after dosing with ^{203}Hg-labelled mercuric chloride, phenylmercuric acetate, methoxyethyl mercuric hydroxide and methyl-mercuric hydroxide, were studied in most cases. With few exceptions, methylmercury was absorbed faster and retained longer than were the other compounds. Phenylmercury and methoxyethylmercury exhibited lower concentration factors than methylmercury but concentration factors observed for inorganic mercury were still lower. An example is shown in Fig. 7 where concentration factors for three of the mercury compounds in tissues of pike *Esox lucius* exposed in ponds are given. Apart from the large differences in net uptake of each compound, some differences between the compounds in tissue distribution are evident. Similar data were reported by Olson *et al.* (1973) in studies of the uptake of methylmercuric chloride and mercuric chloride by rainbow trout *Salmo gairdneri* exposed to these compounds at 275 μg/litre in water. The tissue distribution of mercury differed according to the compound used for exposure, suggesting that inorganic mercury was not methylated prior to uptake (or, indeed, subsequently). Concentrations attained by tissues of fish exposed to methylmercury were 1·3 to 19·8 times greater than those for fish exposed to inorganic mercury, kidney and muscle tissues exhibiting the greatest difference. Esophageal ligation did not affect the uptake rates of either compound, suggesting that uptake occurred across the body surface and that drinking was an unimportant route, as expected for freshwater finfish. It should be noted, however, that the study of mercury uptake from solution alone does not truly reflect natural conditions, especially as methylmercury has never been found in solution in natural waters to any significant extent. Drummond *et al.* (1974), in studies of the effects of mercury on cough frequency in brook trout *Salvelinus fontinalis*, found a much greater uptake of methylmercury than of inorganic mercury by gills and red blood cells and this difference was increased still further by decreases in ambient pH. Data from other authors (e.g. Miettinen *et al.*, 1969) support the above-noted differences between the uptake and retention of organic and inorganic mercurials.

The unique time-integration capacity of each species–trace metal pairing is paralleled by organochlorines. Thus, different species vary in their uptake and retention of any one organochlorine and different organochlorines exhibit marked variation in kinetics in any one species although, in general, these pollutants often exhibit shorter biological half-lives than do trace metals. The higher flux of organochlorines than trace metals through biota such as oysters (Brodtmann, 1970) necessitates more frequent sampling of indicator organisms for monitoring studies on the former pollutants (Butler, 1966, 1969a). Thus, the extensive National Monitoring Programme in the USA for organochlorines in estuarine bivalves was conducted by sampling at monthly intervals (Butler, 1971, 1973). However, the difficulties involved in the comparison of data from different species were also acknowledged by Butler and were ascribed to the variation in organochlorine kinetics in different bivalves. Studies on the net uptake and excretion of organochlorines from solution by the marine clams *Mya arenaria* and *Mercenaria mercenaria* (Butler, 1971) illustrate this point well

(Table 7). These data indicate that most organochlorines were taken up at slower rates by the hard clam than by soft clams and were also excreted at slower rates by the former animal. Differences between the kintetics of each organochlorine studied were considerable in either species and these differences were not consistent between the species. Thus, the ratios of the organochlorine concentrations attained in each species were not the same,

TABLE 7

THE COMPARATIVE UPTAKE AND EXCRETION OF ORGANOCHLORINES IN SOFT CLAMS, *Mya arenaria*, AND HARD CLAMS, *Mercenaria mercenaria*, EXPOSED TO A MIXTURE OF THE SEVEN COMPOUNDS IN FLOW-THROUGH BIOASSAYS. (AFTER BUTLER (1971).)

Pesticide	Five-day exposure concentration (μg/litre)	*Mya arenaria* (a) and *Mercenaria mercenaria* (b)					
		Initial tissue residue		Residue after seven-day flush		Residue after fifteen-day flush	
		(a) (μg/kg)	(b) (μg/kg)	(a) (μg/kg)	(b) (μg/kg)	(a) (μg/kg)	(b) (μg/kg)
Aldrin	0·5	2 300	190	290	120	22	70
DDT	0·1	880	126	200	36	47	18
Dieldrin	0·5	870	380	20	40	10	12
Endrin	0·5	620	240	10	42	nd	25
Heptachlor	0·5	1 300	110	90	26	10	nd
Lindane	5·0	200	63	10	nd	nd	nd
Methoxychlor	1·0	1 500	470	nd	43	nd	nd

nd = not detected.

suggesting that uptake was a function of the organism as well as of the biochemical partitioning of the pollutant. A comparison of these data with those of Courtney and Denton (1976) for PCB kinetics in *M. mercenaria* indicates a much longer biological half-life of the PCB components than of the pesticide organochlorines in this species; however, the effects of uptake route and exposure time on the biological half-lives of trace metals noted above are probably equally important for organochlorines and the data provided by different authors should be compared with caution, if at all.

Finfish in general exhibit rather greater time-integration of organo-chlorines than do bivalve molluscs (Bulter, 1971). At first sight this might suggest that use of finfish rather than bivalves in monitoring surveys could lead to substantial savings in money and effort, as a longer sampling interval would accrue. However, the response of each indicator type to different portions of the total organochlorine load on an ecosystem would suggest that monitoring surveys for these pollutants might profitably use both indicator types rather than either type alone. In any event, finfish are frequently used as indicators of organochlorine availability in aquatic environments. The available evidence again highlights the dependence of time-integration on both species used and organochlorine considered. For example, in freshwater salmonids, the excretion rates of ΣDDT in *Salmo salar* and *Salmo gairdneri* appear quite similar (Reed, 1966; Sprague *et al.*, 1971) but *Salvelinus fontinalis* excretes ΣDDT much faster (Cole *et al.*, 1967). Differences between the time-integration of different organo-chlorines in any one species have also been reported. Macek *et al.* (1970) found ^{14}C-labelled DDT to be better assimilated from food by rainbow trout *Salmo gairdneri* than was similarly labelled dieldrin. In addition, the biological half-life of DDT in whole fish was much longer than that of dieldrin (160 $\pm$ 18 days compared with 40 $\pm$ 4 days, respectively). As might be expected from the similarities between aldrin and dieldrin (the latter is the epoxy derivative of aldrin), the biological half-life of aldrin is also shorter than that of DDT in salmonids (Addison *et al.*, 1976). However, it is important to guard against extrapolation of data on one compound to any other compound, however closely related; for example, Watkins and Yarbrough (1975) found mosquitofish (*Gambusia affinis*) to take up dieldrin eight times faster than aldrin at the same exposure concentration of 10 μg/litre in water.

To some extent, the retention of organochlorines by biota reflects the water–lipid partitioning of each individual compound. Thus, Gakstatter and Weiss (1967) found the accumulation rates of DDT, dieldrin and lindane in both bluegills *Lepomis macrochirus* and goldfish *Carassius auratus* to decrease in the order DDT > dieldrin > lindane. Excretion rates decreased in the inverse order, as do the solubilities of each component in water. The importance of direct partitioning of organochlorines between water and lipid in determining the uptake of these pollutants by biota will be dealt with further in Chapter 3.

It is interesting to compare the persistence of organochlorines such as those discussed above with that of PCBs. Commercial PCBs are, in fact, complex mixtures of several chlorinated biphenyl isomers. The compounds present in commercial preparations may differ according to both degree and position of chlorination. Each isomer present may exhibit its own unique persistence in biota, i.e. the uptake and elimination rates of each PCB component vary. In addition, this variation is (as noted previously for pesticide-type organochlorines in clams) not consistent between organisms. Thus, Sanders and Chandler (1972), in studies of Aroclor 1254 uptake by

TABLE 8

ENRICHMENT FACTORS FOR DIFFERENT COMPONENTS OF AROCLOR 1254 IN SCUD, *Gammarus pseudolimnaeus*. THE ENRICHMENT FACTOR FOR EACH COMPONENT REPRESENTS THE RELATIVE PEAK AREA OF THE SAMPLE PEAK AND THE EQUIVALENT PEAK IN AROCLOR 1254. (AFTER SANDERS AND CHANDLER (1972).)

Peak No.	Relative retention time	Number of chlorines	Concentration factor Sample		Average 1 + 2	Aroclor 1254 RPA
			1	2		
1	0·27	3	2·00	2·00	2·00	0·03
2	0·37	4	1·69	1·72	1·71	0·29
3	0·45	4	1·81	1·81	1·81	0·11
4	0·50	4	1·80	2·00	1·90	0·05
5	0·63	5	1·31	1·31	1·31	0·51
6	0·77	5	1·00	1·00	1·00	1·00
7	0·98	5	1·13	1·16	1·15	0·38
8	1·07	5	1·07	1·16	1·12	0·57
9	1·19	6	0·33	0·66	0·49	0·03
10	1·31	6	0·84	0·85	0·85	0·65
11	1·59	6	0·55	0·55	0·55	0·33
12	1·67	6	0·80	0·80	0·80	0·30
13	1·79	7	0·43	0·57	0·50	0·07
14	2·04	6	0·56	0·60	0·58	0·45
15	2·61	6	0·50	0·62	0·56	0·08
16	3·22	7	0·25	0·50	0·37	0·04
17	3·68	7	0·25	0·25	0·25	0·04

crustaceans, found that the scud *Gammarus pseudolimnaeus* preferentially accumulated the isomers of lower chlorination (Table 8). Thus, a gradual decrease in enrichment of different components was evident when residues in scud were compared with those in the exposure mixture, average enrichment factors being 2·00 for a trichloro isomer, 1·71 to 1·90 for tetrachloro isomers, 1·00 to 1·31 for pentachloro isomers, 0·49 to 0·85 for hexachloro isomers and 0·25 to 0·50 for heptachloro isomers. The absence of isomers in scud containing less chlorine atoms than any component of the parent mixture suggested that reductive dechlorination of the isomers did not occur, i.e. the observed preferential enrichment of isomers of lower chlorination was due to uptake differences between components rather than metabolism of isomers.

This pattern of greater retention of the lower chlorinated PCB components is not typical of most organisms. Thus, Sanborn *et al.* (1975), in studies on the kinetics of DDT, DDE and three pure polychlorinated

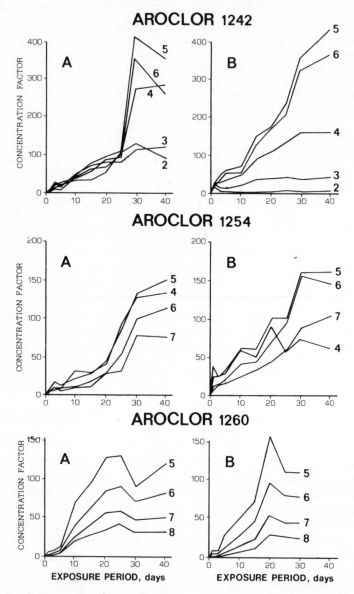

Fig. 8. Concentration factors for PCB components in Aroclor 1242, Aroclor 1254 and Aroclor 1260, as observed after accumulation of these components from aluminium oxide particles in water by (A) *Macoma balthica* and (B) *Cerastoderma edule*. (After Langston (1978a).)

biphenyl isomers in green sunfish, *Lepomis cyanellis*, reported concentration factors of 17 500 for DDT, 1510 for the pentachlorobiphenyl, 890 for DDE and 460 and 54 for the tetra- and trichlorobiphenyl, respectively. In this case, therefore, the higher chlorinated PCBs exhibited a greater biological affinity. Defoe *et al.* (1978) reported similar conclusions based on comparisons of the accumulation of Aroclor 1248 and 1260 by fathead minnows, *Pimephales promelas*. Residues in several seal species from the coasts of the United Kingdom, the Baltic Sea and Canada also revealed a greater ratio of high chlorine: low chlorine components than that of Aroclor 1254 (Holden, 1972*a*); however, this profile may have been a result of similar ratios in ingested food and need not imply any preferential accumulation in seals. Langston (1978*a*, *b*) has performed extensive studies on the accumulation of Aroclors 1242, 1254 and 1260 by the marine bivalves *Macoma balthica* and *Cerastoderma edule*. Both these species exhibited preferential accumulation of pentachlorobiphenyl isomers; isomers containing less chlorine atoms were accumulated in decreasing amounts from 4 to 2 atoms and those with more chlorine atoms in decreasing amounts from 6 to 8 atoms (Fig. 8). The uptake of PCB components by other bivalves, however, does not always follow this pattern. Thus, although Nimmo *et al.* (1975) found preferential accumulation of pentachlorobiphenyls in *Crassostrea virginica*, Denton (1974) observed a greater persistence of lower chlorinated isomers in the clam *Mercenaria mercenaria* and Vreeland (1974) reported decreased accumulation of penta- to dichlorobiphenyls than of hexachlorobiphenyls in the oyster *Crassostrea virginica*.

In the later report, Langston (1978*b*) noted that the persistence of PCB isomers in *Macoma balthica* and *Cerastoderma edule* depended not only on their degree of chlorination but also on the position of the chlorine atoms in the molecule. Thus, within each group of isomers containing the same number of chlorine atoms, isomers with the most 'ortho'-substituted chlorine atoms were least persistent. Differences were also noted in this study between the excretion of components by the two bivalve species; *C. edule* excreted dichlorobiphenyls much faster than did *M. balthica*. The effects of chlorine positioning in the PCB molecule on its retention by biota no doubt account for the variation in enrichment factors exhibited by scud (Table 8 and discussion above) for PCB components containing either 4, 5, 6 or 7 chlorine atoms per molecule.

The differences in biological retention of the various component molecules of a commercial PCB preparation may be severe. There is therefore a very strong argument in favour of treating each component as a separate pollutant. To date this has not been the practice of most researchers, partly due to inadequate separation of components during analysis and to the difficulties of accurate identification of multiple components. However, the recent research on purified PCB components is a significant advance and the quantification of PCB in biota as a group, by crude comparison of total peak areas with those in commercial PCB preparations, may be considered outmoded in a few years time. The same argument applies to the analysis of DDT and its metabolic products, DDE and DDD, especially as these are easier than PCB components to separate analytically.

D. CONCLUSIONS ON THE PRELIMINARY SELECTION OF INDICATOR ORGANISMS

This chapter has defined three basic requirements of an organism which should be addressed prior to its selection as an indicator species. The first of these concerns basic pre-requisites, which must be satisfied by any selected organism. Secondly, an organism should be selected with reference to the type of pollutant to be monitored and its behaviour in the ecosystem. For pollutants which are mainly adsorbed to inorganic particulates, a filter-feeder is generally considered the best type of indicator organism. However, for pollutants mainly occurring in solution, it may be preferable to use a primary producer, avoiding food chain effects (such as differences in preferred diets of different populations of higher consumers). If a particular outfall is to be monitored, data describing the physico-chemical form of pollutants of interest in the outfall may be most useful in deciding on an indicator species. Thirdly, the frequency of sampling of biota in monitoring surveys should be defined by the kinetics of contaminants in the chosen organism(s); occasionally, this parameter may be of over-riding importance and may cause alteration of any decision made on the basis of other considerations. This is most likely to occur for organochlorine monitoring (or that of hydrocarbons), as some such compounds may exhibit very short half-lives in some species; this is rarely, if ever, the case for trace metals. In general, the intervals between sampling for surveys of organochlorines in biota are very much shorter than those for surveys of trace metals in indicator species and this may be correlated both to the greater seasonal changes in organochlorine availability to aquatic organisms (due to seasonal spraying of pesticides) and to their shorter residence times in indicator organisms. Thus, most large-scale programmes to date concerned with trace metal indication sampled annually, whereas the programme for organochlorine monitoring in estuaries of the United States used monthly sampling. This parameter is obviously of great importance economically; possibly the best scheme is to sample as frequently as possible in the beginning of any programme to define the magnitude of seasonal variation and sample less frequently if possible in subsequent years. This aspect will be further discussed in later chapters.

CHAPTER 3

The Effects of Lipid on the Accumulation of Organochlorines and Trace Metals by Biota

A. INTRODUCTION

Discussion of the effects of lipid on the accumulation of pollutants by biota is vital here, as differences in the lipid contents of organisms or their tissues may underlie much of the variability in the concentrations of at least organochlorines noted in biota. Thus, the effects of several parameters—such as species, season or animal size—on the concentrations of organochlorines in organisms may be partly or wholly mediated by changes in the body lipid of the organisms.

Organochlorines, composed of an aliphatic or aromatic hydrocarbon chain with substituted chlorine atoms (Fig. 1), are universally highly soluble in fatty tissues (or organic solvents) and are extremely hydrophobic. The low solubilities of organochlorines in water have already been alluded to (Chapter 1) and this hydrophobic, lipophilic character is responsible to a large extent for the extreme persistence of organochlorines in aquatic biota.

The extreme affinity of organochlorines for lipid material has consequences in terms of the biological accumulation and storage of these compounds at all hierarchical levels of the organism and the biosphere. These consequences will be studied here in turn, considering first the biochemical basis of variations in organochlorine sequestration and graduating through tissues and entire organisms to the aquatic food web.

B. THE BIOCHEMICAL BASIS OF ORGANOCHLORINE SEQUESTRATION

As noted above, all organochlorines are lipophilic in nature and are therefore sequestered by organisms in lipid-rich tissues. Most publications concerning organochlorines estimate lipids crudely (if at all), the normal extraction method being based on solvation in a 2:1 v/v mixture of chloroform and methanol (or other organic solvents), followed by a washing process to remove non-lipid material into an aqueous phase. However, lipids vary considerably in nature and total amount between different aquatic organisms. Organochlorines will undoubtedly respond to this variation, as the affinity of any organochlorine for a binding or sequestration site subcellularly must depend on the exact lipids present. Published data concerning lipids in aquatic biota are increasing rapidly; excellent reviews may be found in Love (1970) and Morris and Culkin (1976, 1977). The present work does not attempt to review lipid chemistry in aquatic biota, but certain generalisations are possible concerning the variation in lipids with species and with factors such as season in any one species. These differences in lipid types and amounts in organisms undoubtedly have much bearing on the persistence of organochlorines in aquatic biota.

(i) Variation in Total Lipid in Whole Organisms

In most aquatic organisms, lipid is usually the second largest biochemical fraction after protein. Several parameters are known to affect the amount of total lipids in aquatic biota. Of these, the most important is season, and the variation in organism lipid with season is related to the sexual cycle and to the water temperature (which are, in turn, often co-related, changes in water temperature often triggering spawning). In general, the lipid content of aquatic biota increases prior to—and during—gonad development, decreases being evident during and after spawning. Curiously, this lipid cycle may not be entirely restricted to mature animals; at least in the case of teleosts, total lipids sometimes follow a similar (although less marked) cycle in immature fish to that in mature fish (Graham, 1924; Hickling, 1934; Rae, 1967a, b). Diet is also an important determinant of total lipids in aquatic biota; starvation results in the progressive depletion of neutral lipid reserves and proteins are utilised as an energy source only after lipid contents reach critically low levels. In this connection, it is interesting that deep sea biota often exhibit high lipid contents, presumably due to their larger size and to the energy-limiting ambient conditions.

Total lipid contents of many aquatic organisms also increase with age or size. Such variation is particularly marked in certain finfish and may be related to the greater proportion of body weight taken up by ripe gonads as fish age. This increase in the ratio of gonad weight to the weight of the rest of the body is also evident in bivalves, which thus also often exhibit increased total lipid contents with age. The extent of the lipid/age correlation depends on the seasonal state of the organism, however, because of this relation to spawning; thus, fish taken prior to spawning may exhibit very marked increases in total body lipid with age, whereas those taken immediately after spawning may, in fact, show an inverse relationship due to a greater exhaustion of the lipid reserves in older fish during spawning.

(ii) Variation in Specific Lipid Components in Whole Organisms

Although no general quantitative differences are seen between total lipids in freshwater and marine finfish, the fatty acid component of these lipids does differ between fish from the two habitats. Thus, freshwater fish typically contain 18:2, 18:3 and 18:4 acids, whereas marine fish lipids contain large amounts of long-chain polyunsaturated acids, particularly 20:5 and 22:6. Terrestrial organisms possess fatty acids similar to those of freshwater fish. These differences are almost certainly related to the diet of each class; freshwater blue–green algae contain high levels of 18:2 and 18:3 acids and few polyunsaturated longer-chain acids whereas marine diatoms exhibit the reverse profile (Morris and Culkin, 1976). The same conclusion was reached by authors noting differences between the two classes of finfish for other lipid components, e.g. for linoleic acid, which Gruger *et al.* (1964) found to be more prevalent in freshwater finfish than in marine species. However, to some extent both classes are able to synthesise some polyunsaturated fatty acids from non-fatty precursors (Lovern, 1935; Kelly *et al.*, 1958). More recent papers have confirmed these conclusions (Ackman, 1967; Ackman *et al.*, 1967; Stansby, 1967), and the fatty acids of crustaceans from marine and fresh waters appear to show similar differences (R. J. Morris, 1971). The sterol component of lipids may also vary in importance in freshwater and saltwater biota, e.g. cholesterol levels as a percentage of total lipids are much lower in marine bivalves than in those from freshwaters, and some crustaceans also exhibit such differences. Anadromous finfish—which normally live in marine environments but return to freshwater to breed—present an interesting test of the differences in lipid character in organisms of the two environments. The available data show that these fish contain fatty acids characteristic of the environment in which they are living, e.g. a change occurs from a typical marine lipid pattern to the freshwater lipids on migration up estuaries. This change takes some time to become complete, presumably because pre-existing lipids must be broken down to be replaced by the new dietary lipid forms (Lovern, 1942; Stansby, 1967; Morris and Culkin, 1976). The differences noted here in the fatty acids of marine and freshwater biota may be general for secondary and higher consumers, assuming that they are due to diet and that the biotransformation of lipids by organisms is not great. It is noteworthy here, in addition, that sterols appear to be mostly accumulated via the diet rather than biosynthesised. Thus, Morris and Culkin (1977), in their review of the sterol literature, state that crustaceans appear unable to synthesise sterols from acetate or mevalonate precursors. Amongst molluscs, herbivorous gastropods are capable of sterol synthesis whereas carnivorous species obtain cholesterol from their diet in general, although biosynthesis may be inducible in the latter organisms. The more simple sterol compositions of finfish (possessing cholesterol usually as 80 per cent or more of total sterols) and higher aquatic mammals (almost totally dominated by cholesterol and cholesterol ester) presumably indicate an even greater possibility of diet dependence.

Most of the parameters noted in section (i) above as effective in eliciting fluctuations in the total lipids present in organisms may also elicit changes in the proportions of the different types of lipids present. Changes in lipid chemistry with season may be broadly correlated to two different effects—spawning and water temperature. During times of depletion of lipid reserves at spawning, specific lipids may be preferentially depleted, thus changing the total lipid chemistry of the organism. For example, Lovern (1934*a*) noted a decreased proportion of fatty acids with chains of 14 and 16 carbon atoms as the salmon *Salmo salar* drained its reserves of lipids and this catabolic selectivity was more marked in males than in females. Marine fish such as cod *Gadus morhua* and herring *Clupea harengus* preferentially utilise the more highly unsaturated lipids during times of reserve depletion. A decreased proportion of phospholipid concomitant to reductions in some protein fractions was noted in starved cod and herring by Wilkins (1967), indicating the occurrence of actual tissue breakdown. Reserve depletion in fish may thus be extreme (see also Love, 1970) and may lead to very great changes in condition, especially in older fish.

Changes in lipid composition with the ambient water temperature appear quite general throughout aquatic biota. Many species thus exhibit alterations in lipid component proportions such that the melting points of the total lipids closely follow the environmental temperature. Presumably this process has value in that membrane mobility is maintained at all times. In general it is found that the proportion of long-chain unsaturated fatty acids in lipids of organisms decreases as water temperature is raised, and vice versa. An example of this is shown in Fig. 9, for freshwater planktonic copepods (Farkas and Herodek, 1964). This effect seems quite general, occurring not only in crustaceans but also in phytoplankton and in finfish. The existence of such an effect in organisms which are not primary producers may be based on their change of diet with season, i.e. it may be that phytoplankton lipid changes are reflected by secondary and higher consumers via the food web. However, as pointed out by Morris and Culkin (1976), diet is not the only factor involved. Thus, exceptions to the general rule of increased lipid unsaturation with lowered water temperature do exist; possibly these exceptions may be explained by the existence of temperature-dependent changes in the rate of biosynthesis of lipids.

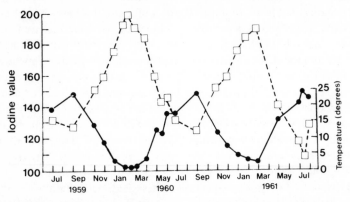

FIG. 9.   Seasonal changes in the iodine values of the lipids of copepods (a measure of the degree of unsaturation of lipids; broken line) and in water temperature (unbroken line) for Lake Balaton. (After Farkas and Herodek (1964).)

The effects of age on the total lipid content of organisms discussed previously are quite possibly accompanied by changes in the lipid types present. Unfortunately, data on this effect are inadequate and even the total lipid increase with age is contested by some authors as the amounts of lipid present in fish are greatly affected by administration of an artificial diet, for example. Thus, much of the published data which concerns lipids in salmonid species maintained on artificial diets has been criticised with respect to its relevance to finfish in the environment. However, some examples are known in which the proportions of lipid components change with age of an organism; thus, Lovern (1934*b*) reported changes in the lipids of salmon *Salmo salar* during the parr–smolt transition and similar changes may occur in sterol chemistry with age in finfish (Morris and Culkin, 1977).

The changes in total lipids and in the relative proportions of lipid components noted above for aquatic biota with factors such as season, age and diet undoubtedly elicit alterations in the kinetics of lipophilic pollutants to which these organisms might be exposed. Thus, the ability of an organism to sequester an organochlorine must depend on the number and type of binding sites available, which varies with both the total lipid content and the lipid chemistry of the organism (Harvey *et al.*, 1974). Unfortunately, our current understanding of the actual binding mechanisms involved in the sequestration of organochlorines is very poor, as indeed is our knowledge of cell membrane organisation in higher organisms. Although Roubal (1974) has published data on spin-labelling studies of hydrocarbon binding to lipids of the neural membrane of coho salmon *Oncorhynchus kisutch*, no such studies are known for organochlorines. Thus, although it is certain that organochlorine binding and retention in aquatic biota will vary with changes in the lipid components of the organisms, the actual qualitative and quantitative variation is not known.

The uptake and sequestration of trace metals may also be affected by total body lipid contents or by the presence or absence of specific lipids. Evidence for a relationship between lipid and trace metal accumulation by biota will be considered later in this chapter, but here it is worth noting that Morris and Culkin (1977) speculated that trace metal uptake across biological membranes may depend on the presence of specific sterols in such membranes. The sterol composition of membranes has been found to affect membrane permeability to some cations, and it may be that specific sterols are required as components of carrier or transport systems currently being proposed by some authors as mechanisms for the uptake of trace metals across the body surfaces of organisms (e.g. see George and Coombs, 1977*b*).

C. ACCUMULATION OF ORGANOCHLORINES BY INDIVIDUAL TISSUES OF BIOTA

Individual tissues of any organism vary in their lipid content. This variation, which may in some cases be extreme, may be the primary cause of the asymmetric distribution of organochlorines in biota. Data correlating organochlorine distributions in aquatic organisms with the lipid contents of the tissues mostly concern finfish or marine mammals, although a limited amount of information also exists for bivalve molluscs and crustaceans.

Nimmo *et al.* (1970, 1971*a*) have reported studies on the uptake of both DDT and PCBs (from Aroclor 1254 exposure) by pink shrimp, *Penaeus duorarum*. The distribution of both compounds was similar, maximal

TABLE 9

CONCENTRATIONS OF TOTAL PCBS, DDT AND ITS METABOLITES, OR TOTAL DDT PLUS METABOLITES (ΣDDT) IN TISSUES OF THE YELLOW GURNARD, *Trigla lucerna*, THE PLAICE, *Pleuronectes platessa*, THE BRILL, *Scophthalmus rhombus*, AND THE QUEEN SCALLOP, *Chlamys opercularis*. CONCENTRATIONS BASED ON BOTH WET WEIGHTS AND LIPID WEIGHTS OF EACH TISSUE ARE SHOWN. (AFTER ERNST *et al.* (1976).) MEANS CALCULATED BY THE AUTHOR

Species	Tissue	Individuals	Per cent lipid	PCBs[a]		DDT		DDE		DDD		ΣDDT	
				Wet weight	Lipid weight	Wet weight	Lipid weight	Wet weight	Lipid weight	Wet weight	Lipid weight	Wet weight	Lipid weight
Trigla lucerna	Muscle	7	0·58	0·06	10·6	0·006	1·17	0·005	0·78	0·002	0·32	0·012	2·29
Trigla lucerna	Liver	7	26·61	0·93	3·4	0·09	0·36	0·11	0·39	0·038	0·15	0·235	0·91
Trigla lucerna	Intestinal adipose tissue	7	80·46	3·70	4·6	0·41	0·52	0·60	0·74	0·094	0·12	1·136	1·39
Pleuronectes platessa	Muscle	3	0·33	0·03	7·4	0·002	0·76	0·001	0·33	0·001	0·27	0·004	1·21
Pleuronectes platessa	Liver	3	24·30	1·23	5·0	0·096	0·33	0·083	0·35	0·068	0·27	0·247	0·97
Scophthalmus rhombus	Muscle	1	0·08	0·02	32·0	0·003	4·10	0·001	1·60	No data		0·005	6·30
Scophthalmus rhombus	Liver	1	30·80	2·80	9·2	0·490	1·60	0·270	0·88	0·140	0·44	0·900	2·90
Chlamys opercularis	Adductor muscle	4	0·20	0·034	19·2	0·003	1·78	0·001	0·86	No data		0·005	2·96
Chlamys opercularis	Digestive gland	4	7·80	0·154	2·0	0·027	0·40	0·028	0·34	0·014	0·41	0·069	0·94

[a] Quantitated by comparing peak heights of three major sample peaks with corresponding peaks in Clophen A60 standard.

uptake being observed in hepatopancreas and least uptake in abdominal muscle or exoskeleton. A general agreement was noted between the organochlorine distribution and the lipid content of the tissues.

Ernst *et al.* (1976) reported similar conclusions concerning the tissue distributions of DDT and its metabolites, and PCBs, in three species of finfish and the scallop *Chlamys opercularis*, all organisms being collected in the English Channel. The most intensively studied species was the yellow gurnard, *Trigla lucerna*. Residue concentrations in this species, when based on wet tissue weights, exhibited marked variation between the tissues, increasing with lipid content in the order musculature < liver < visceral adipose tissue. Basing the concentrations on lipid weights decreased the magnitude of the differences between the tissues and concentrations increased in a different order: liver $\lesssim$ visceral adipose tissue $\lesssim$ musculature (Table 9). Organochlorine concentrations in the liver (digestive gland) and muscle tissues of the other two finfish species and the scallop exhibited similar profiles, liver concentrations always being greater on a wet weight basis but muscle often exhibiting higher concentrations when these were based on lipid weights (Table 9). The diminution of tissue-to-tissue differences when lipid weights are used as a basis for organochlorine concentrations confirms the effect of tissue lipid on organochlorine sequestration. The residual differences between the lipid weight-based concentrations of the pollutants are presumably related to different modes of pollutant binding in each tissue, possibly correlating to variation in dominant lipid types between the organs. Other factors, such as the ability of each tissue to detoxify and/or excrete organochlorines, may also be involved.

Concerning data for the effects of lipid on the tissue distribution of organochlorines in finfish, Holden (1962) reported that the distribution of ^{14}C-DDT among the tissues of brown trout exposed to this compound experimentally was directly related to the lipid content of the tissues. The DDT was suggested to be transported through the fish body by dissolution in blood lipids. Similar conclusions concerning the relationship between tissue lipid content and their ability to sequester organochlorines were reported by Yoshida *et al.* (1973) for ^{14}C-PCBs in carp *Cyprinus carpio*, and by Tooby and Durbin (1975) for lindane (γ-BHC) in rainbow trout *Salmo gairdneri* and roach *Rutilus rutilus*; these data were also based on the results from laboratory exposure experiments, using either a food or solution route of exposure to the pollutant. By contrast, Grzenda *et al.* (1970, 1971) failed to correlate the tissue distributions of either DDT or dieldrin in goldfish, *Carassius auratus*, exposed to these compounds in the laboratory to the lipid levels in each tissue, although an increased concentration of dieldrin in maturing ovaries was ascribed to concomitant increases in lipid content of this tissue. The disagreement evident here between authors has not been explained to date but again may depend on differences between the lipid chemistries of tissues and the catabolic ability of tissues for organochlorines. The importance of organochlorine biotransformation in determining the tissue distribution and equilibrium levels of these pollutants in finfish has been emphasised by Ernst and Goerke (1974).

Some information concerning the effect of lipid on organochlorine concentrations found in different tissues of finfish is also available from studies of fish taken directly from the environment for analysis. Linko *et al.* (1974) reported similar data for pike, *Esox lucius*, from the Baltic Sea to those cited above for gurnard from the English Channel (Ernst *et al.*, 1976). The concentrations of total PCBs and ΣDDT in the different tissues of pike varied widely on a wet weight basis, decreasing in the order liver > ovary > kidney > testis > muscle. This variation was much reduced by basing concentrations on lipid weights, and the tissues then decreased in concentration in the order ovary > liver ≥ muscle > kidney ≥ testis.

The tissue dependence of organochlorine concentration—and its correlation to lipid contents of the tissues—reaches its extreme in the axial muscle of some finfish. Thus, most authors treat axial muscle of finfish as a single tissue and assume homogeneity of pollutant concentration throughout the tissue. However, at least for some fish, this is far from the case; both organochlorines and trace metals may vary significantly in concentration with variation in the part of the muscle studied, and these fluctuations in pollutant levels depend (at least in the case of organochlorines) on differences in total lipid contents of different muscle areas. The fluctuation of biochemical constituents in finfish muscle areas has been discussed by Love (1970). Many finfish store lipids preferentially in the extreme dorsal and ventral areas of musculature, possibly because these areas take less part in swimming activity and thus present a convenient sequestration point for lipids. In addition to this 'vertical profile', differences are found in total lipid content of muscle areas longitudinally in the fish. The classical studies of *Clupea harengus*, published by Brandes and Dietrich (1953) may be used as an example (Fig. 10), although it should be noted that quantitative—and, to some extent, qualitative—differences exist between different species in the variation of muscle lipids.

Correlation of such profiles for muscle lipids to variations in organochlorine concentration in finfish was first reported by Reinert (1969) for coho salmon, *Oncorhynchus kisutch*, from Lake Michigan. Stout *et al.* (1972) cited these results to suggest that organochlorine contamination of fish for human consumption might be significantly reduced by selective removal of muscle areas containing high lipid contents. More extensive results were reported for the same species in a later paper (Reinert and Bergman, 1974). Very considerable differences in the wet weight-based

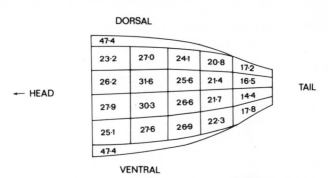

FIG. 10. The variation in total lipids as a percentage of biochemical components in different parts of the axial musculature of the herring, *Clupea harengus*. Differences between right and left muscle fillets were not observed. (After Brandes and Dietrich (1953).)

concentrations of ΣDDT in different muscle areas were noted, agreeing with the previous study. In addition, the concentrations fluctuated seasonally in a tissue-dependent fashion, i.e. ΣDDT levels by wet weight varied differently with season in different muscle areas (Table 10). Conversion of these data to concentrations based on lipid weights, however, clarifies the situation completely (see Phillips, 1978*b*). As seen in Table 10, the differences between muscle areas in ΣDDT concentrations become insignificant on lipid weight-based data, and the seasonal fluctuations are shown to be similar in each muscle region, increasing by a factor of between 6 and 8 between August, 1968 and January, 1969. The large fluctuations in organochlorine content with muscle region and with season are thus seen to depend almost entirely on variation in the total lipid content of the muscle regions (similar to those in Fig. 10) and the differences in lipid metabolism in each muscle area with season. It should be noted that this finding has repercussions for tissue sampling practices in those monitoring surveys of organochlorines employing finfish as indicators; obviously, subsampling procedures for axial muscle would need to be considered very carefully in such programmes, especially if data were based

TABLE 10

MEAN CONCENTRATIONS OF ΣDDT (mg/kg) BY WET WEIGHT OR BY LIPID WEIGHT AND
PERCENTAGE OF LIPID IN TISSUES OF COHO SALMON, *Oncorhynchus kisutch*, TAKEN
FROM LAKE MICHIGAN ON THREE OCCASIONS. (AFTER REINERT AND BERGMAN (1974).)
DATA FOR RESIDUES BY LIPID WEIGHTS CALCULATED BY THE PRESENT AUTHOR

Sample	Collection date	ΣDDT (wet weight)	Lipid (per cent)	ΣDDT (lipid weight)
Whole fish[a]	21 August, 1968	12·3	13·2	93·2
	18 October, 1968	12·6	7·1	177·5
	31 January, 1969	12·3	2·8	439·3
Whole muscle	21 August, 1968	14·9	16·2	91·9
	18 October, 1968	16·3	7·1	230·0
	31 January, 1969	18·4	2·3	800·0
Loin region	21 August, 1968	5·6	5·4	103·7
	18 October, 1968	4·7	2·3	204·3
	31 January, 1969	10·1	1·7	594·1
Dorsal region	21 August, 1968	61·1	62·1	98·4
	18 October, 1968	106·1	39·2	270·7
	31 January, 1969	59·6	8·2	726·8
Medial region	21 August, 1968	41·1	44·5	92·4
	18 October, 1968	59·8	22·4	266·9
	31 January, 1969	41·3	7·7	536·4
Ventral region	21 August, 1968	66·0	67·0	98·5
	18 October, 1968	106·4	41·5	256·4
	31 January, 1969	68·5	8·5	805·9
Brain	21 August, 1968	1·2	8·7	13·8
	18 October, 1968	2·4	5·8	41·4
	31 January, 1969	5·0	7·7	64·9
Eggs	21 August, 1968	7·4	10·9	67·9
	18 October, 1968	10·2	8·6	118·6
	31 January, 1969	7·9	9·4	84·0
Adipose fat[b]	21 August, 1968	88·9	85·6	103·9

[a] Average weights of whole fish were 3514, 3486 and 3770 g, respectively for each
sampling date. Two 25-mm thick steaks and the brain had been removed from whole
fish samples.
[b] Fish collected in October, 1968 and January, 1969 lacked adipose fat.

only on wet sample weights. It is noteworthy also in these results (Table 10)
that concentrations of ΣDDT in adipose fat were similar to those in whole
fish (at the same period) when based on lipid weights. By contrast,
concentrations of ΣDDT based on lipid weights were much lower in the
brain and eggs of coho salmon than in any of the other tissues sampled, and
the seasonal profile of ΣDDT in eggs did not agree with that of muscle

tissues, brain or whole fish. These differences in ΣDDT content almost certainly depend on differences between the lipid types present in each tissue, and such an effect may also explain the unusual seasonality of concentrations in the eggs. The low capacity of brain lipids to accumulate organochlorines has been noted in other species also, e.g. for cutthroat trout (Allison *et al.*, 1963), mackerel (Duffy and O'Connell, 1968) and salmon (Anderson and Fenderson, 1970), as well as for marine mammals (see below).

TABLE 11

CONCENTRATIONS OF ΣDDT BY WET WEIGHT AND BY LIPID WEIGHT (mg/kg) IN SIX TISSUES OF A SINGLE PORPOISE, *Phocaena phocaena*, FROM THE COAST OF SCOTLAND. (AFTER HOLDEN AND MARSDEN (1967).)

Parameter	Blubber	Kidney	Liver	Muscle	Spleen	Brain
ΣDDT by wet weight	3·8	0·04	0·58	0·56	0·12	0·02
Per cent lipid	67·0	1·4	13·2	6·1	5·1	8·3
ΣDDT by lipid weight	5·6	2·9	4·8	9·2	2·4	0·27

Data concerning organochlorines in marine mammals are quite numerous and most papers published include some information on the tissue distributions of these compounds. Holden and Marsden (1967) first reported the dependence of organochlorine concentration in porpoise (*Phocaena phocaena*) tissues on the lipid content of the tissues, basing these data on analyses of ΣDDT in one individual only (Table 11). Concentrations of ΣDDT based on wet weights differed considerably between the tissues, a factor of 95 being recorded between blubber and kidney. By contrast, basing concentrations on lipid weights reduced the variation amongst tissues to a factor of less than 4 if the brain is omitted from the calculation. ΣDDT levels in the brain were the lowest of all tissues on either a wet or lipid weight basis, the difference in concentration being a factor of almost an order of magnitude on lipid weights. This was correlated by the authors to the unusual lipid composition of the brain compared with other tissues. The effects of total lipid—and of lipid chemistry—on the accumulation and sequestration of DDT and its metabolites were thus clearly demonstrated.

More recent studies have confirmed these observations and extended them to other marine mammals, including seals and sea-lions (see, for example, Gaskin *et al.*, 1971 for porpoises, Frank *et al.*, 1973 and Gaskin *et*

TABLE 12

MEAN CONCENTRATIONS (mg/kg BY WET WEIGHT) OF DDT, DDE, DDD AND PCBS IN THE BRAIN AND BLUBBER OF HARBOUR SEALS, *Phoca vitulina*, AND THE RATIOS OF THE CONCENTRATIONS IN EACH TISSUE. SEE TEXT FOR EXPLANATION OF RATIO COMPARISONS. (AFTER DRESCHER *et al.* (1977).) RATIOS CALCULATED BY THE PRESENT AUTHOR

Age	Per cent lipid		DDT			DDE			DDD			PCBs		
	Brain	Blubber	Brain	Blubber	Ratio	Brain	Blubber	Ratio	Brain	Blubber	Ratio	Brain	Blubber	Ratio
0–6 months	6·60	87·10	0·052	4·26	82	0·026	4·83	186	0·017	1·08	63	1·14	167·8	147
13–18 months	7·42	88·33	0·050	3·14	63	0·030	4·56	152	0·020	1·05	52	1·38	162·8	118
3–5 years	7·90	85·60	0·023	1·88	82	0·009	2·22	247	0·006	0·49	82	0·48	71·1	148
					$\bar{x}=75{\cdot}7$			$\bar{x}=195{\cdot}0$			$\bar{x}=65{\cdot}9$			$\bar{x}=137{\cdot}7$

Comparison of ratios:　DDT　:　DDE　:　DDD　:　PCBs
　　　　　　　　　　　75·7　:　195·0　:　65·9　:　137·7
　　　　　　　　　　　1　:　2·6　:　0·9　:　1·8

al., 1973 for seals and Delong *et al.*, 1973 and Buhler *et al.*, 1975 for sea-lions). In all cases, differences between tissues were significantly diminished by basing organochlorine concentrations on lipid weights; in addition, the sequestration of organochlorines in the brain was found to always be low compared with that of other tissues. Similar conclusions may be inferred from the data of Anas and Wilson (1970*a, b*) for fur seals, *Callorhinus ursinus*. A more recent report by Drescher *et al.* (1977) on organochlorines and trace metals in harbour seals, *Phoca vitulina*, from the North Sea coast of Germany permits some interesting (but tentative) observations on the ability of brain tissue of this species to store organochlorines. Data comparing concentrations (by wet weight) of DDT, DDE, DDD and PCBs in blubber and brain of harbour seals of known age are shown in Table 12. These figures indicate that the differences in residue concentration between the two tissues are approximately two orders of magnitude on a wet weight basis. Adjustment of the data to a lipid weight basis decreases the tissue-based difference to about a factor of 10, as noted in the discussion above. However, if the ratio of the concentrations in blubber and brain is considered, consistent profiles emerge for each of the organochlorines, irrespective of age. Using this method, the ratio of concentrations in blubber to those in brain for DDT is found to closely approximate that for DDD, whereas PCBs are relatively less concentrated by brain tissue and DDE is concentrated 2–3 times less efficiently than is DDT by this tissue compared with blubber tissues. (Ratios calculated by using lipid weights, although lower than those based on wet weights, exhibit the same comparative relationship between each organochlorine, as the lipid weight data for each compound are generated using the same percentage lipid figures.) These differences in the brain : blubber ratios presumably reflect the biochemical differences between the lipids in each organ; although brain lipids concentrate all organochlorines less effectively than do those of blubber, DDE is selected against more strongly than is DDT or DDD, whereas PCBs are intermediate in this respect. Attempts to confirm such conclusions by use of data from Gaskin *et al.* (1973) on the same species from the Bay of Fundy and the Gulf of Maine were only partially successful; although similar trends are evident, the smaller number of individuals exceeding detection limits for the DDT group of compounds frustrated strong conclusions. Frank *et al.* (1973) published information on the concentrations of ΣDDT, PCBs and dieldrin in harp seals, *Pagophilus groenlandicus*, from eastern Canada. These results suggest that blubber : brain ratios may vary with age of the seal; sex differences may also be present. Evidently the relative concentrations of these compounds in different tissues are affected by several parameters, each of which presumably alters the specific lipid composition of the tissues, by dietary changes or otherwise. Reports such as that of Ackman and Hooper (1974) confirm the widespread tissue- and species-based differences in the lipid chemistries of seals. Tissue differences reach their ultimate in the report of Anas and Worlund (1975), where organochlorines (measured as ΣDDT plus PCBs) were found to be non-uniformly distributed in blubber samples from fur seals, *Callorhinus ursinus*. As these data were quoted by wet weights, the differences between different parts of the sample tissue may have been due to changes in lipid amounts. Ackman *et al.* (1965) have reported changes in the total lipid content of blubber sections from finback whales, *Balaenoptera physalus*, the percentage lipid content decreasing with depth of the blubber sample from the epidermal surface.

D.   VARIATION BETWEEN SPECIES IN THE ACCUMULATION OF ORGANOCHLORINES

Just as tissue lipid contents are important determinants for the distribution of organochlorines within organisms, and this effect of lipid extends similarly to whole individuals of any given species, so is total body lipid an important parameter contributing to the variation of organochlorine levels found in different species. Duffy and O'Connell (1968) suggested that the relatively high levels of DDT and its metabolites in mackerel, *Scomber scombrus*, compared with other fish such as perch or trout were due to the higher fat content of mackerel. Jensen *et al.* (1969, 1972), in extensive studies of biota from Swedish waters for organochlorines, preferred to base concentration data on lipid weights because of the large effect of lipid on the accumulation of these compounds. Differences between finfish species such as herring, *Clupea harengus*, and cod, *Gadus morhua*, for organochlorine concentration were correlated to the fat content of axial muscle in the two species, herring containing much greater amounts of fat and therefore exhibiting higher concentrations of organochlorines if these were based on wet tissue weights. Use of lipid weights for concentrations almost eliminated this species difference.

Similar conclusions have been reached by other authors, studying both freshwater and marine biota. Studies of finfish from the Great Lakes by Reinert (1970) showed convincingly that species differences in whole fish levels of DDT and dieldrin were mainly due to the different lipid contents of the species; an example concerning four species from Lake Michigan is

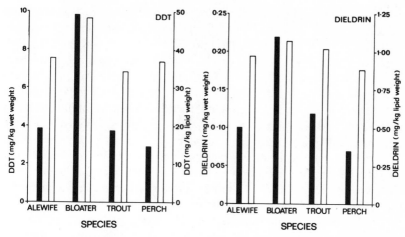

FIG. 11. Concentrations of DDT and dieldrin by wet weights (solid bars) or by lipid weights (open bars) in four species of finfish from Lake Michigan. All data refer to whole fish; data for lake trout are means of four size groups. Species names are as follows: Alewife, *Alosa pseudoharengus*; bloater, *Coregonus hoyi*; lake trout, *Salvelinus namaycush*; yellow perch, *Perca flavescens*. (After Reinert (1970).)

shown in Fig. 11. Hannon *et al.* (1970) also found that species differences were markedly less on a lipid weight basis than on a wet weight basis for ΣDDT, aldrin and its metabolite dieldrin, heptachlor and its expoxide, lindane, and toxaphene in 14 species of finfish from Lake Poinsett in South Dakota. Frank *et al.* (1974) analysed similar but even more extensive data for 38 species of finfish from four lakes in Southern Ontario to reveal similar trends, but concluded that other factors such as age and feeding habits of the fish were also implicated in the determination of residue levels of DDT and its metabolites, and dieldrin. These ancillary factors will be discussed in subsequent chapters. More recently, Hattula *et al.* (1978*a*), in studies of over 1700 individuals (twelve species) of finfish from the Finnish Lake Päijänne, sampled over five consecutive years, confirmed the relationship between fat contents of fish and their ability to sequester DDT, DDE or PCBs. However, these same authors could not show any correlation between the lipid contents of fish species and their concentrations of DDD, lindane (γ-BHC), aldrin or dieldrin, and other authors also have failed in this respect, e.g. Henderson *et al.* (1969, 1971) in studies of various species of freshwater fish in the US National Pesticide Monitoring Programme, and Kelso and Frank (1974), who reported data for organochlorines and trace metals in three species from Lake Erie. The failure of these authors to reach any substantial conclusion in this respect is due to one of several factors. Hattula *et al.* (1978*a*) felt that the concentrations of organo-chlorines other than DDT, DDE and PCB were very low, and the high standard deviation of mean levels masked any organochlorine–lipid correlation. The sample sizes of Henderson *et al.* (1969, 1971) were probably inadequate to overcome the effects of individual variation between fish of the same species, and this may also be true for data of Kelso and Frank (1974). Certainly, each of these studies suffered from the combined and interactive effects of other parameters also, such as season or fish size. In later chapters it will become evident that sample sizes of biota have to be large to accurately define concentrations of either organo-chlorines or trace metals; furthermore, interfering parameters (such as size, season, sex, animal condition and so on) must be normalised in the sample for studies of any single variable to be effective (see Zitko *et al.*, 1974).

Because of the abundance of parameters affecting the concentrations of organochlorines in biota, the basis of species differences in sequestration of these compounds is difficult to detect experimentally. Presumably, however, the amount of a lipophilic pollutant accumulated by an organism depends not only on its total lipid content, but also on the specific lipids present, as discussed in the previous sections. The affinity of the pollutant for a subcellular binding site will, to a large extent, define the rate of its excretion. These contentions are implicit in the comments of Langston (1978*b*) concerning the variation in PCB kinetics in different species of bivalve molluscs (see Chapter 2), that '... variation in the persistence of PCBs in bivalves may, therefore, be the result of inter-specific differences in the chemical structure and percentage composition of their lipid pools...'.

An interesting possibility with respect to the effects of lipid composition in biota is presented when data on finfish from Swedish waters are considered. Jensen *et al.* (1972) found that samples of herring, *Clupea harengus*, and cod, *Gadus morhua*, from the Baltic Sea exhibited higher mean concentrations of ΣDDT and PCBs than did those from the west of Sweden, either on a fresh weight or lipid weight basis. By contrast, a later report (Jensen *et al.*, 1975) could not confirm this distinction for samples of eel, *Anguilla anguilla*, or pike, *Esox lucius*, collected during the same period. The authors attempted to correlate such differences in the profiles obtained from these species to differences in the degree of contamination of deep waters (to which the pelagic cod and herring are exposed) and surface waters (which the coastal and territorial pike and eel inhabit). Admittedly, such differences are possible causative factors, and diet or migration effects may also be involved. However, a factor which was not considered was the difference in lipid chemistries of the organisms, as affected by the ambient salinity. The herring and cod samples thus presumably contained lipids typical of marine species (e.g. large amounts of polyunsaturated fatty acids; see Section B above), whereas the lipids of the anadromous species would be expected to vary in composition with the ambient salinity, which defines the lipid composition of the phytoplankton base of the food web. A disagreement between the organochlorine profiles obtained from the two studies might therefore be based on the alterations in the lipid chemistries of the fish from area to area. This argument is reminiscent of that used by Phillips (1977c, 1978a) to explain the differences between the trace metal concentrations found in mussels from Scandinavian waters, which did not correlate to changes observed in algae (Phillips, 1979a). In this case, phytoplankton species composition was believed to be responsible for the profiles found; again, the basic diet organism may be the root of the difference.

Concentrations of organochlorines in seals were noted in the previous section to be highly lipid-dependent in terms of tissue distribution. However, it is difficult to reach any strong conclusion concerning differences between the sequestration of organochlorines by different species of seals. This is at least partly due to the fact that few reports are available which include data for several seal species in one geographical area. Thus, differences in organochlorine levels in seals due to location interfere with attempts to delineate species differences. Table 13 shows published data for organochlorines in seal blubber, ranked approximately from lowest to highest reported levels. It can be seen that no consistent species difference occurs, i.e. no species is found to contain only low or only high levels; the correlation of the data to location is far more evident, seals from the Arctic or Alaska being relatively low in organochlorines, whereas those from the coasts of the USA, Canada and Sweden contain high levels commensurate with the known pollution of these waters by DDT and PCB compounds.

The few reports describing organochlorine levels in more than one species of seal from the same geographical region in general support the concept of little species difference in seals, at least in blubber levels. Helle *et al.* (1976a) found no significant difference between the concentrations of either ΣDDT or PCBs in ringed seal, *Pusa hispida*, and grey seal, *Halichoerus grypus*, from the Gulf of Bothnia (Table 14), although both species exhibited decreased levels of each compound with distance north in their respective ranges. These data correlate quite well with the data for cod and herring noted above (Jensen *et al.*, 1972), maximal pollution being centred in the southern Baltic Sea. Holden (1972a) reported data for grey seals, *Halichoerus grypus*, and common seals, *Phoca vitulina*, from the

TABLE 13

CONCENTRATIONS OF ORGANOCHLORINES (mg/kg BY LIPID WEIGHT) IN BLUBBER OF VARIOUS SPECIES OF SEALS FROM THE WORLD'S OCEANS. SAMPLES ARE RANKED IN APPROXIMATE ORDER OF CONTAMINATION BY DDT AND ITS METABOLITES. (SEE ALSO TABLE 14 AND FIG. 12.)

Location	Species	n	DDT	DDE	DDD	ΣDDT	PCBs	Author(s)
Canadian Arctic	*Pusa hispida*	28	0·03–1·11	0·14–1·34	—	—	1–6	Addison and Smith (1974)
Canadian Arctic	*Pusa hispida*	3	1·54	1·21	0·20	2·95	3·3	Holden (1972a)
Norwegian Arctic	*Pusa hispida*	2	1·67	0·95	0·29	2·90	1·8	Holden (1972a)
Scotland	*Halichoerus grypus*	?	—	—	—	2·4–14·8[a]	—	Holden and Marsden (1967)
Magdalen I., Canada	*Cystophora cristata*	1	7·75	4·38	0·69	12·82	3·7	Holden (1972a)
North Sea coast, Germany	*Phoca vitulina*	63	1·17–4·89	2·37–5·55	0·01–0·02	5·37–11·83	83–193	Drescher et al. (1977)
Pribiloff I. Alaska	*Callorhinus ursinus*	5[b]	0·22–1·40[a]	0·35–45·0[a]	0·07–1·50[a]	0·64–47·9[a]	—	Anas and Wilson (1970b)
Eastern Canada	*Pagophilus groenlandicus*	78	—	—	—	2·06–50·0	1·2–26·0	Frank et al. (1973)
Sable I., Canada	*Halichoerus grypus*	5	22·3	30·0	2·4	54·7	32·5	Holden (1972a)
Basque I., Canada	*Halichoerus grypus*	2	27·5	28·9	2·2	58·7	37·6	Holden (1972a)
Gulf of Finland	*Halichoerus grypus*	2[c]	23	—	—	42·0	6·5	Jensen et al. (1969)
Baltic (N. Sweden)	*Pusa hispida*	1	1·5	43·6	27·0	72·1	66·7	Holden (1972a)
Gulf of Maine	*Phoca vitulina*	10	4·0–67·7	5·5–61·3	0·2–22·5	9·7–147	8·0–254	Gaskin et al. (1973)
Gulf of Bothnia	*Pusa hispida*	2	56	—	—	120	13	Jensen et al. (1969)
Stockholm archipelago	*Halichoerus grypus*	3	17	—	—	170	30	Jensen et al. (1969)

[a] By wet weight: no conversion factor quoted.
[b] All nursing pups.
[c] Both pups.

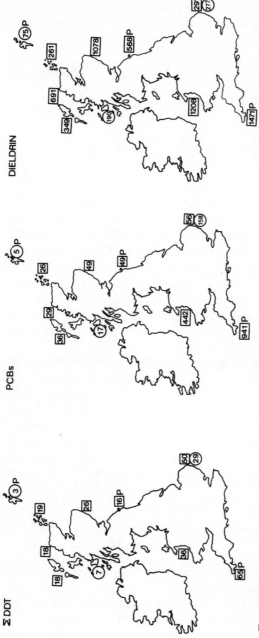

FIG. 12. Mean concentrations of ΣDDT and PCBs (mg/kg by lipid weight) and of dieldrin (μg/kg by lipid weight) in the blubber of seals from the coast of the United Kingdom. Figures in circles denote common seals, *Phoca vitulina*; figures in squares denote grey seals, *Halichoerus grypus*. P denotes that the sample was composed of pups rather than adults. All data from Holden (1972a); two locations omitted due to inadequate data for calculation of lipid-based concentrations (the Wash) or because the original data were cited for a mixture of species (the Clyde).

TABLE 14

CONCENTRATIONS (MEANS ± STANDARD ERRORS, mg/kg BY LIPID WEIGHTS) OF ΣDDT AND PCBS IN THE BLUBBER OF RINGED SEAL, *Pusa hispida*, AND GREY SEAL, *Halichoerus grypus*, FROM THE BOTHNIAN BAY, THE GULF OF BOTHNIA AND THE BALTIC SEA. (AFTER HELLE *et al.* (1976a).)

Area	Ringed seal			Grey seal		
	Number of individuals	ΣDDT	PCB	Number of individuals	ΣDDT	PCB
Bothnian Bay	40	110 ± 10	69 ± 4·4	—	—	—
Gulf of Bothnia	33	200 ± 28	110 ± 15	15	210 ± 28	100 ± 18
Baltic Sea	—	—	—	18	420 ± 53	140 ± 17

coasts of the United Kingdom. Both species were taken in only one location (Scroby, eastern England) and blubber samples from these five individuals indicated lower levels of dieldrin, DDT and DDD in the common seal than in the grey seal; by contrast, levels of DDE and PCBs in the two species were similar in these samples, either on a wet or a lipid weight basis. Consideration of the other results reported by Holden (1972a) for these species supports the concept of lower levels of dieldrin and ΣDDT in the common seal, but PCB differences appear less well defined (Fig. 12), as location-based differences interfere with interpretation of the data. It is interesting to note the localisation of the pollutants in these profiles; ΣDDT appears more widespread and varies less between samples than do dieldrin or PCBs. Presumably this reflects the usage of each of the compounds in the United Kingdom, PCBs and dieldrin being discharged from specific industries (see Peakall and Lincer, 1970 and Holden, 1972b for details) whereas DDT was more widely used as an agricultural pesticide and inputs would be expected to be more extensive and diffuse as a result. It is, perhaps, surprising that seals should reflect such asymmetric inputs of these pollutants, as not only do they themselves move from area to area, but their food supply is also far from sedentary.

E.   THE VARIATION IN ORGANOCHLORINE CONCENTRATIONS WITH TROPHIC LEVEL

(i) Evidence for Trophic Level Variations in Organochlorine Accumulation: Field and Model Ecosystem Studies

As an introduction to the discussion of this subject, it is difficult to improve on the following:

'Marine food webs are very complicated and there is much disagreement among marine biologists on prey–predator relationships. Many marine organisms are very opportunistic and flexible in their diets. Any attempt to use a chemical tracer for food web information will be confounded by these facts, as well as by differences between individuals of a species. Thus, we must accept "order of magnitude" comparisons.' (Harvey *et al.*, 1974.)

Given this cautionary note, it is nevertheless important to consider the changes in organochlorine levels with position of organisms in the food web, and to define the basis of these changes. However, even current data include considerable controversy; authors discussing this subject have reached opposite conclusions according to their selection of examples from the literature. Thus, for example, Portmann (1975) suggested, on the basis of data from Europe and the North Atlantic, that ΣDDT exhibited trophic level amplification on either a wet weight or a lipid weight basis (Table 15)

TABLE 15

RANGE IN ΣDDT CONCENTRATIONS (μg/kg) IN VARIOUS MARINE ORGANISMS, ON BOTH WET WEIGHT AND LIPID WEIGHT BASES. (AFTER PORTMANN (1975).)

| Organism | Concentration of ΣDDT | | Author(s) |
	Wet weight	Lipid weight	
Phytoplankton	0·2–0·5	40–100	Harvey *et al.* (1973)
Zooplankton	0·01–9·5	up to 154	Harvey *et al.* (1973)
Flying fish	0·6–4·0	180–1 480	Harvey *et al.* (1973)
Mollusc	8–100	800–10 000	ICES (1974)
Cod	3–50	1 500–2 500	ICES (1974)
Seal	10–20 000	20–40 000	Holden (1972*a*)

and dieldrin exhibited similar increases in concentration up food chains. By contrast, Hargrave and Phillips (1976) could find no evidence for ΣDDT amplification with trophic level when residues from organisms in areas remote from direct DDT inputs (except atmospheric inputs) were based on lipid weights (Fig. 13). Such comparisons, which frequently use data exhibiting wide ranges of concentration for individual phyla and may compare samples taken at different times or locations, are probably of limited value. However, some authors have considered the amplification of residues through biota from single areas in large-scale studies, and these conclusions may be of greater validity. Finally, a few studies of model ecosystems or simple food chains have been published, and results from

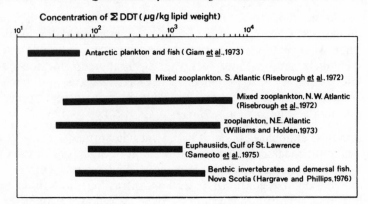

FIG. 13. Range in ΣDDT concentrations (μg/kg by lipid weight) in various organisms from areas not receiving direct inputs of DDT. (After Hargrave and Phillips (1976).)

these are of even greater import because the predator–prey relationships are better established.

Robinson *et al.* (1967) studied dieldrin and DDE levels in marine biota and several birds from the coasts of the United Kingdom; most samples were derived from the Farne Islands. Both compounds exhibited increased concentrations by wet weight with trophic level, the difference between trophic levels 1 and 3 being between one and two orders of magnitude. No data for lipid contents were quoted, so these data cannot be compared on a lipid weight basis. However, it is notable that the results quoted by these authors for sea birds and marine mammals (both of which represent trophic levels 4 or 5) were for liver or blubber tissues, which both contain large amounts of lipids. Increased concentrations (by wet weight) of these compounds noted between trophic levels 3, 4 and 5 were probably due mainly to the differing lipid contents of these samples. Woodwell *et al.* (1967) reported similar data for ΣDDT in biota of a salt marsh on Long Island, claiming an increase of greater than three orders of magnitude from 0·04 mg/kg in plankton to an extreme value of 75·5 mg/kg ΣDDT in an immature ring-billed gull (whole body analysed). Again, no data for lipid contents of the studied organisms were included.

Jensen *et al.* (1969) reported levels of ΣDDT and PCBs in biota from Swedish waters, using both wet and lipid weight bases. No primary producers or zooplankton were studied, however, and these results therefore refer to organisms of trophic levels 2 (mussels) to 4 or 5 (seals and sea birds). Extraction of data representing simplified food chains (fish to seal, fish to sea birds) suggested amplification of residues by a factor of at least 10 on either a wet or a lipid weight basis; however, this was admitted by the authors to be a gross simplification and an underestimate of the flexibility of the diet of higher predators. These authors also reported differences in the DDT:DDE ratios of higher predators; sea birds contained mostly DDE, whereas seals (and some fish) contained large proportions of ΣDDT residues as DDT. This distinction is confirmed by the results of many other authors as a general rule (e.g. see Table 13 above) and it would appear that the seal is the anomalous result. In general, as organochlorines are transferred through the food chain, one would expect increased proportions of metabolites (i.e. increased ratios of DDE to DDT, and of dieldrin to aldrin), although this depends to some extent on the time-integration of parent compound and metabolite in the organisms from each trophic level. The differences between seals and other high ranking predators in this respect must be based on an unusual relationship of the half-lives of DDT and DDE in the former animals, as differences in the ratio of these compounds in ingested food do not appear significant. It should be noted here that although some of the earlier analyses of marine biota included PCBs in the quantification of DDE due to the overlapping of peaks in analysis by gas–liquid chromatography, more recent results which take this into account have confirmed the differences in DDT:DDE ratios of seals and other high ranking predators (e.g. compare Risebrough, 1969, with Holden, 1972a). Holden (1972a) confirmed the high proportion of DDT in various seal samples by hydrolysis with alcoholic alkali and this anomaly remains unsolved. The same author also reported an amplification of dieldrin, ΣDDT and PCBs from cod and salmon food items to seals from Scottish waters, the difference between predator (blubber) and prey being factors of 50, 200 and 200 by wet weight but generally less than a factor of 10 by lipid weight.

Harvey *et al.* (1974) conducted extensive studies of DDT and its metabolites, and PCBs in biota from the open Atlantic Ocean. No correlation of residue levels (by wet or lipid weights) with trophic level could be demonstrated and, in fact, plankton exhibited the highest average concentrations of both compounds. No evidence of any correlation of residue levels with depth of habitat, lipid content, migratory habits or age of the organisms studied was found either and these authors dismissed food chain amplification as a major factor affecting residue levels in this ecosystem. Interestingly, however, the ratio of total PCBs to ΣDDT was correlated to trophic level, decreasing from about 30 in the atmosphere, surface water and plankton to approximately 3 in high predators and in

TABLE 16

MEAN CONCENTRATIONS OF ORGANOCHLORINES BASED ON BOTH WET WEIGHTS (μg/kg) AND LIPID WEIGHTS (mg/kg) IN ORGANISMS TAKEN FROM THE NORTH SEA AND THE DUTCH WADDEN SEA, 1972–3. (AFTER TEN BERGE AND HILLEBRAND (1974).)

Organism	DDT		DDE		DDD		PCBs		Dieldrin		Endrin		Pentachloro-benzene		Hexachloro-benzene		α-BHC		γ-BHC	
	Wet	Lipid	Wet	Lipid	Wet	Lipid	Wet	Lipid	Wet	Lipid	Wet	Lipid	Wet	Lipid	Wet	Lipid	Wet	Lipid	Wet	Lipid
Phytoplankton	0·05	0·11	0·05	0·12	0·13	0·31	3·5	8·4	0·30	0·69	0·12	0·27	0·05	0·14	0·06	0·13	0·09	0·22	0·21	0·49
Zooplankton	0·30	0·11	0·19	0·11	0·82	0·34	20·0	10·3	1·5	0·65	0·60	0·24	0·12	0·05	0·21	0·10	0·50	0·23	0·72	0·31
Shrimp	nd	nd	2·0	0·18	0·91	0·08	83·0	7·2	2·4	0·21	nd	nd	1·8	0·16	0·70	0·06	4·5	0·39	1·2	0·11
Mussel	1·5	0·09	1·8	0·11	5·7	0·36	237	15·0	8·9	1·56	8·6	0·55	0·40	0·03	0·53	0·034	4·7	0·30	3·2	0·20
0-Group herring	9·9	0·28	13·1	0·43	22·7	0·64	765	22·4	45·2	1·20	10·6	0·27	2·6	0·08	9·5	0·33	17·1	0·46	11·3	0·29
0-Group plaice	1·5	0·09	4·4	0·26	5·1	0·31	290	17·8	10·5	0·64	3·1	0·19	1·1	0·07	2·2	0·14	5·0	0·30	3·3	0·20
3-Group herring	28·8	0·45	26·0	0·41	21·6	0·34	413	6·6	33·7	0·52	nd	nd	nd	nd	8·3	0·13	11·3	0·18	6·4	0·10
3-Group plaice	14·1	1·07	15·3	1·10	14·0	0·72	331	22·1	10·6	0·52	nd	nd	nd	nd	3·0	0·16	2·5	0·10	2·0	0·08
3-Group cod	1·6	0·70	2·5	1·25	1·2	0·59	51·7	23·6	1·4	0·68	nd	nd	0·28	0·17	1·0	0·57	0·27	0·13	0·38	0·15
Greatest difference with respect to phytoplankton	576x	9·7x	520x	9·2x	175x	3·9x	219x	2·8x	151x	3·3x	88x	2·0x	52x	4·7x	158x	4·4x	190x	2·2x	54x	6·1x

nd: Not detected. No detection limits quoted. Data for greatest difference does not include samples below limit of detection.

mesopelagic organisms. Exceptions to this general rule were observed, but no conclusion was reached as to why these compounds exhibited ratio differences.

Ten Berge and Hillebrand (1974) reported data for several organo-chlorines in biota from the North Sea and the Dutch Wadden Sea. All concentrations were reported using both wet weights and lipid weights as a basis. The results of these extensive studies are shown in Table 16. For all compounds, an increased concentration by wet weight was noted with trophic level. Differences in residue concentrations (wet weight) in phytoplankton and in the most contaminated higher organism varied from a factor of about 50 for pentachlorobenzene and γ-BHC (lindane) to about 200 for PCBs and over 500 for DDT and DDE. On a lipid weight basis, such differences were in all cases less than an order of magnitude and no consistent trends in concentration with trophic level were observed with the exception of DDT and DDE, where moderate increases in residue levels in higher organisms were found. These data are some of the most extensive reported to date; it is unfortunate that no high ranking predators were included.

Most of the above reports suffered from an inability to accurately define food-chain relationships in the studied organisms, in addition to non-synchronous collection of organisms of different trophic levels, or collection at differing locations. Fowler and Elder (1978) recognised these limitations and avoided them by sampling organisms of a relatively well-defined pelagic food chain (microplankton/macrozooplankton/shrimp/fish, confirmed by analysis of stomach contents), at a single location in the northern Mediterranean. Results from these studies were reported by dry weights of the organisms and, most unfortunately, lipid weights were not recorded. However, profiles based on dry weights (Table 17) were most unusual, revealing a decrease in concentrations of both DDE and PCBs with increased trophic level with the sole exception of DDE concentrations between trophic levels 1 and 2. Although other authors have occasionally noted similar trends (e.g. see Harvey *et al.*, 1974, discussed above), the elimination of time- and space-dependence of these data lend particular confidence to these results.

Data are also available in the literature which permit estimates of the amplification of organochlorines with trophic level in freshwater ecosystems. The classical paper by Hunt and Bischoff (1960), written almost 20 years ago, distinctly indicated amplification of DDD residues in the biota of Clear Lake, California, after this compound was used extensively as a pesticide against the gnat, *Chaoborus astictopus*. Although the concentrations of DDD in plankton were not established, these authors suggested (on the basis of concentrations by wet weight) that trophic level amplification was occurring, residues from fish being the major route of DDD uptake by the western grebe, *Aechmophorus occidentalis*, and causing high enough rates of ingestion to elicit death—as well as reproductive failure—in the birds. Some of these data were quoted as DDD in both edible flesh and visceral fat of the samples; this approximates a wet

TABLE 17

CONCENTRAIONS (μg/kg DRY WEIGHT) OF DDE AND PCBS IN PELAGIC COMPONENTS OF A DEFINED FOOD CHAIN, COLLECTED IN NOVEMBER, 1974 OFF VILLEFRANCHE-SUR-MER IN THE MEDITERRANEAN SEA. (AFTER FOWLER AND ELDER (1978).)

Organism(s)	Species name	Trophic level	DDE	PCBs
Microplankton	See note below[a]	1 and 2[a]	<0·5	4 500
Macrozooplankton	*Meganyctiphanes norvegica*	2	26	620
Shrimp	*Sergestes arcticus*	3	15	470
Shrimp	*Pasiphaea sivado*	3	5	210
Finfish	*Myctophus glaciale*	3 or 4[b]	1	50

[a] Microplankton consisted mainly of copepods, unidentified small crustaceans, chaetognaths, phytoplankton and detritus.
[b] *M. glaciale* preys on *Meganyctiphanes norvegica* (trophic level 2) and other pelagic crustaceans of trophic levels 2 and 3.

weight: lipid weight basis for concentrations and the data, although incomplete, suggested that food chain amplification was less or absent on a lipid weight basis. A later report on Clear Lake (Herman *et al.*, 1969) substantiated these general conclusions and also included data describing the correlation of DDD residue levels in grebe tissues to the total lipid contents of the tissues (Fig. 14); residues in eggs and hatchlings were also extremely concentrated, again due mainly to the high lipid contents of these life stages.

More recently, Hannon *et al.* (1970) reported the results of a systematic investigation of organochlorines in ecosystem components of Lake Poinsett in South Dakota. Data from this paper concerning food chain amplification of organochlorines were reported by wet weight only. Using this weight basis, ΣDDT was found to increase with trophic level and this was correlated to lower ratios of DDT to its metabolites, DDE and DDD. A similar increase in epoxide metabolites of aldrin and heptachlor (dieldrin and heptachlor epoxide) compared with their parent compounds was also noted with trophic level. These data suggest that DDT, aldrin and

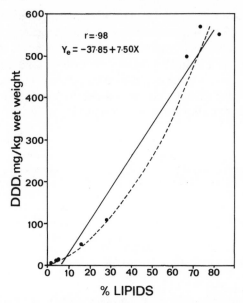

FIG. 14.   Mean concentrations of DDD (mg/kg wet weight) in the tissues of western grebes, *Aechmophorus occidentalis*, from Clear Lake and their relation to total lipid contents of the tissues. Tissues plotted, in order of increasing lipid levels, are leg muscle, liver, breast muscle, ovaries, uropygial glands, subcutaneous fat, visceral fat and thigh fat. Brain and testes omitted due to analytical difficulties in the extraction of lipids. Data were fitted by both linear and exponential regressions; the correlation coefficient is for the linear regression and is significant at $p < 0.001$.
(After Herman *et al.* (1969).)

heptachlor were transferred between organisms of successive trophic levels mainly by ingestion of food, with direct uptake of such compounds from water playing a relatively minor role; breakdown of the parent compounds to their metabolites may have occurred at several points of the food chain (see also Woodwell *et al.*, 1967).

Hamelink *et al.* (1971) studied the concentrations of DDT and its metabolites in components of experimental ecosystems, one of which was natural and four artificial. The comparison of the levels of ΣDDT in fish from ecosystems where the food chain was intact and functioning, and where the food chain was broken by removal of invertebrates, suggested that the food chain was not instrumental in the accumulation of ΣDDT residues by the higher predator. However, residue levels (by wet weights) in each component of the food chain were consistent with trophic level amplification, i.e. concentrations of ΣDDT increased with each step in the food chain in all studies (Table 18). The authors suggested that these data could be explained only if the food chain were insignificant in the dynamics of ΣDDT in the studied ecosystems and therefore proposed that DDT was absorbed directly from water by the organisms by a lipid–water partition process. Data for invertebrates supported this theory, a linear correlation being found between ΣDDT concentrations in water and those in the organisms. Consideration of the concentration factors attained by

TABLE 18

CONCENTRATION FACTORS (WHOLE ORGANISM CONCENTRATION BY WET WEIGHT RELATED TO THAT IN THE WATER) FOR ΣDDT IN ALGAE, INVERTEBRATES AND FINFISH OF VARIOUS SPECIES USED IN STUDIES OF DDT DYNAMICS IN LENTIC ENVIRONMENTS BY HAMELINK *et al.* (1971)

| Year | Study | DDT addition | Concentration factor attained | | |
			Algae	Invertebrates	Fish
1965	Natural pond study	15 μg/litre to water	20 000	28 750	363 000
1966	Artificial pool study	5 μg/litre to water	5 789	27 868	317 000
1967	'Pool hydrosoil' study	0·05 mg/kg to sand[a]	7 700	20 000	78 500
		1·0 mg/kg to sand[a]	1 843	11 687	76 000
		10·0 mg/kg to sand[a]	770	5 941	23 125

[a] Concentrations in sand by dry weight; no addition to water.

invertebrates in 1965 and 1966 studies (Table 18) and their fat content of about 2 per cent, suggested a partition coefficient of the order of 10^6, although it was noted that this was species- and lipid-dependent, as well as time-dependent (equilibration would not be instantaneous). In fish, the authors suggested DDT was taken up primarily at the gills, passing by direct partitioning from water to blood and thence to lipids in the different tissues (see also Holden, 1962). Partition coefficients were suggested to be about 10^4 between blood and water and 10^3 between lipid and blood, i.e. a combined total of about 10^7. A lipid content of 1 per cent in the fish would then lead to an observed concentration factor of about 10^5, in reasonable agreement with the experimental data shown in Table 18. This suggestion of lipid–water partitioning as the major route of organochlorine uptake by organisms is attractive for several reasons. First, it explains the differences in net uptake of different organochlorines, as each will exhibit a partition coefficient based on its water solubility (increased solubility leading to lower partition coefficients) and its affinity for the specific lipids present in organisms. Several authors have supported the concept of organochlorine persistence in aquatic biota being related to the water solubility of the compound considered (see below). Secondly, the entire dependence of organochlorine levels on lipid contents and distribution in biota may be readily understood given this mechanism of uptake. (However, the dependence of organochlorines on lipid may also be explained on the basis of a food chain amplification hypothesis.) Finally, Hamelink *et al.* (1971) also suggested that such a mechanism might explain the differences in organochlorine persistence in biota of oligotrophic and eutrophic lakes, the latter containing a greater organic content in bottom sediments and therefore sequestering more of the water-borne contaminant. Other mechanisms may also explain such a difference, however; for example, in eutrophic lakes a higher standing crop of phytoplankton might be expected to accumulate less contaminant per cell at a given exposure level, thus leading to lower concentrations in secondary and higher consumers if the food chain were predominant in the passage of residues through the biota of ecosystems.

These suggestions of Hamelink *et al.* (1971) have received some support from other authors. Sanborn and Yu (1973) studied dieldrin dynamics in the model ecosystem used previously by Metcalf *et al.* (1971) for studies of DDT and methoxychlor. The behaviour of DDT and dieldrin was similar in some respects; both accumulated to high levels in the biota (although concentration factors for DDT were generally greater than those noted for dieldrin), and dieldrin was resistant to biodegradation; DDT was metabolised to DDE, but this compound resisted further degradation. The concentrations of each compound attained in components of the ecosystem did not vary consistently with trophic level when based on organism wet weights; unfortunately lipid weights were not quoted. The inability of these authors to demonstrate consistent residue amplification with trophic level may be interpreted as support for lipid–water partitioning theory of organochlorine uptake, although confidence in this conclusion would be greater if lipid weight-based data were available for support. Similarly, Södergren *et al.* (1972) found that levels of ΣDDT and PCBs in organisms from streams in the south of Sweden bore no consistent relationship to trophic level. In addition, no consistent trends in the DDT: DDE ratio were evident with position of the sampled organisms in the food web and these data are probably more understandable on the basis of a lipid–water partitioning theory of organochlorine uptake than by food chain amplification mechanisms. In a later paper, Södergren (1973) published the results of studies on DDT, DDE and PCBs (Clophen A50) in a model freshwater ecosystem. Algae absorbed all compounds rapidly and the author assumed that concentrations in higher organisms were attained via the food web, as the concentrations of organochlorines in the water and air phases of the ecosystem were below detection limits. However, this conclusion is patently insufficient as a test of uptake routes, as significant lipid–water partitioning could occur dynamically with only minute amounts in the water column at any one time. The metabolic transformation of DDT to DDE observed represents somewhat better evidence of food chain transfer, but both this and the selective loss of PCB components might be explained by selective uptake of the compounds from solution, or by metabolism after uptake from solution.

More recently, Hamelink and Waybrant (1976) reported investigations of the fate of DDE and lindane in the natural ecosystem of a limestone quarry in Indiana. The great difference in water solubility of these two compounds (Gunther *et al.*, 1968) correlated to their behaviour after addition, DDE being largely removed from the water column by sedimentation in association with inorganic and organic particulates, whilst lindane remained in solution throughout the experiment. DDE was nevertheless available to pelagic biota, presumably via a sediment/water dynamic equilibrium, which may have been temperature sensitive. Concerning biota, the concentration factors observed for DDE were about 10^3 times greater than those for lindane in zooplankton, whereas in invertebrates and bluegills the ratio of concentration factors was about 150. Lindane exhibited faster equilibration than DDE, which could be related to the smaller amount of the former compound absorbed by the organisms. These results in general supported a lipid–water partitioning theory of organochlorine uptake, although such a mechanism was affected by other parameters also; age of the organism selected was considered to be one of these interfering parameters (see Chapter 8).

(ii) Laboratory Studies of Organochlorine Kinetics in Food Chains or Single Species

Both the positive and negative aspects of the use of laboratory studies to clarify field situations may be seen in the reports of authors employing such methods to investigate the apparent trophic level amplification of organochlorines. The positive aspect is that laboratory studies may investigate organochlorine kinetics in single species or defined food chains and the exposure route may be varied at will. The negative aspect is that, too often, results are obtained using exposure levels which are completely unrepresentative of those in the field; thus conclusions from these studies may not be realistically applied to the environment.

The most basic difference between the lipid–water partitioning and food chain amplification hypotheses of organochlorine accumulation by biota is that the former presupposes that these compounds are derived mainly from solution whereas, under a food chain amplification theory, organochlorines are derived mainly via ingested food (with the exception of primary producers). Results from laboratory studies may be considered in the light of this distinction in an attempt to clarify the major method involved in the accumulation of organochlorine by biota.

It is clear from various reports in the literature that both marine and freshwater organisms will accumulate organochlorines relatively rapidly from either water or food. With respect to marine biota, Brodtmann (1970) demonstrated a rapid uptake of DDT by the oyster, *Crassostrea virginica*, when this species was exposed for six hours to various concentrations of this compound in water, adsorbed to powdered milk. Uptake was apparent in gills especially, and possibly via the gut. Elimination of DDT was also found to be rapid in these experiments. Nimmo *et al.* (1970) also found rapid uptake of DDT from solution; these authors used polyethylene glycol as a solubilising agent for studies on adult pink and white shrimp, *Penaeus duorarum* and *P. setiferus*. Residues in the body correlated to the lipid contents of the tissues. Wildish and Zitko (1971), in studies of PCB uptake by the littoral amphipod, *Gammarus oceanicus*, used a non-ionic surfactant for solubilisation. Again, uptake from solution was rapid and may have occurred across the general integument. The amount of PCB accumulated was apparently dependent on the surface area of the organism (size), the exposure time and the exposure concentration. Amongst other reports on the accumulation of organochlorines via food are those of Petrocelli *et al.* (1975*a*, *b*), in which dieldrin transfer through a food chain comprising the phytoplankter, *Dunaliella peircei*, the clam, *Rangia cuneata*, and the blue crab, *Callinectes sapidus*, was studied. A 'biomagnification' of 54 times was claimed between the phytoplankter and the clam, but this refers to the concentration in the clam versus the concentration in the water after algae were added, which is a curious comparison at best. A much better comparison is that of algal concentration of dieldrin versus clam concentration, which leads to a factor of 0·15. Therefore, in terms of the wet weight concentration of dieldrin in these organisms, levels in the clam were about one-seventh of those in the food; the low final concentration in the clam may be due to the short feeding time of only 24 h; equilibrium conditions were obviously not attained. In the later paper (Petrocelli *et al.*, 1975*b*), calculations of 'biomagnification' were again most unusual. Recalculation of these data, some of which are extremely variable for no apparent reason, resulted in average magnification factors (dieldrin concentration in crabs versus that in food) of 0·17 for a five-day exposure and 0·13–0·53 for a ten-day exposure. Obviously, equilibrium conditions were again not attained. Unfortunately, no lipid data are quoted and calculation of the ratio of lipid-based residue levels in 'predator' and food is thus impossible.

Concerning organisms from freshwater environments, several reports exist which show that, like marine biota, these species accumulate organochlorines rapidly from either solution or via food. Crosby and Tucker (1971) produced similar results for DDT uptake by *Daphnia magna* to those of Wildish and Zitko (1971) cited above. DDT, introduced in acetone, was rapidly taken up, principally through the carapace. Final concentration factors were between 16 000 and 23 000 at exposure concentrations of 8 and 50 μg/litre DDT. Johnson *et al.* (1971) found rapid uptake of both DDT and aldrin by ten species of freshwater invertebrates when exposed to these compounds at levels below one part per billion (10^9) in solution. Uptake was time-dependent, concentration factors increasing in a linear fashion with exposure period. Some degradation of DDT to DDE, DDD and more polar metabolites was observed. For finfish, several authors have demonstrated a similar rapid uptake of DDT and other organochlorines from solution, occurring principally across the gills (e.g. see Holden, 1962; Gakstatter, 1968; Murphy, 1970, 1971). Grzenda *et al.* (1970, 1971) have shown that DDT and dieldrin are also absorbed from ingested food by goldfish, *Carassius auratus*, and this uptake is dose-dependent, although some differences were noted between the uptake kinetics of the two compounds. Warlen *et al.* (1977) also observed dose-dependent uptake of DDT from the diet by Atlantic menhaden, *Brevoortia tyrannus*. Uptake by this species was linear with time for an exposure period of 48 days; at this time, the concentrations attained were similar to those present in the food. The percentage retention of DDT was rather less with an increase in the dietary concentration, however, varying from 27 per cent at exposure levels of 0·58 μg/kg in food, through 17 per cent at 9 μg/kg to 19 per cent at 92 μg/kg exposure.

It is therefore abundantly clear that both exposure routes permit the uptake of organochlorines by biota. However, the studies cited above concern one route or the other only, and it is thus difficult to compare the relative importance of each route in the environment. However, a few reports exist in which both routes were studied for the same species, and these may lead to a clearer picture. Epifanio (1971, 1972, 1973) published excellent studies on the uptake of dieldrin by larvae of the crab, *Leptodius floridanus*. Both solution and food routes were studied independently, exposure levels in the later studies being 0·5 µg/litre in solution and 213 µg/kg (by dry weight) in food, consisting of nauplii of the brine shrimp *Artemia salina*. The results are shown in Fig. 15. Accumulation of dieldrin from solution was 19·1 times faster than that from food at the exposure levels tested. At first sight these data suggest that the food route is insignificant for the uptake of organochlorines. However, to relate these

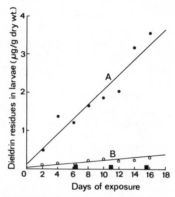

FIG. 15. The uptake of dieldrin by larvae of the crab, *Leptodius floridanus*, exposed to this compound in (A) water, at 0·5 µg/litre, and (B) food, at 213 µg/kg by dry weight. Crab larvae were exposed from the time of hatching; reference marks on the horizontal axis indicate mean times of zoeal moults. Regression lines were calculated by least-squares analysis. (After Epifanio (1973).)

data to the environment one must consider the ratio of the concentrations used in each route. Epifanio (1973) includes this calculation at the end of his paper, suggesting field concentrations of 0·002 µg/litre in solution and 20 µg/kg in food. This is a ratio of 10^4, as opposed to the ratio of 416 actually used in his experiments. Use of these data reveals that crab larvae in the field would accumulate dieldrin from water only 1·2 times as fast as from food. Thus one might expect 45 per cent of the total body load to be derived from food and 55 per cent to be derived from water under field conditions.

More recently, Scura and Theilacker (1977) reported laboratory studies on the transfer of PCBs through a marine food chain, using the novel method of bubbling the ambient air through test solutions as a method of introducing PCBs. No surfactant or organic compound was used for solubilisation of the contaminant and exposure levels were very low, being similar to the concentrations found in near-shore waters of California (2·3–14·0 ng/litre or parts per 10^{12}). The food chain consisted of a phytoplankter, *Dunaliella* sp., the rotifer, *Brachionus plicatilis*, and the larva of the northern anchovy, *Engraulis mordax*. The first samples were taken after five days of exposure, at which time each trophic level was found to be at equilibrium concentrations; uptake of PCBs was thus rapid by all organisms. More importantly, anchovy larvae were found to exhibit the same concentration of PCBs at day 5 and thereafter, whether fed or not fed, the concentration at equilibrium apparently depending on that in the

TABLE 19

MEAN CONCENTRATIONS OF PCBS (μg/g BY DRY WEIGHTS OR LIPID WEIGHTS; QUANTITATED BY REFERENCE TO AROCLOR 1254) IN ALGAE, ROTIFERS AND ANCHOVY LARVAE DURING AN EXPOSURE PERIOD OF 45 DAYS, ALL ORGANISMS BEING AT EQUILIBRIUM THROUGHOUT. (AFTER SCURA AND THEILACKER (1977).)

Organism	Per cent lipid	PCB concentration (μg/g)		Mean exposure concentration (ng/litre)	Partition coefficient[a] ($\times 10^6$)
		Dry weight	Lipid weight		
Dunaliella sp.	6·4	0·25	3·91	8·2	0·48
Brachionus plicatilis	15·0	0·42	2·80	8·2	0·34
Engraulis mordax	7·5	2·06	27·46	2·0	13·73

[a] Calculated as ratio of concentration in organism by lipid weight and exposure concentration.

seawater. These authors therefore supported a lipid/water partitioning mechanism as the major uptake route of PCBs. However, other data from the same paper lead to different conclusions. Thus, consideration of the concentrations attained with trophic level showed a stepwise amplification of residues if dry weights were used as a basis (Table 19). Using lipid weights as a basis abolished the difference between the alga and the rotifer, but concentrations of PCBs in the anchovy larvae were an order of magnitude greater. If these organisms were at equilibrium and PCB concentrations were dominated by lipid–water partitioning, the concentrations should have been similar in each organism by lipid weights, i.e. the calculated partition coefficients should have been similar. The fact that partition coefficients for the anchovy larvae were some 28–40 times greater than those for the other organisms studied (Table 19) is difficult to explain on the basis of simple chemical partitioning unless a large difference in lipid type exists between the species used. In addition, calculations of the dietary intake of PCBs indicated that the amount in the diets of the rotifer and the fish larvae were adequate to account for the entire body load of PCBs in these predators. It is clear, therefore, that in this case the argument concerning the derivation of PCBs was meaningless; either route could apparently account for the total body load of PCBs in the fish larvae and, in fact, continuous dynamic exchange of PCBs might have been occurring throughout the maintenance of equilibrium conditions.

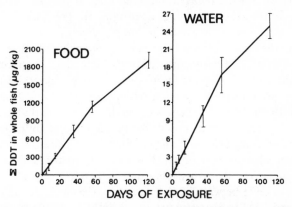

FIG. 16. Concentrations of ΣDDT (μg/kg by wet weight) in brook trout, *Salvelinus fontinalis*, exposed to either $3 \cdot 0 \pm 0 \cdot 15 \, \mu g/g$ DDT in dry pellet feed, or $3 \cdot 0 \pm 0 \cdot 3 \, ng/litre$ DDT in water. (After Macek and Korn (1970).)

Considering freshwater biota again, a few studies have been reported in which both food and solution routes of organochlorine uptake were studied. Macek and Korn (1970) studied the kinetics of DDT uptake in brook trout, *Salvelinus fontinalis*. Exposure levels were considered to approximate those in Lake Michigan, being $3 \cdot 0 \, ng/litre$ in solution and $3 \, mg/kg$ in food, using $1 \cdot 5$ per cent body weight per day rations. Net uptake curves are shown in Fig. 16; mean final concentrations of ΣDDT attained were $1920 \, \mu g/kg$ in fish receiving contaminated food and $25 \cdot 6 \, \mu g/kg$ in fish exposed to DDT in water. Neither group of test fish reached equilibrium conditions, or perhaps equilibrium conditions were altering in such a fashion as to mimic constant uptake; this last possibility is included speculatively as these fish were fed high-lipid rations and may have exhibited significantly increased total body lipid contents during the experiment. Unfortunately, no lipid data were included in the paper. Clearly, uptake from food was highly predominant in this study. However, two criticisms are necessary. First, the DDT in water was introduced as a water/acetone stock solution. Although subsequent dilution of this stock solution would decrease the acetone content greatly, the presence of even minute amounts of an organic chemical must alter the lipid–water partition coefficient, as noted by Scura and Theilacker (1977). Secondly, the ratios of the DDT content of food and water are perhaps rather high, as noted by Reinert (1972), although this would probably not account for a large proportion of the difference noted between the two routes.

Reinert (1967, 1972) reported somewhat contradictory data to this, based on studies of the accumulation of dieldrin by the green alga, *Scenedesmus obliquus*, *Daphnia magna*, and the guppy, *Poecilia reticulata*. Both *D. magna* and the guppy accumulated more dieldrin directly from water than from food which had been exposed to the same dieldrin concentration in water. The results of previous authors were cited as support for this pattern of dieldrin accumulation by biota (see Lenon, 1968 and Chadwick and Brocksen, 1969). The differences between this report and that of Macek and Korn (1970) cited above could be based on the differences in the compound studied. However, the solubility of dieldrin in water is about $100\,\mu g$/litre, whereas that of DDT is at least ten times and probably a hundred times less than this. One would therefore expect the partition coefficient of DDT between lipids and water to be much greater than that of dieldrin, and DDT to be taken up from water by biota at a correspondingly faster rate. Both authors used acetone to solubilise the studied compound in stock solutions. Possibly, as Reinert (1972) suggests, the difference between the studies may be due to differences in complexation of the organochlorines in the test solutions, leading to large variation in the amount which was actually available for uptake by biota.

More recently, Jarvinen *et al.* (1977) published the results of investigations concerning the uptake of DDT from food and water by the fathead minnow, *Pimephales promelas*. The food source consisted of chopped tissue from five species of clams previously exposed to ^{14}C-DDT; DDT was maintained in solution during all exposures by use of acetone. Use of the ^{14}C label only in food allowed separation of the DDT from this route and that taken up from solution. The results showed that residues accumulated from food were additional to those taken up directly from solution in minnows exposed to DDT from both routes simultaneously; mortality rates of the exposed fish and their progeny confirmed this observation. At nominal exposure levels of $2 \cdot 0\,\mu g$/litre for both food organisms and test organisms (mean measured concentrations of $1 \cdot 48$–$1 \cdot 53\,\mu g$/litre), the uptake of DDT from food constituted about 27 per cent of the total uptake, with no particular time-dependence being observed in this value. Equivalent figures from other authors are 10 per cent for guppies (Reinert, 1967, 1972) and 16 per cent or less in sculpins (Chadwick and Brocksen, 1969).

(iii) Conclusions Concerning Trophic Level Variations in Organochlorines

At first sight one would expect that the elucidation of the major uptake routes of organochlorines in biota would be relatively simple. However, this is clearly not the case, as evidenced by the contradictions in the published data cited above. In the laboratory, studies have been hampered by the practical difficulties of solubilising organochlorines in water. Even if the final concentration of toxicant used is less than the solubility of that compound, the design of most continuous flow bioassay equipment entails the use of a more concentrated stock solution, in which an organic solvent must be present to afford reasonable homogeneity of the solution. In this respect, the method of Scura and Theilacker (1977) (see above) appears of considerable value as a means of toxicant introduction to test solutions; however, the air used should be monitored for other contaminants also, some of which might conceivably alter the uptake of organochlorines by the test organism. In addition, laboratory studies must employ toxicant concentrations which are known to be below the limit of solubility of the compound used. If this simple precaution is not observed, the apparent partition coefficient will be underestimated (Butler, 1970). Finally, it is necessary to reiterate the warnings of Harvey *et al.* (1974), with which this section was started; the feeding habits of aquatic organisms in the field are often poorly understood and may vary from population to population. Laboratory studies, either on simple food chains or on model ecosystems, cannot accurately mimic field conditions; indeed, the aim should not be to duplicate conditions in the environment but to simplify the essential aspects of field situations, thus aiding the ready interpretation of data from both laboratory and (by extension) true environmental studies.

Production of an all-embracing hypothesis which satisfies all the data cited above is not easy. Most of the data suggest that organisms absorb organochlorines more rapidly from water than from food and that the contribution per unit time of residues from the food chain to the total body load of an organism is rather less than 30 per cent. However, this in itself must depend on the trophic level considered. The most important parameter which defines the relative uptake of organochlorines from each route is the relative concentration of these compounds in the food and water to which an organism is exposed. Thus, Macek and Korn (1970), using a ratio of 10^6, (3 μg/g in food and 3 ng/litre in water) found predominance of the food route, whereas the studies of Reinert (1967, 1972), Lenon (1968),

Chadwick and Brocksen (1969) and Jarvinen *et al.* (1977), all of which used food:water exposure concentration ratios between 1 and 2 orders of magnitude less than that of Macek and Korn, agreed that uptake of organochlorines from solution was the more important route.

If this argument is extended to members of different trophic levels in aquatic environments, the situation is somewhat clarified. Phytoplankton and other primary producers obviously take up organochlorines from solution, presumably by a mechanism approximating lipid–water partitioning. It may be noted that this step is by far the greatest amplification of residues found in any single step of the food chain. By contrast to primary producers, all organisms of trophic level 2 or greater are exposed to organochlorines in both water and food. However, the ratio of the concentrations in solution and in food differs with trophic level, because of the well established increase in wet weight-based levels of organochlorines up the food chain. For organisms of trophic level 2, which feed on primary producers, a typical food:water concentration ratio would be about 10^3 or 10^4. By contrast, seals of trophic level 5, which might feed on salmon or cod, for example (Holden, 1972a), would be exposed to food concentrations of organochlorines at least 10^5 or 10^6 times greater than those in the ambient water. In addition, seals or other high ranking aquatic predators are of a generally greater size than are finfish, which, in turn, are larger than most biota representing the second trophic level. A larger size of biota is accompanied by a decreased surface area:volume ratio and equilibration of residues by lipid–water partitioning at the body surface would thus be a much slower process. The increased predominance of the food route of organochlorine uptake with each step up the food chain is accompanied by an increase in the storage of lipid by organisms, which provides a larger sequestration pool for residues. These effects of total body lipid on the uptake of organochlorines were graphically illustrated by Roberts *et al.* (1977) in studies of chlordane uptake by a single species of freshwater finfish, the northern redhorse sucker, *Moxostoma macrolepidotum*. Using methylmercury labelled with ^{203}Hg as a tracer, these authors showed that tissue retention of both the *cis*-isomer and the *trans*-isomer of chlordane was directly proportional to the size of the lipid pool in the individual, i.e. to individual fatness or adiposity. This increased retention of chlordane by fish containing greater amounts of lipid was observed whether uptake occurred from solution or via ingested food. The authors calculated that the equilibrium concentration of chlordane in these fish would not exceed that in the food unless the adiposity of the individual were greater than average. A similar effect of total body lipid on the extent of hydrocarbon

TABLE 20

LEVELS OF ORGANOCHLORINE COMPOUNDS IN THE MUSCLE AND LIVER OF COHO SALMON, *Oncorhynchus kisutch*, AND IN THE EGGS OF HERRING GULLS, *Larus argentatus*, RELATIVE TO THEIR LEVELS IN POOLED STOMACH CONTENTS OF THE SALMON (ALEWIVES AND SMELT). THESE DATA REPRESENT A 'BIOMAGNIFICATION RATIO' FROM PREY TO EACH PREDATOR. (AFTER NORSTROM *et al.* (1978).)

Species and tissue	mg/kg:mg/kg in alewives and smelt									
	PCBs	DDE	DDD	Mirex	Photomirex	HCB	β-HCH	Oxychlordane	Heptachlor epoxide	Dieldrin
Coho salmon muscle	2·6	2·1	2·3	2·5	3·7	4·0	6·0	1·6	5·0	3·0
Coho salmon liver	1·0	0·9	1·6	1·1	1·4	2·7	5·0	1·3	2·3	2·1
Herring gull egg	60	37	3	48	55	22	39	20	41	11

accumulation was reported for the oyster, *Crassostrea virginica*, by Stegeman (1974) but, surprisingly, these are the only two such reports known to date.

On the basis of the above arguments, lipid–water partitioning is suggested to be more important in organisms of lower trophic levels, whilst the uptake of organochlorines from food is predominant in biota of higher trophic levels. The result of this is a general increase in the concentration of organochlorines on a wet weight basis with increased trophic level; lipid weight-based data would exhibit a less marked increase. It should also be noted that for lower trophic levels, where lipid–water partitioning predominates, organisms are more likely to be equilibrated with ambient levels. If this is so, the uptake of organochlorines via both routes is balanced by their excretion, and the argument as to which route predominates becomes meaningless, except as a means of maintaining equilibrium by excretion. The data of Norstrom *et al.* (1978) are interesting in this respect. These authors studied the levels of several organochlorines in fish and herring gulls from Lake Ontario. Both coho salmon, *Oncorhynchus kisutch*, and herring gulls depend largely on alewives and smelt for food in this ecosystem, but the salmon exhibited much lower levels of organochlorines than did the eggs of the gulls, despite similar lipid contents (Table 20). Unfortunately, no data were reported concerning the gulls themselves. However, it would appear probable that the salmon, although ingesting similar amounts of organochlorines from food as gulls (and taking up more organochlorines from solution than gulls), are nevertheless far more able to excrete these compounds and maintain low concentrations. Presumably gulls may lose organochlorines only in faeces and urine, whereas the salmon may take advantage of the lipid–water partition to achieve organochlorine loss. Thus lipid–water partitioning may be as important for excretion of organochlorine residues in aquatic biota as for their uptake.

F.   INTERACTIONS BETWEEN ORGANOCHLORINE EXPOSURE AND LIPID CONTENT IN BIOTA

Occasional reports have appeared in the literature which suggest that the exposure of biota to organochlorines may increase or decrease lipogenesis in biota. Thus, not only are lipids important in the storage of organochlorines, but these compounds may also alter the percentage of lipids present in some organisms which may, in the case of positive effects on lipogenesis, lead to a circular interaction of organochlorine uptake/

increased lipogenesis. All these reports concern freshwater finfish. It is noteworthy in this respect that the lipid contents of finfish kept in the laboratory may increase due to the unusual lipid constituents in commercial pellet food (see Section B(ii) above); thus it is important to consider whether these reports of increased lipids ascribed to the exposure of finfish to organochlorines are, in fact, due to the feeding regime employed.

TABLE 21

PERCENTAGE LIPIDS (OF THE DRY CARCASS WEIGHT) IN WHOLE RAINBOW TROUT, *Salmo gairdneri*, EXPOSED TO DDT AND/OR DIELDRIN AT VARIOUS LEVELS IN PELLET FEED FOR 140 DAYS. VALUES FOR LIPIDS ARE EXPRESSED AS A MEAN ± STANDARD ERROR FOR EIGHT INDIVIDUALS PER TREATMENT AND WERE ESTIMATED BY EXTRACTION WITH DIETHYL ETHER. (AFTER MACEK *et al.* (1970).)

Treatment	Dietary exposure level (mg/kg/week)	Percentage lipid
Control	$<0.03^a$	10.34 ± 0.3
DDT	0.20	9.02 ± 1.7
DDT	1.00	14.52 ± 2.0^b
Dieldrin	0.20	12.70 ± 1.4^b
Dieldrin	1.00	13.20 ± 1.4^b
DDT + dieldrin	$1.00 + 1.00$	17.06 ± 0.8^b

[a] Untreated pellet food contained ΣDDT equivalent to a dosage of 0.014–0.028 mg/kg per week.

[b] Significantly different from control group by Student's t test ($p < 0.05$).

Buhler *et al.* (1969) studied the uptake of DDT from the diet in juveniles of both coho salmon, *Oncorhynchus kisutch*, and chinook salmon, *O. tshawytscha*. The lipid content of whole coho salmon increased as the DDT content of the diet increased; however, no such effect was recorded for chinook salmon. In a similar report, Macek *et al.* (1970), in long-term studies of the kinetics of DDT and dieldrin in rainbow trout, *Salmo gairdneri*, exposed to these compounds in the diet, found increased lipogenesis in treated fish compared with controls. Over the 140 days of exposure neither organochlorine affected growth of the trout (in terms of weight or length), and no significant mortality increase over controls was found. However, fish treated with high DDT concentrations, dieldrin or both pollutants in combination, exhibited significantly increased lipid levels compared with controls; by contrast, fish exposed to the lower DDT concentration did not differ from controls (Table 21). The effects of DDT

TABLE 22

TOTAL BODY LIPIDS (MEAN ± STANDARD ERROR, $n = 10$; CHLOROFORM–METHANOL EXTRACTION) AND RELATIVE PERCENTAGES OF MONO-, DI- AND TRIGLYCERIDES IN WHOLE MATURE MALE GOLDFISH, *Carassius auratus*, EXPOSED TO ENDRIN AT VARIOUS DOSAGE LEVELS IN PELLET FOOD FOR 104 DAYS. DIFFERENTIAL GLYCERIDES WERE DETERMINED BY TLC ON TWO POOLED SAMPLES OF FIVE FISH EACH FOR EACH TREATMENT. (AFTER GRANT AND MEHRLE (1970).)

Parameter	Control	Dosage level (μg endrin per kilogramme body weight per day)			
		4·30	14·3	43·0	143·0
Total body lipids (per cent)	6·11 ± 0·41	6·83 ± 0·64	11·31 ± 1·28[a]	7·92 ± 0·26[a]	8·69 ± 0·78[a]
Differential glycerides:					
Monoglycerides (per cent)	20	9	18	13	10
Diglycerides (per cent)	40	29	18	25	13
Triglycerides (per cent)	40	62	64	62	77

[a] Significantly different total body lipids from control ($p < 0.05$ on Fisher's t test).

and dieldrin in combination were additive, fish from this treatment group exhibiting higher lipid contents than those of any other exposure group. These changes in the lipid contents of treated trout were not apparent at 84 days after the commencement of treatment, but were apparent at 140 days —the time of the next sampling. They did not appear to be artefacts of the artificial diet, as both controls and treated fish were fed at the same level of 2 per cent of body weight per day.

Endrin is also known to affect the lipid contents of freshwater finfish when administered in the diet. Grant and Mehrle (1970) fed endrin-contaminated pellet food to goldfish, *Carassius auratus*, for 157 days at doses of 4·3 to 430 µg endrin per kilogramme body weight per day, maintaining a control group on the same food with no endrin added. Decreased growth was evident in the test group receiving the highest endrin concentration, but was not found at lower exposure levels. Serum cholesterol appeared unaffected at all exposure concentrations. However, both total and differential body lipids were affected by endrin exposure (Table 22). Total body lipids increased in proportion to exposure level between 0 and 143 µg/kg/day, but body lipids in the fish exposed to higher endrin concentrations, whilst significantly greater than controls, were less than those of fish fed on 14·3 µg/kg/day. The use of thin layer chromatography revealed that changes occurred in the relative proportions of mono-, di- and triglycerides, a general decrease in mono- and diglycerides occurring concomitant to increased triglyceride levels. A later report concerning the effects of dietary endrin on rainbow trout, *Salmo gairdneri* (Grant and Mehrle, 1973), did not include study of total body lipids but, in this case, serum cholesterol was found to be affected by exposure to endrin.

Resistance to endrin, or to other organochlorines, is known to occur in finfish populations which receive chronic organochlorine inputs, usually in areas of agricultural use of these compounds as pesticides (see, for example, Grant, 1976). The level of resistance may correlate to the degree of contamination and is also species-dependent, as well as varying with the particular organochlorine considered. The phenomenon of resistance appears to be hereditary, i.e. is genetically based. Several methods of resistance appear to occur, including decreased permeability to the pollutant, unusually high excretion rates and tolerance of extremely high tissue concentrations of organochlorines. In at least one instance, tolerance of high concentrations of endrin in the tissues has been shown to be due to an increase in total body lipids which provide a sequestration point for the toxicant (Fabacher and Chambers, 1971). This represents an unusual example of the effects of organochlorines on lipogenesis in fish in that it is hereditary in nature, but it may be used to indicate that the effects of organochlorines on the lipid content of finfish are not restricted to the laboratory.

The effects of dieldrin on lipids in freshwater finfish may differ somewhat from those of DDT or endrin. Silbergeld (1973) exposed johny darters, *Etheostoma nigrum*, to 2·3 μg/litre dieldrin in solution for 30 days and noted a resulting weight loss and reduction in lipid content of treated fish compared with controls. The reduced lipid content might be a function of either decreased lipogenesis or increased lipolysis in the dieldrin-exposed fish and the latter could be linked to a decreased efficiency of lipid assimilation from the diet. Phillips and Buhler (1979), in studies of dieldrin effects on growth and body composition of fingerling rainbow trout, *Salmo gairdneri*, fed a natural or artificial diet, observed similar effects. Thus, dieldrin reduced fat elaboration in trout fed tubificid worms, but such an effect was not found in trout fed on artificial pellet food.

Amongst other aspects of the interaction between organochlorines and lipids in finfish, the effects of lipid on the metabolism of DDT might be mentioned. It is, of course, well known that DDT can be metabolised to either DDE or DDD by a wide range of organisms, although some species lack such an ability and most exhibit a fairly specific breakdown to one metabolite or the other. To a large extent, the persistence of DDT in the aquatic environment depends not on its own ubiquity but on that of its metabolite DDE, which is often present in amounts exceeding those of the parent compound. By contrast, DDD is less common in aquatic biota, as it is much less persistent than either DDT or DDE; an exception is Clear Lake, where DDD was actually employed as a pesticide in its own right (see discussion of Hunt and Bischoff, 1960, in section E(i) above).

The ability of marine and freshwater finfish to metabolise DDT to one or other of the primary metabolites is well documented (e.g. see Greer and Paim, 1968; Cherrington *et al.*, 1969; Ernst and Goerke, 1974; Addison and Zinck, 1975; Addison *et al.*, 1976). Such metabolism is often slow, and may be due to some extent to intestinal microorganisms; the rate of degradation may be temperature-sensitive (Zinck and Addison, 1975).

The metabolism of DDT to DDE, DDD and further metabolites is important in terms of the persistence of such compounds in biota, as each of these species exhibits a unique biological half-time in any organism (see Chapter 2). Jensen *et al.* (1975) have suggested that the ratios of DDT to DDE and/or DDD in finfish might depend on the amount of body lipid present in the fish, as low-fat fish would be expected to turn over lipid reserves faster than high-fat fish. Lipid turnover presumably liberates sequestered DDT, allowing its relocation and possible metabolism. This concept is supported by a recent report of Addison and Zinck (1977). These authors injected fingerlings of the brook trout *Salvelinus fontinalis* with DDT, DDE, DDD or DDMU. The dehydrochlorination of DDT was found to be unaffected by pretreatment with any of the metabolites or with DDT itself, suggesting that metabolism of the parent compound is not inducible, in contrast to the situation in insects. However, statistical analysis of the data showed that the rate of DDT dehydrochlorination to DDE was inversely correlated to the weight and lipid content of the fish studied (weight and lipid content were positively correlated to each other). Obviously, the dependence of the rate of DDT metabolism on weight and lipid content could be caused by a number of factors which may only be separated by further experimentation; however, speculation based on the suggestions of Jensen *et al.* (1975), noted above, is tempting. If the lipid content of finfish does affect the rate of metabolism of DDT to its more polar metabolites, such an interaction has important consequences with respect to age/concentration profiles. This aspect of the effect of lipid on organochlorine levels in organisms will be further discussed in Chapter 8.

G.   THE EFFECTS OF LIPID ON THE ACCUMULATION OF TRACE METALS BY BIOTA

This chapter would be incomplete without some reference to the accumulation of trace metals by aquatic biota, and the effects of lipids thereon. Most trace metals are thought to be taken up in the ionic form and indeed this form is generally considered to be that of greatest toxicity. The affinity of trace metals for biological material depends not on the lipid–water partition which is so important for organochlorines, but on the affinity of metals for subcellular proteins and other molecules. Thus most trace metals can bind more or less specifically to sulphydryl groups of proteins, for example (see Vallee and Ulmer, 1972, for more details). In addition, some trace metals are important constituents of enzymes or co-factors, although the physiological requirements of aquatic biota for trace metals are generally considered to be much smaller than the actual metal content in most organisms. For example, Pequegnat *et al.* (1969) estimated the maximum zinc requirements of marine organisms as approximately $2 \cdot 7 \, \mu g/g$ on a soft tissue fresh weight basis. This calculation obviously depends on the number of metal-containing enzymes in an organism, but seems a fair approximation, and is supported by the deliberations of Wolfe (1970*b*) on zinc enzymes in the oyster *Crassostrea virginica*.

Some trace metals are known to exist in several different forms in aquatic biota. The best known example of multiple speciation of metals *in vivo* concerns mercury, which may exist in inorganic or organic forms in biota, the latter being mostly or completely a methylated species. Other metals found in inorganic and organic forms include lead and arsenic, although the kinetics of these forms are not nearly as well documented as is the case for mercury. Several authors have shown that lead can be methylated by microorganisms in the laboratory, with the production of tetramethyl lead (Jarvie *et al.*, 1975; Wong *et al.*, 1975; Schmidt and Huber, 1976), but until recently the importance of this species in the environmental cycling of lead was unknown. However, a recent report claims 10–40 per cent of the total lead in samples of cod or mackerel muscle as tetraalkyl lead (Sirota and Uthe, 1977). In addition, Harrison and Laxen (1978) have concluded that the intertidal mud flats in Morecambe Bay give rise to an appreciable amount of tetraalkyl lead in the coastal air masses, as profiles of this compound in air indicated an input from the coast or sea distinct from that deriving from urban areas. The presumption from this study is that lead is undergoing bio-alkylation, probably by microorganisms in the coastal mud flats. The status of arsenic is also somewhat controversial; however, in a recent report, Wrench *et al.* (1979) have suggested that the organic arsenic derivative found in large amounts in many shellfish is synthesised primarily by phytoplankton and is then passed through the food chain without modification. This concept is now receiving support from other authors (Bottino *et al.*, 1978, Waslenchuk and Windom, 1978).

If some trace metals occur in alkylated forms in organisms, it might be expected that the greater lipophilic nature imported by the alkyl group to such compounds would lead to a greater tendency not only for bioaccumulation in general but also for association with lipids. Certainly, the uptake of methylmercury by organisms resembles that of organochlorines to some extent, uptake from water and food occurring rapidly, with subsequent swift inter-tissue transport of the compound (presumably via blood cells and conceivably by reversible binding to lipids in these; see McKim *et al.*, 1976; Olson *et al.*, 1978). The importance of the lipid solubility of mercury derivatives in determining their uptake and toxicities has been emphasised by Bryan (1976), who correlated the toxicity of nine mercury forms to their relative partition coefficients between seawater and ethyl ether (Table 23). The differences in the uptake rates, persistence and tissue distribution of inorganic mercury and methylmercury may be related to the greater solubility of the latter compound in body lipids, therefore. If this were so, some indication of this tendency should be evident in organisms from the field, and we might expect to see differences between the concentrations of methylmercury in tissues, individuals and species which depended partly at least on the amount of lipids present. However, a study of the published literature tells us little of this aspect, perhaps because of the

TABLE 23

THE TOXICITIES OF NINE MERCURY DERIVATIVES RELATIVE TO MERCURIC CHLORIDE ($HgCl_2$) USING THREE SPECIES OF CRUSTACEANS AS TEST ORGANISMS, COMPARED WITH THE RELATIVE PARTITION COEFFICIENTS OF THE TEST COMPOUND AND $HgCl_2$ BETWEEN SEAWATER AND ETHYL ETHER. (AFTER BRYAN (1976).)

Mercury derivative	Ratio of toxicities, $\dfrac{\text{test compound}^a}{HgCl_2}$			Ratio of partition coefficients, $\dfrac{\text{test compound}^c}{HgCl_2}$
	Acartia clausii	*Elminius modestus*[b]	*Artemia salina*[b]	
CH_3HgCl	2·1	4·7	15	16
C_2H_5HgCl	2·0	6·8	17	63
$n\text{-}C_3H_7HgCl$	3·1	9·7	54	255
$n\text{-}C_4H_9HgCl$	2·7	16	294	879
$n\text{-}C_5H_{11}HgCl$	3·8	20	980	2 490
$i\text{-}C_3H_7HgCl$	—	2·4	25	42
$i\text{-}C_5H_9HgCl$	—	16	450	1 641
C_6H_5HgCl	2·4	4·3	23	360
HgI_2	1·7	4·6	24	19

[a] Comparison of LC_{50} values.
[b] Larvae.
[c] Partition coefficient using $HgCl_2$ was 0·26 at 15 °C.

tendency of most authors to quote data for total mercury as opposed to separating the two forms present. Even though methylmercury commonly accounts for greater than 90 per cent of the total mercury in muscle tissues of finfish and marine mammals (see reviews by Ackefors, 1971 and Peterson *et al.*, 1973), the proportion of total mercury present in methylated form in tissues such as the liver may be very low and it is considered by some authors that this is indicative of a capacity of some tissues of seals or finfish for demethylation (Smith and Armstrong, 1975; Olson *et al.*, 1978). The existence of this demethylation capability—and the further existence of specific metallothioneins which are known to bind both inorganic and methylated mercury forms—thus serves to obscure any correlation which might exist between the lipid content and mercury accumulation capacity of biota or their tissues.

The correspondence between the ecosystem kinetics or cycling of methylmercury and the organochlorines is nevertheless quite marked. None of these compounds occurs in true solution in water to any great extent, but all exhibit high affinities for biological material. The rapid uptake of each of these compounds from solution and food is paralleled by a general increase of their concentration with trophic levels, and frequently both methylmercury and organochlorines exhibit increased concentrations with age of organisms (Chapters 7 and 8). However, by contrast to the controversy surrounding the basis of organochlorine amplification through the food web (Section E above), most authors support a concept of food chain amplification of methylmercury (e.g. see Peterson *et al.*, 1973; Sergeant and Armstrong, 1973; Ratkowsky *et al.*, 1975), although even here there is apparently some disagreement (Williams and Weiss, 1973). It is tempting to speculate that the increase in lipid amounts with trophic level may thus be involved in the food chain dynamics of methylmercury and other organometallic species, but such speculation is rarely supported by hard data, even in cases where data for lipid contents are quoted with mercury levels allowing the necessary correlative calculations (e.g. see Kelso and Frank, 1974). Perhaps the general similarity between methylmercury and the organochlorines in respect of their cycling in ecosystems reflects merely their similar persistence but is based on different methods of sequestration. Olson *et al.* (1973) considered the binding of methylmercury to red cells of the rainbow trout *Salmo gairdneri* to depend on the availability of sulphydryl groups on the surface of the cells. Furthermore, these authors speculated that the availability of —SH groups may limit the uptake of mercury species; thus the faster uptake of methylmercury than of inorganic mercury might be explained by the requirement of each form for —SH groups, methylmercury requiring only one free group whereas inorganic mercury will bind to two such groups.

Clearly, studies on the subcellular binding and sequestration of organometals are needed to clarify the basis of the persistence of these species in biota. The distribution of binding sites appears in some cases to be non-uniform even within a single tissue. Kelly *et al.* (1975) thus found a heterogeneous distribution of total mercury in muscle fillets of walleye, *Stizostedion vitreum vitreum*, and a similar report is available for zinc and copper in muscle of the blue shark, *Prionace glauca* (Stevens and Brown, 1974; see Fig. 17). These differences, although reminiscent of the non-uniform distribution of organochlorines in trout due to lipid variations

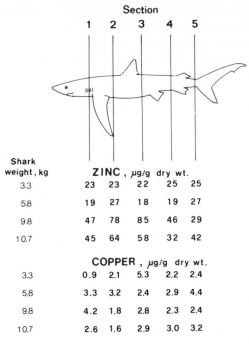

Section

1   2   3   4   5

Shark weight, kg	ZINC , μg/g dry wt.				
3.3	23	23	22	25	25
5.8	19	27	18	19	27
9.8	47	78	85	46	29
10.7	45	64	58	32	42

	COPPER , μg/g dry wt.				
3.3	0.9	2.1	5.3	2.2	2.4
5.8	3.3	3.2	2.4	2.9	4.4
9.8	4.2	1.8	2.8	2.3	2.4
10.7	2.6	1.6	2.9	3.0	3.2

FIG. 17.   Mean concentrations (μg/g dry weight) of zinc and copper in muscle tissues taken from five transverse sections of blue sharks, *Prionace glauca*. Four individuals were used and all were caught in the north-east Atlantic Ocean. (After Stevens and Brown (1974).)

(Reinert and Bergman, 1974; see Section C and Table 10 above), are probably not a function of lipid variation but depend almost certainly on the changes in protein binding sites (especially —SH group availability) with tissue area. This contention is supported by the studies of Arima and Umemoto (1976), in which the mercury distribution in muscle of tuna *Thunnus obesus* and *T. thynnus* and swordfish *Xiphias gladius* was correlated to the different biochemical components of the muscle. The amount of mercury bound was linearly related to the amounts of myofibrillar protein present in the muscle at low levels; at higher concentrations, some mercury was also incorporated into sarcoplasmic protein. Such differences in the microdistribution of elements in finfish are obviously most important in their use as indicators of trace metals; any monitoring survey should include a scheme for the reproducible subsampling of tissues of organisms. Finally, it is notable that although the report of Scott and Armstrong (1972) correlated the concentrations of total mercury in freshwater finfish of several species from lakes in Canada to both size and fish condition or fatness, the relationship between mercury and condition (lipid content) could not be confirmed in a later, more detailed, study of four of these species (Scott, 1974). The relationship between organometallic species and tissue lipids therefore remains obscure and is certainly an area for further research interest.

H. CONCLUSIONS ON THE EFFECTS OF LIPID

Data considered in this chapter have shown that the amount of lipid present in a tissue or an organism exerts a powerful influence on the amount of organochlorine accumulated. It is evident, in addition, that not only is total lipid important, but the specific types of lipid present, and their relative proportions, also affect the ability of an organism or its tissues to bind and sequester organochlorines. By contrast, the evidence linking the retention of trace metals by biota to their content of lipids is far more tenuous, even for those metals which are present in organisms partially or almost completely in organic forms.

As will be seen in the following chapters, the effects of several extraneous variables (such as season or organism age) on the organochlorine content of indicator organisms may be partially or wholly explained, at least in some instances, by the covariance of body or tissue lipid.

Given the highly significant effects of body lipids on the accumulation of organochlorines by biota, and the inherent variability of the lipid contents found in biota of any one species even at one point in space and time, the question arises as to whether the results of indicator surveys should be based on the lipid weights, rather than wet weights, of the studied organisms. Phillips (1978b) has addressed this problem in some detail and has identified the deficiencies inherent in the use of either of these weight bases. Clearly, if the results of indicator surveys for organochlorines are based on wet weights, differences in the lipid contents (either total lipid or specific lipid components) of an indicator species from multiple locations will interfere with the interpretation of results. Thus, a sample exhibiting a high concentration of organochlorine might be interpreted as evidence of local pesticide contamination whereas, in fact, the high concentrations may be merely due to an unusually high lipid content of that sample compared with samples from other locations. By extension, the use of wet weights as the sole basis for organochlorine concentrations is justifiable only if all samples contain similar amounts of total lipid and similar lipid components. This is clearly unattainable when individuals of a single population can vary in total lipid content by greater than an order of magnitude (e.g. see Brandes and Dietrich, 1953 and Jensen *et al.*, 1969).

The use of lipid weights as a basis for the concentrations of organochlorines in aquatic organisms is known to substantially decrease variability between individuals in a given population (e.g. see Jensen *et al.*, 1969, 1970; Kelso and Frank, 1974 and Linko *et al.*, 1974), and this would permit a more sensitive definition of inter-sample (inter-location) differences in organochlorine concentrations in monitoring surveys for these compounds. However, the use of lipid weights as a basis for concentrations has two major disadvantages. First, basing organochlorine concentrations on total lipid (measured by the customary simple organic extraction procedure) does not distinguish between the different binding and sequestration capacities of the several components of total body lipids. Secondly—and perhaps more importantly—this method presupposes that organisms attain the same concentration of organochlorines in body lipids at a given exposure level regardless of the size of the body pool of lipids. This last supposition is tantamount to a suggestion that organisms are in equilibrium with the environmental organochlorine insult, which appears unlikely at least in cases where organochlorines are taken up mainly via the food chain. It is clear that in cases where organisms are not in equilibrium with the ambient organochlorine concentration, a given incremental uptake would be dispersed throughout the body lipids, and this would lead to an inverse relationship between the concentrations of organochlorines recorded in a species and its total body lipid. Such a relationship has rarely been recorded. However, Addison and Smith (1974) observed an inverse relationship between ΣDDT concentrations and blubber thickness in male ringed seals, *Pusa hispida*, suggesting that the same DDT input per individual was shared amongst differing total lipid pools. Similarly, Earnest and Benville (1971) found significant negative correlations between the concentrations of DDT, DDE, DDD or ΣDDT (by wet weights) and the total lipid content of dwarf perch, *Micrometrus minimus*, from San Francisco Bay. Seven other species of finfish from this study exhibited the more conventional positive correlation of ΣDDT to lipid contents, however.

The uncertainty surrounding the precise role of body lipids in determining the kinetics of organochlorines in aquatic biota suggests that lipid weights should not be used as the sole basis for concentrations of these compounds found in these organisms. Nevertheless, the amounts of lipid present in biota should certainly be determined as a matter of course in any studies which are designed to compare the organochlorine levels of a species with temporal or spatial changes. The conclusion that organochlorine concentrations should be based on both wet weights and lipid weights of the studied organisms appears inescapable. The comparison of results over space or time should be made using both sets of data, as each holds valuable information concerning either the physiological state of the organism or the ambient organochlorine levels in the environment. The data based on lipid weights should, in most cases, provide the more accurate reflection of ambient organochlorine availability; however, the assumptions inherent in the use of lipid weights as a basis for organochlorine concentrations should be borne in mind at all times.

CHAPTER 4

Introduction to Seasonal Variation

The seasonal variation of pollutant concentrations in organisms is a major source of interference in monitoring surveys. Whilst it is quite simple in many cases to minimise—or even eradicate—the effects of season (by sampling all study areas at a similar period), many authors have ignored this important variable.

This brief introductory chapter serves to summarise the main causes of seasonality in pollutant levels in aquatic biota. It will be seen that seasonal variations in trace metals are not always temporally coincident with those of organochlorines; hence each pollutant type will be considered separately in Chapters 5 and 6.

It is intuitively evident that three major inter-related factors may contribute to seasonality of pollutants in aquatic biota. These factors are as follows:

(i) Pollutant delivery to the aquatic environment.
(ii) Organism physiology, particularly the sexual cycle.
(iii) Changes of ambient water quality parameters such as temperature or salinity.

The changes occurring in pollutant concentration in biota with time may reflect any, or all, of these three contributing factors. However, considerable differences exist between the trace metals and the organochlorines in respect of the mechanism and direction or magnitude of effect of these parameters. For example, the delivery of trace metals to the aquatic environment varies mainly with run-off, although this variation may depend on the nature of the source of trace metals in the catchment. Phillips (1979b) has contrasted theoretical profiles for the delivery of cadmium to estuarine biota from catchments including either natural or industrial sources of the element. If the source is mainly industrial, a relatively steady total load input per unit time may be expected (although this is by no means always the case); with a steady input, concentrations in the receiving waters near the outfall will vary inversely with the extent of run-off. In a tidal estuary, however, higher run-off will lead to a slower dilution of river water by the salt-receiving waters of a less contaminated nature; thus, a 'cross-over' may occur, at which point the concentration of available metal is independent of run-off (Fig. 18(A)). Sites upstream from this point will exhibit metal concentrations which vary inversely with run-off, whilst concentrations at sites downstream may vary directly with run-off. It may be noted that this type of profile should also be characteristic for organochlorines which are derived from industries if they are discharged at relatively uniform rates. However, profiles of trace metal delivery in estuaries which are dominated by natural sources of the elements may be quite distinct from those discussed above. Periods of high run-off will, in these cases, be accompanied by a large delivery of inorganic and organic particulates with associated adsorbed contaminants because of the high scouring action; a relatively slower dilution of freshwater by the receiving salt water (as above) will increase the degree of difference between concentrations of metals present in high and low run-off conditions in a downstream direction (Fig. 18(B)). Such profiles may approximate those seen for organochlorines from agricultural usage only if application occurs throughout the year (which is most unusual). In practice, most organochlorines which are employed as pesticides are applied to crops at a particular season to protect the crops from pests during growth. In non-equatorial areas with well defined growing seasons, application commonly occurs in early summer. In these cases, a large peak in organochlorine delivery inevitably occurs immediately following pesticide application; concentrations delivered to rivers—and thence to estuaries—in the rest of the year will be much lower and will represent, in most cases, compounds which are carried away from application sites by adsorption to suspended particulates in rivers. In areas closer to the equator, multiple cropping and harvesting may occur, with associated multiple peaks (one after each pesticide application) in organochlorine delivery to rivers and the receiving waters of estuaries and adjacent coasts. It should be noted that in most contaminated areas studied to date, trace metals have been found to be predominantly derived from industries, and organochlorines are predominantly derived from their use in agriculture. The seasonal profiles for trace metal and organochlorine delivery to aquatic environments thus differ greatly, organochlorines being of an episodic nature whilst trace metals are commonly abundant throughout the year. Exceptions of course occur, such as the DDT input

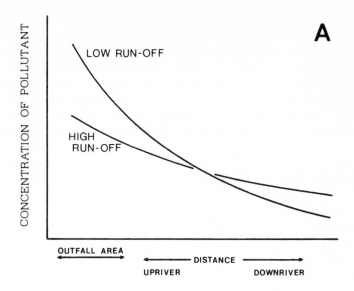

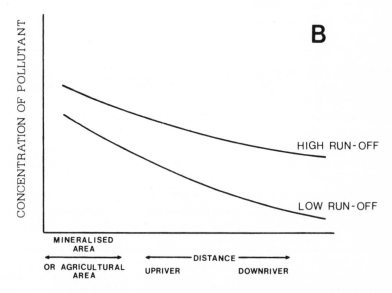

FIG. 18. Theoretical profiles for the concentration of pollutants present in waters of estuaries draining (A) an industrial area and (B) an area in which pollutants are derived by leaching of natural (trace metals) or agriculturally applied (organochlorines) pollutants. (Adapted from Phillips (1979*b*).)

from industries manufacturing this compound in the Los Angeles Hyperion outfall; however, such exceptions are rare.

The effects of organism physiology on the seasonality of pollutants in aquatic biota are also very different for trace metals and organochlorines. Seasonality of organochlorines in biota is thus mainly linked to the changes in lipid content of the organism which are, in turn, related to the sexual cycle (see Chapter 3). Fluctuations of trace metals in biota depend not on lipid changes, but on changes in organism weight, which is also linked to the sexual cycle. Thus, whilst organochlorines typically exhibit a pre-spawning maximum in biota, correlated to the high lipid content and subsequent enhanced ability for sequestration of these compounds, trace metals are commonly most concentrated after spawning, when the organism body weight is minimal.

Changes in salinity and temperature of the ambient water are intimately involved in both the above factors. Thus, pollutant delivery in an estuary depends on run-off and on the exact rate of freshwater–saltwater mixing, i.e. on the seasonal changes in the salinity profile. Temperature is commonly an important parameter in determining the timing of spawning in aquatic biota. In addition, however, both salinity and temperature may have direct effects on the uptake of pollutants by biota. In general, increases of ambient temperature lead to increased net uptake of pollutants by organisms, which may correlate to physiological changes linked to metabolism (e.g. filtration or ventilation rates). Decreases in salinity commonly also lead to increased uptake of pollutants, although exceptions may be quite common here.

The seasonal profiles of pollutants in aquatic organisms should thus be envisaged as a mosaic of these three major perturbations and should be interpreted on the basis of these changes. An understanding of the basis of pollutant seasonality is important in the design of monitoring surveys using biological indicator organisms, as a decision must be reached as to the correct timing of sampling. As trace metals and organochlorines commonly exhibit quite distinct seasonal profiles in aquatic biota, they are considered separately in subsequent chapters.

CHAPTER 5

Trace Metal Seasonality in Aquatic Biota

The major parameters involved in determining the seasonal fluctuation of trace metal levels in aquatic biota are the extent of pollutant delivery to the aquatic environment (and the associated dilution of polluted waters with receiving waters), the weight changes occurring in the organism, and the direct effects of salinity, temperature and other water quality parameters which alter seasonally. Other parameters such as migration of organisms may also be important in specific instances.

A. CHANGES IN POLLUTANT DELIVERY TO AQUATIC ECOSYSTEMS WITH SEASON

The preceding chapter included discussion of the changes in trace metal abundance in rivers and estuaries exposed to a steady industrial source of elements or to a natural leachable source. It is clear that the effects of altered run-off vary according to the type of source present in a catchment. It is also evident that seasonal profiles of trace metal availability may vary according to estuarine position. For example, biota of the lower estuary in Fig. 18(A) would be expected to exhibit higher rates of trace metal uptake in the season of high run-off, whilst those of the upper reaches of the river would exhibit maximal element uptake in the season of low rainfall. These profiles are, of course, extremely simplified. In real situations, it is known that the concentrations of trace metals in estuaries fluctuate widely over both the short- and the long-term and that parameters other than run-off may be responsible for many of these perturbations. Phillips (1977b) included stratification of waters, tides and currents and the intermittent flow of industrial effluent as additional factors which may elicit changes in trace metal levels in estuarine or coastal waters. To these may be added the changes in water chemistry which occur with time and which may sequester

95

normally available metals in complexes which are not biologically available (e.g. Foster and Morris, 1971; Fukai *et al.*, 1975), as well as the abundance of phytoplankton (A. W. Morris, 1971, 1974; Abdullah and Royle, 1974).

An ideal biological indicator organism will of course smooth out or time-integrate such fluctuations in water quality; indeed, this ability is one of the major advantages in the use of indicator biota over classical methods of water analysis. However, the temporal change in levels of metals in aquatic biota is often highly dependent on those changes occurring in the ambient water mass, and nowhere is this more apparent than in situations where episodic inputs occur. Occasional studies have thus been reported in which biota are exposed to markedly episodic influxes of trace metals; in these areas, the seasonal profiles found in the biota are often most unusual. Examples of this phenomenon are seen in the work of Boyden (1975) on the biota of Poole Harbour, UK, which was contaminated by effluents from a chemical manufacturing industry. Romeril (1977) cited a further instance, where concentrations of copper, iron and zinc in macroalgae—*Fucus serratus* and *F. spiralis*—and the limpet *Patella vulgata* varied in concert with the discontinuous effluent discharge from a nearby desalination plant employing flash distillation methods.

It should be emphasised that the fluctuation of trace metal concentrations in biota includes the decrease in element concentration as well as its increase. It is clear that an increased ambient supply of a metal will lead to more rapid uptake of that metal by biota; however, the changes occurring in biota when a decrease in ambient metal availability occurs are also of importance. The events which take place at this period depend, to a large extent, on the metal half-life in the organism. As noted in Chapter 2, half-lives of metals vary enormously between species and within a species. Certainly some trace metals may persist long enough after episodic increases in their uptake rates to obviate the possibility of their being excreted *in toto* prior to the next influx. Such a situation was described by Luoma (1977*a*, *b*) for mercury kinetics in the shrimp *Palaemon debilis* and the polychaete *Nereis succinea*. Total mercury concentrations in these animals from Ala Wai Canal in Hawaii fluctuated over almost two orders of magnitude in 1973–1974 (Fig. 19(A)), profiles being similar in each organism. A mathematical model developed for the exchange of mercury in the shrimp species indicated that equilibrium concentrations were never attained under field conditions over the entire 13-month study period. The accumulation of mercury by each organism was apparently dominated by rapid uptake of the element from solution during conditions of storm run-off, when biologically available mercury washed rapidly into the estuary

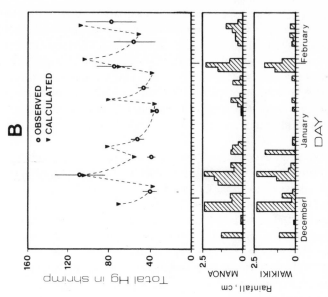

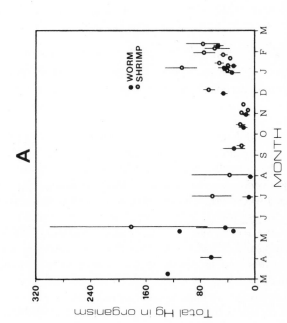

FIG. 19. (A) Means and ranges in concentration of total mercury (μg/kg wet weight) in shrimp, *Palaemon debilis*, and the polychaete worm, *Nereis succinea*, taken from Ala Wai Canal in Hawaii during 1973 and 1974. (B) Observed concentrations of total mercury (means and ranges, μg/kg wet weight) in shrimp, *P. debilis*, collected from Ala Wai Canal between December, 1973 and February, 1974, and the relationship of these to rainfall in the two major watersheds of the estuary or to mercury profiles calculated using the mathematical model of mercury kinetics in this organism. (After Luoma (1977a).)

and was subsequently flushed out. A short-term comparison of rainfall data and observed mercury levels in the shrimp fitted this hypothesis neatly, and calculated values using the mathematical model of element flux also agreed closely with observed field data (Fig. 19(B)). Two further points may be of interest in these studies. First, the loss of mercury was apparently not so slow as to elicit an increase in metal concentration with age of the shrimp (see Chapter 7). Secondly, the uptake of mercury from solution by the polychaete was increased in periods of storm run-off by a direct effect of salinity, although the shrimp was not thus affected (see Section C below).

The effects of episodic exposure of biota to trace metals on their accumulated concentrations are also particularly well shown by a series of studies on the discharge of radionuclides in the Columbia River. The outflow from this river is responsible for both lowered salinities and elevated radionuclide levels in the area of the northeast Pacific Ocean bordering the coasts of Oregon and California. A large low-salinity surface plume is generated in summer and directed southwards along the western coast of the USA by winds and currents. In winter, run-off is less and the plume is indistinct, but is mainly driven northwards by the prevailing winds. Radionuclides originated from the use of Columbia River water to cool the Hanford nuclear reactors; the major nuclide released was ^{65}Zn, of 245-day half-life. Nelson (1961) estimated the release of ^{65}Zn to the sea (when eight reactors were being used) to be 38 Ci/day and the effects of such an output have been noted at distances of hundreds of kilometres from the estuary of the Columbia River. Osterberg *et al.* (1964) used the euphausiid *Euphausia pacifica* to study the dissipation of these wastes. In general, profiles of ^{65}Zn in these organisms correlated well to the observed salinity patterns, although some discrepancies were noted. The seasonal fluctuation of ^{65}Zn in *E. pacifica* was not as marked as expected, although it did appear to be dependent on the degree and location of plume discharge. Vertical migration of the test animal and a long biological half-life of ^{65}Zn in *E. pacifica* are sufficient to account for much of the observed activity in winter, which probably represents to a large extent residual ^{65}Zn activity accumulated during the previous summer. By contrast to these results, Pearcy and Osterberg (1968) found that livers of the albacore *Thunnus alalunga* caught in the same region off Oregon and Washington contained highly labile levels of ^{65}Zn and ^{54}Mn. The albacore is a species of tuna of considerable commercial importance; it is known to migrate in the north Pacific between Japan and the west coast of America. Fish caught off Washington and Oregon during the summer exhibited rapid increases in ^{65}Zn levels and specific activities, attributable directly to time spent in the contaminated Columbia River plume. In later autumn and winter months ^{65}Zn decreased markedly in these fish livers. Albacore taken from Baja California and southern waters exhibited ^{65}Zn concentrations an order of magnitude lower than those taken off the Oregon coast and no definite seasonal trends could be established. Levels of ^{54}Mn and ^{60}Co in livers of the same species exhibited a different pattern, however. ^{54}Mn decreased during the summer period when fish were present off the Oregon coast, suggesting a greater availability of this radionuclide in offshore waters; probably most of the activity present was a result of nuclear weapons testing in 1961–1962 (Pearcy and Osterberg, 1968). A similar conclusion was reached by Krygier and Pearcy (1977) concerning ^{60}Co in livers of the same species and, although seasonal data were rather inadequate to support the hypothesis of a fallout-dominated source, annual data agreed well with this suggestion (Fig. 20). It was notable that peak concentrations of ^{60}Co lagged the nuclear testing by about one year in fish from the northern area whereas a lag of 1–2 years was found for fish from the southern region (Hodge *et al.*, 1973); this difference has been correlated to differences in migration between the two albacore populations (Laurs and Lynn, 1977). A later addition to these elegant studies, concerning ^{65}Zn levels in the migratory Pacific hake *Merluccius productus*, will be considered in Chapter 7.

In Chapter 2, it was pointed out that different indicator species respond to different portions of the total trace metal load on an ecosystem. Thus, profiles for trace metal concentrations in one organism do not always match those seen for another species from the same locations (e.g. Bryan and Hummerstone, 1977; Ireland and Wootton, 1977; Phillips, 1979*a*). This phenomenon is important also in determining the seasonal changes in availability of metals to coastal biota. Clearly, if the uptake of metals occurs from solution only (e.g. in macroalgae; see Section C below), seasonal variations in the trace metal uptake rates exhibited by the alga will depend on the temporal fluctuations in soluble metals of available form. A filter-feeder, by contrast, accumulates metals not only from solution but also from inorganic particulates (Raymont, 1972; Preston *et al.*, 1972; Boyden and Romeril, 1974) and the seasonal fluctuation in total available metal in these animals is therefore a composite of the changes in metal availability in both these phases. Organisms in which trace metal uptake is dominated by the food route will respond to the fluctuations in content of trace metals in that food, which may be a function of either species changes with time (if annual changes in preferred food occur) or of the response of the food organism(s) to variation in the available quantities of trace metals in different

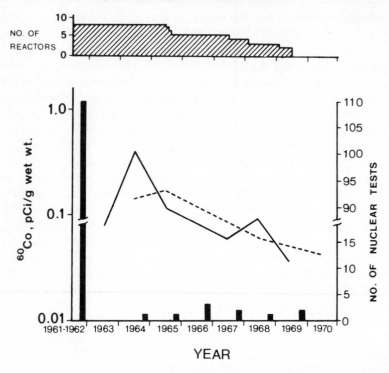

FIG. 20.   Mean concentrations of ^{60}Co (pCi/g wet weight) in livers of the albacore, *Thunnus alalunga*, from the west coast of America in 1963–1969, and the relationship of these to nuclear weapons testing (fallout affecting the north Pacific) and to nuclear reactor discharge at Hanford, Washington. Vertical bars show nuclear test data; solid line indicates the data of Krygier and Pearcy (1977) for albacore from Oregon and Washington coasts; broken line shows levels recorded by Hodge *et al.* (1973) for albacore from southern California coasts. (Adapted from Krygier and Pearcy (1977).)

phases. The exact importance of each route of exposure to trace metals in determining uptake rates is unknown. However, several authors have reported correlations between the average amounts of metals in solution and concentrations in macroalgae (e.g. see Morris and Bale, 1975; Foster, 1976; Seeliger and Edwards, 1977), and these results confirm the conclusions of laboratory experiments which also suggest that large benthic algae respond to metals in solution only (Gutknecht, 1961, 1963, 1965; Bryan, 1969, 1971) and time-integrate ambient concentrations over a long period (see Section C below). Filter-feeders such as the bivalve molluscs of the genera *Mytilus* or

Crassostrea will take up metals rapidly from solution or from food, but the latter route is probably predominant in most areas which do not receive direct metal inputs (Preston, 1971; Pentreath, 1973a; Phillips, 1976a). The uptake of metals from particulates is probably more important for those metals which exhibit a preference for particulate association rather than remaining in solution; this would include iron, lead and manganese amongst other elements. Ayling (1974) has emphasised the uptake of trace metals from sediments by oysters and has shown a general correlation between metal levels present in these two ecosystem components. He further suggests that this route is so important that concentration factors for metals in oysters should be based on the element levels in ambient sediments rather than water. This suggestion has not received much support to date, as many authors feel that the correlation of sediment and oyster levels of trace metals may reflect the same particulate input routes rather than depending on each other. Although bivalves undoubtedly respond to metals in sediments, the importance of this response in determining total body loads of metals in the organism probably varies with both species and metal (Boyden and Romeril, 1974) and a generalisation cannot be completely defended because of this variation. A scheme showing the pathways involved in the uptake of ^{65}Zn by oysters in estuarine environments was published by Wolfe (1970a) and is shown in Fig. 21. This

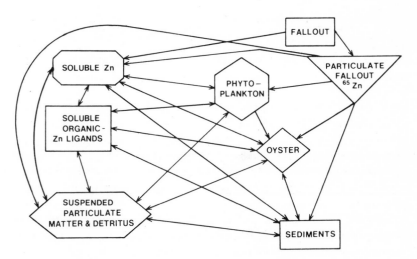

FIG. 21. Schematic representation of the pathways of trace metal cycling with respect to the exposure of oysters to ^{65}Zn. (After Wolfe (1970a).)

scheme is equally applicable to stable trace elements, the only change being the substitution of aerial and aquatic sources of stable metals for the fallout components shown for ^{65}Zn. Finfish probably respond very little to metals present in inorganic particulates, but absorb metals both from solution (directly across the body surface and, after drinking, across the gastrointestinal wall) and from food; in most cases the ingestion of metals in food probably predominates. Further comments on these aspects may be found in Phillips (1977b).

B. THE SEXUAL CYCLE: WEIGHT CHANGES AND OTHER FACTORS

Several physiological changes occur with season in organisms and may affect the seasonal fluctuations in trace metal levels present in either the whole organism or its component tissues. These changes superimpose those due to the effects of changes in ambient metal availability discussed above. One of the major physiological perturbations which exerts a significant effect on temporal trends in trace metal levels of higher organisms is the sexual cycle. Indicator organisms such as bivalves and other molluscs, and finfish, undergo dramatic physiological changes with season which are related directly to maturation of gametes and spawning. These changes involve fluctuations of all biochemical components (proteins, lipids, carbohydrates) as well as animal weight, water content and condition. Details of the temporal variation in biochemical components of bivalve molluscs may be found in the reviews of Galtstoff (1964), Giese (1969) and Bayne (1976); finfish are dealt with in the work of Love (1970), of Morris and Culkin (1976, 1977) and of other authors. A full description of these seasonal changes is considered to be outside the scope of the present work, as little is known of the relationship between trace metal sequestration in organisms and their biochemical composition. However, the changes occurring in organism weight and condition are important with respect to trace metal seasonality and brief general comments are included below on these aspects.

  Galtstoff (1964), in his classical review of the taxonomy, anatomy, physiology and chemical composition of the American oyster, *Crassostrea virginica*, included an oft-quoted figure for the percentage of total body weight contributed by the ripe gonad. Under ideal conditions, the ripe gonad comprised between 31·2 and 40·7 per cent of the total body wet weight (exclusive of the shell) and accounted for 32·8 to 33·4 per cent of the total bulk volume of the soft parts. Whilst these high percentages are unusual, they are by no means unique, and serve to emphasise the enormous involvement of the gonad in determining whole tissue weights when the bivalve is in a fully mature condition. Sexual maturity is usually attained by oysters within a year of settling of larvae; the actual time taken depends mainly on the ambient temperature and the availability of food. In tropical climates, sexual maturity may be attained in the astonishingly short time of 20 to 30 days subsequent to settling (Stenzel, 1971), but this is again somewhat unusual. The fecundity of bivalves depends on their age, increasing steadily as the animal grows in size. Non-incubatory bivalves produce smaller and more numerous eggs than do incubatory species; members of the genus *Crassostrea* can produce, in one spawning season, over a hundred million eggs. Incubatory oysters such as *Ostrea edulis*, however, contain a mere two million larvae at any one time (Stenzel, 1971). The incidence of spawning is again temperature dependent, varying from intermittent spawning throughout the year in tropical climates to situations where spawning may fail several years in succession due to cold weather.

Finfish of some species may also exhibit large body weight changes due to spawning. The process reaches its climax in species which spawn only once prior to death; most important amongst these are the five species of Pacific salmon *Oncorhynchus*, the eel *Anguilla* and the lamprey *Lampetra*. *Salmo salar* is said to generally survive spawning in America, but all males and many of the females die on spawning in European rivers (Love, 1970). Death in these cases is probably due to the excessive weight loss and reserve depletion; salmon, for example, lose 31 to 44 per cent of their initial weights on spawning (Belding, 1934). Castration studies support this hypothesis, as castrated fish may live well beyond their usual spawning-associated death point (Robertson, 1961). Species of finfish which do not exhibit spawning death on the first occasion generally exhibit increased fecundity with age, just as bivalve molluscs increase gamete production with age and size. Gonad maturation is accomplished by utilisation of body proteins, and the water content of tissues other than the gonad rises as spawning approaches. After spawning, fish condition is poor because of this utilisation of reserves and structural proteins. It should be noted that differences exist between male and female fish with respect to gonad weights and the corresponding depletion of the fish; in general females exhibit markedly greater gonad weights than males. An example is shown in Fig. 22, and may be considered fairly typical. This sex difference is of importance both from the point of view of body weight changes (and associated trends in trace metal concentrations) and because of the associated lipid changes (which affect organochlorine levels; see Chapter 6). Such a difference has not been noted amongst bivalve molluscs, where hermaphroditism and ambisexuality (rhythmical changes in sex) in any case confuse the situation completely, at least in some species.

The loss of gametes—and concomitant loss of body weight—in organisms at spawning has consequences for trace metal seasonality. These

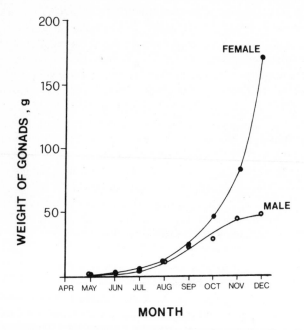

FIG. 22. The increase in weight of male and female gonads of the rainbow trout, *Salmo gairdneri*, during maturation prior to spawning. (After Sano (1960).)

consequences must be considered on two levels—those of the total body load of metals and those of the concentration of elements. It is immediately evident that unless gametes contain no metals whatsoever, their loss at spawning produces a decrease in the total body load of trace metals. The extent of this decrease depends on the total amount (weight) of gametes discharged and on the concentration of each metal in the gonads or, more accurately, in the gametes themselves. Unfortunately, there have been very few attempts to quantitate trace metals in either ova or sperm; most data currently available concern whole gonad analyses. An exception is the report of Greig *et al.* (1975), in which the concentrations of five metals were quoted for both eggs and adults of artificially spawned oysters, *Crassostrea virginica*. These data are shown in Table 24. It should be noted that only two female oysters from each sampling location were used to produce the eggs analysed and that more than these adults were analysed to elucidate trace metal concentrations of the adult animals; considering the well known variability in metals of oysters, this would seem an unfortunate

TABLE 24

CONCENTRATIONS (MEANS ± STANDARD DEVIATIONS, $\mu g/g$ DRY WEIGHTS) OF FIVE TRACE METALS IN ADULT FEMALE OYSTERS AND IN OVA FROM TWO FEMALES. ALL DATA REFER TO THE AMERICAN OYSTER, *Crassostrea virginica*, SAMPLED IN CONNECTICUT, USA. TWELVE ADULTS WERE ANALYSED FROM THE HOUSATONIC RIVER AND THIRTEEN ADULTS FROM BRANFORD. FOR BOTH LOCATIONS, FOUR POOLS OF EGGS FROM TWO ADULTS WERE ANALYSED. (AFTER GREIG *et al.* (1975).)

Location	Metal	Adults Mean ± SD	Ova Mean ± SD
Housatonic River	Silver	12·1 ± 4·45	<1·6
	Cadmium	28·1 ± 7·49	<1·6
	Copper	2 208 ± 793	28·9 ± 3·96
	Lead	<4·2	<10·0
	Zinc	10 460 ± 2 483	82·4 ± 8·05
Branford	Silver	16·4 ± 6·02	<1·2
	Cadmium	15·6 ± 3·46	<1·2
	Copper	1 260 ± 415	27·8 ± 7·80
	Lead	7·1 ± 2·45	<9·9
	Zinc	8 300 ± 1 800	65·9 ± 19·6

experimental design. In addition, concentrations of silver, cadmium and lead were below the detection limits of the analytical method used for ova from oysters of each location, so little can therefore be deduced for these elements. However, the data for copper and zinc reveal much lower concentrations in ova than in adults (which is obviously true also for the other metals) and eggs are thus relatively metal-deprived compared with adults. With respect to location, the copper concentrations in adults of the Housatonic River sample were statistically greater than those of the other population sampled, although no such differences were observed in the eggs. The concentrations of zinc in either adults or eggs of the two populations did not differ significantly, although a trend towards higher concentrations in both life stages is seen in the Housatonic River data. No comparable data are known for teleosts, but Forrester *et al.* (1972) reported very low levels of total mercury in embryos of the spiny dogfish *Squalus acanthias* from the Strait of Georgia in British Columbia. Concentrations of mercury in these embryos were age independent in contrast to the age-dependent (and much greater) concentrations found in adult dogfish.

TABLE 25

CONCENTRATIONS (μg/g WET WEIGHT) OF CADMIUM, COPPER, LEAD AND ZINC IN TISSUES OF SIX SCALLOPS, *Pecten maximus*, FROM KILBRENNAN SOUND, FIRTH OF CLYDE, SCOTLAND. (AFTER TOPPING (1973).)

Tissue	Scallop	Cadmium	Copper	Lead	Zinc
Gonads	1	0·73	2·9	0·2	51·0
	2	0·63	3·2	0·7	46·8
	3	0·88	2·6	0·3	110·0
	4	0·30	3·0	<0·2	51·0
	5	0·58	2·6	0·5	46·2
	6	0·75	4·7	1·7	62·5
	Mean	0·64	3·2	*	61·2
Muscle	1	0·88	0·4	<0·2	18·0
	2	1·03	0·5	0·2	18·0
	3	0·55	0·5	<0·2	16·2
	4	0·55	0·4	<0·2	16·7
	5	0·90	0·4	0·3	14·5
	6	0·73	0·5	0·5	18·7
	Mean	0·77	0·45	*	17·0
Viscera	1–6 (bulk sample)	15·4	11·5	0·8	17·6

* No mean calculated because of samples below detection limits.

Data from reports which include comparative tissue analyses in general support the hypothesis that gametes of organisms are relatively poor in metal content compared with adults. Thus, gonad tissues are not often found to possess large amounts of trace metals. For example, amongst bivalve molluscs, Pentreath (1973*a*) observed slow accumulation of the radionuclides [58]Co, ^{59}Fe, [54]Mn and [65]Zn by gonads of the mussel *Mytilus edulis* compared with other tissues. A similar conclusion was reached by

Cunningham and Tripp (1975*b*) for the accumulation of ^{203}Hg by tissues of *Crassostrea virginica*; these authors also noted slow rates of elimination of mercury or methylmercury from gonads. Metals in gonads thus appear to be tightly bound and to exchange slowly with metals in the other tissues. Stable isotopes of trace metals are also known to be present at low concentrations in gonads of bivalves relative to most other tissues (e.g. see Mullin and Riley, 1956; Bryan, 1973) and most trace metals are concentrated in the digestive gland, kidneys and gills of bivalves, which commonly account for more than 75 per cent of the total body load of elements. Exceptions to this general pattern do exist, however. Table 25 shows analytical results for the concentrations of four metals in scallops *Pecten maximus* from the Firth of Clyde, Scotland (Topping, 1973). Although a certain amount of individual variation is apparent, it is clear that cadmium, copper and, to some extent, lead, are not particularly accumulated by gonads compared with other tissues. However, zinc levels in the gonads exceed those in the other tissues and one might therefore expect spawning to affect zinc levels in this species quite severely. Segar *et al.* (1971) also published extensive data on the tissue distributions of trace metals in *P. maximus* and in the mussel *Modiolus modiolus*. It is clear from Table 26 that these authors found copper, lead and zinc levels in the gonads of *P. maximus* to exceed those in whole soft parts; spawning may once again be important, therefore, in terms of its effects on the total body load and concentrations of these metals. Some disagreement exists between the two sets of results for *P. maximus* (compare Tables 25 and 26); this presumably arises because metal seasonality varies considerably in different tissues of this species (Bryan, 1973). The data for *Modiolus modiolus* reveal that of all the metals studied, only copper is present in gonads at concentrations which exceed those present in whole soft parts (Table 27).

Differences in metal concentration also apparently exist between male and female bivalves of some species, which may be ascribed to the variation in metals of gonad tissues. Alexander and Young (1976) reported female gonads of *Mytilus californianus* to contain more copper and zinc than male gonads although lead exhibited the opposite profile; concentrations of silver, chromium and nickel did not differ in gonads of each sex. Gordon *et al.* (1978) confirmed the higher levels of copper and zinc in female *M. californianus* than in males of this species, although the differences between the sexes in this report were greater than those quoted by Alexander and Young (1976). Watling and Watling (1976*b*), in studies of the South African Mytilid species, *Choromytilus meridionalis*, found higher concentrations of copper, iron, manganese and zinc in whole soft parts of females compared

TABLE 26

MEAN CONCENTRATIONS (μg/g DRY WEIGHT) OF TRACE METALS PRESENT IN THE TISSUES OF THE SCALLOP, *Pecten maximus*, COLLECTED FROM PORT ERIN IN THE IRISH SEA. (AFTER SEGAR *et al.* (1971).)

Sample	Entire soft parts	Muscle	Gut and digestive gland	Mantle and gills unwashed	Mantle and gills washed	Gonad unwashed	Gonad washed	Mixed shell	Upper valve shell	Lower valve shell
Dry weight (per cent)	28·3	Nd	24·3	Nd	7·7	Nd	21·1	—	—	—
Iron	170	30	2 900	240	570	160	100	30	37	49
Manganese	140	22	410	200	4·0	31	8·6	16	12	4·9
Cobalt	8·5	0·34	0·68	0·45	0·58	2·7	0·18	0·31	0·20	0·20
Nickel	49	1·7	0·96	0·30	0·82	0·44	1·5	0·21	1·2	2·4
Cadmium	13	1·9	96	17	3·1	2·5	2·5	0·04	0·04	0·04
Copper	3·3	1·2	25	4·4	2·8	13	14	1·1	0·09	0·09
Lead	8·3	17	1·7	2·8	1·5	31	0·40	2·0	0·62	0·60
Zinc	230	70	1 100	160	420	360	180	6·6	4·1	6·1
Silver	Nd	Nd	8·9	Nd	0·36	Nd	0·059	Nd	Nd	Nd
Chromium	Nd	Nd	1·8	Nd	0·76	Nd	0·45	Nd	Nd	Nd

Nd: not determined

TABLE 27

MEAN CONCENTRATIONS (μg/g DRY WEIGHT) OF TRACE METALS PRESENT IN THE TISSUES OF THE MUSSEL, *Modiolus modiolus*, COLLECTED FROM PORT ERIN IN THE IRISH SEA. (AFTER SEGAR *et al.* (1971).)

Sample	Shell	Entire soft parts[a]	Entire soft parts[a]	Mantle and gills	Muscle	Gonad	Gut and digestive gland
Dry weight (per cent)	—	25·0	20·8	9·1	16·7	15·4	11·1
Iron	15	350	300	220	51	130	1 100
Manganese	20	47	150	160	71	49	140
Cobalt	0·30	5·5	0·49	2·9	0·30	0·72	1·1
Nickel	0·20	133	9·4	3·2	2·0	1·2	0·59
Cadmium	0·03	7·1	4·5	7·0	2·8	4·6	4·2
Copper	1·9	10	44	42	14	19	45
Lead	1·9	42	23	18	7·5	25	22
Zinc	6·2	530	320	180	68	140	190
Silver	Nd	Nd	0·26	0·24	0·03	0·07	0·81
Chromium	Nd	Nd	0·14	0·15	0·20	0·20	0·19

[a] Different individuals
Nd: not determined.

with males. A later report (Watling, 1978) suggested the differences were almost twofold for manganese and zinc, although copper was only slightly elevated in females. These differences are presumably due to differences in the gonad tissue itself, or in the gametes contained in the gonads. The quantitative disagreement between the reports concerning *Mytilus californianus* may have been caused by differences in the degree of gonad maturity in the samples studied. Bryan (1973) has shown that metal levels in the gonad/foot of the scallop, *Chlamys opercularis*, vary inversely with gonad

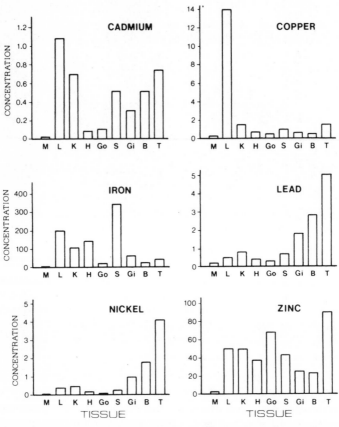

FIG. 23. Geometric mean concentrations (μg/g wet weight throughout) of six trace metals in the tissues of the snapper, *Chrysophrys auratus*, taken from waters off the east coast of North Island, New Zealand, between March and July, 1973. M = muscle, L = liver, K = kidney, H = heart, Go = gonad, S = spleen, Gi = gills, B = backbone and T = tail. (After tabulated data in Brooks and Rumsey (1974).)

condition. Thus, mean weights of this tissue fraction as a percentage of whole soft parts were maximal in early spring just prior to spawning. At this time, metal concentrations were low in the gonad, but increased after spawning to reach a maximum in winter. It is possible that the metal changes with maturation are not completely synchronised in male and female bivalves of some species, leading to differences in male:female ratios found with timing of sampling.

Some information is also available concerning the trace metal levels in gonads of finfish compared with other tissues. One of the most extensive studies, concerning eight species of marine finfish from New Zealand waters, was reported by Brooks and Rumsey (1974). The tissue distribution of each metal varied little between species, but considerable differences were noted in the distributions of each of the metals in any one species. Thus, copper and iron tended to concentrate in soft organs of the fish, whereas lead and nickel were mainly present in bony organs (see also Patterson and Settle, 1977); cadmium and zinc were, to some extent, intermediate in their tissue distribution profile. Data for snapper, *Chrysophrys auratus*, are shown in Fig. 23 and may be considered to be fairly representative of these extensive studies. It is immediately noticeable that gonads contain extremely low concentrations of all elements other than zinc. In most cases the only tissue with a lower level of each metal was axial muscle, in which many metals appear to be strictly regulated (Phillips, 1977b). By contrast to this profile, zinc levels were quite high in the gonads of each of the species studied compared with other tissues (Fig. 24), ranking in each case amongst those tissues which exhibit markedly elevated concentrations of the element. This disparity between the accumulation of zinc and that of other elements by gonad tissues of finfish may reflect a metabolic requirement of this organ for the element, and the same may be true for bivalve molluscs (above). Reports of other authors in general agree with the tissue distributions for trace metals found by Brooks and Rumsey (1974); examples may be found in the work of Windom *et al.* (1973), of McDermott and Young (1974), of Stevens and Brown (1974) and of Wright (1976), all of whom deal with marine fish. Most data for freshwater finfish species concern mercury; here again, gonad tissues exhibit very low concentrations of the element either in fish from the field (Johnels and Westermark, 1969; Lockhart *et al.*, 1972) or in fish exposed to inorganic or methylmercury in the laboratory (McKim *et al.*, 1976; Olson *et al.*, 1978). The limited information available for the tissue distributions of other metals also suggests that accumulation is low in gonads compared with other tissues (Eaton, 1974; Benoit *et al.*, 1976; Holcombe *et al.*, 1976).

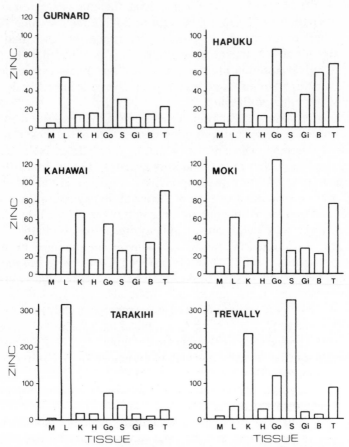

FIG. 24.   Geometric mean concentrations (μg/g wet weight throughout) of zinc in tissues of six species of finfish from the east coast of North Island, New Zealand. Species were gurnard, *Trigla kumu*, hapuku, *Polyprion oxygeneios*, kahawai, *Arripis trutta*, moki, *Latridopsis ciliaris*, tarakihi, *Cheilodactylis macropterus*, and trevally, *Caranx lutescens*. Abbreviations are as in Fig. 23. (After tabulated data in Brooks and Rumsey (1974).)

These data therefore suggest that, in general, concentrations of trace metals present in gonads or gametes are considerably lower than those found in the rest of the tissues. If the gametes lost during spawning of biota contain lower concentrations of trace metals than the remaining soft parts, spawning will be associated with an increase in metal concentration of whole soft tissues, despite the decreased total body load of elements. As we shall see below, several authors consider this to be the case. However, a few reports concerning the uptake of trace metals by bivalves in the laboratory have ascribed *decreases* in metal levels noted during experiments to spawning. Cunningham and Tripp (1973, 1975*a*), in extensive studies on the uptake of mercury by the American oyster, *Crassostrea virginica*, observed a drop in metal concentrations in oysters exposed to 10 or 100 μg/litre of mercury in solution. No such decrease was evident in control animals, but the report does not clearly state whether the control oysters spawned at the same time as the experimental animals. Phillips (unpublished data) has observed spawning in mussels, *Mytilus edulis*, exposed to zinc in the laboratory; as control animals did not spawn, exposure to the metal appeared to be the stimulus responsible. Consideration of a later paper (Cunningham and Tripp, 1975*b*), reveals that gonads contain low concentrations of mercury compared with the rest of the soft parts of *Crassostrea virginica*; one would therefore expect spawning to be accompanied by an increase in metal concentration in the oysters. This anomaly has not yet been solved.

In field situations, agreement between authors is rather better. Galtstoff (1964), in studies of oysters, *Crassostrea virginica*, from Long Island Sound, observed that gonad condition was related to glycogen content of whole soft parts of oysters. Gametogenesis utilises glycogen reserves and an annual minimum in glycogen content marks completion of spawning. Subsequent to spawning, glycogen reserves are accumulated once again until the next spawning approaches. *C. virginica* from Long Island Sound was thus found to spawn once only each year, in July-August (Fig. 25). At this time, the seasonal profiles of copper, iron and zinc exhibited marked increases in metal concentration. This pattern confirms the hypothesis suggested above, that the metal levels in the whole soft parts of bivalves increase when tissue weights drop because of the loss of gametes which have relatively low metal contents. The extensive studies of Frazier (1975, 1976) on seasonal fluctuations of trace metals in the same species from Chesapeake Bay, show essentially similar trends, at least for cadmium, copper and zinc. Spawning of these genetically similar hatchery-reared oysters occurred at the same time as in the studies of Galtstoff, and again a marked increase in concentrations of the three metals was noted (Fig. 26). However, although the seasonal fluctuation of iron and manganese in these Chesapeake Bay oysters appeared to be similar to that of the other metals, the maxima lagged those of cadmium, copper and zinc by some 4–6 weeks. Frazier suggested that manganese was more intimately involved with the annual fluctuation in shell growth and convincing evidence for this was

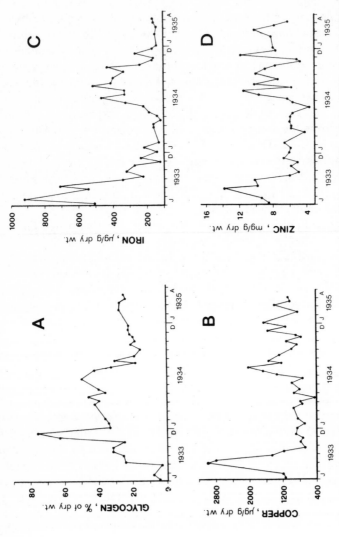

FIG. 25. Seasonal fluctuation in (A) glycogen content, and in concentrations of (B) copper, (C) iron and (D) zinc in adult oysters, *Crassostrea virginica*, from Long Island Sound. All samples were 5 to 7 years of age. (After Galtstoff (1964).)

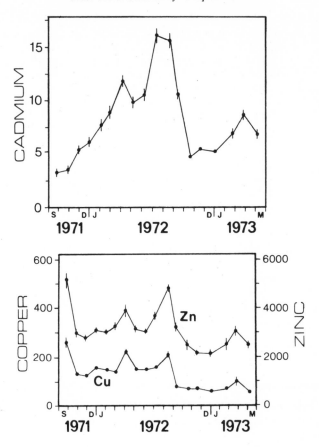

FIG. 26. The seasonal fluctuation in concentrations (means ± standard errors, μg/g dry weight) of cadmium, copper and zinc in oysters, *Crassostrea virginica*, from Chesapeake Bay. All data refer to whole soft parts of hatchery reared oysters, ten individuals per sample. Lack of error bars indicates standard error was less than size of symbol used for the mean. (After Frazier (1975).)

produced by the analysis of metal levels in shells. The amount of manganese deposited in the shell during one growing season was far greater than the range of total body burden of this element throughout the season. By contrast, very little cadmium, zinc or copper was integrated into the shell compared with the body load; iron was intermediate (Table 28). The seasonal fluctuation in manganese (and, to some extent, iron) concentrations thus correlated rather better with shell growth than spawning

TABLE 28

RANGES IN TOTAL BODY BURDENS OF THE METALS CADMIUM,
COPPER, IRON, MANGANESE AND ZINC, AND TOTAL AMOUNTS
OF EACH METAL DEPOSITED IN THE SHELL, DURING THE 1972
GROWING SEASON FOR OYSTERS, *Crassostrea virginica*, IN
CHESAPEAKE BAY. (AFTER FRAZIER (1975).)

Metal	Range of body burden (μg)	Amount deposited in shell (μg)
Cadmium	0·5–7·0	<0·6
Copper	30–80	1
Iron	50–180	112
Manganese	2–13	3 020
Zinc	600–1 800	15

(Fig. 27), and manganese in particular was under constant flux, over 20 μg per day being incorporated into the shell, when only about 10 μg was present at any one time in the entire soft parts. These data certainly raise doubts concerning the ability of *C. virginica* to act as an accurate indicator of iron and manganese; however, the ambient levels of the other metals are no doubt reflected in this oyster and, if seasonal perturbations can be overcome, *C. virginica* appears a capable indicator of cadmium, copper and zinc.

The reciprocality of bivalve weights and their trace metal concentrations was noted also in studies by Phillips (1976a) on the mussel, *Mytilus edulis*, in Port Phillip Bay, Australia. This author found that the total body burdens of cadmium, copper, lead and zinc in mussels varied little throughout the year, although their concentrations varied quite appreciably because of the fluctuation in tissue weights of each individual caused by gametogenesis and spawning. Seasonal maxima in metal concentrations thus coincided with the annual minimum in tissue weight immediately subsequent to spawning (which takes place in the spring in these waters) and, conversely, metals were at minimum concentrations prior to spawning, when the gonads were full of gametes of low metal content. Fowler and Oregioni (1976) supported this conclusion and reported, in addition, some interesting differences between the degree of seasonal variation in the concentration of different metals in the mussel *Mytilus galloprovincialis* from the north-west Mediterranean. Each metal exhibited significant seasonality, but some metals fluctuated in concentration far more than others. Thus, chromium was found to vary most in concentration with season, exhibiting an 8·8-fold difference between maxima and minima; the

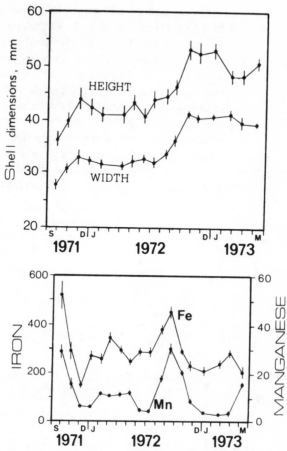

FIG. 27.   Seasonal variation in shell dimensions and in concentrations of iron and manganese (means ± standard errors, μg/g dry weight), in oysters, *Crassostrea virginica*, from Chesapeake Bay. Sample size was ten individuals in all cases; data for metal concentrations refer to whole soft parts. Lack of error bars indicates standard error was less than size of symbol used for the mean. (After Frazier (1975).)

difference for zinc was only two-fold, by contrast. These differences no doubt correlate to the amount of metal enrichment in mussel tissues in relation to the gametes; it is interesting that zinc was found to vary least, and is known to be unusually concentrated in the gonad, almost to levels seen in the rest of the tissues. However, other factors must also be involved in determining the absolute magnitude of seasonal fluctuation, such as temporal changes in influx rates from natural or anthropogenic sources to coastal areas. The pattern of seasonality noted in the above studies has nevertheless been seen by other authors also (e.g. see Karbe *et al.*, 1977, for *M. edulis* from coasts of Germany and Harrison, 1978 for *C. gigas* from the Humboldt Estuary, USA). A very recent report concerning the uptake kinetics of lead and zinc in *M. edulis* (Simpson, 1979) has strongly supported the view that metal concentrations in bivalves depend greatly on the body weight (and hence on the reproductive state) of the individuals studied. This author emphasises the importance of the reproductive state in defining element concentrations in mussels and points out that monitoring studies should employ mussels of similar condition from all sites.

Data for finfish are not so easily found. As noted above, the concentrations of most trace metals (with the possible exception of zinc)

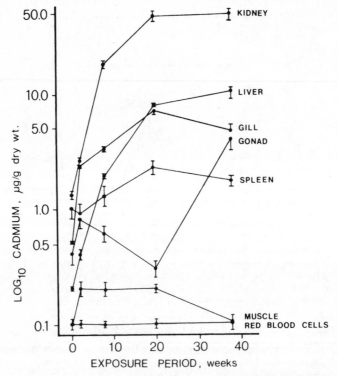

FIG. 28.   Concentrations of cadmium in tissues of first generation brook trout, *Salvelinus fontinalis*, exposed to 3·4 μg/litre of the metal in solution (added as the chloride salt). Each point represents the mean and standard deviation of ten samples. (After Benoit *et al.* (1976).)

appear to be low in the gonads (or gametes) of finfish compared with other tissues and an increase in whole-body metal concentrations would be anticipated at spawning. Benoit *et al.* (1976) noted an increase in the concentration of cadmium in gonad tissues of yearling brook trout, *Salvelinus fontinalis*, exposed to this element in solution (Fig. 28). This increase occurred between the 20th and 38th weeks of study and was correlated by the authors to spawning. Benoit *et al.* suggested that atrophy of the gonads subsequent to spawning was the main cause. It will be noted that the other tissues studied exhibited little change in cadmium levels during this period and whole-body levels of the metal were probably close to steady-state conditions. Holcombe *et al.* (1976) have reported essentially similar data for the uptake of lead from solution by tissues of the brook trout; the changes occurring before and after spawning elicited observable changes in the accumulation of lead by the gonads.

If it is accepted that spawning of organisms alters their whole-body trace metal concentration, it is clearly important to take account of this in decisions on the timing of indicator surveys. A collation of results reported for trace metal seasonality in bivalves of the genera *Mytilus* and *Crassostrea*, about which most is known (Table 29), reveals several interesting facts. First, the degree of seasonality is not only metal-dependent (as noted above by Fowler and Oregioni, 1976), but also appears to be species dependent. Thus, the ratio of seasonal maxima and minima for trace metals is often greater in oysters than in mussels for the same metals. However, different populations of the same species also exhibit different degrees of metal fluctuation, e.g. compare the data of Goldberg *et al.* (1978) for *M. edulis* in Narragansett Bay with those of other authors for the same species. This location dependence may be a function of either the degree of fluctuation in ambient available trace metals with season (which might change, for example, with proximity to terrigenous sources), or of the amount of weight lost at spawning in each population. Mussels which are stressed by either natural or anthropogenic factors produce fewer and smaller eggs than do unstressed mussels (e.g. see Bayne *et al.*, 1978) and this would lead to a smaller decrease in the total body load of metals, and a smaller increase in metal concentration, of stressed mussels at spawning compared with unstressed populations. These two factors may, in some instances, act in concert—i.e. a population receiving a highly seasonally dependent metal input might be stressed by that metal input and might spawn less vigorously as a result. This was quite possibly the case with the highly polluted population of mussels, *Mytilus edulis*, in the estuary of the River Yarra, which is exposed to industrial and domestic discharges from

TABLE 29

SEASONAL MAXIMUM AND MINIMUM CONCENTRATIONS OF CADMIUM, COPPER AND ZINC (μg/g DRY WEIGHT) AND THE RATIO OF THE TWO IN WHOLE SOFT PARTS OF THE MUSSELS *Mytilus edulis*, *M. californianus* AND *M. galloprovincialis* AND THE OYSTERS *Crassostrea virginica* AND *C. gigas*

Author	Location	Species	Cadmium Max.	Cadmium Min.	Cadmium Ratio	Copper Max.	Copper Min.	Copper Ratio	Zinc Max.	Zinc Min.	Zinc Ratio
Phillips (1976a)[a]	Port Phillip Bay, Australia	*M. edulis*	4·52	1·48	3·05		No data		445	143	3·11
Boyden (unpublished)	Helford Estuary, UK	*M. edulis*	2·40	1·10	2·18	17·4	7·6	2·29	225	106	2·12
Cossa (unpublished)	St. Lawrence Estuary, Canada	*M. edulis*	0·60	0·18	3·33		No data			No data	
Goldberg et al. (1978)	Narragansett Bay, USA	*M. edulis*	2·0	1·1	1·82	13·2	6·7	1·97	199	81	2·46
Majori et al. (1978)[a]	Gulf of Trieste, Italy	*M. edulis*		No data			No data		222	74	3·00
Fowler and Oregioni (1976)	North-west Mediterranean Sea	*M. galloprovincialis*	b	b	4·60	b	b	3·92	b	b	1·98
Goldberg et al. (1978)	Bodega Head, California, USA	*M. californianus*	12·4	6·1	2·03	8·0	5·1	1·57	140	100	1·40
Frazier (1975)	Chesapeake Bay, USA	*C. virginica*	16·0	3·0	5·33	280	60	4·67	5 100	2 200	2·32
Boyden (unpublished)	Helford Estuary, UK	*C. gigas*	4·5	1·5	3·00	700	120	5·83	5 100	900	5·67
Harrison (1978)	Humboldt, USA	*C. gigas*		No data			No data		9 000	3 300	2·73

[a] Data converted from wet to dry weights using a ratio of 13·5 per cent.

[b] No maximum and minimum values quoted because ratios are means of the two at 15 stations, calculated individually.

the city of Melbourne (Phillips, 1976*a*, *b*, 1977*a*). Mussels from this estuary exhibited mass mortalities every year during storms, which were probably due to the combined effects of high tissue zinc levels and fluctuating salinities.

Whatever the exact reason for the location dependence of the data in Table 29, it is clear that seasonality of trace metals is severe in bivalves. Widespread monitoring surveys such as those of ICES (Holden, 1973) or the 'mussel watches' conducted in the USA (Goldberg *et al*., 1978) and Scandinavia (Phillips, 1977*c*, 1978*a*, 1979*a*) have shown that trace metal concentrations in bivalves of a given species rarely differ by more than a factor of 10 between highly polluted and relatively clean locations. If seasonal effects can account for 15–60 per cent of this difference (Table 29) it is obviously most important to eliminate these effects.

However, the elimination of the effects of spawning of organisms on the results of monitoring surveys for trace metals is not a simple matter. Synchronous sampling of indicator organisms at all study locations is unfortunately not always sufficient, as the exact timing of spawning in an organism may differ from site to site, even within a relatively small area. In bivalves, partial spawning is quite common, and occasionally oysters will fail to spawn at all, despite favourable conditions; in these cases the gametes are reabsorbed later, usually in the autumn (Galtstoff, 1964). Spawning is controlled by both endogenous and exogenous parameters, the most important of the latter being water temperature. Seed (1975, 1976) has reviewed the spawning of the mussel *Mytilus edulis* in detail, and this species may be taken as a representative example. Figure 29 shows the spawning cycle of *M. edulis* from the North Yorkshire coast of Great Britain, over five years. In general it may be seen that gonad development begins in October–November; gametogenesis occurs throughout the winter until early spring when the gonad is fully ripe. Spawning occurs intermittently through the late spring and summer, sometimes accompanied by intervening periods of gametogenesis. Gametes are usually completely absent from mussels by late August–September, at which time the majority of the population is resting prior to the development of gonads for the next year. In terms of eliminating the effects of spawning or gonad condition on the trace metal content in these mussels, it is important to select a sampling period where all animals (from all sites) exhibit similar gonad indices. This is not simple, as even in the populations shown in Fig. 29, which differ only in shore habitat and local area, very considerable differences exist in the gametogenesis–spawning cycle. Selection of a post-spawning period in about September, for example, would yield samples from each of the five

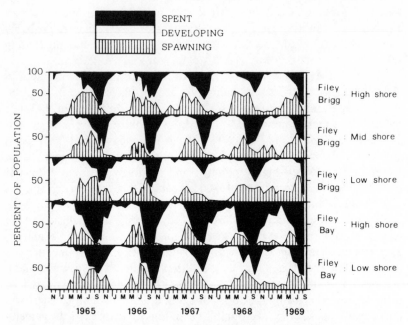

FIG. 29. Seasonal variation in the percentage distributions of developing, spawning and spent individuals in five populations of the mussel, *Mytilus edulis*, between 1964 and 1968. (After Seed (1975).)

locations which differed completely in the relative percentages of developing and spent animals. The period during which least inter-site variability occurs is, in fact, prior to the commencement of spawning, in about January to March; it can be seen that all five populations contain almost all animals in a developing condition, of high (and comparable) gonad index, and little difference occurs from year to year. Unfortunately, this period corresponds to the time when the mussel is of greatest tissue weight and consequently contains the lowest seasonal concentration of trace metals. Although this tends to diminish the accurate definition of inter-site differences in trace metal levels (as well as leading to greater analytical difficulties), the synchrony of condition of the animals analysed would tend to outweigh these disadvantages. This is confirmed by consideration of the data shown in Tables 30 and 31, which are taken directly from the review of Seed (1976). In almost all populations of *M. edulis* studied to date, sampling in the latter half of winter would give mussels in a developing, pre-spawning state; this site-to-site synchrony of

TABLE 30

THE TIMING OF SPAWNING IN POPULATIONS OF THE COMMON MUSSEL, *Mytilus edulis*, FROM THE COASTS OF THE UNITED KINGDOM (AFTER SEED (1976).)

Locality	Authority	Spawning period: Comments
England		
General	White (1937)	Spring, with second, possibly more important, spawning later in the summer
	Raymont (1963)	Especially spring–July/August; but almost any time according to conditions
	Baird (1966)	Over at least 8 months of the year in England/Wales; March–October
Plymouth	Matthews (1913)	Early spring; January–March in 1911
	White (1937)	January–March; spent mussels common May and August
	Lebour (1938)	April–June; some ripe at almost any time; veligers dominant late spring–early summer
	Chipperfield (1953)	May–early June
	Seed (1971)	March–August but especially May–June
Padstow	Chipperfield (1953)	Late April–early June
Brixham	Chipperfield (1953)	May
River Dart	Raymont and Carrie (1964)	March/April–August/September; extended spawning possibly due to local increase in water temperature by power station
Southampton Water	CEGB (1965)	Starts May with intermittent spawning over following 18 weeks
Brighton	Campbell (1969)	April–May; secondary phase in October
The Wash	Savage (1956)	April
Brancaster	Chipperfield (1953)	May–early June
North Yorkshire	Seed (1969, 1975)	March–November but especially April–May and July–August
Northumberland	Lebour (1906)	May–August/September
	Mitchell (cited in Lebour, 1906)	Two spawnings, one in the spring another about August.
	King (cited in Lebour, 1906)	July–September; earlier in warmer years
North-east coast of	McIntosh (1891)	March–May/June
Lancashire	Johnstone (1898)	July–early August; second spawning earlier in year with possibly a slow emission from April onwards; variable
	Daniel (1921)	April–May; as early as March in warm years

TABLE 30—*contd.*

Locality	Authority	Spawning period: Comments
Liverpool	Chipperfield (1953)	May–early June
Morecambe Bay	Herdman and Scott (1895)	May
	Dare (1973)	April–May but some spawning until September–October
Isle of Man	Scott (1901)	Early May–mid July
	Bruce (1926)	May
	Chipperfield (1953)	May
	Roberts (1972)	Mid June–early July. Also October
Wales		
Conway	Cole (cited in Graham, 1956)	Major settlements in March–April
	Chipperfield (1953)	May
	Savage (1956)	Especially April, but also May, June, August
	Baird (1966)	April–May
Menai Bridge	Bayne (1964)	April–June
Cardigan Bay	Wright (1917)	Spawning begins late April or May
Scotland		
St. Andrews	McIntosh (1885)	Mature April; spawn late May–June; larvae abundant July–August
Bay of Nigg	Wilson (1886)	Mature April–May; nearly empty July
	Williamson (1907)	April–June
Millport	Elmhirst (1923)	April–June
	Pyefinch (1950)	Heavy settlements June–July suggest May–June spawnings
Loch Sween	Mason (1969)	Spring
Isle of Skye	Chipperfield (1953)	May–early June
Ireland		
Cromaine	Crowley (1970)	Spring–summer
River Boyne	Meaney (1970)	Late spring–early summer
Carlingford and Belfast Loughs	Wilson and Seed (1975)	Especially April–June, but repeated spawnings may continue throughout the summer until October–November

TABLE 31

THE TIMING OF SPAWNING IN POPULATIONS OF THE COMMON MUSSEL *Mytilus edulis* FROM THE NORTHERN HEMISPHERE, OTHER THAN THE UNITED KINGDOM. (AFTER SEED (1976).)

Locality	Authority	Spawning period: Comments
USSR		
East Murman	Kuznetzov and Mateeva (1948)	May–October; larvae abundant July–August
	Mateeva (1948)	May–October
White Sea	Palichenko (1948)	June–August
	Savilov (1953)	Mid July–early September
Greenland	Madsen (1940)	October
Norway		
Oslofjord	Bøhle (1965)	May–June; also autumn; larvae abundant June–July
	Bøhle (1971)	Starts early May; second spawning mid-June
Trondheimsfjord	Jensen and Sakshaug (1970)	Spring–autumn; extended spawning
Southern Norway	Runnström (1929)	March–June
Finland	Heinonen (1962)	Maximum spawning late May–late June
Denmark		
Limfjord	Spärck (1920)	May–June
The Sound	Jørgensen (1946)	Veligers appear end May–early June and are abundant until September–October; also in December–January and even the spring
Isefjord	Jorgensen (1946)	Veligers appear end May; spawning rapidly completed; by mid July veligers no longer found
General	Vorobiev (cited by Palichenko 1948)	May–September

TABLE 31—*contd.*

Locality	Authority	Spawning period: Comments
Germany		
Helgoland	Kändler (1926)	Larvae common April–December, especially April–June
Cuxhaven	Kühl (1972)	Starts May–June; larvae common May–September
Kiel	Boje (1965)	Starts June
Holland		
General	Berner (1935)	March–April; not later than early May
Zeeland	Lambert (1935)	Mainly June; starts March; smaller emissions May and July
Zuidersee	Havinga (1929)	Summer
General	Havinga (1964)	Most of the year but especially spring–early summer
North Sea	Werner (1939)	Spring–autumn
France		
General	Field (1909)	February–September
Normandy	Le Gall (1970)	End December–early January and March–April even as late as June
Luc-sur-Mer	Lubet and Le Gall (1967)	Sometimes as early as late January–early February; mainly March–April; partial emissions May–June
Brittany	Kriaris (1967)	Larvae abundant during the winter, less abundant in the summer. Especially late October and mid-May
Arcachon	Lubet (1957)	Feeble spawning December and early January; Main spawning late March–June, especially April–May

Baie d'Aiguillon	Herdman (1893)	Early spring
	Berner (1935)	February–March; not later than early April
	Lambert (1950)	Early spring
North Atlantic		
North-west Spain	Stubbings (1954)	February–September, especially April–June
	Andreu (1963)	*edulis* (?) April–May and November–January
	Andreu (1968)	Extended spawning; starts February and ends early summer; secondary spawning in the autumn
		May–June and January–February
Mediterranean		
Black Sea	Fox (1924)	*edulis* (?) February–October
	Vorobiev (cited by Palichenko, 1948)	
North America		
Western Canada	Stafford (1912)	Veligers abundant June–late autumn
New Brunswick	Battle (1932)	Mid June–mid September, especially August
Long Island	Engle and Loosanoff (1944)	May; settle early June–end August
Atlantic Coast	Field (1922)	April–September
Woods Hole	Field (1909)	Early February–end August
	White (1937)	June–September
Western USA	Ahmed and Sparks (1970)	Late April/early May–late August
Pacific coast	Field (1922)	Mainly cold months
	Somer (cited by White, 1937)	Mainly winter
California	Moore and Reish (1969)	Mature ♂ throughout the year but especially October–February; mature ♀ November–May but especially November–February
Japan	Sagiura (1959)	Mature November–April; recently spent mussels May–July
	Hirai (1963)	December–May

TABLE 32

THE TIMING OF SPAWNING IN MYTILIDS OTHER THAN *Mytilus edulis* FROM LOCATIONS IN BOTH THE NORTHERN AND SOUTHERN HEMISPHERES. (AFTER SEED (1976).)

Locality	Authority	Spawning period: Comments
M. galloprovincialis		
South-west England	Seed (1971)	Especially July–August
Brittany	Bouxin (1956)	Extended spawning starts March (sometimes February) ends July, sometimes August
Arcachon	Lubet (1957)	Starts September arrested by low temperature; restarts late March and continues until early July
Provence	Berner (1935)	Extended spawning September–October, December–January
Toulon	Bourcart and Lubet (1965)	Autumn, winter and early spring, ends May–June
Naples	Lo Bianco (1899)	Mature March–April
	Renzoni (1961)	Mature and spawn February–April
	Renzoni (1963)	End winter–early spring; second spawning in autumn
Trieste	Favretto (1968)	Mature end winter–early spring
	Valli (1971)	Mid October–mid December; mid January–early February; March
Messina	Guiseppe (1964)	November–May; inactive till following September
Syracuse	Renzoni (1962)	Ripen and spawn April–May; again ripe October–November
Yugoslavia	Lubet (1961)	Spawning extended but especially March–April and autumn
Black Sea	Kiseleva (1966)	Mass spawning spring/autumn; larvae always abundant
	Ivanov (1971)	Late May–December
Adriatic	Hrs-Brenko (1971)	Especially late January; several less intense spawnings later
M. californianus		
California	Stohler (1930)	Two periods; maximum in July and November–December
	Coe (1932)	Larval abundance suggests June–September
	Whedon (1936)	October–November; also January–February and May–June; more or less continuous
	Young (1942)	Starts early September and at maximum in mid-winter; at minimum from May–August; some limited summer spawning

Species / Location	Reference	Spawning
M. viridis		
India	Fox and Coe (1943), Young (1946)	More or less any season but especially spring and autumn October–March; less intense March–September; some spawning more or less throughout the year
India	Paul (1942)	More or less continuous but mainly March–November; especially August–September
M. edulis diegensis		
California	Coe (1946)	All seasons but especially March–June and early winter
M. edulis plamulatus		
Sydney	Wisely (1964)	June–mid August
Western Australia	Wilson and Hodgkin (1967)	Ripe April–July; some spawning April–May, main spawning July; secondary spawning September with other minor periods
Perna perna (= *M. perna*)		
Venezuela	Carvajal (1969)	Three peaks of larval abundance correspond to three peaks of spawning; December–January, March, June–July
Brazil	Lunetta (1969)	More or less continuous but especially April–June and September
M. aeoteanus		
New Zealand	Pike (1971)	Spring especially
M. platensis		
Argentina	Moreno et al. (1971)	Early spring especially
Perna canaliculus		
New Zealand	Pike (1971)	Spawning rare before January; minor spawning over the summer with another heavy spawning in the autumn
M. crassitesta		
Japan	Miyazaki (1935)	Variable, but especially late December–early April
M. smaragdinus		
Philippines (?)	Obusan and Urbano (1968)	Throughout year but especially May and November
Crenomytilus grayanus		
Japan (?)	Suburo and Sakamoto (1951)	Starts July; maximum late July and August
Peter the Great Gulf	Sadykhova (1970)	Extended but with two peaks

condition would thereby allow the elimination of the interfering effects of spawning on the trace metals present in the samples.

It should be noted here that the timing of spawning in bivalves is species dependent. Thus, Table 32 shows data for mytilids other than *M. edulis*; considerable variation is found between species, but within a single species the location dependence is generally not so great as to lead to great difficulty in selecting a pre-spawning period for sampling during which all populations are in similar condition. In warm regions, it is clear that spawning periods may be extended over much of the year (e.g. see data for *M. californianus* in Table 32); in these cases, the condition of animals can rarely be estimated at any time without empirical study. The lack of large changes in condition in this species decreases the need for strict synchrony of sampling of study areas here, and decisions on the timing of sampling could be made with reference to other factors such as run-off rates. It is interesting that trace metal seasonality in *M. californianus* is very small, the concentrations of most metals only varying by a factor of 2 or less (John H. Martin, pers. comm.); this tends to confirm the suggestion that much of the metal fluctuation in mussels is caused by weight changes occurring at spawning.

Whilst much less is known concerning the effects of spawning in finfish on their trace metal levels, it is clear that similar changes could occur in whole-body trace metals to those outlined above for bivalves. If a monitoring survey is designed for the use of finfish for either trace metal or organochlorine studies, the possible influence of spawning on whole-body concentrations of pollutants should be kept in mind. Finfish are known to exhibit within-species variability in the timing of spawning, which may sometimes be correlated with geographical location and/or water temperatures. Love (1970) cited an example for cod, *Gadus morhua*, which spawns in Scottish waters about two months earlier than in Canadian waters. Other finfish may exhibit similar location dependence in spawning dates. Often, however, authors studying the concentrations of trace metals in finfish for monitoring purposes employ a single tissue as an indicator rather than using the whole animal; muscle tissue is, of course, the most common. In these cases the changes occurring at spawning probably affect the results much less, if at all, and consideration of the timing of spawning in the design of surveys using fish muscle is therefore relatively unimportant. Data for organisms other than bivalves and finfish are rather rare and allow no strong conclusions as to the effects of spawning on seasonality. However, it is reasonable to assume that all higher organisms which lose an appreciable proportion of their whole tissue weights at spawning will exhibit some changes in their residual trace metal levels. Ireland (1974) has shown that metals in the barnacle, *Balanus balanoides*, undergo seasonal fluctuations similar to those of mussels and oysters and has ascribed this to changes in weight connected with the reproductive cycle. The egg mass was analysed independently of the rest of the tissues for two populations of barnacles and was found to contain very low concentrations of copper, lead and zinc compared with the other tissues (Fig. 30), just as is seen in bivalves.

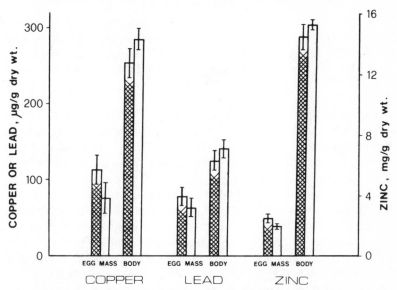

FIG. 30.   Mean concentrations and standard errors (bars) of copper, lead and zinc in the egg mass and body tissues of barnacles, *Balanus balanoides*, from Alltwen (cross-hatched) and Constitution Hill in Cardigan Bay, Wales. Six replicates were analysed for each result. (After Ireland (1974).)

Seasonal profiles for these metals in adult barnacles exhibited maxima generally in the spring, minima occurring in the autumn. The rapid increase in metal concentrations which occurred in early spring was a result of the loss of eggs at spawning. Similar conclusions were reached by Betzer and Pilson (1974, 1975) and Betzer and Yevich (1975) concerning the seasonality of copper in the channelled whelk, *Busycon canaliculatum*. The conclusions of these studies are thus essentially identical to those discussed above for bivalves. Crustaceans other than barnacles probably also exhibit such effects, but in decapods the situation is further complicated by the loss of metals at moulting (see Section C(i) below). However, as stated above, in the absence of data it is safe to assume that most higher organisms will exhibit alterations of whole-body metal levels at spawning and the design of indicator surveys should be adjusted accordingly to attempt to eliminate this variable.

C. OTHER FACTORS: GROWTH, SALINITY AND TEMPERATURE

Of the parameters other than those discussed in previous sections, only three of real importance exist, all of which may lead to significant seasonal perturbations in trace metal levels of aquatic biota. These three parameters are growth, salinity and water temperature, and the effects of each will be discussed in turn here.

(i) Growth

Growth of organisms may, in some cases, be an important influence defining seasonal profiles of trace metal concentration. It is evident that the concentration of a metal in an organism is a function of the balance between its rate of uptake and its rate of excretion; the difference between these two (the rate of net uptake) defines the amount of metal which is to be distributed about the tissues. If this rate of net uptake of metal is the same in two populations of an organism, but one of the populations exhibits twice the average growth rate of the other, the rates of change in metal *content* will be the same, but the rates of change in metal *concentration* will differ. This simply means that the concentration of a metal in an organism is a result of the balance between the net uptake rate of the metal and the rate of growth.

There can be no doubt that variations in growth rates cause changes in the trace metal concentrations of aquatic biota, metals being diluted by fast growth and concentrated by slow growth (or by atrophy; see Fig. 28 and discussion of Benoit *et al.*, 1976, above). However, the quantitative effect of growth rate variation on trace metal levels in biota is often uncertain. Most of the data which relate growth rate to trace metal concentrations in organisms concern either studies on metal retention by biota, or studies on trace metal seasonality in macroalgae. However, one exception to this is the report of Pentreath (1976c), in which the effects of different feeding rates on growth and mercury accumulation from solution were studied using plaice, *Pleuronectes platessa*. Plaice were exposed to ^{203}Hg-labelled methylmercury chloride in seawater for 97 days and two separate groups were fed at different rates. The results (Fig. 31) indicated that the fish fed greater rations

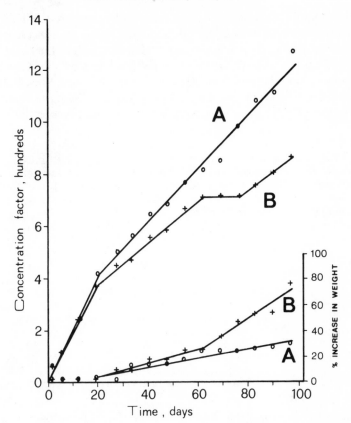

FIG. 31. Concentration factors describing the accumulation of [203]Hg-labelled methylmercury from solution by O-group plaice, *Pleuronectes platessa*, fed different rations to induce different rates of growth. Both A and B groups were fed 1·5 per cent of body weight per day for 20 days, at which time group A were changed to 2 per cent body weight per day for the rest of the experiment, whilst group B were fed 4 per cent body weight per day from day 20 to day 62, and 6–7 per cent body weight per day from day 62 to day 97. (After Pentreath (1976c).)

grew faster and exhibited weight increases approximately double those of the less well-fed group. Despite exposure of each group to the same concentration of methylmercury, the fast-growing fish exhibited lower final concentrations of the metal in their tissues, although the total amounts of metal accumulated by fish of each group were similar. This example thus clearly shows the dependence of tissue levels of metals on growth rates of biota.

Data from transplantation studies designed to elucidate the biological half-lives of trace metals often produce interesting results concerning the effects of growth on trace metal levels found in biota. Thus, Lockhart *et al.* (1972) transplanted pike, *Esox lucius*, from the mercury polluted Clay Lake in Ontario to the relatively clean Heming Lake in Manitoba. Muscle biopsy samples indicated a slow loss of mercury over the first 12 months (Table 33) and the tissue distribution of the metal was found to change very little. The

TABLE 33

TOTAL BODY BURDENS OF MERCURY IN NORTHERN PIKE, *Esox lucius*, AFTER 3-, 6-, 9- AND 12-MONTH PERIODS SUBSEQUENT TO THEIR TRANSPLANTATION FROM CLAY LAKE, ONTARIO, TO HEMING LAKE, MANITOBA. (AFTER LOCKHART *et al.* (1972).)

Sample date	Number	Original weight (g)	Original mercury (μg)	Recapture weight (g)	Recapture mercury (μg)[a]
January, 1971 (3 months)	9	9 560	67 200	9 370	70 600 (105 per cent)
April, 1971 (6 months)	18	16 160	140 800	16 210	117 200 (83 per cent)
July, 1971 (9 months)	17	18 500	146 000	22 040	120 300 (82 per cent)
October, 1971 (12 months)	5	3 920	32 700	8 360	23 100 (71 per cent)

[a] Figures in parentheses are percentages of original total body load of mercury.

results shown in Table 33 are quoted in terms of total body loads; in terms of concentrations, the loss of metal would appear greater due to growth of the fish subsequent to transplantation. Laarman *et al.* (1976) performed similar studies with yellow perch, *Perca flavescens*, and rock bass, *Ambloplites rupestris*, transferring the fish from the polluted Lake St. Clair to uncontaminated earthern ponds. After 26 months, concentrations of total mercury in muscle fillets had decreased 53 per cent in the perch and 59 per cent in the bass, but mean fish weights had increased 88 and 183 per cent, respectively during that period. The *decrease* in metal concentration was entirely attributable to growth, and a net *increase* in total body burdens of mercury was apparent for both fish during the 26-month period of study. The growth dilution effect is shown in Fig. 32. It should be noted that the effects of growth on metals retained by biota are very significant when studies attempt to determine biological half-life values for metals. Other authors have also observed growth dilution effects, e.g. see Branson *et al.*

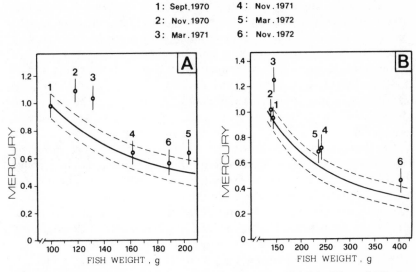

FIG. 32. Mean concentrations of mercury (μg/g wet weight) in fillets of (A) the yellow perch, *Perca flavescens*, and (B) the rock bass, *Ambloplites rupestris*, at intervals after their transplantation from Lake St. Clair to relatively uncontaminated earthern ponds. Mean concentrations ± 95 per cent confidence limits actually observed are shown by vertical lines. The curve shown for each fish indicates the expected mean concentrations (± 95 per cent confidence intervals) of mercury, allowing for growth of original transplants but no accumulation or loss of the metal. (After Laarman *et al.* (1976).)

(1975) for PCBs in rainbow trout, *Salmo gairdneri*, and Spehar (1976) for zinc and cadmium in flagfish, *Jordanella floridae*. This subject was mentioned in relation to the biological half-lives of metals in Chapter 2 also, where several other extraneous factors affecting apparent metal retention by biota were discussed.

These effects of growth on the trace metal levels found in aquatic organisms may contribute to the seasonality of elements in biota. It was stated above that the concentration of a metal in an organism is a result of the balance between the net uptake rate of the metal and the rate of growth. In a hypothetical situation in temperate waters where the amount of available metal does not differ throughout the year, an organism would exhibit cyclical annual maxima and minima in metal concentration because of the changes in growth rates with season. Metals would thus be diluted in the summer period of rapid growth and concentrated in the winter, when growth is slow. Obviously, this profile is simplistic, as the amounts of available metal are also changing with season, as discussed in Section A above; nevertheless, seasonal changes in growth rates of biota may be important in some instances in determining trace metal fluctuations with time. It is notable that growth is only an important factor if it differs throughout the year (i.e. if a seasonal cycle in water temperature and/or food availability exists); in tropical regions, few such effects would be expected. In a sense, the effects of organism growth parallel those of gonad development; in both cases, trace metal concentrations are subject to fluctuations because of cyclic temporal changes in tissue weights.

The best evidence for growth-related seasonality of trace metals in aquatic biota comes from studies of macroalgae. Laboratory experiments have suggested that macroalgae respond mainly to trace metals in solution, acting similarly, in some ways, to an ion-exchange column. (Interestingly enough, this property is not restricted to aquatic plants; terrestrial bryophytes absorb metals from the atmosphere and have, in consequence, been used as indicators of air quality.) Bryan (1969, 1971, 1976) has published much information on the uptake of metals by *Laminaria digitata*. The relationship between metals in the alga and those in water is shown in Fig. 33. It is evident that whilst uptake is not precisely

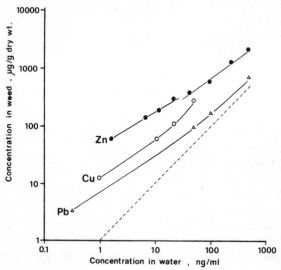

FIG. 33.   The relationship between the concentrations of metals in seawater and those in the macroalga, *Laminaria digitata*, after 30–31 days' exposure. 3 × 1 cm pieces of weed from the growing region were exposed in continuous light at 12–13 °C. Proportionality is shown by the broken line. (After Bryan (1969, 1976).)

proportional to seawater concentrations of the elements, it certainly approaches proportionality. Similar conclusions were reached by Morris and Bale (1975) and Seeliger and Edwards (1977) in field studies. Morris and Bale (1975) compared previously reported values for metal concentrations in *Fucus vesiculosus* from the Bristol Channel, UK (Fuge and James, 1974) with their own long-term data for element levels in water of that site. A general agreement between the metal levels in each component was evident for cadmium, copper and zinc, but data for manganese were less convincing (Fig. 34). Seeliger and Edwards produced similar data for the relationship between concentrations of copper and lead in the waters of Raritan Bay near New York and in four species of algae from the Bay. Overall correlation coefficients for the relationship of metal levels in water and algae were 0·98 for copper and 0·97 for lead. The extensive studies of these authors therefore suggest that seaweeds of this type could be extremely useful indicators of soluble metals. In addition, the time-integration capacity of macroalgae for metals is considered to be very high —i.e. once bound, metals are lost extremely slowly. This high time-integration capacity was suspected from measurements of half-lives of metals in the laboratory (Gutknecht, 1965; Bryan, 1969; Young, 1975), but has recently been confirmed by transplantation studies in the field (Myklestad *et al.*, 1978).

Seasonality of trace metal concentrations in macroalgae has been observed by several authors. Fuge and James (1973, 1974) used whole plants, or parts of plants including stipe, thallus and growing tips, to study the seasonal variation in metal levels of *Fucus vesiculosus* from the coasts of Wales. A typical result is shown in Fig. 35. Concentrations of each metal were found to increase in the autumn and winter to a maximum in late winter, subsequently decreasing during the spring and summer. These profiles are reciprocal to the pattern of seasonal growth in macroalgae from temperate waters; growth begins in the spring, continues throughout the summer and virtually ceases in the autumn and winter. Therefore, if the entire plant is considered, the concentrations of metals are found to depend on the rate of growth dilution of pre-existing levels. This suggests that older parts of the plant contain higher concentrations of metals than do young growing tips and that metals are retained for long periods once bound to the plant. Both these hypotheses are known to be generally true (see Bryan, 1969; Bryan and Hummerstone, 1973*a* and discussion above). A parallel may be drawn between the seasonal fluctuations in macroalgae due to growth and those in bivalves due to gonad maturation. In both cases, the synthesis and development of new tissue occur at one time of year faster

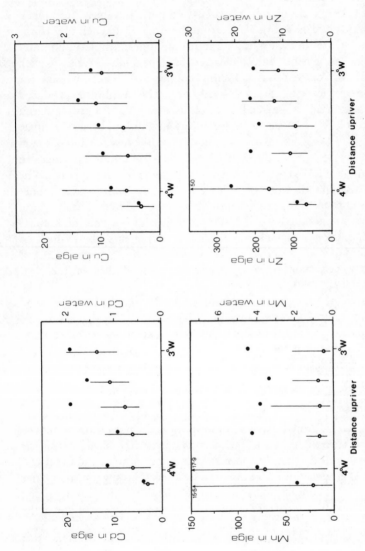

FIG. 34. Profiles of cadmium, copper, manganese and zinc in water and in the alga, *Fucus vesiculosus*, plotted with distance down the Bristol Channel, UK. Open circles and range bars indicate mean and overall range of metals (μg/litre) in water, right-hand scale. Closed circles referred to left-hand scale indicate mean concentrations of metals in *Fucus vesiculosus* (μg/g dry weight). (After Fuge and James (1974) and Morris and Bale (1975).)

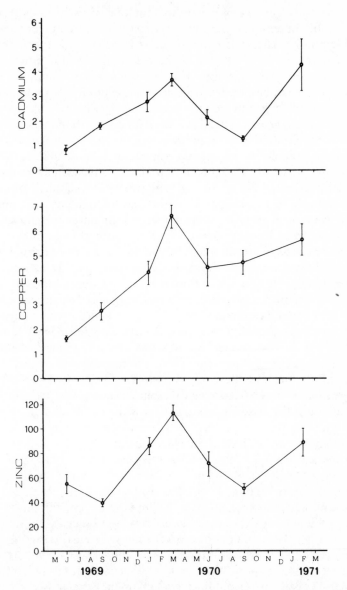

FIG. 35. Fluctuation in concentrations of cadmium, copper and zinc (means ± standard deviations, μg/g dry weight) in the macroalga, *Fucus vesiculosus*, with season. All data refer to samples from Nefyn, Caernarvon Bay in the Irish Sea; sample size was 30 throughout. (After Fuge and James (1973, 1974).)

than the rate of uptake of metals, and dilution of metal levels therefore occurs. In the case of the bivalve, however, spawning produces the reconcentration of metals noted, whereas in macroalgae this is brought about by cessation of growth in the cold season whilst metal uptake continues throughout the year. The elegance of the example cited above cannot, of course, be matched at all locations, as growth-dependence of the profile depends not only on inclusion of the growing tips but also on a relatively constant level of available metal for uptake. If the concentrations of available metals in the ambient water mass fluctuate, the plant responds, and the variations in net uptake superimpose those due to growth, sometimes obscuring the growth dependence altogether. The seasonal profiles reported for zinc in *Ascophyllum nodosum* from the Trondheimsfjord by Haug *et al.* (1974) and for zinc and manganese in *Fucus vesiculosus* from the Tamar Estuary (Bryan and Hummerstone, 1973*a*) are cases in point. Metal availability at both these sites appears complex in its temporal variation, as is often the case in estuaries draining industrialised catchments. Bryan and Hummerstone (1973*a*) found that copper levels in *F. vesiculosus* from the Tamar Estuary varied little with season, although concentrations of aluminium, iron, manganese and zinc all exhibited significant seasonality. Manganese and zinc both exhibited site-dependent seasonality—i.e. the seasonal fluctuation of metal levels was different at different sites. This was ascribed to temporal changes in available metal levels at each site. These studies in any case employed older parts of the main thallus only as samples, which tends to preclude observation of growth-dependent seasonal changes. It is therefore clear that although the seasonal variation in growth rates of an organism must elicit temporal variation in trace metal concentrations, this effect is rarely predominant and is most frequently obscured by the fluctuation of available metal levels. Only in instances where ambient metal levels are relatively constant—and organism growth varies greatly throughout the year—are effects likely to be noted in field studies.

Organism growth may, however, be important in one further instance, which should be seen as a special case. Crustaceans such as crabs, lobsters and prawns possess a chitinous exoskeleton which must be shed regularly during periods of growth; this process of moulting may have importance in determining the temporal changes in metal concentrations present in the animal. The control of moulting is complex in the extreme, being achieved by hormonal changes in which both moult-accelerating and moult-inhibiting hormones are involved. The production of these hormones occurs in response to both external stimuli (light, temperature, etc.) and internal or physiological stimuli. However, the effect of temperature is important enough to commonly elicit seasonal changes in the rate of moulting in decapod crustaceans. Thus, moulting is generally infrequent in the winter when growth rates are low, but the increased metabolism and growth in summer temperatures elicits more frequent moulting. As noted above for growth rate changes in macroalgae, such comments obviously apply only to temperate climes with well-defined temperature seasonality.

Several authors have found that the amounts of trace metals present in the exoskeleton of crustaceans represent a very significant proportion of the total body load of elements. Loss of part of the exoskeleton at moulting therefore removes, in a quantum fashion, a certain percentage of the whole-body metal content. Studies by Fowler and his co-workers are of particular note, and have included reports on the effects of moulting on the excretion of ^{65}Zn, ^{75}Se, ^{137}Cs and ^{144}Ce by euphausiids (Fowler *et al.*, 1971; Fowler and Benayoun, 1976a), ^{65}Zn by the amphipod *Gammarus locusta* (Fowler *et al.*, 1975), and ^{75}Se or ^{109}Cd by the shrimp *Lysmata seticaudata* (Fowler and Benayoun, 1974, 1976c). The large amounts of either radionuclides or stable metals accumulated by the exoskeleton relative to the total body load of isotopes in crustaceans have also been noted in studies by other authors (e.g. see Pequegnat *et al.*, 1969; Small, 1969; Jennings and Rainbow, 1979; Wright and Brewer, 1979). It is important to understand, however, that the amount of trace metals lost in cast moults is not the same as that accumulated by the exoskeleton. For example, Fowler and Benayoun (1976b) reported that whilst the exoskeleton of *Lysmata seticaudata* accounts for about 22 per cent of the body burden of selenium in animals from the field, cast moults contain only a little over 2 per cent of the body burden (Table 34). Clearly, only 10 per cent of the total selenium present in the exoskeleton is lost in the moult, which represents some 70 per cent of the biomass of the exoskeleton. It therefore appears that, for selenium at least, much of the metal contained in the exoskeleton is bound to deep tissues which are not lost with the cast moult. The opposite conclusion may, however, be reached by authors studying the uptake of metals from solution. If uptake from solution predominates, metals in the exoskeleton commonly account for more than half of the total body load of elements and this may be correlated to the capacity of the carapace to adsorb large amounts of metals in a non-specific fashion. The apparent loss of metals at moulting then depends on the exposure period, as the non-specific binding of metals to the carapace is much more rapid than is metal uptake by the soft parts. If moulting occurs early during exposure, a large proportion of the total body load of metals is lost; if later, a much smaller proportional

TABLE 34

COMPARATIVE TISSUE DISTRIBUTION OF SELENIUM IN THE SHRIMP, *Lysmata seticaudata*, IN TERMS OF BOTH ELEMENT CONCENTRATIONS AND TOTAL LOADS. DATA REFER TO THE STABLE ISOTOPE AND TO SHRIMP FROM THE REGION OF THE PORT OF MONACO. (AFTER FOWLER AND BENAYOUN (1976*b*).)

Tissue	Selenium concentration μg/g dry	μg/g wet	Tissue wet weight (per cent total animal)	Per cent total Se body burden
Whole animal	2·69[a]	0·65[a]	(100)	(100)
Viscera	7·06	2·26	8·2	31·6
Muscle	1·98	0·40	62·8	42·8
Eyes	4·86	1·22	1·8	3·8
Exoskeleton	1·51	0·47	27·2	21·8
Moults	0·32	0·07	19·0	2·1

[a] Measured value, not reconstructed.

decrease occurs (Fowler and Benayoun, 1974). In a later paper (Fowler and Benayoun, 1976*c*), these differences were emphasised by comparing selenium kinetics in shrimp exposed to ^{75}Se in food or water separately. Figure 36 shows the retention of ^{75}Se in each case; it is clear that shrimp exposed to the nuclide in water alone lost greater proportions of the body load than did those which had accumulated the nuclide from food. The difference in retention was found to be mainly due to the amounts of selenium lost in cast moults; shrimp exposed to ^{75}Se in solution subsequently lost 65 per cent of their total body load at moulting, whilst those exposed to contaminated food lost insignificant amounts of the nuclide at moulting (cf. the estimate for the loss of the stable isotope, cited above).

The effect of moulting on the use of decapod crustaceans as indicators of trace metals thus depends on the relative importance of element uptake from food and from solution, as this dictates the amount of a metal which is incorporated into, or adsorbed on to, the exoskeleton. As the predominance of each route of uptake is rarely known in the field, no quantitative estimate of the interference of moulting in indicator surveys can be made. Nevertheless, the seasonal dependence of the incidence of moulting in crustaceans from non-tropical waters, allied to changes in water temperature and other factors throughout the year, suggests that the effects of moulting on the trace metal contents of these animals will be

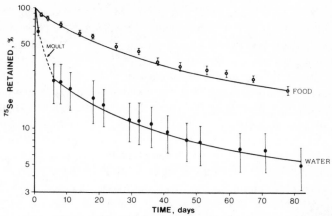

FIG. 36. The retention of [75]Se (+ 4) by whole shrimp, *Lysmata seticaudata*, after their exposure to the radionuclide in food or water for 51 days. All values represent means ±1 standard deviation for four individuals. (After Fowler and Benayoun, 1976c).)

greatest in the summer. An additional factor of interest is the report of Vernberg *et al.* (1977), in which the incidence of moulting in the grass shrimp, *Palaemonetes pugio*, was found to be significantly altered by exposure of the animals to cadmium. Moderate body burdens of the element were accompanied by stimulation of moulting frequency, whereas high body burdens apparently lead to inhibition of moulting.

Because of these effects of moulting, the use of decapod crustaceans in indicator surveys designed to monitor the relative abundance of trace metals in different locations cannot be recommended unless the effects of moulting can be quantitatively evaluated. In addition, some metals appear to be regulated within definite limits in crabs and lobsters at least (see Chapter 14), thus eliminating any possibility of their use as biological indicators of trace metals in aquatic environments.

(ii) Salinity

The effects of salinity on the seasonality of trace metals in aquatic biota may be divided into two components. The first of these follows from the discussions in Section A of this chapter, where the influence of run-off on the delivery of trace metals to the marine environment was considered. The amounts of trace metals maintained in the water column in estuaries are commonly found to be a simple function of salinity. Thus, several authors have published profiles describing the decrease in concentrations of trace metals in river or estuarine waters with increases in salinity; examples are shown in Fig. 37. If the salinity dependence of metal concentrations is linear, the metal is said to behave conservatively and the process may be adequately described by the rate of mixing of freshwater with relatively uncontaminated marine receiving waters. However, if departures from linearity occur, the metal must be responsive to additional events other than freshwater–saltwater mixing. Thus, the metal must exhibit desorption from particulates into solution or, alternatively, adsorption on to particulates from solution, or some other change, concurrently to mixing of the two water masses; in these instances the metal is termed non-conservative. Whatever the changes involved, it is clear that an increase in the rate of run-off will lead to the maintenance of lower salinities further downriver, i.e. in increased run-off, mixing of the two water masses in an estuary is slower. Sedentary biota in the estuary will therefore be exposed to altered concentrations of metals incidental to the lower salinities during periods of greater run-off. The possible implications of this in terms of the seasonal fluctuations in metal availability to estuarine biota have already been discussed and will not be repeated here.

The second effect of salinity on the uptake of trace metals by biota is more direct in nature and does not depend on the presence of higher ambient levels of metals occurring concomitantly to lowered salinities. Thus, salinity affects the physiology of aquatic organisms directly, leading to alterations in filtration or feeding rates or even to cessation of feeding in some instances. Many of the direct physiological effects are more important in terms of their bearing on the indicator ability of an organism rather than as mechanisms producing trace metal seasonality in biota; these effects will be considered elsewhere. Discussion here will be restricted to the direct effects of salinity on metal uptake by biota. The earliest report known to the present author to suggest that the accumulation of trace metals by biota is salinity dependent is that of Rucker and Valentine (1961). These authors investigated the concentrations of boron, copper, magnesium, manganese, sodium and strontium in the shells of oysters, *Crassostrea virginica*, taken from eleven stations on the east coast of the United States. Correlations of the resulting metal concentrations with mean annual salinities of each sampling location produced significant coefficients for manganese and sodium; some correlations between groups of elements and salinity were also noted.

More recently, several authors have discovered direct effects of salinity on the rates of net uptake of trace metals by marine, estuarine or brackish-water biota. Hannerz (1968) reported that the uptake of methoxyethylmercury and methylmercury direct from solution by pike, *Esox lucius*, and cod,

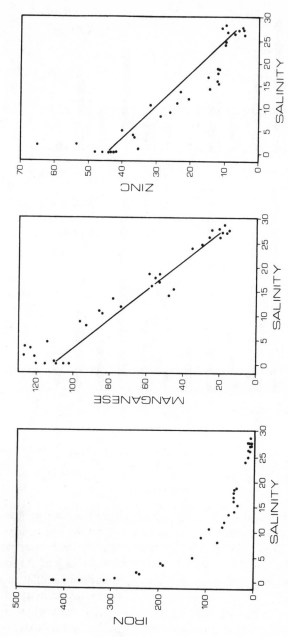

FIG. 37. Relationship between concentrations of 'dissolved' ($<0.45 \mu$) iron, manganese or zinc and salinity in the Beaulieu Estuary, southern England; samples taken on 5 February, 1974. All metal concentrations are in μg/litre; salinities are in parts per thousand. Manganese and zinc appear mainly conservative in behaviour, whereas iron is markedly non-conservative, probably because of its removal from solution by precipitation during freshwater–saltwater mixing. (After Holliday and Liss (1976).) For further examples, see Graham *et al.* (1976) and Duinker and Nolting (1976, 1977).

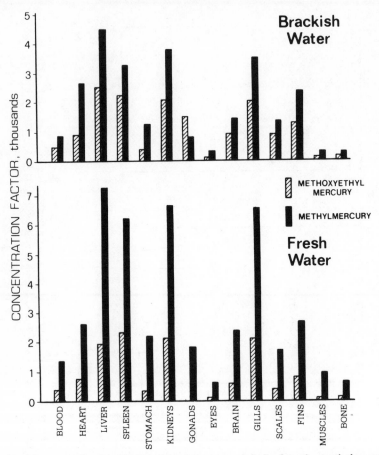

FIG. 38.   Concentration factors (based on wet weights) of methoxyethylmercury and methylmercury attained by different tissues of the pike, *Esox lucius*, after exposure to these compounds (as hydroxides) in brackish water (5·8‰ S) or fresh water. (After Hannerz (1968).)

Gadus morhua, varied with the ambient salinity. Results for several tissues of the pike, analysed individually, are shown in Fig. 38. The uptake of methylmercury is clearly less in brackish water than in freshwater; on a whole body basis the former was stated to be about 60 per cent of the latter. Tissue distributions of the accumulated methylmercury are similar in the two instances. By contrast, the uptake of methoxyethylmercury from brackish water by pike did not differ significantly from that from freshwater. The results for cod are shown in Fig. 39; in this case, both

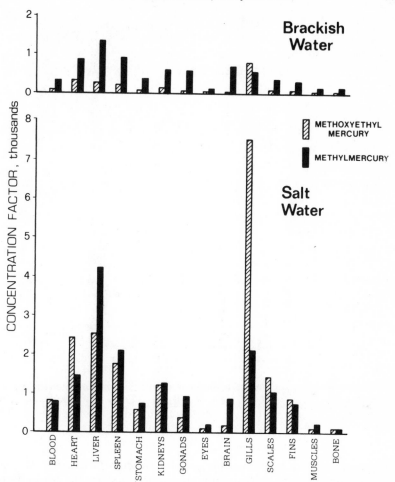

FIG. 39. Concentration factors (based on wet weights) of methoxyethylmercury and methylmercury attained by different tissues of cod, *Gadus morhua*, after exposure to these compounds (as hydroxides) in saltwater (33·7‰ S) or in brackish water (6·38‰ salinity). (After Hannerz (1968).)

compounds were accumulated much more rapidly from saltwater than from brackish water, differences being a factor of 2·2 for methylmercury and 8·3 for methoxyethylmercury. As muscle tissues are of particular interest, because of their extensive use in indicator surveys, data for the uptake of these compounds by muscle of each species are shown in Fig. 40. These data conform to the general pattern outlined above with the

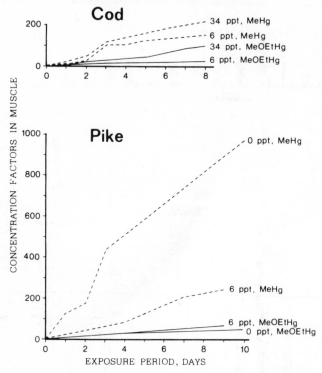

FIG. 40.   Concentration factors (based on wet weights) attained by muscle tissues
of pike, *Esox lucius*, and cod, *Gadus morhua*, exposed to methoxyethylmercury
(continuous lines) or methylmercury (dashes) in water of differing salinities. (After
Hannerz (1968).)

exception of the quantitative degree of difference between each pairing.
This report remains the only paper known to date in which the *direct* effects
of salinity on the uptake of a metal by a finfish have been studied. Similar
data have, however, been published for organochlorines (see Chapter 6).

Differences in salinity also elicit changes in the rates of uptake of trace
metals by other organisms, including bivalve molluscs, crustaceans and
polychaetes. Concerning bivalves, Phillips (1976a) found that both salinity
and temperature affected the uptake of trace metals by the mussel *Mytilus
edulis*. Mussels were exposed (after an acclimation period of 21 days) to a
mixture of cadmium, copper, lead and zinc in solution at four
salinity–temperature combinations. The uptake of metals was studied at 6
and 14 days; results are shown in Table 35. Zinc concentrations attained by

TABLE 35

CONCENTRATIONS (μg/g WET WEIGHT, MEANS $\pm$ STANDARD DEVIATIONS FOR $n = 10$) OF ZINC, CADMIUM, LEAD AND COPPER IN WHOLE SOFT PARTS OF MUSSELS, *Mytilus edulis*, EXPOSED TO A MIXTURE OF 400 μg/LITRE ZINC, 40 μg/LITRE CADMIUM, 20 μg/LITRE LEAD AND 20 μg/LITRE COPPER FOR 14 DAYS AT FOUR SALINITY–TEMPERATURE COMBINATIONS. (AFTER PHILLIPS (1976*a*).)

Sample	Metal	Tank 1	Tank 2	Tank 3	Tank 4
		18 °C, 35‰ S	18 °C, 15‰ S	10 °C, 35‰ S	10 °C, 15‰ S
Control	Zn	$21\cdot2 \pm 5\cdot8$	$22\cdot5 \pm 4\cdot6$	$23\cdot5 \pm 7\cdot3$	$27\cdot7 \pm 14\cdot4$
	Cd	$0\cdot47 \pm 0\cdot13$	$0\cdot49 \pm 0\cdot07$	$0\cdot51 \pm 0\cdot18$	$0\cdot52 \pm 0\cdot07$
	Pb	$1\cdot80 \pm 0\cdot68$	$1\cdot82 \pm 0\cdot44$	$1\cdot68 \pm 0\cdot32$	$1\cdot58 \pm 0\cdot72$
	Cu	BDL[a]	BDL[a]	BDL[a]	BDL[a]
6 Days	Zn	$40\cdot7 \pm 14\cdot4$	$40\cdot6 \pm 16\cdot2$	$36\cdot5 \pm 9\cdot1$	$29\cdot3 \pm 5\cdot1$
	Cd	$1\cdot01 \pm 0\cdot41$	$2\cdot23 \pm 0\cdot40$	$0\cdot99 \pm 0\cdot27$	$1\cdot55 \pm 0\cdot34$
	Pb	$3\cdot55 \pm 1\cdot04$	$2\cdot14 \pm 0\cdot58$	$3\cdot15 \pm 0\cdot55$	$1\cdot74 \pm 0\cdot51$
	Cu	$0\cdot32 \pm 0\cdot15$	$0\cdot98 \pm 0\cdot42$	$0\cdot58 \pm 0\cdot30$	$1\cdot05 \pm 0\cdot57$
14 Days	Zn	$45\cdot8 \pm 26\cdot8$	$51\cdot9 \pm 24\cdot4$	$51\cdot4 \pm 20\cdot1$	$41\cdot4 \pm 12\cdot7$
	Cd	$1\cdot22 \pm 0\cdot57$	$6\cdot52 \pm 2\cdot04$	$1\cdot42 \pm 0\cdot41$	$2\cdot25 \pm 0\cdot66$
	Pb	$4\cdot78 \pm 1\cdot82$	$2\cdot63 \pm 1\cdot11$	$4\cdot76 \pm 1\cdot33$	$2\cdot90 \pm 1\cdot18$
	Cu	$1\cdot10 \pm 0\cdot67$	$3\cdot13 \pm 1\cdot26$	$1\cdot19 \pm 0\cdot47$	$1\cdot75 \pm 1\cdot23$

[a] BDL = below detection limits for these samples.

mussels in all treatments did not differ significantly, but cadmium uptake was always greater at lower salinities, whilst lead uptake was increased at higher salinities. Temperature effects were insignificant for zinc and lead, but cadmium uptake at the lower salinities was increased by higher temperatures. The uptake of copper was extremely erratic; this and other data (see Chapter 13) lead to suggestions that the mussel is a poor indicator of copper, its uptake responding to many interacting variables. A later report by Jackim *et al.* (1977) confirmed the effects of salinity and temperature on the uptake of cadmium by *M. edulis* from solution and extended these observations to the bivalves, *Mulinia lateralis* and *Nucula proxima*; in each case, decreases in salinity increased the net uptake of cadmium from a given exposure level in solution (Table 36). Ünlü and Fowler (1979) have recently shown that inorganic arsenic is also taken up faster from solution by *Mytilus galloprovincialis* when salinities are lowered; such effects may be quite widespread amongst many organisms.

It is important here to distinguish true effects of salinity *per se* on the uptake of metals by bivalves (which may be observed in acclimated animals which are not unduly stressed) from the effects of salinity stress on metal

TABLE 36

THE EFFECT OF SALINITY ON THE NET UPTAKE OF ^{109}Cd BY WHOLE
SOFT PARTS OF THREE MARINE BIVALVE MOLLUSCS MAINTAINED IN
DIFFERENT SALINITY–TEMPERATURE REGIMES. EXPOSURE WAS AT
20 μg/LITRE CADMIUM FOR 21 DAYS; ALL RESULTS ARE IN μg/g DRY
WEIGHTS AND REFER TO POOLED SAMPLES OF TEN OR MORE
INDIVIDUALS. (AFTER JACKIM *et al.* (1977).)

Species	10 °C		20 °C	
	20‰ S	30‰ S	20‰ S	30‰ S
Mytilus edulis	83·16	32·08	108·12	86·62
Mulinia lateralis	52·27	24·35	36·91	8·78
Nucula proxima	2·08	0·61	5·35	2·61

uptake. For example, zinc uptake was seen above to be unresponsive to
salinity in *Mytilus edulis* (Phillips, 1976a). However, if these mussels are
repeatedly stressed by rapid large-amplitude fluctuations of salinity,
perturbations of zinc uptake can occur. Thus, Phillips (1977a) reported
that mussels exposed to a rapid decrease in salinity, followed by a salinity
increase and concurrent exposure to zinc, accumulate larger amounts of
metal than do mussels which are not stressed in this way. The report of
Jackim *et al.* (1977) unfortunately does not state whether the bivalves
tested were salinity acclimated; whilst both stress effects of salinity and
'direct' effects of salinity on metal uptake by biota may be important in the
field, the comparison of acclimated and non-acclimated animals may help to
differentiate the mechanisms by which salinity affects trace metal uptake.

In organisms other than bivalves, the dependence of metal uptake on
salinity and/or temperature is similar to that noted above. O'Hara (1973a,
1973b) found both parameters to alter uptake and toxicity of cadmium in
the fiddler crab, *Uca pugilator* (Fig. 41); in general, cadmium was taken up
more rapidly at lower salinities and at higher temperatures. The effect of
temperature was markedly greater at lower salinities, as noted by Phillips
(1976a) for *Mytilus edulis* (Table 35 and discussion above). Hutcheson
(1974) reported very similar data concerning the uptake of cadmium by the
blue crab, *Callinectes sapidus*, and Wright (1977a) found increases in
cadmium uptake from solution at lower salinities for the shore crab, *Carcinus
maenas*. Vernberg *et al.* (1977) also noted increases in cadmium uptake at
lower salinities, in this case for the grass shrimp *Palaemonetes pugio*;
mortalities followed the same profile (Fig. 42). Amongst Nereid worms, the
direct effects of salinity on metal uptake vary with the metal concerned (*cf.*

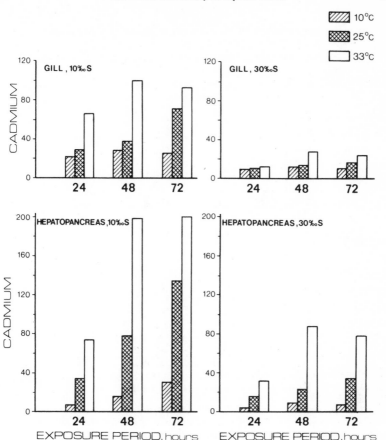

FIG. 41. Concentrations of cadmium (means of four individuals, μg/g wet weight) in gill and hepatopancreas tissues of fiddler crabs, *Uca pugilator*, exposed to 10 mg/litre cadmium in solution for 72 h at two salinities and three temperatures. (After tabulated data in O'Hara (1973*b*), as shown in Phillips (1979*b*).)

Phillips 1976*a* above). Bryan and Hummerstone (1971) noted anomalies in the relationship between copper in *Nereis diversicolor* and that in sediments for the Restronguet Creek and Tamar estuaries in southern England. These were suggested to be due to an effect of salinity on the rate of net uptake of copper by the worms, although no direct evidence was cited. In a later review, Bryan (1976) stated that copper absorption by this organism increased as salinities were lowered, but again no data were cited and none could be found in the literature. The data for zinc absorption are available,

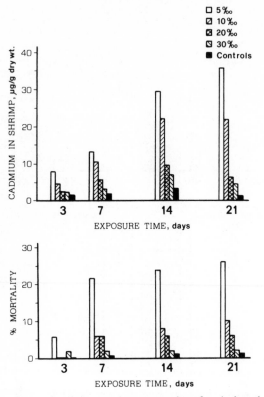

FIG. 42.   The effects of salinity on the net uptake of cadmium by whole grass shrimp, *Palaemonetes pugio* (top), and on cumulative per cent mortalities of the same organisms (bottom). All salinities pooled for control data. (After Vernberg *et al.* (1977).)

however; Bryan and Hummerstone (1973*b*) showed that *N. diversicolor* from both the Avon and Restronguet Creek estuaries exhibited increased rates of zinc uptake at lower salinities (Fig. 43(A)). A similar result was reported for the uptake of manganese by the Avon population in a subsequent paper, and this is shown in Fig. 43(B) (Bryan and Hummerstone, 1973*c*). More recently, Luoma (1977*a*) found that the uptake of dissolved mercury by the related species *Nereis succinea* was also responsive to salinity, but in this case uptake was slower at the lower salinities, at least below a salinity of 16‰ (Fig. 43(C)). By contrast, no effect of salinity was noted on ^{203}Hg uptake from solution by the shrimp, *Palaemon debilis*, tested under similar conditions (Luoma, 1977*a*). These

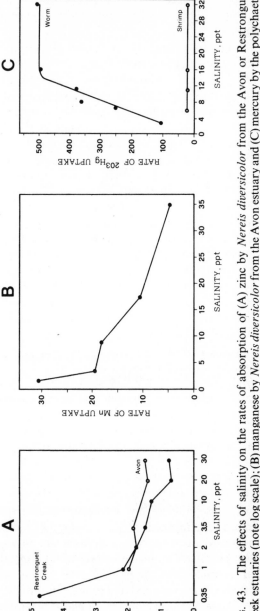

FIG. 43. The effects of salinity on the rates of absorption of (A) zinc by *Nereis diversicolor* from the Avon or Restronguet Creek estuaries (note log scale); (B) manganese by *Nereis diversicolor* from the Avon estuary and (C) mercury by the polychaete, *Nereis succinea*, or the shrimp, *Palaemon debilis*, from Ala Wai Canal, Hawaii. Exposure concentrations were 1 mg/litre for (A) and (B), and 1 μg/litre for (C). Units for vertical axes are (A) μg/g wet weight/day; (B) μg/g dry weight/day; (C) pg/mg wet weight/day. (After Bryan and Hummerstone (1973b, 1973c) and Luoma (1977a), respectively.)

effects did not appear to be dependent on the period of acclimation, as mercury uptake did not change with pre-acclimation of animals of four hours or four days.

Such effects of salinity were suggested by Phillips (1976a) to be due to changes in the ratio of major ions to added trace metals; in particular, the uptake of cadmium might be responsive to the ambient calcium availability, as has been noted in mammals (see, for example, Friberg *et al.*, 1974). Some support for this theory has been published recently by Wright (1977a, b, c), in extensive studies on cadmium uptake by the shore crab, *Carcinus maenas*. Bryan (1976) has also postulated that the salinity effect on manganese uptake by *Nereis diversicolor* could be related to calcium availability. Wolfe and Coburn (1970) reported that the uptake of ^{137}Cs by the clam, *Rangia cuneata*, increased with decreases of salinity or with increasing temperature, possibly because of its co-transport with potassium. However, although ion co-transport and competition at uptake appears likely, other factors also exist which may be important. For example, George and Coombs (1977b) have found that chelation of cadmium promotes its uptake into the mussel, *Mytilus edulis*, from solution. The relationship of this to ionic effects is obscure and we no doubt still have much to learn concerning the biochemical processes involved in the passage of ions across the body surfaces of aquatic organisms. Whatever the mechanisms involved, the changes in apparent metal availability or rate of uptake into biota with salinity may be important in certain cases in defining seasonal profiles of trace metals. Thus, in estuaries of regions where well-defined wet and dry seasons exist, biota will be exposed to seasonal variations in mean salinity, and the direct effects of salinity on metal uptake could lead to marked changes in metal abundance in such biota. The probability of greater delivery rates of metals to estuaries under conditions of higher run-off tends to compound the seasonal effect which would occur.

(iii) Temperature

In temperate regions, seasonal change is accompanied by a well-defined cycle of change in water temperature. These seasonal fluctuations in ambient water temperature elicit alterations in organism physiology and metabolism which lead to effects on the net uptake of trace metals. Effects may occur whatever the major route of metal uptake, as both ventilation rates and feeding rates of organisms respond to temperature fluctuations. Much of the published data, however, concern the effects of temperature on the uptake of trace metals from solution. Some examples have already been cited above; it is clear that increases of temperature in general cause an increased net uptake of trace metals, although exceptions do exist.

In contrast to the complete lack of research to date on the effects of salinity on trace metal accumulation by macroalgae, some information is available on the effects of temperature. Gutknecht (1961, 1963) found temperature effects on the uptake rate of ^{65}Zn by *Ulva lactuca* to be substantial, uptake occurring much faster at higher temperature (Fig. 44(A)). In the later paper, ^{65}Zn loss from *Porphyra umbilicalis* was also found to be increased by higher temperatures (Fig. 44(B)). A consideration

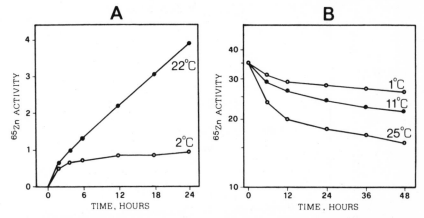

FIG. 44.   (A) The effect of temperature on the net uptake of ^{65}Zn by *Ulva lactuca*. (After Gutknecht (1961)). (B) The effect of temperature on loss of ^{65}Zn from *Porphyra umbilicalis*, exposed previously to 16 μCi/litre ^{65}Zn for 35 h in the light. In both cases, activity of ^{65}Zn was measured as thousands of counts/minute/unit area. (After Gutknecht (1963).)

of these papers in comparison with other published studies (that of Bryan, 1969, for example) leads one to expect that much of the data published by Gutknecht refer to the preliminary binding process only between metal ions and the macroalga cell surface, as bound metals appear particularly labile in the studies of this author. However, it is interesting to speculate on the overall effects of temperature on the accumulation of metals by macroalgae. If increased temperatures promote metal uptake, they also promote faster growth, and the one effect tends to counteract the other by a growth dilution process (see discussion above). Clearly, further study is needed before any definite conclusions may be reached.

The studies of Phillips (1976a) and Jackim *et al.* (1977) on the effects of ambient water temperatures on trace metal uptake by bivalves have already been referred to; further data from the latter authors is shown in Fig. 45. It can be seen that the net uptake of ^{109}Cd from solution is faster at 20 °C than at 10 °C for both *Mya arenaria* and *Mulinia lateralis*; by contrast, the differences were insignificant for *Mytilus edulis*. This lack of a temperature effect on cadmium uptake at high salinity by *M. edulis* was also noted by

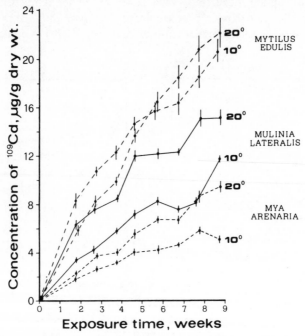

FIG. 45.   The effect of water temperature on the net uptake of ^{109}Cd from solution by the bivalves, *Mytilus edulis*, *Mulinia lateralis* and *Mya arenaria*. Exposure concentration was 5 μg/litre in all cases, at 28‰ S; each point represents a mean ± 1 standard deviation of ten individuals. (After Jackim *et al*. (1977).)

Phillips (1976*a*), but this author observed that temperature effects were significant at low salinities (see Table 35). The uptake of copper by *Mya arenaria* is also known to be faster at higher temperatures (Pringle *et al*., 1968). Fowler and his co-workers have published several papers on the effects of environmental parameters, including temperature, on radionuclide uptake and retention by the mussel, *Mytilus galloprovincialis*, and the shrimp, *Lysmata seticaudata*. The influence of temperature on the net uptake of metals by these species is interesting, as species differences exist.

Thus, Fowler and Benayoun (1974) showed that the uptake of ^{109}Cd from solution increased with temperature in the shrimp but not in the mussel (*cf. Mytilus edulis*, above). Temperature effects on ^{109}Cd retention were insignificant for either animal. The uptake of ^{75}Se (+4), by contrast, exhibited the opposite temperature dependence, mussels attaining higher concentrations of the nuclide at higher temperatures but shrimp being unaffected by temperature (Fowler and Benayoun, 1976c); patterns of ^{75}Se loss followed the same profile, shrimp again being unaffected. Finally, both inorganic mercury and methylmercury tended to be taken up or lost more rapidly by mussels at high temperatures than at lower temperatures, although the differences for these pollutants were not great; no data were reported for the effects of temperature on mercury flux in the shrimp in this latest report (Fowler *et al.*, 1978a). The reason for these differences between the response of each species–metal pair to changes in the ambient temperature is not clear. However, it is certainly apparent that the effects of temperature are not based on a general change in organism physiology (e.g. filtration rate, metabolism) which influences all metals, or all species, in the same qualitative fashion. Temperature effects on the uptake of trace metals from solution by organisms are thus brought about by some far more subtle mechanism, perhaps involving ion transport mechanisms at the gill surface. Conceivably, the difference in temperature response depends on the immediate need for metabolic energy in the transport of some metals— but not others—across the gill surface, although perhaps this, too, is simplistic. It is important to realise that uptake profiles such as those shown in Fig. 45 are, in fact, composites of uptake and excretion occurring simultaneously; clearly, the effects of temperature on each component may vary both qualitatively and quantitatively for different metals. In addition, the process of element transport to storage sites which must occur subsequent to uptake may be temperature-dependent; this is certainly the case for mercury in the fiddler crab, *Uca pugilator*, where an unexpected increase in mercury toxicity at lower temperatures was found to correlate to build up of the metal in gills, with subsequent lethal effects (Vernberg and O'Hara, 1972; Vernberg and Vernberg, 1972).

The effects of temperature on trace metal uptake by finfish are better documented than are those of salinity, although reports are restricted mainly to mercury. Exceptions to the preoccupation with mercury kinetics were the studies of Westernhagen *et al.* (1974) and Westernhagen and Dethlefsen (1975) on cadmium uptake by eggs of the herring, *Clupea harengus*, and the flounder, *Pleuronectes flesus*. The effects of salinity on this accumulation of cadmium are shown in Fig. 46; it is clear that the eggs of both species take

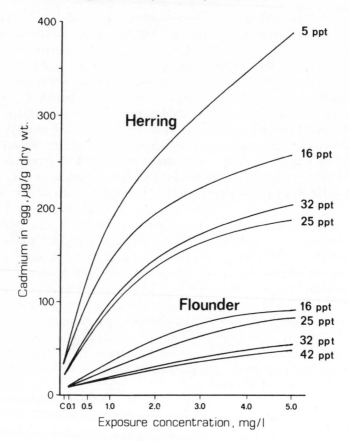

FIG. 46.   Concentrations of cadmium (μg/g dry weight) in eggs of the herring, *Clupea harengus*, and flounder, *Pleuronectes flesus*, after their exposure to cadmium in solution at different concentrations and at various salinities. (After Westernhagen and Dethlefsen (1975).)

up greater amounts of the metal at lower salinities, notwithstanding the differences apparent between species. The species differences were ascribed to differences in thickness of the chorion of eggs of these fish; the effects of salinity were suggested to be caused by competition between calcium and cadmium for binding to mucopolysaccharides on the egg surface.

Temperature effects on the net uptake of mercury by fish were noted by MacLeod and Pessah (1973) for rainbow trout, *Salmo gairdneri*. Accumulation of mercuric chloride was much faster at 20 °C than at lower temperatures (Fig. 47(A)); toxicity was also increased at higher temperatures. Similar data were reported by Reinert *et al.* (1974) for methylmercury uptake by the same species (Fig. 47(B)) and by Ruohtula and Miettinen (1975), again for methylmercury in *S. gairdneri*. More recently, Cember *et al.* (1978) found bluegill sunfish, *Lepomis macrochirus*, to accumulate methylmercury faster at higher temperatures, and the response in this case was exponential with water temperature and independent of the ambient methylmercury concentration. For marine species, reports are less

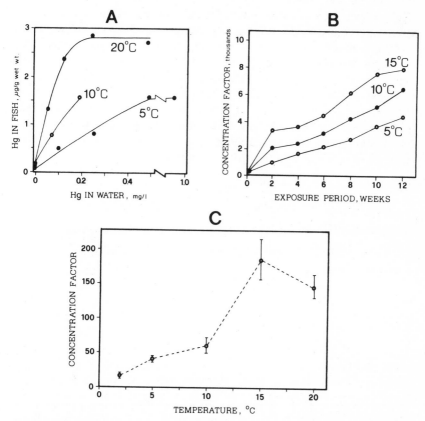

FIG. 47. The effect of temperature on the uptake of mercury from solution by finfish. (A) refers to mercuric chloride uptake by rainbow trout, *Salmo gairdneri*, exposed for 4 days. (After MacLeod and Pessah (1973).) (B) refers to the same species and methylmercury uptake. (After Reinert *et al.* (1974).) (C) concerns uptake of mercuric chloride (^{203}Hg-labelled) in 8 days of exposure by the plaice, *Pleuronectes platessa*. (After Pentreath (1976b).)

common, although Pentreath (1976*b*) showed that concentration factors describing the uptake of mercury from solution increase with increasing temperature in the plaice, *Pleuronectes platessa* (Fig. 47(C)).

In addition to the laboratory studies reported above, reports on field studies have occasionally been published which suggest that metal uptake rates vary seasonally. For example, Seymour (1966), in extensive studies of ^{65}Zn kinetics in oysters, *Crassostrea gigas*, using transplantation methods, found that oysters transplanted into contaminated areas accumulated the radionuclide more rapidly in the spring and summer than in the winter. Whilst effects such as tissue weight fluctuations may have been involved here, temperature could also have been a significant parameter. Eisler (1977) also noted greater rates of metal uptake in the summer than in the winter, in this case for the softshell clam *Mya arenaria*, exposed to a complex mixture of six trace metals. Metal toxicities were also discovered to be seasonally dependent by Eisler (1977), being greater in the summer than in the winter; similar data were cited by Perkins (1974) for oysters exposed to chromium, molybdenum and nickel, and the review of Cairns *et al.* (1975) contains much information on the effects of temperature on the toxicities of various pollutants to aquatic biota.

CHAPTER 6

Seasonality of Organochlorines in Aquatic Biota

As noted in Chapter 4, the seasonal fluctuation in organochlorine concentrations of biota is primarily a function of the temporal changes in organochlorine availability (from industrial sources or, more commonly, episodic application of agricultural pesticides) and of the lipid variations in organisms, which are generally allied to the sexual cycle. These factors will be considered in turn here, prior to brief discussion of the allied effects of temperature and salinity variation on organochlorine accumulation by aquatic biota.

A. EFFECTS OF ORGANOCHLORINE DELIVERY TO THE AQUATIC ENVIRONMENT

Examples of the effects of episodic pollutant delivery to aquatic ecosystems on the concentrations of organochlorines found in biota are common in the literature. For compounds which exhibit relatively short half-lives in either organisms or ecosystems, the correlation of measurable pollutant levels in biota to application periods in the water catchment is most evident. However, for relatively persistent compounds such as DDT or its metabolites, an initial peak after application may be followed by a steady or fluctuating decline in residue levels which may persist until the subsequent application of the pesticide. It should be noted that the dependence of the concentrations of organochlorines in biota on the agricultural application period is most evident in waters immediately draining the treated catchment (usually rivers); the severity and acute nature of this peak is dampened by passage of the residues from the area of application to the open ocean. This is primarily a function of the different flux of organochlorines through each portion of the biosphere and the rapid and variable dilution of pesticides through estuaries and coastal waters.

161

Few data are available concerning seasonal changes in the concentrations of organochlorines in either phytoplankton or zooplankton. In situations where acute episodic inputs occur (e.g. in rivers draining agricultural land receiving periodic applications of pesticides), plankton presumably reflect the rapid increase in available concentrations of pollutant. Although data from the field are sparse, such changes may be inferred from laboratory studies of the uptake of organochlorines by single plankton species (e.g. see Södergren, 1968; Wheeler, 1970; Crosby and Tucker, 1971; Reinert, 1972; Petrocelli *et al.*, 1975a). By contrast, seasonal changes in the delivery of the pollutant to coastal waters are masked by the changes in species composition of coastal plankton. Thus, studies such as those of Jensen *et al.* (1970) and Williams and Holden (1973) correlated temporal changes in organochlorine contents of mixed plankton samples to the species succession of the plankton, rather than to the episodic nature of organochlorine availability. In terms of the transmission of organochlorines through the food web, the changes in residue levels of mixed or total plankton are, of course, more important than those of any single species. However, the changes in species composition may serve to obscure any possible correlation of residue levels in any one species with the rate of organochlorine delivery to coastal waters. There is, in fact, a possibility that the species succession in plankton may be linked to organochlorine inputs; several authors have produced data showing that the species composition of mixed phytoplankton samples may be altered by quite low concentrations of organochlorines such as DDT or PCBs (e.g. see Mosser *et al.* 1972b, Fisher *et al.*, 1973 and Harvey *et al.*, 1974).

By contrast to the uncertain position for plankton, residue levels in higher organisms have frequently been found to exhibit seasonal profiles dominated by the episodic nature of organochlorine delivery. As noted above, such effects are more severe in freshwaters close to the site of pesticide application. Correlation of seasonal organochlorine profiles to the timing of upriver usage of pesticides was thus seen by Bedford *et al.* (1968) in studies of the use of freshwater mussels as indicators of DDT and its metabolites, aldrin and methoxychlor in a Michigan river. Godsil and Johnson (1968) produced similar results for biota of the Tule Lake National Wildlife Refuge in the USA, which was severely polluted by seasonal applications of endrin and other pesticides. Concentrations of endrin in the waters of the lake exhibited a sharp peak between the end of July and October; concentrations in biota increased in August, were maximal in October and had decreased to reach values representative of winter samples by early January. The lag in endrin levels of biota compared with those in water reflects the transport of the chemical from one to the other component, as well as the differences in persistence of endrin in each component. Pollution of Tule Lake by pesticides reached a magnitude sufficient to elicit a large number of deaths in fish-eating birds in the 1960s. Kelso *et al.* (1970) correlated the seasonal changes in DDT and dieldrin of six species of fish from Grand River, Ontario, to applications of these compounds in the catchment. Lockhart *et al.* (1977) found the periodic use of methoxychlor against blackfly larvae in the catchment of an Alberta river to lead to greatly increased methoxychlor levels of caged or wild fish subsequent to the spraying period. Amongst salmonids, several authors have noted the characteristic peak in residue levels some one or two months subsequent to DDT application in the relevant catchment (Reed, 1966; Cole *et al.*, 1967; Sprague *et al.*, 1971). In each of these cases, the influx of pesticides during and after spraying completely dominated the seasonal fluctuations noted in biota of the rivers draining the agricultural areas involved.

This total dependence of the seasonal residue fluctuation in biota on the timing of pesticide application has been noted occasionally in coastal waters also, although these waters commonly drain an agricultural area directly. Organisms of coastal waters or estuaries receiving organochlorines from more distant sites often exhibit seasonal fluctuations in residues which may correlate to both gross inputs and organism physiology, i.e. in these sites the predominance of the episodic pesticide inputs in determining seasonal profiles in biota is reduced and variations in the lipid contents of the organisms may also be effective in dictating seasonal trends in their organochlorine levels. Butler (1969b, 1971, 1973) and Butler *et al.* (1972) considered the seasonal profiles of organochlorines noted in bivalves used in the US National Monitoring Programme of pesticides in estuaries to reflect almost entirely the availability of these compounds in run-off waters; little, if any, evidence was noted to suggest that lipid fluctuations in bivalves were of importance in this respect. An example is shown in Fig. 48; it may be seen that levels of ΣDDT in oysters, *Crassostrea virginica*, were approximately proportional to the extent of usage of this compound in the catchments of each estuary. In addition, increased levels of DDT occurred in oysters following each application; whereas crops were sprayed once in the catchments of Matagorda Bay and San Antonio Bay, the Laquna Madre supported multiple harvesting and three applications of DDT were necessary in order to protect crops in each year. Juvenile menhaden of the genus *Brevoortia* also exhibited multiple organochlorine peaks annually in the latter estuary (Butler *et al.*, 1972). Furthermore, the exact timing of the ΣDDT maxima in the oysters from

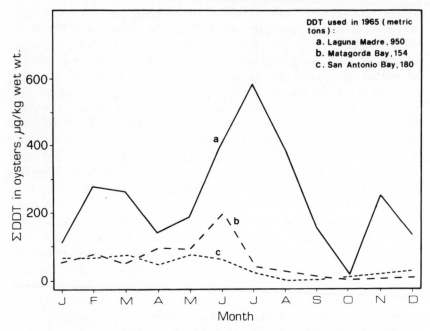

FIG. 48. Seasonal variation in concentrations of ΣDDT (μg/kg by wet weights) in whole soft parts of oysters, *Crassostrea virginica*, from three Texas watersheds in 1966. Catchment (a) involved multiple harvesting and DDT was applied thrice annually; catchments (b) and (c) were sprayed only once in each year. (After Butler *et al.* (1972).)

this estuary was found to correlate not only to pesticide application periods but also to rainfall in each year, which produced the necessary run-off to wash applied residues through the catchment to the estuary in which the oysters grew.

Hansen and Wilson (1970), in monitoring studies of fish in Escambia Bay and Pensacola Bay, Florida, found differences in the seasonal fluctuation of DDT according to the site of fish sampling. Species from the lower estuary exhibited a relatively well-defined seasonal peak in ΣDDT levels in late summer, corresponding to the timing of spraying of the adjacent land mass. By contrast, the catchment of the upper estuary was not subjected to application of DDT at any time, and levels of ΣDDT in fish from this area varied little throughout the year. Consideration of the residue ratios (DDT: DDE + DDD) revealed higher ratios in the fish from the lower estuary, indicating that local DDT was absorbed by these fish and confirming the local spraying as the basis of the seasonal changes. By contrast to this profile, seasonal changes in dieldrin levels present in the northern quahog, *Mercenaria mercenaria*, in Narragansett Bay were consistent throughout the study area (Check and Canario, 1972). All six stations studied thus supported quahogs which exhibited a seasonal maximum between February and April and a minimum in August or September. Consistent differences between the absolute concentrations of dieldrin in quahogs from each site at all sampling periods indicated a source in the upper reaches of the Bay, which may have been residues introduced by the Providence River. Several other authors have produced similar results which indicate the presence of this simple relationship between organochlorine application for agricultural purposes and the seasonality of organochlorines in biota of the surrounding aquatic environment (see, for example, Conte and Parker, 1975; Livingston *et al.*, 1978). Unfortunately, these authors do not quote data for the amounts of lipids in seasonal samples and it is therefore difficult to separate the effects of lipid from those of organochlorine applications in the surrounding catchments. In some cases at least, the peak in organochlorines present in the water as a result of run-off subsequent to crop spraying may coincide with the lipid maximum in aquatic biota, as organisms frequently spawn in late spring or summer, when crops are most often treated with pesticides. This would appear to be the case at least in the studies of Bjerk (1973) on cod in Norwegian waters although, in this area, the organochlorines released in spring were those applied in the previous growing season and were brought down to the marine life by the enormous run-off pursuant to the spring ice break-up.

The simple profiles discussed above are always found in areas where the major organochlorine source is agricultural. If the source is mainly industrial, however, seasonal profiles of the residues in biota tend to be far more erratic. In addition, the effects of changes in run-off are different in the two cases (see Chapter 4 and Fig. 18). Both Butler (1969*b*) and Foehrenbach (1972) have recognised this essential difference. The studies of Foehrenbach (1972) were performed on bivalves from Long Island which are exposed to effluents from industries in New York as well as to organochlorine residues applied in local spraying programmes. The seasonal fluctuations in organochlorines present in bivalves differed according to the relative importance of the two sources in determining the local levels of pesticides in water. In addition, some evidence of species-dependent differences in seasonality of organochlorines was noted and this certainly depends on organism physiology or, more specifically, on the timing of spawning (and hence lipid cycle) in the different bivalves studied. A knowledge of the spawning cycle—and associated lipid variations—in an indicator organism to be used for studies of organochlorines is most useful in aiding the correct interpretation of results; as noted in Chapter 3, if organochlorine concentrations are based both on wet and lipid weights, confusion as to the exact seasonal change in ambient abundance of organochlorines should be avoided.

It might be noted with respect to differences in the seasonal availability of organochlorines and its dependence on the source that PCBs are completely industrial by source and are never used agriculturally. Thus one might suspect differences between the seasonality of PCB residues and of DDT or other agricultural pesticides in biota. Data from Escambia Bay which was, at one time, severely polluted by Aroclor 1254 from an industry discharging to Escambia River, support this notion. Thus, in contrast to the location-dependent seasonal profiles for ΣDDT in fish noted above (Hansen and Wilson, 1970), PCB levels in oysters were found to peak in June and to decrease rapidly when leakage of the compound from industry was controlled (Duke *et al.*, 1970). This is, of course, a special case, and a summer maximum could not be expected elsewhere; however, the contrast between this profile and those for ΣDDT in fish illustrates the importance of the consideration of sources in planning monitoring surveys. A further example was provided by the studies of Clegg (1974) who noted differences in the seasonal profiles of ΣDDT in oysters *Crassostrea commercialis* (or *Saccostrea cuccullata*; see Stenzel, 1971; and Ahmed, 1975) from two sites in Moreton Bay, Australia. These differences were correlated to the dominant sources of DDT in the two areas, the Brisbane site being exposed to industrial sources whilst a more southerly site was exposed to agricultural run-off from a rural area in which DDT was employed as a pesticide (see Phillips, 1978*b* for further discussion).

B. EFFECTS OF THE SEXUAL CYCLE

Notwithstanding differences between industrial and agricultural areas, the reports cited above all suggest that the seasonal changes in organochlorine concentrations found in biota are predominantly input dependent. By contrast to this situation, several authors have found that organism physiology has a marked effect on organochlorine seasonality in biota. As noted in Chapter 3, lipids are frequently vitally important in determining the concentrations of organochlorine residues present in biota as they represent the sequestration site for these compounds. A change in lipid level in an organism may thus affect organochlorine flux markedly, and most organisms exhibit a well-defined seasonal variation in lipid levels which correlates to the sexual cycle. In addition, lipid levels and chemistries are known to correlate to water temperature. In this subsection, the effects of lipid variations associated with maturation and spawning of aquatic organisms will be discussed; the possible effects of temperature are discussed in Section C below.

In general, aquatic organisms exhibit increases in whole-body lipid contents during pre-spawning maturation. These changes in lipid content are due mainly to the enormously increased lipid levels of gonad tissues which contain greater and greater amounts of lipid-rich gametes as spawning approaches. The amplitude of such lipid fluctuations varies with age. Immature animals often exhibit no marked changes in lipid contents with season although, in some cases, a change in lipid levels occurs which mimics that seen in adults even though spawning does not take place; however, even in these instances, the seasonal variation found in immature individuals is not so great as in adults of the same species. As a species attains sexual maturity, gametes are produced and the classical lipid cycle appears. However, the amplitude of lipid fluctuations continues to increase with age in most organisms, as fecundity is greatest in older animals. These fluctuations in the amount of lipid present in the organism present a greater or lesser pool of lipids in which organochlorines may accumulate; thus, if organochlorines are available in the ambient water or in ingested food, the total body load of these pollutants will increase. The changes which occur on spawning depend entirely on the content and concentration of organochlorines in the gametes themselves relative to the rest of the tissues in the organism. If organochlorines were distributed uniformly amongst the tissue lipids (i.e. ignoring all differences in the sequestration capacity of different lipid types), it is clear that the loss of lipid-rich gametes would lead to a marked fall in the concentration of organochlorines (based on wet weights) and in total organochlorines present in the whole body of the organism. On a lipid weight basis, however, the concentration of organochlorines in the whole organism would be unchanged by spawning, despite the large decrease in total body load of the pollutant.

Several reports which contain information concerning the organochlorine contents of gonads are available for comparison with the above theoretical profile. Most of these concern either bivalve molluscs or finfish. Amongst the bivalves, Butler (1966) recorded high concentrations of ΣDDT in gametes of both male and female oysters; this report does not name the species used, but it was probably *Crassostrea virginica*. The authors of several reports concerning the uptake of pesticides in the laboratory have ascribed sudden decreases in uptake curves to spawning of the test bivalve (Lowe *et al.*, 1971, 1972; Roberts, 1972); these decreases are evident for uptake curves using both total body loads and concentrations when the latter are based on wet weights.

It was mentioned in the previous subsection that different species of bivalves taken in any one area can exhibit differences in the seasonal fluctuation of their accumulated organochlorine residues (see, for example, Foehrenbach, 1972). There are two possible explanations for this phenomenon. First, bivalves may respond differently to the various exposure routes by which they could accumulate organochlorines. To take a theoretical and oversimplified example, one might consider a species which accumulates most of its organochlorines from ingested phytoplankton and a second species which takes up the majority of its total body load of organochlorines from inorganic particulates. If the seasonal variation in organochlorine levels of phytoplankton and inorganic particulates does not match, the bivalve species will differ in their seasonal profiles. Secondly, bivalves of different species spawn at different times of the year. If spawning (and the lipid cycle) is important in determining organochlorine concentrations, the seasonal profiles will again be unique in each species. To extend these ideas, a single species may exhibit different organochlorine seasonality according to location; again, either of the above mechanisms may operate. Thus, a mussel in an estuary could be exposed to entirely different concentrations of organochlorines in phytoplankton than the same species in open water; alternatively, the two populations may spawn at different times of the year. Non-synchronous spawning of bivalves was also noted as a problem in trace metal monitoring with respect to its effects on seasonality of metals in these organisms (above); the same comments as to the design of sampling programmes apply in the case of organochlorines as in the case of trace metals. The results of Marchand *et al.* (1976) and Risebrough *et al.* (1976) are amongst those found in the literature where effects such as these apply. Spawning effects may be overcome to a large extent by basing organochlorine concentrations on lipid weights (analogous to consideration of total body loads rather than concentrations for trace metals); however, the effects of different exposure route predominance are more difficult to combat and a knowledge of local hydrology and input sources would seem essential in aiding correct interpretation.

The data available on the effects of lipid seasonality in finfish and its effects on fluctuations of organochlorines throughout the year are somewhat more detailed than those for bivalve molluscs. Most reports concern laboratory studies of organochlorine uptake or field studies of commercially important species; information for freshwater species is more abundant than for marine species.

Burdick *et al.* (1964) investigated the effects of DDT on reproduction of the lake trout, *Salvelinus namaycush*, subsequent to unexplained losses of lake trout fry from a hatchery at Lake George in New York State. The catchment of this lake was estimated to be exposed to some 8700 to 16 200 lb (4000–7400 kg) of applied DDT annually in the late 1950s and early 1960s, and female trout taken from it exhibited the highest lipid weight-based concentration of DDT in their tissues of any of the New York State lakes. Interestingly, the correlation of trout residues to application rates was better when total residue weight applied to the catchment was considered rather than residues applied per unit area, although both correlations were significant (Fig. 49). The comparison of residue levels in eggs with those in the parent female is shown in Fig. 50, concentrations being based on lipid weights. A general correlation between residue levels in the parent tissues and its eggs was noted; this is not surprising in view of the relative homogeneity of organochlorine concentrations in lipids of different tissues of an individual (Chapter 3). The lack of a strict relationship between DDT concentrations in the two tissues may have been a result of changes in the DDT content of the female subsequent to deposition of lipids in the eggs. It is, however, evident that the concentrations of DDT based on lipid weights were similar in both parent and egg—a finding which agrees with the theoretical profile discussed above.

The losses of lipid-rich gametes and their associated DDT residues were also convincingly shown in studies of the spotted seatrout, *Cynoscion nebulosus*, by Butler *et al.* (1972); these results are shown in Fig. 51. Eggs of trout from the Arroyo Colorado in Texas exhibited steadily increased levels of ΣDDT (by wet weight) as maturation occurred from January towards the September spawning period. Ovaries of mature females reflected these changes and also exhibited a sharp drop in residue levels at spawning; unfortunately, no data for lipids were reported and results cannot, therefore, be expressed on a lipid weight basis.

A comparison of organochlorine levels in ovaries of finfish with those in other tissues is possible using the extensive data of Linko *et al.* (1974) for pike, *Esox lucius*, from the Turku Archipelago in the northern Baltic Sea. Figure 52 shows mean concentrations of ΣDDT and PCBs by lipid weights in muscle, liver and ovaries of female pike from six different areas. It may be seen that despite differences in the absolute magnitude of contamination of

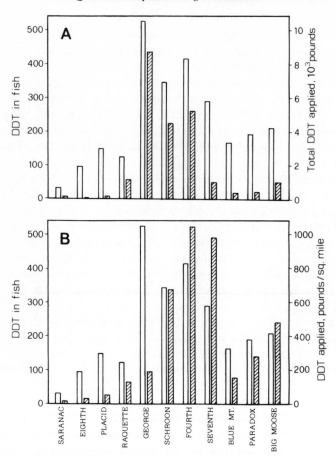

FIG. 49. Comparisons of DDT levels in muscles of female lake trout, *Salvelinus namaycush*, (μg/g lipid weights, open bars) with (A) total poundage of DDT applied to each lake catchment and (B) poundage applied per unit surface area of water in each lake. (After Burdick *et al.* (1964).) Means calculated by present author.

different areas, the relative concentrations of ΣDDT and PCBs in muscle and liver are quite constant. By contrast, levels of the two compounds in ovaries varied enormously in relation to the other tissues, being less than those in muscle or liver in fish from area 2, but much greater in fish from areas 1 and 3. This variability, which was also seen in the wet weight-based concentrations, suggests differences in maturity of the ovary in fish from different areas; in addition, the lipid chemistry in the ovary may change

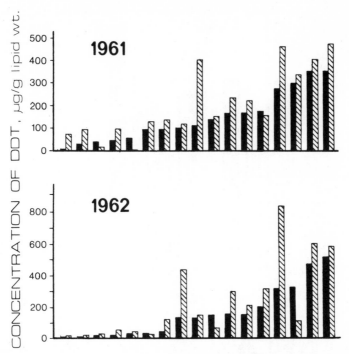

FIG. 50. Concentrations of DDT (μg/g lipid weights) in the eggs (black bars) and body muscle (cross-hatched bars) of female lake trout, *Salvelinus namaycush*. Each pair of bars represents one individual fish, taken from one of ten lakes in New York State; data are presented in order of increasing DDT content of eggs for both 1961 and 1962. (After Burdick *et al.* (1964).)

during maturation, affecting organochlorine storage in this organ. A similar conclusion may be reached with respect to the uptake of dieldrin by goldfish, *Carassius auratus*; Grzenda *et al.* (1971) ascribed increases in dieldrin concentrations in ovaries to maturation of the fish and the associated lipid changes.

By contrast to the rather severe effects of ovarian development and egg production on the levels or organochlorines in female finfish, the loss of these compounds by male fish in milt appears to be relatively small. Anderson and Everhart (1966) and Anderson and Fenderson (1970), in very extensive studies of DDT residues in Atlantic salmon, *Salmo salar*, from the landlocked Sebago Lake in Maine, found a much greater effect of gonad maturity on female than on male organochlorine levels as a result of this difference. As will be seen below, the same appears true of marine mammals,

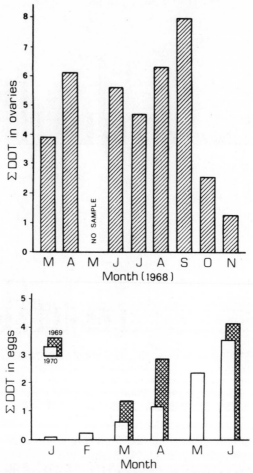

FIG. 51. Mean concentrations of ΣDDT in the ovaries of mature spotted sea trout, *Cynoscion nebulosus*, taken from the Arroyo Colorado in 1968 and in eggs of the same species in the period prior to spawning in 1969 and 1970. Spawning is complete by October; all data are μg/g wet weights. (After Butler *et al.* (1972).)

and this sex difference appears to be quite general amongst higher organisms which interact sexually. Differences of such a nature in organisms which reproduce by releasing gametes to join the plankton and fuse randomly have not been recorded, however.

The above examples deal mainly with the changes in whole-body levels or contents of organochlorines and the direct effects of spawning on these

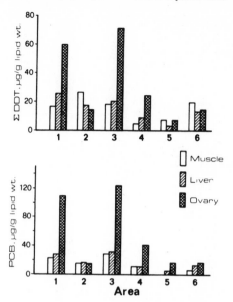

FIG. 52. Mean concentrations (μg/g lipid weight) of ΣDDT and PCBs in pike, *Esox lucius*, from six areas in the Turku Archipelago in the northern Baltic Sea. Levels of organochlorines in muscle, liver and ovary are shown in each case. (After tabulated data in Linko *et al.* (1974).)

levels. However, examples also exist of lipid dependence in the organochlorine seasonality in other tissues of finfish. Thus, Reinert (1970) and Reinert and Bergman (1974) reported differences in the seasonality of ΣDDT in whole coho salmon from Lake Michigan and Lake Erie. Concentrations of ΣDDT based on wet weights thus exhibited an increase of only 1·7-fold in Lake Erie salmon between the spring and the autumn, whilst four year-classes in Lake Michigan exhibited increases of 3·4-, 3·8-, 4·8- and 5·5-fold. At first sight a difference in input sizes might be suspected on the basis of these data. However, calculation of the concentrations by lipid weights (present author) reveals that much of the difference may be ascribed to differences in the lipid cycles of the fish from the two lakes (Table 37). Data based on lipid weights thus show an increase of 3·5-fold in Lake Erie salmon and similar increases of 2·4-, 2·6-, 3·2- and 4-fold in Lake Michigan fish.

Amongst crustaceans, Sprague and Duffy (1971) reported ΣDDT to be nine times as concentrated in eggs as in muscle for the lobster, *Homarus americanus*, collected from New Brunswick coastal waters; however, no

TABLE 37

AVERAGE WEIGHTS, LIPID CONTENTS AND CONCENTRATIONS OF ΣDDT (μg/g BY WET OR LIPID WEIGHTS) FOR WHOLE COHO SALMON, *Oncorhynchus kisutch*, COLLECTED ON DIFFERENT DATES FROM LAKE MICHIGAN AND LAKE ERIE. DATA FOR CONCENTRATIONS OF ΣDDT BY LIPID WEIGHTS WERE CALCULATED BY THE PRESENT AUTHOR. (AFTER REINERT AND BERGMAN (1974).)

Lake	Year-class and date of collection	Number of fish	Weight (g)	ΣDDT (wet weight)	Lipid (per cent)	ΣDDT (lipid weight)
Michigan	1965 year-class					
	21–22 April, 1968	5	1054	3·3	7·4	44·6
	4–7 May, 1968	3	1180	3·5	5·3	66·0
	21 August, 1968[a]	10	3514	12·3	13·2	93·2
	18 October, 1968[a]	10	3486	12·6	7·1	177·5
Michigan	1966 year-class					
	1 May 1969	4	1328	3·5	9·0	38·9
	3–11 September, 1969	10	3903	11·8	11·6	101·7
Michigan	1967 year-class					
	4 May, 1970	5	967	2·9	6·9	42·0
	21–28 August, 1970	13	3663	14·0	13·8	101·4
Michigan	1968 year-class					
	17 April, 1971	12	1029	1·8	7·6	23·7
	28 August, 1971	15	4254	9·9	13·0	76·2
Erie	1966 year-class					
	4 April, 1969	6	811	1·3	10·8	12·0
	5 May, 1969	5	1050	2·1	10·0	21·0
	7–8 October, 1969	10	2027	2·2	5·2	42·3

[a] Two 25 mm-thick steaks and the brain had been removed from these fish.

indication of the lipid contents of each tissue was quoted. Sheridan (1975) found the stage of gonad development in the blue crab, *Callinectes sapidus*, to be a major factor determining the presence of DDE and DDD in terms of both their absolute and their relative concentrations. This author noted that gonad development includes the transfer of lipids from the hepatopancreas to the ovaries and, to a lesser extent, the testes. As the hepatopancreas is the major storage organ of organochlorines (and trace metals) in crustaceans (Nimmo *et al.*, 1970, 1971*a*), it is tempting to speculate that both lipids and organochlorines translocate from this organ to the gonads during maturation, with subsequent loss of these on spawning.

Marine mammals represent a rather special case in terms of organochlorine loss during reproduction. In males, production of sperm by the testes presumably leads to a loss of a certain amount of the accumulated body load of organochlorines, but this is probably minute in comparison with the large amounts of these compounds stored in blubber. However, in females, a large foetus is, of course, produced, which must lead to fairly severe losses of organochlorines from the adult; in addition, lactation presents a further excretion route for the female. The presence of relatively high concentrations of organochlorines in both newborn or immature seal pups and in milk of lactating female seals was established by several authors (Anas and Wilson, 1970*a*, *b*; Holden, 1972*a*) and such data can be correlated to low levels of these compounds in mature lactating females (e.g. Frank *et al.*, 1973; Gaskin *et al.*, 1973). Similar profiles are evident in porpoises (Gaskin *et al.*, 1971). Addison *et al.* (1973) found an age-based variation in ΣDDT and PCBs present in harp seals, which was ascribed to parturition and lactation. A later report (Addison and Smith, 1974) confirmed this hypothesis for Arctic ringed seals, *Pusa hispida*, in which DDT, DDE and PCBs were found to increase in concentration with age in males but not in females. Frank *et al.* (1973) had previously also found a plateau for residue levels in mature female harp seals, *Pagophilus groenlandicus*. Finally, a recent report from Addison and Brodie (1977), concerning grey seals, *Halichoerus grypus*, from Nova Scotia, contained even more information. In this species, ΣDDT and PCB concentrations in milk lipid were about 60 per cent and 30 per cent, respectively of those in maternal blubber lipid. A partial barrier to transfer of residues through mammary tissue was thus demonstrated; however, significant amounts of the two compounds are nevertheless lost by lactation. Concentrations of ΣDDT and PCBs in lipids of pup blubber were similar to, or greater than, those in milk lipid. The authors estimated annual losses of 30 per cent of the total body load of ΣDDT and 15 per cent of that of PCBs from mature females through parturition and lactation and suggested that such losses were balanced by the ingestion of each group of compounds in food. The conclusions of these elegant studies may be extended by consideration of the possible interaction between organochlorines and parturition in marine mammals. Helle *et al.* (1976*a*, *b*) have demonstrated that reproductive failure in ringed seals, *Pusa hispida*, from the area of the Baltic is correlated to elevated levels of ΣDDT and PCBs in mature females (Table 38). This effect appears to be self-propagating, as once a pregnancy

TABLE 38

CONCENTRATIONS OF ΣDDT AND PCBS (MEANS ± STANDARD ERRORS) IN EXTRACTABLE FAT FROM BLUBBER OF RINGED SEALS, *Pusa hispida*, FROM SIMO IN THE BOTHNIAN BAY. (AFTER HELLE *et al.* (1976*b*).)

Sample	Number	ΣDDT (mg/kg)	PCB (mg/kg)
Pregnant females	24	88 ± 9·7	73 ± 6·6
Non-pregnant females with normal uteri	8	100 ± 15	89 ± 11
Non-pregnant females with stenosis and occlusions	29	130 ± 13	110 ± 7·8
Foetuses	24	62 ± 4·3	49 ± 3·0
Males	24	130 ± 18	100 ± 13

fails, organochlorine levels in the female increase because ΣDDT and PCBs cannot be lost to the foetus or by lactation; the likelihood of further reproductive failure therefore increases. The effect appears to occur by stenosis of the uterine horns, occluding the horn completely and preventing passage of the ovary. In females which exhibit such pathological uterine changes, blubber levels of ΣDDT and PCBs are similar to those in males, whilst females with normal uteri exhibit lower levels of each group of compounds and blubber from pregnant females exhibits yet lower concentrations. Premature pupping in the Californian sea lion, *Zalophus californianus californianus*, (Delong *et al.*, 1973) may be due to similar causes. However, in the case of the sea lion, only about 8 per cent of the populations on San Miguel and San Nicolas Islands appear affected, although this estimate is undoubtedly a minimum as it was produced by spot counts over part of the birth period only. In the Bothnian Bay, by contrast, only 27 per cent of mature ringed seal females were pregnant in

1973–1974, compared with 80–90 per cent in other, less polluted areas (Helle *et al.*, 1976*a*).

The seasonal fluctuation in organochlorine residues in some organisms may be affected severely by one additional factor which may be seen as a special case of change in ambient organochlorine availability. This factor is seasonal migration, and it is most important amongst certain finfish and marine mammals. Many coastal teleost species spawn in estuarine areas and migrate to these grounds prior to spawning from feeding grounds further offshore. The seasonality of organochlorines in water is frequently more pronounced in estuaries than in offshore areas (see Butler, 1966 and discussion above) and adult fish present in the estuary for spawning in the spring or summer may be exposed to the sudden spikes in organochlorine availability produced after pesticide spraying in the estuary catchment. Robinson *et al.* (1967) suggested migration as the basis of seasonal changes of DDE and dieldrin in cod, *Gadus morhua*, and sand eels, *Ammodytes lanceolatus*, from the Farne Islands, off the east coast of the United Kingdom. These results, shown in Fig. 53, reveal similar profiles for DDE and dieldrin in each fish, although the seasonal maximum in sand eels may be somewhat earlier than that in cod. Unfortunately, the data quoted allows no conversion to a lipid weight basis and the contribution of lipid fluctuations to the profiles cannot therefore be separated from the effects of a change in ambient organochlorine availability. In addition, the precise movements of the two species are not well established and the amount of inter-population mixing which occurs is unknown. However, authors studying organochlorines in cod and herring, *Clupea harengus*, in the Baltic Sea have also suggested the importance of migration in determining whole-body levels of these pollutants (e.g. see Jensen *et al.*, 1972).

A more definitive example of the effects of migration on organochlorine levels in finfish is afforded by the studies of Smith and Cole (1970) on the winter flounder, *Pseudopleuronectes americanus*, in the Weweantic River estuary, Massachusetts. These studies were initiated by the discovery of unusually high larval mortality in winter flounder from this site compared with other areas. Concentrations of DDT, DDE and heptachlor and its epoxide, in ovaries of mature flounder (Table 39) were found to increase as the spawning season approached, as noted by Butler *et al.* (1972) for sea trout (discussed above). It was notable that the heptachlor was mostly present as the epoxide metabolite in later samples; this suggests an early episodic input with subsequent metabolism and this is further discussed below. Although ΣDDT levels were somewhat short of the concentrations reported to affect survival of larval lake trout (2·95 μg/g wet weight; see

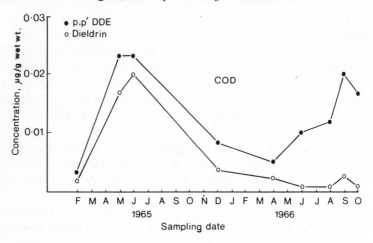

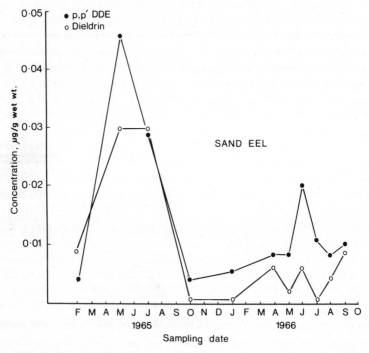

FIG. 53.   Concentrations of DDE and dieldrin (µg/g by wet weights) in cod, *Gadus morhua*, and sand eels, *Ammodytes lanceolatus*, from the Farne Islands, UK. (Redrawn from Robinson *et al.* (1967).)

TABLE 39

MEAN CONCENTRATIONS (μg/g WET WEIGHT) OF ORGANOCHLORINES IN OVARIES OF MATURE WINTER FLOUNDER, *Pseudopleuronectes americanus*, FROM THE WEWEANTIC RIVER ESTUARY, MASSACHUSETTS, USA. SPAWNING OCCURS IN EARLY SPRING, AT OR ABOUT LATE MARCH AND EARLY APRIL. (AFTER SMITH AND COLE (1970).)

Sampling date	Number of fish	DDT	DDE	Heptachlor	Heptachlor epoxide	Dieldrin
30 October, 1966	3	0·11	0·02	0·07	—	<0·01
25 January, 1967	3	0·16	0·04	<0·01	<0·01	<0·01
29 March, 1967	4	0·40	0·22	<0·01	0·65	<0·01

Burdick *et al.*, 1964 and discussion above), the high mortalities of flounder in the Weweantic estuary were probably due to these residues or to a combination of these and other organochlorines.

The seasonal profiles for organochlorines in adult and juvenile flounder were most interesting. The estuary contained both migratory adults (ages III and above) and resident juveniles. Migration of the adults involved entering the estuary in late October, spawning in the estuary between mid-winter and early spring and moving offshore by early May. Juveniles exhibited no such migration, being resident in the estuary until attaining age III. Seasonality of organochlorines in muscle tissues from the juveniles is shown in Table 40. Unfortunately, no lipid data were quoted, and the

TABLE 40

MEAN CONCENTRATIONS (μg/g WET WEIGHT) OF ORGANOCHLORINES IN MUSCLE OF JUVENILE WINTER FLOUNDER, *Pseudopleuronectes americanus* (1964 YEAR-CLASS) FROM THE WEWEANTIC RIVER ESTUARY IN MASSACHUSETTS, USA. (AFTER SMITH AND COLE (1970).)

Sampling date	Number of fish	DDT	DDE	Heptachlor	Heptachlor epoxide	Dieldrin
20 July, 1966	5	0·19	0·04	<0·01	<0·01	0·05
16 August, 1966	5	0·12	0·04	<0·01	0·11	0·04
29 September, 1966	6	0·05	0·03	<0·01	0·06	0·03
30 October, 1966	6	0·06	0·03	—	0·04	0·03
25 January, 1967	7	<0·01	1·07	1·10	<0·01	<0·01
29 March, 1967	6	<0·01	0·22	0·98	0·44	<0·01
24 April, 1967	6	0·04	0·04	0·08	0·03	<0·01
25 May, 1967	6	0·13	0·14	0·53	0·14	<0·01
16 June, 1967	6	0·31	0·13	0·07	0·14	<0·01

possibility of lipid fluctuations affecting interpretation of residue availability therefore exists. However, the data suggest a DDT input in May–June, with subsequent slow breakdown to DDE possibly occurring; by contrast, heptachlor levels were highest in the winter and the metabolism of this compound to the epoxide occurred in about two months. The source of DDT was uncertain, but the high levels noted correlated to the spring thaw and subsequent high run-off. Heptachlor sources were also uncertain but were clearly different from those of DDT if the timing of the seasonal maxima in resident juveniles is to be considered as representative of the availability of the two compounds. Dieldrin exhibited no marked seasonality in juvenile flounder. A comparison of the organochlorine levels in flounders of different ages generally confirmed the picture of organochlorine availability suggested above (Table 41). Migratory adults

TABLE 41

MEAN CONCENTRATIONS ($\mu g/g$ WET WEIGHT) OF ORGANOCHLORINES IN MUSCLE OF WINTER FLOUNDER, *Pseudopleuronectes americanus*, AGED BETWEEN I AND IV. ALL FISH WERE COLLECTED IN THE WEWEANTIC RIVER ESTUARY, MASSACHUSETTS, ON 25 JANUARY, 1967. (AFTER SMITH AND COLE (1970).)

Age	Number of fish	DDT	DDE	Heptachlor	Heptachlor epoxide	Dieldrin
I	5	<0·01	0·72	1·55	0·56	<0·01
II	7	<0·01	1·07	1·10	<0·01	<0·01
III	4	<0·01	0·18	1·27	<0·01	<0·01
IV	3	<0·01	0·21	0·62	<0·01	<0·01

exhibited much lower concentrations of ΣDDT than juveniles, whereas the amounts of heptachlor were only slightly lower in adults than in juveniles. The adults thus appear to be exposed to similar amounts of heptachlor as juveniles, but lower amounts of DDT; this correlates to the presence of adults in the estuary at the supposed maximum heptachlor input in winter and to their absence from the estuary during the June peak in DDT input. Other explanations are possible for these data, and it must be remembered that profiles based on lipid weights could differ substantially from those based on wet weights; however, the existence of age-based differences in seasonality of organochlorine levels is clearly a factor which must be considered in any monitoring survey.

The situation for marine mammals with regard to migration is somewhat distinct from that of finfish which spawn in estuaries. Thus, mammals such as seals may exhibit seasonal migration patterns for breeding purposes, but few differences exist between the movements of seal pups and those of adults, as the immature pups migrate to and from the breeding grounds either with the mature adults or soon afterwards (e.g. see Sergeant, 1965). Hence, although migration may affect the levels of organochlorines in seals in a seasonal fashion, age-based differences in seasonality may not be expected (see Anas and Wilson, 1970*a*; Delong *et al.*, 1973).

Finally, it is important to note that migration of an animal introduces problems of data interpretation if the animal is to be used as an indicator. The basic requirements of indicator organisms suggested by Butler *et al.* (1971) and discussed in Chapter 2 thus included a desire for the organism to be sedentary in order to be representative of the study area. This prerequisite has been much abused by authors using indicator organisms to monitor pollution; for example, the use of pelagic finfish is frequent. The concentrations of pollutants found in such non-sedentary organisms represent, at best, a time-integrated indication of the water quality in a large area through which the organism moves. Unfortunately, space- and time-dependence cannot be clearly delineated, as inadequate knowledge exists concerning the rate of pollutant flux in organisms. If the exact degree of time-integration is unknown, any amount of information on the movements of the organism is useless in attempts to discover the area of water indicated by a pelagic organism. The superimposition of the effects of variables such as diet changes, lipid fluctuations, salinity and temperature of the ambient water mass, and so on, leads to a mass of data which cannot be unequivocally interpreted. It is to be hoped that authors will pay more attention in future studies to the basic indicator requirements, at least if the intention is to complete meaningful monitoring studies.

C. EFFECTS OF SEASONAL CHANGES IN WATER QUALITY

The dependence of organochlorine availability to biota of freshwater or estuarine regions on the run-off rate has already been alluded to. Authors have often found that concentrations of organochlorines in such organisms are maximal when heavy rains bring residues from an agricultural catchment into the watercourse and flush them into the estuary.

In addition to such effects, water quality changes occur with season which may have marked effects on the accumulation of organochlorines by biota. Three changes in water quality may be considered as being particularly important—turbidity, salinity and water temperature.

The importance of turbidity is allied to the tendency of organochlorines to adsorb to inorganic particulates. These pollutants might be lost to sediments if calm conditions prevail in an estuary, permitting rapid sedimentation of larger particulates. However, in high run-off conditions, waters are typically more turbid in both rivers and estuaries; indeed, coastal waters may also be turbid if rain is accompanied by strong winds. The exact importance of turbidity in the overall organochlorine availability to aquatic biota is uncertain. However, filter-feeders in the water column are likely to respond to residues adsorbed to particulates and many benthic organisms may also take up organochlorines from sediment particles. Burnett (1971) found that the sand crab, *Emerita analoga*, contained increased concentrations (by wet weight) of ΣDDT after the winter period of stormy weather. These crabs, sampled off the polluted Los Angeles sewage outfall, not only exhibited increased ΣDDT levels but also contained higher ratios of DDE to DDT after the winter. This was interpreted as evidence for an indirect exposure, i.e. an exposure to DDE after DDT had been metabolised. It was suggested that DDT adsorbed to sediment particles was metabolised to DDE and that these particulates were resuspended by rough seas to become available to the crab. Unfortunately, no data for lipids were quoted and the effects of lipids could not therefore be determined. Other authors have also reported data suggesting that sediments may be a significant source of organochlorines. Young *et al.* (1976) suspended mussels, *Mytilus californianus*, at different depths in the water column off the Palos Verdes Peninsula, close to the outfall mentioned above. These mussels were derived from a relatively uncontaminated region (Point Sal, about 250 km north-west of the study site). The concentrations of ΣDDT and PCBs in these animals are shown in Fig. 54. It is evident that a graded increase in organochlorine availability with depth was present. The outfalls which represent the major source of these pollutants are submarine in nature, discharging effluent 3 km south-east of the study site. The presence of a thermocline tends to diminish vertical mixing of the effluent and the receiving waters; hence the profiles seen in Fig. 54 may not be completely a result of the uptake of organochlorines from resuspended bottom sediments, although the authors considered this to be a major source. A later report (Young *et al.*, 1977) noted the presence of elevated levels of ΣDDT and PCBs in Dover Sole, *Microstomus pacificus*, from this outfall region also, and it would appear that most, or all, of the sedentary benthic organisms are contaminated in this area. The enforced decrease in the amounts of DDT and PCBs discharged at this site in recent years tend to confirm the hypothesis that sediment-bound organochlorines are now the

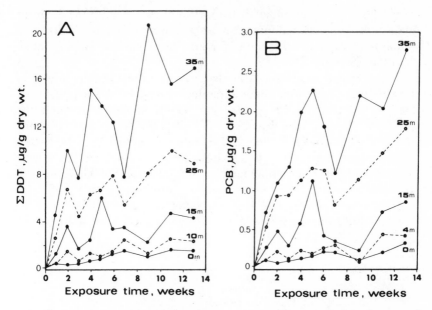

FIG. 54.   The net uptake of (A) ΣDDT and (B) PCBs by whole soft parts of mussels, *Mytilus californianus*, transplanted in June, 1974 from Point Sal to various depths in the water column at Palos Verdes. (After Young *et al.* (1976).)

major source of these compounds for biota indigenous to the Palos Verdes coast. Indeed, the relative constancy of the organochlorine concentrations in biota over the period of effluent control suggests that sediments may have been a major source of organochlorines throughout, with relatively little DDT or PCB being taken up direct from water even when the discharges were highly contaminated. This conclusion is supported by data reported recently by Fowler *et al.* (1978*b*), who studied the uptake of PCBs from sediments and water by the polychaete, *Nereis diversicolor*. PCB uptake from sediments equilibrated in two months, with concentration factors of 3 to 4. By contrast, the accumulation of PCBs from water by the polychaete reached equilibrium in two weeks and concentration factors approximated 800. At first sight one would expect the uptake of these compounds from solution to predominate in the field; however, a consideration of environmental levels of PCBs in water and sediments reveals that the sediment-derived route is the most important, accounting for perhaps 90 per cent or more of the total body load of PCBs in the worms. This predominance may be greater for benthic infauna than for epifauna because of the more intimate contact of the former organisms with the sediment milieu and with enriched interstitial waters; nevertheless, the importance of this route cannot be discounted for any organism which lives in contact with the sea bed.

The ecosystem of the Palos Verdes coast (above) is of interest also in terms of the relative proportions of residues of the DDT group found in its components. Studies by MacGregor (1974), mostly concerning the myctophid fish, *Stenobrachius leucopsarus*, included a considerable volume of data on the outfall constituents. This author suggested that DDE would be the residue of greatest importance at a theoretical offshore site, at least after several years of continuous discharge. (Figure 55.) The extremely great persistence of DDE is instrumental in producing such a profile. By contrast, levels of DDT and DDD were computed to increase for some 5–10 years subsequent to the start of discharge, but to level off at that time when

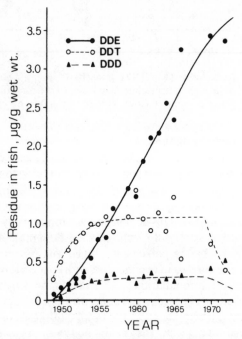

FIG. 55. Computed trends of DDT, DDE and DDD in the myctophid fish, *Stenobrachius leucopsarus*, from a theoretical offshore site some 20 nautical miles from the discharge point of residues near Palos Verdes, southern California. For details of assumptions and discharge data, see original author. (After MacGregor (1974).)

metabolism'and dispersion rates equal the rates of input. It is notable in Fig. 55 that DDD values increased in 1972; this was a result of sewer cleaning operations which caused a large discharge of sequestered DDD in that year. The theoretical profile shown was largely confirmed by a study of DDT and its metabolites in the offshore sediments of the Palos Verdes coast; DDT:DDE ratios were much higher in deep sediments than in surface sediments, suggesting a continually increasing importance of DDE compared with DDT at this site (MacGregor, 1976). A similar time-dependence of DDT:DDE ratios might be expected at all sites receiving chronically polluted wastes of the type discharged at Palos Verdes.

The effects of salinity on the accumulation of organochlorines have received very little attention to date. This is most unfortunate, as estuarine organisms are certainly at great risk from this form of pollution (Butler, 1969a, 1969b, 1971). Clearly, an increased concentration of organochlorines in biota of estuarine sites compared with those of areas of higher salinity may be interpreted in terms of either a higher absolute level of these compounds in the former sites (correlated perhaps to sources in the catchment and to run-off) or a higher biological availability of organochlorines in estuaries. One might envisage a situation where the absolute concentrations of organochlorines in water are similar throughout a large area but estuarine biota within this area could .nevertheless accumulate a greater or smaller residue load than would open-ocean biota because of some direct effect of salinity (e.g. on the lipid/water partitioning of a pesticide, or on filtration rates of the organism). If the intention of a monitoring survey using a biological indicator is to define areas of high organochlorine abundance ('hot spots'), the inability to differentiate between absolute abundance and salinity dependent availability is a serious disadvantage. Only one study on the effects of salinity on organochlorine uptake is known. Murphy (1970) exposed the mosquitofish, *Gambusia affinis*, to DDT, DDE or DDD in waters of differing ambient salinity. The results (Fig. 56) revealed a faster uptake of each compound at lower salinities. Differences between the sizes of the fish in each test group were not sufficient to explain this phenomenon and an explanation based on stress effects of salinity changes (e.g. see Phillips, 1977a) also appears inadequate; thus the results seem to be a *bona fide* example of a direct effect of salinity on organochlorine uptake. No other examples of this effect are known and this is obviously an area for further research.

The effects of water temperature on the net uptake of organochlorines by aquatic organisms have received rather more attention than have salinity effects. An increase in ambient water temperature may elicit several

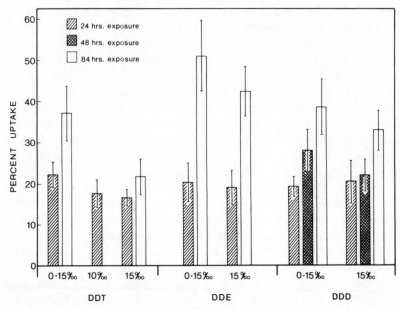

FIG. 56.   The percentage uptake of DDT, DDE and DDD from solution by the
mosquitofish, *Gambusia affinis*. Vertical bars show one standard deviation above
and below the mean. (After Murphy (1970).)

changes, each of which could alter the net uptake of an organochlorine in
the water. First, the organochlorine itself will be more soluble in water of
higher temperature. Although the absolute solubilities of organochlorines
in water are a matter of some disagreement, all authors agree that
temperature changes affect organochlorine solubility in a direct fashion;
examples are shown in Table 42. As discussed by Phillips (1978*b*), this effect
of temperature will lead to a shift in the relative amounts of organochlorines
in solution and in particulate-adsorbed forms. A higher proportion of the
total pollutant present may, therefore, be expected to exist in solution in the
hot, compared with the cold, season. If the organochlorine is more readily
available from solution than from particulates (as would generally be the
case), a greater uptake of organochlorines by biota at higher temperatures
would be anticipated. In addition, seasonal changes in water temperature
are known to be accompanied by changes in the lipid chemistry of aquatic
organisms (see Chapter 3). Such alterations in the lipids present will have
marked effects on the ability of the organisms to sequester organochlorines
in their tissues. This effect is quite distinct from the lipid fluctuations

TABLE 42

THE SOLUBILITIES OF ORGANOCHLORINES IN WATER AS A FUNCTION OF TEMPERATURE.
PARTICLE SIZE EQUIVALENT TO 5 μm. (AFTER BIGGAR *et al.* (1966).)

Organochlorine compound	Purity (per cent)	Solubility in water (μg/litre)			
		15 °C	25 °C	35 °C	45 °C
p,p' DDT	99+	17	25	37	45
DDT (Technical grade)	*a*	23	40	55	—
Lindane	99+	2 150	6 800	11 400	—
Aldrin	99+	105	180	350	600
Dieldrin	99+	90	195	400	650
Endrin	99+	130	250	420	625

a 76 per cent *p,p'* DDT; *o,p'* DDT; *o,o'* DDT; *p,p'* DDD; 2 per cent *p,p'* DDE.

occurring during the sexual cycle (above) and the two may overlap or coincide according to the relationship between spawning times and the maximum water temperature. Finally, a change in water temperature affects the organism itself in diverse ways, eliciting alterations of feeding rates, filtration or pumping rates and oxygen uptake, and metabolism in general. The exact relationship between these changes and any effects on the uptake of organochlorines will depend on the exact route by which these compounds are accumulated but, clearly, the alteration of ambient water temperatures may affect uptake from any route.

Hamelink and Waybrant (1976) studied DDE and lindane kinetics in a natural freshwater ecosystem. It was noted that lindane remained mainly in solution throughout the experiment, whilst DDE was rapidly lost to the bottom sediments, agreeing substantially with the accepted relative solubilities of these two compounds in fresh waters. DDE was later noted to be significantly mobilised from the sediments during the summer; this effect probably reflects the shift in the equilibrium between adsorbed and soluble forms, as suggested above. The direct effects of temperature on the uptake of organochlorines from solution have been studied by some authors also. Murphy and Murphy (1971) studied the uptake of DDT from water by the mosquitofish, *Gambusia affinis*, using fish acclimated to 5 and 20 °C prior to DDT exposure. The rate of DDT uptake was faster at 20 °C than at 5 °C and the difference in uptake rate was very similar to the difference in oxygen consumption, suggesting a link between metabolic or respiration rates and DDT uptake. Reinert *et al.* (1974) reported similar results for DDT uptake by rainbow trout, *Salmo gairdneri*, exposed to this compound in solution. These results are shown in Fig. 57; it will be noticed that the profiles are very

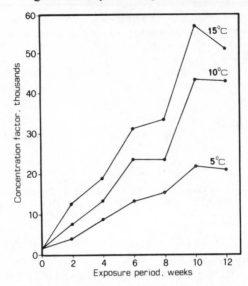

Fig. 57. Concentration factors for DDT (based on wet weights) in whole yearling rainbow trout, *Salmo gairdneri*, exposed to DDT in solution at 5, 10 or 15°C ambient water temperature. Exposure concentrations differed slightly for each group, being 176 ± 13·0, 137 ± 12·9 and 133 ± 8·4 ng/litre for fish held at 5, 10 and 15 °C, respectively. (After Reinert *et al.* (1974).)

similar to those for the uptake of methylmercuric chloride by the same species (see Chapter 5, Fig. 47 and text), although the concentration factors for DDT were about five times as great as those for methylmercuric chloride. These authors also suggested that the uptake rate of the two pollutants was proportional to the metabolic rate of the fish, although no data for metabolic rates were quoted in the paper. It is worth noting that no consistent change in the DDT:DDE ratios occurred with either time or temperature in this study; DDT residues constituted 87·6–93·1 per cent of total residues throughout. Evidently, the temperature effect on DDT accumulation is not, therefore, based on a DDT → DDE metabolic transformation with sequestration of the latter (highly persistent) compound, but is a real phenomenon involving the parent compound itself.

It is clear from this discussion that the changes in water quality which may occur with season may have a direct bearing on the accumulation of organochlorine residues by biota. A typical temperate ecosystem might exhibit a winter season of high run-off causing turbid waters of low salinity to flood the estuary; both these effects would tend to increase organochlorine uptake by biota, although the low winter temperatures would act contrary to this tendency. In some sub-tropical areas, in which the warm weather coincides with the greatest rainfall, all three factors could act in concert. It should be emphasised, however, that in most cases the effects of these parameters will be secondary to the more important changes which occur in organochlorine availability and lipid contents of aquatic organisms with season. Nevertheless, such factors are worthy of study in their own right, and it is to be hoped that additional information on their influence will become available in the future.

CHAPTER 7

The Effects of Age (Size, Weight) on Trace Metals in Aquatic Biota

Many authors have reported that the concentrations of trace metals present in an organism can vary with age of the organism. This effect may be a function of any one of several age-dependent parameters; for example, it may depend on differences between the metabolic, feeding or filtration rates of old and young individuals. Alternatively, age dependence may be a function of the period over which an organism has been exposed to a pollutant; thus, in areas with discontinuous or episodic pollution, young individuals of a species may have been exposed to greater or lesser time-integrated amounts of pollutants than older animals. Differences might also exist in preferred food of young (small) and old (large) individuals of a species, which would lead to age-dependent variations in the amounts of trace metals ingested. Finally, migration may again be an important factor in some instances, and this may be linked to the attainment of sexual maturity; sexual maturity itself may be important in its effects on the total load of pollutants present in an organism, spawning or parturition being an age-dependent method of pollutant excretion. The abundant literature affords examples of each of the above mechanisms producing age-dependent variation in trace metals in aquatic biota, as well as permitting some limited generalisation concerning the differences between different metals.

The generalisation of greatest validity concerning age dependence of metals in biota is that mercury behaves quite differently from most, or all, other metals. It will become clear in the course of the following chapter that whilst mercury concentrations tend to increase with age or size in aquatic biota (especially finfish), other metals commonly exhibit higher concentrations in younger or smaller individuals, growth being accompanied by decreased levels. For this reason, mercury is discussed separately from the other metals.

A. MERCURY

The majority of the data reported to date concerning the changes in mercury levels of biota with age involve finfish, often those species of commercial importance. Part of the reason for this research emphasis is that mercury concentrations in finfish may frequently approach or exceed the limits laid down for the protection of public health (generally 0.5 mg/kg by wet weight). However, some studies have been published which concern other species of conceivable indicator value, and these will be considered first.

De Wolf (1975) found that mercury concentrations in mussels, *Mytilus edulis*, from two sites in Europe did not differ consistently with age (Table 43). However, samples from a third location, Balgzand in The Netherlands,

TABLE 43

CONCENTRATIONS OF TOTAL MERCURY (μg/kg BY WET WEIGHTS) IN INTERTIDAL MUSSELS, *Mytilus edulis* AND/OR *M. galloprovincialis*, FROM THREE LOCATIONS IN WESTERN EUROPE AND THEIR VARIATION WITH SHELL LENGTH OF INDIVIDUALS. (AFTER DE WOLF (1975).)

Size class (cm)	Pointe de Grave (France)	Nieuwstad (The Netherlands)	Balgzand (The Netherlands)
2·5–3·0	160	500	150
3·0–3·5	150	560	130
3·5–4·0	180	530	230
4·0–4·5	120	480	280
4·5–5·0	—	420	200
5·0–5·5	—	460	320
>5·5	—	—	330

exhibited a doubling of mercury levels in large individuals compared with small mussels. No explanation of such location dependence was offered, but the magnitude of the differences may have affected results of the survey published by this author. Davies and Pirie (1978) also noted location dependence in the effects of age on the mercury content of mussels. In this case, mussels from the outer estuary of the Firth of Forth exhibited increased mercury concentration with higher tissue weights, whereas the samples from the inner estuary exhibited no such profile. However, it should be noted that this result concerns mussels from several locations rather than different sized mussels from a single location, and could therefore be produced by an artefact arising from selecting small mussels at relatively uncontaminated locations and large individuals from polluted locations. When the situation at one single location was studied, mussels from that location were found to exhibit increased mercury concentrations with increased tissue weights, but even in this case the data were reported on the basis of 'standard tissue weights', supposedly to eliminate the influence of variations in water content of the individuals. Confidence in the conclusion would have been greater if dry weights had been used as a basis for concentrations of the metal, although this admittedly entails the use of an aliquot of the sample to produce a dry weight:wet weight ratio independently of the portion analysed for mercury (because of the volatility of the element). Interestingly, the freshwater mussel, *Anodonta anatina*, has also been found to exhibit age-dependent changes in mercury concentration in some locations, but not in others (Manly and George, 1977). However, in this case, the mussels exhibiting significant age dependence of mercury levels were found to contain lower concentrations of the metal when larger.

The lack of consistency in the relationship between age or size of bivalves and their concentrations of mercury under field conditions may be explained if the results of laboratory studies are considered. In general, authors studying the kinetics of mercury in bivalves maintained under laboratory conditions have found that small individuals respond more rapidly to changes in ambient levels of mercury. Thus, the uptake of mercury from solution is more rapid in small individuals than in larger ones in both oysters, *Crassostrea virginica* (Cunningham and Tripp, 1975a; see Table 44) and mussels, *Mytilus galloprovincialis* (Fowler *et al.*, 1978a). In addition, the rate of mercury loss is greater in smaller individuals, at least for the mussel, *Pseudanadonta complanata* (Miettinen *et al.*, 1969). Essentially, therefore, smaller individuals appear to time-integrate ambient mercury levels over a shorter period compared with large bivalves of the same species. If this is correct, it will be seen that the apparent age dependence may, in fact, be a function of the differences in response of bivalves of different sizes to temporal fluctuations in mercury availability. Thus, if we assume that a stable environmental availability of mercury exists, all mussels will presumably contain similar concentrations of the metal, regardless of size. A transient increase in ambient mercury levels will then lead to a reciprocal relationship between body size (age, weight, etc.) and mercury concentration. By contrast, a transient decrease in available mercury will give rise to a population exhibiting a direct relationship between body size and accumulated metal. Whilst this theory has not been tested to date, it would appear to explain instances such as those noted

TABLE 44

MEAN CONCENTRATIONS OF TOTAL MERCURY (μg/kg WET WEIGHTS) ACCUMULATED BY OYSTERS, *Crassostrea virginica*, OF TWO SIZE CLASSES. ALL DATA REFER TO WHOLE SOFT PARTS; UPTAKE WAS FROM 10 OR 100 μg/litre IN SOLUTION, ADDED AS MERCURIC ACETATE. (AFTER CUNNINGHAM AND TRIPP (1975*a*).)

Experimental group	Day	Mean mercury residue (ppb)		Student's *t* test
		0–7·85 g	7·86–20·98 g	
Control	0	425 ± 88	471 ± 125	−0·84
	12	425 ± 116	314 ± 89	2·04
	19	409 ± 88	645 ± 57	−1·42
	27	337 ± 140	342 ± 53	−0·09
	34	390 ± 128	520 ± 90	−2·01
	45	322 ± 130	283 ± 60	0·69
		0–6·85 g	6·86–15·58 g	
10 μg/litre	0	—	—	
	12	5 620 ± 2 385	3 486 ± 772	2·10
	19	6 461 ± 4 466	5 480 ± 1 546	0·59
	27	11 802 ± 4 127	2 907 ± 3 148	5·61*
	34	11 741 ± 3 228	11 261 ± 5 454	0·19
	45	15 166 ± 5 845	9 750 ± 1 772	2·50*
				$\chi^2 = 24\cdot38$*
		0–6·70 g	6·71–15·42 g	
100 μg/litre	0	—	—	
	12	12 423 ± 2 861	9 994 ± 3 487	1·37
	19	31 630 ± 13 226	13 725 ± 10 118	2·44*
	27	36 180 ± 13 473	23 963 ± 12 391	1·74
	34	106 285 ± 32 494	86 851 ± 25 989	1·24
	45	106 750 ± 45 918	72 142 ± 29 951	1·70
				$\chi^2 = 21\cdot11$*

* $p < 0\cdot05$.

above, where the relationship of age and concentration in bivalves is found to vary with location.

With respect to finfish, few qualitative differences appear to exist between freshwater and marine species in terms of their profiles of age dependence of mercury levels. The early studies of freshwater fish were pioneered by Swedish scientists, and early reports of the weight dependence of mercury levels in pike, *Esox lucius*, were published in Swedish (e.g. see Westermark, 1965). A later report in English (Johnels *et al.*, 1967) included considerable amounts of data and suggested that the relationship between age or weight of pike and mercury concentrations in axial muscle was location dependent.

Thus, unpolluted locations contained fish which exhibited no increase of mercury with age, whilst fish from polluted areas invariably contained higher levels of mercury when older (Fig. 58). These data were cited in two later publications also (Johnels and Westermark, 1969; Ackefors, 1971). It is notable that the slopes relating mercury concentration to age in the fish, increase in gradient with an increase in the degree of contamination, i.e. age dependence is more important in the more contaminated samples. Most of

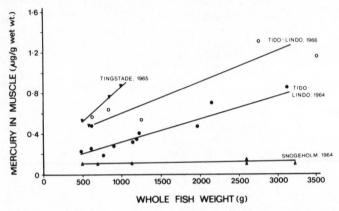

FIG. 58.   Concentrations of total mercury (µg/g wet weight) in axial muscle of pike, *Esox lucius*, from three Swedish lakes in relation to whole fish weight. (After Johnels *et al.* (1967).)

these data regress mercury levels on fish weight rather than age because of the unreliability in methods of age determination using scales in pike. The variation in the slope of the mercury concentration–age/weight regression with the degree of contamination of the study area has been noted in more recent studies also. For example, Olsson (1976) reported extensive studies of the mercury levels in biota of the Morrum River in southern Sweden. The discharge of mercury to this river derived from a paper mill which consumed (and therefore discharged) approximately one ton of phenylmercuric acetate each year until 1965, when mercury usage ceased. Correlations of fish weight to the concentrations of mercury present in axial muscle are given for pike, *Esox lucius*, and roach, *Rutilus rutilus*, for individual years (Fig. 59). It may be seen that the regressions for pike decrease in slope as the degree of contamination decreases, which agrees essentially with the observations of Johnels *et al.* (1967), cited above. The data for roach, however, are somewhat less convincing in terms of changes in gradient of

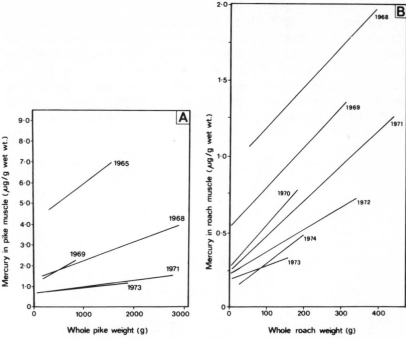

FIG. 59. Regressions relating concentrations of total mercury in axial muscle (μg/g wet weights) and fish weight for (A) pike, *Esox lucius*, and (B) roach, *Rutilus rutilus*, from the Upper Hemsjö hydroelectric power dam lake in southern Sweden. (After Olsson (1976).)

the weight–concentration regressions, although the overall mercury levels undoubtedly decrease from 1968 to 1974, and the magnitude of this decrease appears similar for each species.

These extraneous effects of fish weight (or age) on their content of mercury were recognised by Johnels *et al.* (1967) as significant interference in geographical comparisons of the degree of mercury pollution. These authors suggested weight normalisation as a method of eliminating the effects of size, leading to comparisons of the mercury levels in fish from different locations on the basis of the 'standard 1 kg pike'. It is important to note that such a method places a restraint on the magnitude of location–location difference. Thus, if a 'standard 5 kg pike' were used, it is clear that inter-location variation would be much greater because of the divergence of the regressions (describing weight–concentration re-lationships) with increasing weight of the fish. If the regression lines do not intersect each other, the *qualitative* interlocation differences will be the same, regardless of the standard weight chosen (i.e. locations would rank in the same order of decreasing pollution irrespective of the selected standard weight). However, in the case of roach in 1973 and 1974 from the studies of Olsson (1976; see Fig. 59), the regressions were found to intersect. For roach, Olsson selected a weight of 125 g for normalisation purposes, and this gave rise to higher computed levels in the 1974 fish than in those from 1973 (Fig. 60). If a lower weight (e.g. 50 g) had been selected, however, the

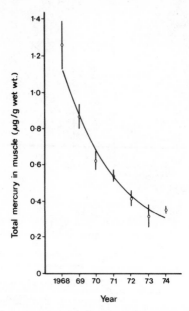

FIG. 60.   Calculated concentrations of mercury (means and 95 per cent confidence intervals, μg/g wet weights) in the axial muscle of roach, *Rutilus rutilus*, of 125 g whole-body weight. For weight-normalisation method, see original author. (After Olsson (1976).)

data would have shown the reverse profile, a continual decrease in levels occurring stepwise from 1968 to 1974, inclusive. It is, of course, possible that the 1973 and 1974 regressions were inaccurate because of an inadequate sample size and that such relationships should never intersect each other. However, other authors have also published intersecting regression lines describing the weight–concentration relationship for mercury in fish (e.g. Hattula *et al.*, 1978*b*) and the problems connected with treatment of such data by weight normalisation methods should be clearly understood, especially as this method appears to be gaining in popularity (e.g. see Linko and Terho, 1977).

It is interesting also to speculate on the basis of such changes in the weight–concentration relationships for mercury in finfish. The differences found between fish in highly contaminated regions and those in relatively unpolluted regions may be explained by the following hypothesis. In areas where available mercury levels are low, it is probable that the indigenous fish are in equilibrium with the environment. Thus, growth of the fish is balanced by the net uptake of mercury (the difference between excretion and uptake) and no increase in metal concentration is apparent with age. If, however, the ambient levels of mercury are increased so that excretion is no longer able to keep pace with uptake (even allowing for the increase in total body load which may occur with growth), the result will be an increase in metal concentration with age. This theory presupposes that the half-life of mercury in fish is long, at least of the order of the age of the fish. Data on mercury half-lives in freshwater fish often support this theory (see Chapter 5, Jarvenpaa *et al.*, 1970 and Lockhart *et al.*, 1972).

Other authors reporting age dependence in the concentrations of mercury in freshwater finfish generally have not reported data as extensive as those of the Swedish studies cited above. However, these reports are worth documenting here as they lead to an understanding of the ubiquity of such effects. Bache *et al.* (1971) found a positive correlation between (eviscerated) whole-body concentrations of mercury and age in lake trout, *Salvelinus namaycush*, from Cayuga Lake, New York State; levels of ΣDDT and PCBs in these fish also increased with age (Bache *et al.*, 1972; Youngs *et al.*, 1972; see Chapter 8). Scott and Armstrong (1972) analysed 53 samples of 11 species of freshwater fish from Manitoba and northwest Ontario. In general a significant positive correlation between total mercury concentration in white muscle of each species and length was noted, although inconsistency of the relationship within each species (as above) was found. One highly unusual result was also recorded; tullibee, *Coregonus artedii*, exhibited a significant *negative* correlation between mercury concentration in muscle and fish length in samples from Elk Island, Lake Winnipeg. This result may, however, have been due to chance; three other samples of this species exhibited either no significant length–concentration relationship or a significant positive correlation, and two other species from Elk Island (burbot, *Lota lota*, and sheepshead, *Aplodinotus grunniens*) both exhibited positive length–concentration relationships. Kelso and Frank (1974) found increased total mercury levels

TABLE 45

RESULTS OF LINEAR REGRESSIONS OF TOTAL MERCURY CONCENTRATION ON WET WEIGHTS OF WHOLE FISH FOR TEN SPECIES FROM FIVE AREAS OF LAKE PÄIJÄNNE, FINLAND, IN 1972–1974. THE FIGURES SHOW THE PERCENTAGE OF TOTAL VARIANCE WHICH IS EXPLAINED BY THE REGRESSION. SIGNIFICANCE OF THE REGRESSION IS SHOWN AS * ($p < 0.05$), ** ($p < 0.01$) OR *** ($p < 0.001$). FOR DETAILS OF STATISTICAL METHODS, SEE ORIGINAL AUTHORS. (AFTER HATTULA et al. (1978b).)

Year		Whitefish	Vendace	Smelt	Pike	Bream	Roach	Burbot	Ruffe	Pikeperch	Perch
1972	Area 1				**36·1	**28·0					**23·4
	Area 2				***67·7	**48·3					
	Area 3				***66·4	***73·9					
	Area 4		**70·8		*28·5	**30·0		***39·0			**43·6
	Area 5	**78·7	*23·7	***77·3	***43·5	***22·2				**55·4	***31·1
1973	Area 1				**23·8						***64·6
	Area 3				***88·5	**45·6	***67·2		***55·6		***47·7
	Area 4				***67·7	*28·7	**17·3	*38·6			***47·8
	Area 5		*21·9	**96·4	*62·9	***37·1	*63·6	*36·0			*13·1
1974	Area 1				*31·8	***83·5					***33·4
	Area 3				*63·6	***56·8	***50·3				
	Area 4		*19·0		***73·1		***45·0			***72·6	***38·8
	Area 5	43·6									***51·1

with weight and age in whole fish of three species (yellow perch, *Perca flavescens*, white bass, *Morone chrysops*, and smallmouth bass, *Micropterus dolomieui*, from Lake Erie; these data will also be discussed in Chapter 8. Walleyes, *Stizostedion vitreum vitreum*, from seven locations in Michigan waters were also found to exhibit age-dependent increases in muscle concentrations of total mercury (Kelly *et al.*, 1975); this study is notable for its sample numbers as well as its excellent comparisons of recent and historical fish samples for mercury levels. It is also interesting that most or all of the data appeared to fit a regression of mercury on standard fish length calculated for all 283 specimens studied; i.e. inter-location variation in the mercury–length relationship was apparently absent, notwithstanding quite severe differences in overall contamination of each location. Finally, the data of Hattula *et al.* (1978b) were mentioned previously. These authors published extensive data covering 12 species of fish from Lake Päijänne in Finland. All species exhibited positive correlations between mercury concentration (whole fish) and wet weights; Table 45 shows the percentage of the total variance within samples due to the effect of weight-dependent variation in mercury levels. It may be seen that weight was a major parameter affecting the intra-population variance in many cases.

The reports of laboratory studies on the kinetics of mercury in freshwater fish present data which is comparable to that noted previously for studies of bivalve molluscs. Thus, smaller individuals appear to accumulate and lose mercury faster than larger individuals. The effects of size on mercury uptake from solution and/or food were studied by Hannerz (1968). Both pike, *Esox lucius*, and pike perch were found to exhibit reciprocal relationships between body length and mercury accumulation. The smaller individuals thus accumulated greater concentrations of the element in a given exposure period (Fig. 61). The most likely explanation suggested by the author was that smaller fish have a larger surface area: volume ratio and would therefore be expected to accumulate mercury faster from solution than would larger individuals. However, it is noteworthy that all fish were of similar length when the exposure period began; growth dilution of the metal accumulated might also be important. Norstrom *et al.* (1976), in studies concerned with the mathematical modelling of pollutant accumulation by finfish, published an interesting figure relating the fractional clearance of methylmercury by fish to their weight; smaller fish exhibited a higher excretion rate for this compound than larger individuals. As noted above in discussions on bivalve molluscs, such size-related differences can lead to weight or size dependence in mercury concentrations in biota under conditions of varying ambient availability of the element. However, the

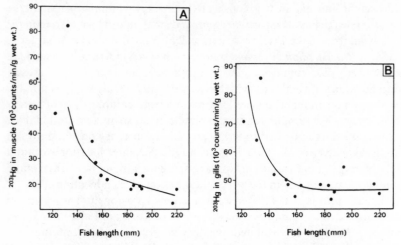

FIG. 61. The accumulation of ^{203}Hg by (A) muscle and (B) gills of pike-perch exposed to labelled phenylmercuric acetate in pond experiments. Initially the fish were all of similar length (78·0 ± 3·6 mm). (After Hannerz (1968).)

relevance of this to field situations appears to be rather less for finfish than for molluscs, presumably because short-term variations due to this effect tend to be masked by the long-term (lifetime) accumulation of residues in finfish. This explanation presupposes that the biological half-life of mercury in finfish is much longer than that in bivalve molluscs. Unfortunately, the differences (which may approach orders of magnitude) between the reports of different authors concerning biological half-lives of metals in biota (see Chapter 2) do not permit any realistic estimate of whether such differences do, in fact, exist in the environmental kinetics of mercury in these organisms. However, it is suggestive that the extremely short biological half-life of mercury in oysters, *Crassostrea virginica*, noted by Cunningham and Tripp (1973, 1975a, b) was of the same order as estimates made more recently by Fowler *et al.* (1978a) for the mussel, *Mytilus galloprovincialis*. Furthermore, the latter authors did not find methylmercury retention to exceed that of inorganic mercury in the mussel by any great amount (biological half-lives of 89–99 days for methylmercury and 46–51 days for inorganic mercury). By contrast, most authors consider the half-life of methylmercury in fish to be extremely long (e.g. see comments on growth effects noted by Lockhart *et al.*, 1972 in Chapter 5), and methylmercury makes up by far the greater portion of the total mercury load in most finfish. Perhaps the differences between the retention of total mercury in finfish and bivalve molluscs depend, to some extent at least, on the selective accumulation of the methylated derivative in finfish compared with bivalves. Thus, not only does total mercury increase with age in finfish, but the fraction present as methylmercury may also rise with age (e.g. see Bache et al., 1971).

Marine and estuarine species of finfish also commonly exhibit age-dependent increases in mercury concentration; indeed, as stated previously, few qualitative differences exist in this respect between the two environments. Studies in the laboratory have again indicated the tendency of small individuals of a species to accumulate mercury faster than large individuals, at least for the plaice, Pleuronectes platessa, and this appears true for both inorganic and organic mercury exposure (Pentreath, 1976b, c). However, plaice from the field exhibit higher concentrations of total mercury in muscle and liver tissues when older (Pentreath, 1976b). These data are shown in Fig. 62 for comparison of field and laboratory studies. A later paper (Pentreath, 1976d) examined the relative importance of uptake from solution and from food, and here perhaps is a clue to the disagreement noted by this and other authors concerning laboratory and field studies of the size dependency of mercury in fish. Experimental data suggested that the uptake of mercury from food would be twice as important as that from solution in a field situation. Clearly, size dependence of uptake from food could vary independently of that from solution (as, for example, factors such as dietary preference of different sized individuals may become important). Restriction of laboratory studies of size dependence in mercury accumulation to exposure of biota to mercury in solution may therefore give a totally biased picture of the real situation in the field.

Amongst other studies of organisms from the environment, that of Barber et al. (1972) reported increases in total mercury concentrations with age in the bathyal-demersal fish, Antimora rostrata, and this species was further studied, together with bluefish, Pomatomus saltatrix, by Cross et al. (1973). The studies of the latter authors are particularly important, as several metals were investigated and the differences between mercury and the other elements in terms of age dependence were unusually well illustrated. The results indicated that mercury was the only element to exhibit significant positive correlations between concentration in white muscle and fish weight. The authors suggested that copper, iron, manganese and zinc were probably regulated by the fish and that these metals were in equilibrium between fish and the ambient environment. Mercury, by contrast, was suggested not to be in equilibrium, presumably

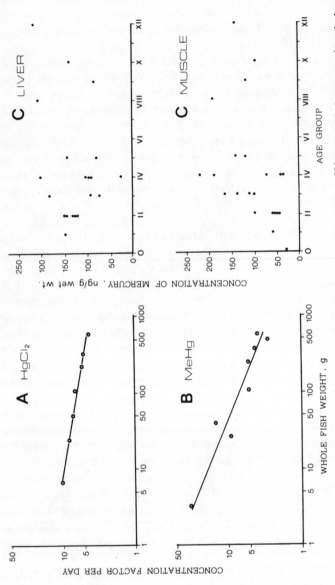

FIG. 62.　The accumulation of (A) inorganic mercury, and (B) organic mercury from ^{203}Hg-labelled seawater by whole plaice, *Pleuronectes platessa*, of different weights. (C) shows the concentrations of total mercury in liver and muscle of the same species from the field, and their variation with fish age. (After Pentreath (1976b, c).)

because excretion rates cannot keep pace with uptake rates of this element, i.e. net uptake is positive throughout the lifetime of the fish. This has important consequences for long-lived fish, which are generally high trophic predators (see below). Such differences between mercury and the other metals will be discussed further in Section B below. It should be noted, however, that species differences also exist; Portmann and Neall (1973) reported that cod, *Gadus morhua*, and plaice, *Pleuronectes platessa*, exhibited quite different profiles of age dependence for a range of metals, even though both species were derived from the same area of the North Sea. The tissue studied is also of importance, presumably because of differences between metals in relative affinity for different tissues (see Chapter 5). Thus, studies of cleithrum bones of cod, *Gadus morhua*, showed unusual profiles of age dependence; mercury did not increase with back-calculated fish lengths, while zinc did increase (Scott, 1977; cf. Papadopoulou *et al.*, 1978 in Section B below). More recently, studies of the sand flathead, *Platycephalus bassensis*, in Tasmanian waters have led to suggestions that this species could be a particularly useful indicator of local mercury pollution (Dix *et al.*, 1976). The correlation between fish size and whole-body mercury concentrations was noted to be significant within populations, but was masked by inter-location differences in mercury availability when the data were treated as a single unit. This is important, as such effects may explain the failure of some authors to generate significant age–concentration relationships for mercury in fish (e.g. see Freeman *et al.*, 1974), especially when sample sizes are small or significant migration of the sampled fish occurs, with populations constantly intermixing. It should be noted that the greatest success with finfish species as indicators of mercury contamination of aquatic environments has arisen from studies on demersal, territorial species of a sedentary nature. The use of pelagic finfish is open to far more variables which often cannot be eliminated; size is but one of these variables.

Amongst high-ranking marine predators, some of the highest levels of mercury have been recorded, and this has been ascribed both to the supposed increase of mercury concentrations with trophic level, and to the long lifetimes of these fish compared with species lower in the food web. Peterson *et al.* (1973) have reviewed data on mercury in tuna and several references are also given here for unpublished studies or little known studies concerning the age–concentration relationship for mercury in finfish. In general, tuna exhibit a positive relationship between mercury concentration in muscle and age; an example from an extensive study of 88 yellowfin tuna, *Thunnus albacares*, from the Gulf of Guinea is shown in Fig. 63. The large

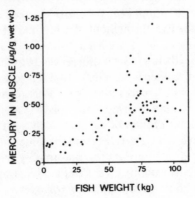

FISH WEIGHT (kg)

Fɪɢ. 63. Concentrations of total mercury (μg/g wet weight) in muscle of 88 yellowfin tuna, *Thunnus albacares*, from the Gulf of Guinea, in relation to whole fish weights. Ivory Coast Fisheries Service, (1972); cited in Peterson *et al.* (1973).

amount of scatter present in the mercury levels of relatively large tuna may reflect differences in the length–concentration relationship in different subpopulations, i.e. these data may be a composite of several intermixed regressions of different slope. In addition, a sex difference is possible because of differences in the growth rates of male and female tuna (see Chapter 9). Significant positive correlations between weight and total mercury concentrations in the muscles of tuna have also been reported by Cumont *et al.* (1972) for three species (*Thunnus albacares*, *T. thynnus* and *T. alalunga*) and by Menasveta and Siriyong (1977) for *Neothunnus albacora* and *Parathunnus sibi*; in addition, four species of shark were reported to exhibit such correlations by the latter authors. Forrester *et al.* (1972) observed a correlation between mercury concentration in the muscle of spiny dogfish, *Squalus acanthias*, and fish length for individuals from the Strait of Georgia; these data will also be referred to in Chapter 9, as a difference between the sexes was again noted. By contrast, Childs and Gaffke (1973) could find no significant length- or sex-based differences in mercury levels of the same species caught off the coast of Oregon; again, it would appear that mixing of several populations masked the differences present in each group, and this is a major problem in the elucidation of variables affecting the metal concentrations of pelagic or wide-ranging biota.

Amongst other reports on sharks, the studies of Walker (1976) are notable for their attempts to differentiate between the effects of species, length, sex and location on the mercury concentrations observed. Both school shark, *Galeorhinus australis*, and gummy shark, *Mustelus antarcticus*, exhibited positive length–concentration relationships for total mercury in muscle, but these were sex dependent and location dependent as well as differing between the two species. It is interesting that location dependence of the regressions describing the length–concentration relationships was noted for gummy shark but not for school shark; this appears to correlate to the relative mobilities of the species, the former being more sedentary than the latter. The extreme importance of length in the variation of mercury levels observed was reflected in the high correlation of length to element concentration; the length variable was responsible for 75–80 per cent of the total variation in mercury levels of school shark and for 43–60 per cent of that for gummy shark (cf. 10 per cent for the sand flathead in the studies of Dix *et al.* (1976)). Finally, the report of Mackay *et al.* (1975b) concerning the black marlin, *Makaira indica*, is worth mentioning. The concentrations of both total mercury and selenium in muscle tissues were positively correlated to length and weight of the fish sampled, although no other metals exhibited such correlations. Mercury and selenium concentrations also correlated to each other in both muscle and liver tissues of the fish. The involvement of selenium here may indicate co-accumulation of the two elements, perhaps affording some protection from the toxic effects of mercury on the teleost, as demonstrated in mammals (see also Koeman *et al.*, 1975; Bernhard, 1978).

This section would be incomplete without some reference to the mercury levels found in seals and other marine mammals. In these cases, age-dependent profiles are easier to produce than are data for weight or other size parameters, as seals can be accurately aged by examination of the canine teeth. Heppleston and French (1973) studied the concentrations of several metals in tissues of the grey seal, *Halichoerus grypus*, and the common seal, *Phoca vitulina*, from the coasts of the United Kingdom. Regional variations in the mercury content of seals were found for brain and liver samples. Age dependence in brain mercury levels was not well defined; however, in livers, mercury concentrations were highly responsive to age in a location dependent fashion. As noted previously for finfish, the age–concentration regressions observed for mercury in seal livers differed significantly in slope between populations from different locations and regressions of greatest slope were found to occur in the most highly contaminated samples. Mercury in seal pups was found to relate to the concentrations in the mother, suggesting placental transfer similar to that known for humans. Sergeant and Armstrong (1973) reported studies of both the above species and of harp seals, *Pagophilus groenlandicus*, and hood seals, *Cystophora cristata*, from the waters of eastern Canada. Tissue distributions of mercury in each species indicated a decrease in total concentrations in the order liver > kidneys > hair > muscle > blubber, and the overall species differences were determined mainly by the diet of each species, although migration patterns may also have been significant. Concentrations of total mercury in liver of each species increased with age; examples for the grey and harp seals are given in Fig. 64(A). It is interesting that the absolute amounts of mercury accumulated by grey seal livers exceed those in livers of harp seals by a factor of about 30, with a maximum of an astonishing 387 μg/g wet weight in a 25-year old male, which is much above the level known to be toxic to humans. A later report showed significant age- and weight-dependent correlations of total mercury concentrations in muscle and in liver of both ringed seals, *Pusa hispida*, and bearded seals, *Erignathus barbatus* (Smith and Armstrong, 1975). Interestingly, mercury in muscle was essentially all present as methylmercury, whereas that in liver was mainly inorganic, suggesting a demethylation capacity of this organ. All species of seal probably exhibit age dependence of mercury levels in at least some of their tissues; Anas (1974) found significant increases in mercury concentrations in liver (but not in muscle or kidneys) with age of fur seals, *Callorhinus ursinus*, and harbour seals, *Phoca vitulina richardi*, confirming an earlier report (Anas, 1970), which concerned the former species only.

The data of Heppleston and French (1973), cited above, were confirmed and extended by studies of Roberts *et al.* (1976) and Koeman *et al.* (1972), who once again observed differences in slopes of the age–concentration relationships for mercury in livers of common seals, *Phoca vitulina*, from the coasts of Great Britain and The Netherlands according to location; these data are shown in Fig. 64(B), which may be compared with the earlier studies. Additional data on *P. vitulina* from the North Sea coast of Germany (Drescher *et al.*, 1977) suggest that the age dependent curve for mercury concentrations in the livers of individuals from this population would fit somewhere between the curves for the East Anglian and Dutch populations in Fig. 64(B).

Other marine mammals have not been studied so extensively as have seals. However, the reports which are available suggest that only minor differences exist between dolphins, porpoises and whales (Gaskin *et al.*, 1972, 1974), and that in general mercury behaves in a similar fashion in these species to its behaviour in seals. Ageing of cetaceans is rather more difficult than in seals; thus Gaskin *et al.* (1972) correlated total mercury levels of *longissimus* muscles and livers in harbour porpoises, *Phocoena*

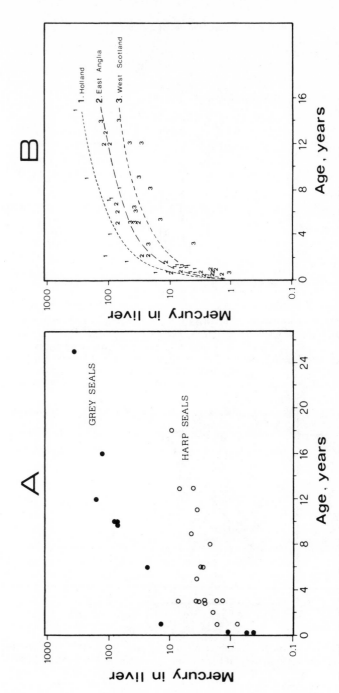

FIG. 64.   Relationships between seal age and the concentration of total mercury (μg/g wet weight) in liver tissues. (A) Profile for grey seals, *Halichoerus grypus*, and harp seals, *Pagophilus groenlandicus*, from tabulated data of Sergeant and Armstrong (1973). (B) Profiles for common seals, *Phoca vitulina*, from two locations on the coasts of Great Britain (Roberts *et al.*, 1976) and The Netherlands (Koeman *et al.*, 1972).

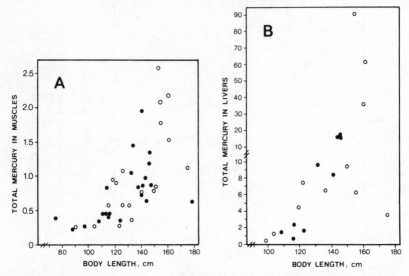

FIG. 65.   Concentrations of total mercury (μg/g wet weight) in (A) *longissimus* muscle and (B) livers of harbour porpoises, *Phocoena phocoena*, from the Bay of Fundy, 1969–1971, in relation to body length. Closed circles indicate males; open circles, females. Note change of scale for concentration axis in (B) (After Gaskin *et al.* (1972).)

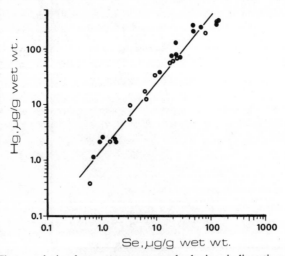

FIG. 66.   The correlation between mercury and selenium in liver tissues of marine mammals. Open circles, dolphins and porpoises; closed circles, common seal. (After Koeman *et al.*, (1973).)

phocoena, to body length of these animals (Fig. 65). The pattern of mercury methylation in the tissues once again reveals lower methylation in livers than in muscles (Gaskin *et al.*, 1974). Selenium may be involved in the protection of all these marine mammals from mercury toxicity, possibly by an involvement in the demethylation process after its co-accumulation with mercury. Koeman *et al.* (1973) have shown that selenium and mercury exist in the livers of marine mammals in approximately a 1:1 molar ratio (Fig. 66) and the involvement of selenium in the detoxification of mercury is suspected from studies on terrestrial mammals also. It would be interesting to attempt to limit or inhibit mercury uptake by aquatic biota by decreasing selenium availability, as the exact relationship between the elements at uptake, storage and excretion is as yet not fully understood. Chapter 11 examines metal–metal interactions in aquatic biota further.

B.   TRACE METALS OTHER THAN MERCURY

As noted in the introduction to this chapter, trace metals other than mercury contrast with mercury in their age dependence in aquatic biota. Thus, whilst most organisms from the field exhibit age dependent increases in mercury concentration, other trace metals commonly either decrease or remain unchanged in concentration as organisms age; however, exceptions are known. The only consistent exceptions to this general profile concern marine mammals, which will be considered last, after data for bivalve molluscs, finfish and other groups have been discussed. As usual, most information which is available concerns bivalves and finfish, although a certain amount of material has been published for crustaceans and other groups.

Amongst bivalves, reports are available concerning both field studies and laboratory experiments. Field studies concerning freshwater bivalves are few in number; the only report of significance which includes data on the size dependence of metals is that of Manly and George (1977) for the mussel, *Anodonta anatina*, from the River Thames. This paper was cited above, where it was noted that mercury–size relationships in *A. anatina* were location dependent. For the other trace metals studied, a similar pattern was noted for cadmium, copper and lead; mussels from some locations exhibited tissue weight-dependent changes in concentration of these metals, whereas those from other locations exhibited no such correlations. Concentrations of nickel did not correlate significantly to tissue weights of individuals at any study location. These data are

TABLE 46

RANGES OF TRACE METAL CONCENTRATIONS IN THE WHOLE SOFT PARTS OF FRESHWATER MUSSELS, *Anodonta anatina*, FROM THE RIVER THAMES, GREAT BRITAIN, AND THE SIGNIFICANCE (AT $p < 0.05$) OF LOGARITHMIC REGRESSION COEFFICIENTS RELATING CONCENTRATIONS TO DRY TISSUE WEIGHTS OF INDIVIDUALS. WHERE SIGNIFICANT RELATIONSHIPS WERE FOUND, THE LOGARITHMIC REGRESSION COEFFICIENTS ARE QUOTED. (AFTER MANLY AND GEORGE (1977).)

Location	Metals (μg/g dry weight)					
	Zn	Ni	Pb	Cd	Cu	Hg
Appleton	219·8–533·1 NS	0·5–7·3 NS	1·5–21·7 NS	0·1–6·1 NS	8·2–36·8 NS	3·1–11·8 S (−0·48)
Pangbourne	152·2–929·4 NS	0·1–7·6 NS	2·1–22·1 NS	0·1–7·1 S (0·52)	38·9–111·1 NS	0·2–9·7 NS
Reading	523·2–3 496·5 NS	11·4–45·4 NS	12·6–79·4 S (0·42)	2·2–9·7 S (0·74)	40·7–137·4 S (−0·7)	1·4–11·2 S (−0·69)
Hurley	303·6–875·0 NS	0·1–12·0 NS	0·1–28·3 NS	0·1–3·4 NS	30·8–250·0 S (−0·86)	0·7–18·1 NS
Bray	200·8–686·3 NS	0·1–8·5 NS	0·1–23·1 NS	0·1–1·2 NS	34·7–222·2 S (−0·93)	0·1–2·1 NS
Lower Sunbury	436·4–2 266·6 NS	9·6–20·2 NS	18·3–134·2 S (0·97)	0·1–21·1 S (0·96)	12·3–144·0 NS	0·5–1·4 NS
Teddington	708·9–3 225·8 NS	0·1–45·9 NS	0·1–44·4 S (0·64)	1·0–6·6 S (0·67)	26·1–106·7 NS	0·4–1·0 NS

NS: not significant.
S: significant.

summarised in Table 46; it will be noted that whilst cadmium and lead levels increased with tissue weight (positive regression coefficients), those of copper and mercury decreased (negative regression coefficients). It is interesting that significant relationships between tissue weight and metal concentration appeared to be restricted to samples of greatest contamination, perhaps with the exception of mercury. Whilst this might suggest that, in conditions of extreme contamination, net uptake would be positive throughout the life of the animal and hence give rise to the observed profiles for cadmium and lead, this is clearly untenable for copper. There seems no alternative but to suggest that copper levels are regulated in this mussel, the degree of regulation varying with age and extent of contamination. Possibly zinc is also regulated in an age-dependent fashion, as whilst no significant regressions could be generated from the data, zinc levels appeared to rise with tissue weight up to a given point, and then to decrease in heavier individuals. The probable metabolic regulation of copper is interesting, as the marine mussel, *Mytilus edulis*, also exhibits unusual handling of this element (Phillips, 1976*a*, *b*; see below).

Marine and estuarine species of bivalves have been more intensively studied than have freshwater varieties. An early report of age dependence was that of Romeril (1971*b*), concerning copper, iron and zinc in the clam, *Mercenaria mercenaria* (Table 47). In this case, metal concentrations apparently increased with age, which is an uncommon profile. Unfortunately, this population has not been further studied since this report, although in-depth studies of seasonal trends in age-dependence of these clams might be most illuminating. Schulz-Baldes (1973) published survey data for lead in the mussel, *Mytilus edulis*, from the Weser Estuary and the German Bight. Detailed studies at one location indicated a moderate (and

TABLE 47

MEAN CONCENTRATIONS OF COPPER, IRON AND ZINC (μg/g DRY WEIGHT) IN CLAMS, *Mercenaria mercenaria*, OF DIFFERENT AGES FROM HAMBLE, SOUTHAMPTON WATER, UK. (AFTER ROMERIL (1971*b*). SEE ALSO ROMERIL (1974).)

Metal	Age of clam (years)		
	3 +	4 +	5 +
Copper	12·9	25·9	32·0
Iron	107·2	194·9	240·8
Zinc	50·5	90·7	131·3

TABLE 48

CONCENTRATIONS OF LEAD (μg/g DRY WEIGHT) IN WHOLE SOFT PARTS OF MUSSELS, *Mytilus edulis*, FROM A SITE IN THE GERMAN BIGHT, AND THEIR VARIATION WITH SIZE (SHELL LENGTHS) OR TISSUE WEIGHTS. FIFTEEN INDIVIDUALS WERE STUDIED IN EACH OF THREE SIZE CLASSES. (AFTER SCHULZ-BALDES (1973).)

Parameter	Group 1	Group 2	Group 3
Shell length (mm)	15	22	35
Mean dry weight (mg)	12	37	139
Lead concentration of individuals	5·7	3·8	4·2
	6·1	4·3	4·4
	6·1	4·7	4·5
	6·2	4·8	4·5
	6·2	4·9	4·6
	6·2	5·3	4·7
	6·3	5·5	4·7
	6·3	5·6	4·8
	7·0	5·9	5·0
	7·1	6·1	5·0
	7·1	6·2	5·0
	7·5	6·8	5·5
	7·7	7·0	5·6
	8·1	7·0	5·8
	8·6	7·3	6·0
Mean lead concentration $\pm$ standard deviation	6·81 $\pm$ 0·85	5·68 $\pm$ 1·06	4·95 $\pm$ 0·54
Differences between groups: significance by Student's t-test	Groups 1–2 = 3·22, $p < 0.01$		
	Groups 2–3 = 2·36, $p < 0.05$		
	Groups 1–3 = 7·12, $p < 0.001$		

significant) size or weight dependence of lead concentrations in whole soft parts. These data are reproduced *in toto* in Table 48, and are useful to emphasise the variability between individuals in each size group. Later laboratory studies of the uptake of lead from solution or from food by the same species revealed that large individuals responded less rapidly to changes in ambient lead levels compared to small individuals; rates of lead uptake and loss were both less in the larger animals (Schulz-Baldes, 1974). Studies of *M. edulis* in Port Phillip and Western Port Bays in Victoria, Australia, were reported by Phillips (1976a, b). Weight-dependent variation in the concentrations of cadmium, copper, lead and zinc was observed during studies of field populations and of mussels exposed to metals in solution in the laboratory. However, the existence of significant tissue weight–metal concentration regressions varied with both the metal considered and the season of study. Cadmium levels were most frequently weight dependent, whilst levels of copper and lead were only occasionally affected and those of zinc were rarely found to depend on tissue weights. The frequent existence of significant relationships between cadmium concentrations and individual (whole soft part) weights permitted this author to use weight normalisation procedures to investigate changes in metal levels with season or time independently of the effects of variations in whole tissue weights. This was unfortunately not possible for other metals because significant weight–concentration relationships were only occasionally noted, mainly in the autumn and early winter, when the mussels underwent gametogenesis in preparation for spring spawning. This finding will be further discussed below.

Amongst other reports dealing with single species of bivalves, that of Mackay *et al.* (1975*a*) is particularly noteworthy as it concerns an oyster which may well become important in the future in monitoring surveys for trace metals. These authors studied the Sydney rock oyster, commonly termed *Crassostrea commercialis*, and noted that it was probably the same species as the ubiquitous subtropical oyster, *Saccostrea cuccullata*. Present information suggests that the Sydney rock oyster should be considered a member of the genus *Saccostrea*, although the population on the east coast of Australia may be reproductively isolated from other populations of *S. cuccullata*. In any event, Mackay *et al.* (1975*a*) found that whilst total body loads of cadmium, copper and zinc increased with age or wet weights of the soft parts of oysters from the Hawkesbury River Estuary, the concentrations of each metal decreased with age or tissue weights.

Both oysters and mussels from South African waters are known to exhibit weight-dependent changes in body load or total metal content per individual (Watling and Watling, 1976*a*, 1976*b*). Unfortunately, these authors did not report concentration changes with tissue weights, but an examination of the graphical relationships published suggests that changes may have occurred in this parameter also. Furthermore, the results for the mussel *Choromytilus meridionalis* (Watling and Watling, 1976*b*) revealed that the changes in total content of metals with tissue weights were sex dependent; these results will be further discussed in Chapter 9.

The burrowing bivalve, *Scrobicularia plana*, has been extensively studied recently by Bryan and his co-workers. Studies in the Tamar Estuary (Bryan and Uysal, 1978) have shown that significant effects of tissue weight on metal concentration exist, but only in animals greater than a threshold size, equivalent to about 0·05 g dry weight of whole soft parts (Fig. 67). In addition, the results showed that whilst the concentrations of copper,

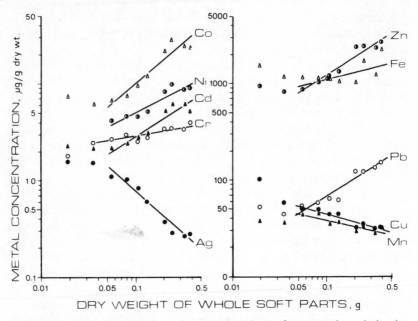

FIG. 67. Relationships between the concentrations of ten metals and the dry weights of whole soft parts of *Scrobicularia plana* from the Tamar Estuary; samples taken in February, 1975. Each point represents about five pooled individuals. (After Bryan and Uysal (1978).)

manganese and silver decreased with increasing tissue weights in this species, those of the other seven metals studied (cadmium, cobalt, chromium, iron, lead, nickel and zinc) all increased with increasing tissue weights. Slopes of all regressions were significantly different from zero, with the exception of iron. A later report concerning metals in the same species from the Gannel and Camel Estuaries of south-west England clearly established location dependence of these patterns, however (Bryan and Hummerstone, 1978). Animals from the Gannel Estuary contained much greater levels of all metals than did those from the Camel Estuary, correlating to the existence of contaminated run-off from old lead mines in the former catchment. Linear regressions describing the relationship between tissue weights and metal concentrations were fitted by an equation $\log_{10}$ concentration $= b \log_{10}$ weight $+ \log_{10} a$, where b is the slope and a the intercept on the Y axis of the plots at lg tissue weight (i.e. a is the weight normalised concentration at lg tissue weight). Values for a and b in regressions relating metal concentrations in whole soft parts to tissue

TABLE 49

RELATIONSHIPS BETWEEN TISSUE WEIGHTS AND METAL CONCENTRATION IN WHOLE SOFT PARTS OF THE BURROWING BIVALVE, *Scrobicularia plana*, FROM THREE ESTUARIES IN THE SOUTH-WEST OF ENGLAND. VALUES OF a AND b ARE GIVEN FROM REGRESSIONS FITTED BY THE EQUATION LOG_{10} CONCENTRATION $= b\,\text{LOG}_{10}$ WEIGHT $+ \text{LOG}_{10}\,a$. VALUES OF b ARE SLOPES OF THE REGRESSIONS; a IS THE WEIGHT NORMALISED METAL CONCENTRATION FOR AN INDIVIDUAL OF $1\cdot0$ g DRY TISSUE WEIGHT. (AFTER BRYAN AND HUMMERSTONE (1978).) DATA FOR TAMAR ESTUARY FOR COMPARISON ARE FROM BRYAN AND UYSAL (1978)

| Metal | Gannel (Nov., 1975) | | Camel (Nov., 1975) | | Tamar (Feb., 1975) |
	a	b	a	b	b
Cadmium	19·2	0·781*	0·26	−0·152	0·606*
Cobalt	80·8	0·542*	4·58	0·314	0·817*
Copper	161	0·279*	30·4	0·283	−0·280*
Chromium	1·79	0·109	1·05	−0·098	0·188*
Iron	1 146	−0·015	670	−0·117	0·241
Lead	586	0·478*	15·3	0·403	0·603*
Manganese	79·2	−0·035	24·3	−0·090	−0·215*
Nickel	13·2	0·270*	4·21	0·147	0·505*
Silver	1·59	0·195*	0·51	0·277	−0·857*
Zinc	4010	0·473*	219	−0·003	0·639*

* Slope significantly different from zero at $p < 0\cdot05$ or better.

weights are given in Table 49, and slopes may be compared in each population to those generated from Fig. 67 above. For bivalves from the Gannel Estuary, concentration–weight relationships were positive and significant statistically for cadmium, cobalt, copper, lead, nickel, silver and zinc. Regressions were not statistically significant for chromium (positive slope) or for iron and manganese (negative slope). Data for the Camel population are less significant because of the much lower amounts of metals and consequent greater scatter; however, it is clear that slopes of the regressions differ considerably from those of the Gannel population. Comparison of the results from Gannel and Tamar animals reveals that slope values are inconsistent, even to the extent of the direction of slope of the weight–concentration regression being different for copper and silver. Clearly, weight–concentration relationships are most inconsistent in this organism. Even weight normalisation procedures will be fraught with problems when two populations are to be compared in anything other than a gross fashion.

Finally, the results of Boyden (1974, 1977) deserve citation and

Quantitative Aquatic Biological Indicators

TABLE 50

RELATIONSHIPS BETWEEN METAL CONCENTRATION AND DRY TISSUE WEIGHTS IN SIX ESTUARINE SPECIES OF MOLLUSC. 'INVERSE' SHOWS THAT CONCENTRATIONS FALL WITH AN INCREASE IN TISSUE WEIGHTS; 'NONE' SHOWS THAT CONCENTRATIONS ARE INDEPENDENT OF TISSUE WEIGHTS AND 'DIRECT' SHOWS THAT CONCENTRATIONS INCREASE WITH TISSUE WEIGHTS. (AFTER BOYDEN (1974).)

Species	Cadmium	Copper	Iron	Lead	Nickel	Zinc
Bivalves:						
Cerastoderma edule	Inverse	Inverse	None	Inverse	None	Inverse
Mercenaria mercenaria	Inverse	Inverse	Inverse	None	None	None
Mytilus edulis	None	Inverse	Inverse	Inverse	None	Inverse
Venerupis decussata	Inverse	Inverse	None	Inverse	None	None
Gastropods:						
Patella intermedia	Not stated	Inverse	Inverse	Inverse	Not stated	Inverse
Patella vulgata	Direct[a]	Inverse	Inverse	Inverse	Not stated	Inverse

[a] Variable in slope with location, but always direct.

discussion. The first paper concerned trace metals in six estuarine species, samples being taken from several locations in southern England. Relationships were elucidated between metal *content* and dry tissue weights for each species, four of which were bivalves and two of which were limpets. The author considered that the results could be fitted into three discrete categories, as follows.

(a) *Case 1:* Metal *content* (μg) relates to dry body weight with a regression coefficient less than 1, approximating 0·75. All species exhibited this type of relationship for copper. In this case, metal *concentrations* (μg/g) decrease with increased body weight.

(b) *Case 2:* Metal *content* (μg) relates to dry body weight with a regression coefficient approximating 1·00. All bivalve species exhibited this direct relationship between element content and body weight for nickel. Here, metal *concentrations* (μg/g) are independent of body weight.

(c) *Case 3:* Metal *content* (μg) relates to the square of body weight, with a regression coefficient approximating 2·00. The only case where this was found to occur involved cadmium in the limpet, *Patella vulgata*, samples being taken from the severely polluted Severn Estuary. In this instance, cadmium *concentrations* (μg/g) were directly proportional to body weight. It was noted that other populations of the same species from less polluted locations exhibited regressions which were less steep, regression coefficients being 1·3 and 1·5. As the changes in concentration of metals with size are considered of greater import than are those of content or total body load, these data are shown in Table 50 to emphasise the relationship of concentration to tissue weights.

With the exception of the instance involving cadmium in *P. vulgata*, Boyden (1974) felt that '... in most cases the regression coefficient relating element content to body weight remains constant irrespective of season or environmental element concentration ...'. If this were so, the effects of size on the trace metal levels in bivalves could be easily and simply eliminated using a weight normalisation process based on a regression line with universal validity.

The later publication (Boyden, 1977) tempered these previous claims somewhat, although the extensive data were still interpreted on the basis of the above three possible cases (Table 51). However, at least in some instances it was admitted that the regressions describing element content–tissue weight relationships could change in slope with either season or the extent of ambient contamination (cf. Section A, above). Cadmium levels in the scallop, *Pecten maximus*, constituted a further departure from the suggested normal pattern; concentrations of the metal exhibited a most

TABLE 51

RELATIONSHIPS BETWEEN THE DRY WEIGHTS OF THE WHOLE SOFT PARTS OF BIVALVE MOLLUSCS AND THEIR CONCENTRATIONS OF SEVEN TRACE METALS. FOR EXPLANATION OF 'INVERSE', 'NONE' AND 'DIRECT', SEE TABLE 50. (AFTER BOYDEN (1977).)

Species	Cadmium	Copper	Iron	Lead	Manganese	Nickel	Zinc
Oysters:							
Crassostrea gigas	Inverse	Inverse	Inverse	Inverse	None	Inverse	None
Ostrea edulis	None	None	Inverse	Inverse	None	Inverse	None
Mussel:							
Mytilus edulis	None	Inverse*	Inverse	Inverse	Inverse	Inverse**	Inverse
Clams:							
Mercenaria mercenaria	Inverse	Inverse	Inverse	None	—	None	None
Venerupis decussata	Inverse	Inverse	None	Inverse	—	None	None
Scallops:							
Chlamys opercularis	None	None	—	None	—	Inverse	None
Pecten maximus	None/Direct†	Inverse	—	Inverse	Inverse	—	Inverse

* Variable depending on extent of contamination.
** cf. Boyden (1974), Table 50.
† Depending on size (see Fig. 68).

unusual size-dependence, being linear and unaffected by body weight below a threshold value of 2·0 g dry weight, then increasing markedly with weight above this limit (Fig. 68).

The suggestions of Boyden concerning constancy of the relationship between body weight and metal concentration in bivalves and gastropod molluscs (for any given species–metal pair) are clearly in disagreement with the results of Phillips (1976*a*, *b*), Manly and George (1977) and Bryan and

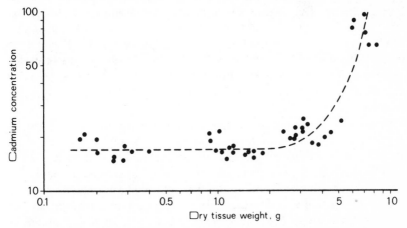

FIG. 68.   Concentrations of cadmium (μg/g dry weight) in whole soft parts of scallops *Pecten maximus* from the English Channel, and their relation to dry weights of the tissues. After Boyden (1977).

Hummerstone (1978), cited above, all of whom found significant differences in the weight–concentration relationships with location and/or season. The seasonal dependence of such relationships noted by Phillips (1976*a*) is of particular interest and may give some clue as to one possible mechanism whereby metals may vary in concentration with organism weight. It was found that significant relationships of non-zero slope were seen more frequently during periods of gametogenesis in the mussel, *Mytilus edulis*. It will be recalled that this period is one of seasonal decrease in trace metal levels in mussels (see Chapter 5), probably because of the dilution effect caused by increased body weights during gamete production whilst total body loads of metals remain relatively constant. If this is so, we may consider the changes involved during gametogenesis in terms of size dependence. It is known that large mussels produce greater numbers of gametes even as a proportion of body weight, i.e. large individuals exhibit greater fecundity and a higher percentage of body weight will be composed of gametes (see Bayne, 1976). It is therefore clear that if a population of mussels contains identical concentrations of a metal in all individuals (of all sizes) prior to the onset of gametogenesis, the concentrations will not be the same when the gonads have attained maturity. Larger individuals, producing proportionately greater amounts of gametes, will dilute body concentrations to a greater extent than will smaller animals, and this will give rise to an inverse relationship between whole tissue weights and metal concentrations. The relationship will, however, disappear at spawning, when the original tissue weights of each individual are attained once again. Whilst this is not suggested here as an explanation which could be universally applied to explain either location-based or season-based changes in the incidence of significant relationships between tissue weights and metal concentrations in biota, it may clearly be involved in some instances.

Reports of size dependence in the metal concentrations exhibited by gastropod molluscs have been somewhat underemphasised above. It should therefore be stated here that significant relationships of this nature have been noted for a variety of species, although studies have been rather less in number compared with those concerning bivalve molluscs. An early report by Mishima and Odum (1963) included investigation of the biological half-life of ^{65}Zn in the snail, *Littorina irrorata*. Individuals of three size groups were exposed to ^{65}Zn in the laboratory and excretion kinetics of the radionuclide were followed under both field and laboratory conditions, the latter at three different temperatures. The slow component of excretion only was considered as representative of that for ^{65}Zn bound to the tissues. The results (Table 52) showed that excretion was faster in animals of smaller size and, in addition, varied directly with the temperature. These data are similar to those described above for metals in bivalves, and show that smaller individuals respond more rapidly to changes in environmental levels of pollutants, i.e. smaller individuals time-integrate ambient metals over a shorter period. The only report known which relates size to metal concentration in field samples of species of *Littorina* is that of Boyden (1977); this concerned *L. littorea* from the highly contaminated Restronguet Creek. As might be expected from the results of Mishima and Odum (1963) above, zinc concentrations were inversely correlated to tissue weights, as were concentrations of iron, lead and manganese. Levels of cadmium and copper, however, were independent of size.

Variation in the concentrations of trace metals present in limpets with

TABLE 52

THE EFFECTS OF BODY SIZE AND AMBIENT TEMPERATURE ON THE BIOLOGICAL HALF-LIFE OF ^{65}Zn IN THE SNAIL, *Littorina irrorata*, UNDER BOTH LABORATORY AND FIELD CONDITIONS. DATA CONCERN THE SLOW COMPONENT OF EXCRETION AND ARE COMPUTED FOR DAYS 11–39 SUBSEQUENT TO LABELLING; VALUES SHOWN ARE MEANS $\pm$ STANDARD ERRORS. (AFTER MISHIMA AND ODUM (1963).)

Location	Temperature (°C)	Biological half-life of ^{65}Zn (in days)		
		Large (15–20 mm)	Medium (10–15 mm)	Small (5–10 mm)
Laboratory	15	40·3 ± 3·4	39·2 ± 3·8	26·2 ± 5·4
Laboratory	25	25·0 ± 2·1	15·4 ± 2·7	13·3 ± 2·7
Laboratory	30	23·3 ± 3·1	16·6 ± 3·8	16·6 ± 4·4
Field	19	18·1 ± 2·5	13·4 ± 2·5	11·3 ± 3·1

size, as seen by Boyden (1974, 1977), was discussed briefly above. Other authors have also noted this phenomenon. Data reported by Nickless *et al.* (1972) was suggestive of an increase in cadmium concentration with size in limpets, *Patella vulgata*, from the Bristol Channel, although the effects of shore level of derivation of the samples influenced the results somewhat. Peden *et al.* (1973) produced rather better data, again concerning *P. vulgata* from the Bristol Channel and Severn Estuary, both of which are severely polluted by metals (especially cadmium) from industrial sources. These results are shown in Table 53; it is seen that whereas concentrations of cadmium increased with size, those of zinc decreased. These trends were later confirmed by Boyden, who published more extensive data for the limpets *P. vulgata*, *P. intermedia* and *Crepidula fornicata*. The results of the studies of Boyden (1977) have been tabulated (see Table 54) to show the differences found between related species in their size–metal relationship. It

TABLE 53

MEAN CONCENTRATIONS OF CADMIUM AND ZINC (μg/g WET WEIGHTS) IN WHOLE SOFT PARTS OF THE LIMPET, *Patella vulgata*, OF THREE SIZE GROUPS FROM FOUR LOCATIONS IN THE CONTAMINATED BRISTOL CHANNEL. (AFTER PEDEN *et al.* (1973).)

Size	Watchet		Kilve		Sand Bay		Clevedon	
	Cd	Zn	Cd	Zn	Cd	Zn	Cd	Zn
Small	46·5	142·0	23·2	76·4	56·4	77·2	34·4	99·2
Medium	54·5	89·0	25·8	61·2	86·4	64·0	46·4	68·4
Large	78·0	53·0	37·6	51·2	81·6	47·6	61·6	47·2

TABLE 54

THE RELATIONSHIP BETWEEN WHOLE SOFT TISSUE WEIGHTS OF GASTROPOD MOLLUSCS AND THEIR CONCENTRATIONS OF SEVEN TRACE METALS. SEE TABLE 50 AND TEXT FOR EXPLANATION. RELATIONSHIPS FOR COBALT WERE NOT TABULATED, BUT WERE INVERSE FOR *B. undatum* AND NONE FOR *S. lignarius*. (AFTER BOYDEN (1977).)

Species	Cadmium	Copper	Iron	Lead	Manganese	Nickel	Zinc
Littorina littorea	None	None	Inverse	Inverse	Inverse	—	Inverse
Buccinum undatum	Direct	None*	None	Inverse	Inverse	Inverse	Direct
Scaphander lignarius	None	None	—	None	None*	None	None
Crepidula fornicata	None*	None*	—	None	Inverse	None	None
Patella intermedia	Direct†	Inverse	Inverse	Inverse	—	—	Inverse
Patella vulgata	Direct†	Inverse	Inverse	Inverse	—	—	None/Inverse†

* Data suggestive of direct relationship, but did not attain statistical significance.
† Variable relationship, possibly depending on extent of contamination.

will be noted that this author considered the tissue weight–concentration relationship for both cadmium and zinc in *P. vulgata* to vary in slope according to the extent of contamination. Cadmium always increased in concentration with size, but the extent of this increase was greater in more polluted locations (Table 55). The regression slopes for zinc, in contrast, varied from significantly below 1·0 in relatively unpolluted areas (indicating an inverse relationship between tissue weights of the limpets and concentrations) towards 1·0 in the polluted Severn Estuary regions (indicating a lack of any change in concentrations of zinc with tissue weights). Comparison of the zinc data here with those in Table 53 may suggest a seasonal change also, as the data for Watchet (at least) appear to disagree.

Finally, one further report exists in which the effects of size of the abalone *Haliotis tuberculata* on its metal content were discussed (Bryan *et al.*, 1977). Data were reported for viscera and for the foot separately, results for whole soft parts being deduced by calculation (Table 56). It is clear that the size dependence of metal concentrations in the two tissue composites did not always agree; for example, copper concentrations increased with weight in the viscera, but decreased with weight in the foot; thus no significant effect of tissue weight was found for this metal in whole soft parts. However, data for whole soft parts show that the concentration of each of the seven other metals was significantly influenced by tissue weights, cadmium and silver increasing with size and iron, lead, manganese, nickel and zinc exhibiting decreases with size.

Laboratory studies of the uptake of trace metals other than mercury by bivalve or gastropod molluscs are few, and most have been cited previously. In general one may conclude from such studies that small individuals take up metals faster than do large animals of the same species and may often also lose metals faster. This, unfortunately, does not throw any light at all on the inconsistencies noted above in field studies. Further discussion of the effects of size on trace metal levels in molluscs is deferred to Section C of this chapter, where the data will be considered in practical terms and an attempt will be made to suggest viable methods of partially or completely eliminating this variable from surveys using molluscs as monitoring organisms.

Apart from finfish, which will be discussed later, the only data of significance concerning size dependence in metals of aquatic biota which have not yet been considered involve crustacean species or the polychaete, *Nereis diversicolor*, although few reports are available. Garcia and Fowler (1972) noted higher concentrations of several elements in smaller

TABLE 55

VARIABILITY OF THE REGRESSION SLOPES RELATING CONTENTS OF CADMIUM AND ZINC IN LIMPETS, *Patella vulgata* AND *P. intermedia*, TO DRY TISSUE WEIGHTS. (AFTER BOYDEN (1977).)

Location	Sampling date	Cadmium			Zinc		
		Regression coefficient (*b*)	Real intercept value (µg)	Soluble environmental cadmium concentration (µg Cd/litre)	Regression coefficient (*b*)	Real intercept value (µg)	Soluble environmental zinc concentration (µg Zn/litre)
				Patella intermedia			
Helford Estuary, Cornwall	3 April, 1973	1·35	4·7	~0·5	0·71	237·8	~10
	10 January, 1974	1·49	6·3		0·76	193·9	
				Patella vulgata			
Watchet, Severn Estuary	18 March, 1974	1·37	190·7	~1·3*	0·89	302·5	~27*
Portishead, Severn Estuary	8 March, 1973	2·05	401·0		0·84	358·3	
	13 August, 1973	1·98	686·4	~5·8*	0·91	354·9	~52*
	11 January, 1974	1·96	716·9		0·93	433·6	
	5 May, 1974	1·70	704·2		0·84	388·2	

* Extracted from Butterworth *et al.* (1972).

TABLE 56

RELATIONSHIP BETWEEN CONCENTRATIONS OF EIGHT METALS IN WHOLE SOFT PARTS, VISCERA, OR FOOT OF THE ABALONE, *Haliotis tuberculata*, AND DRY WEIGHTS OF THE WHOLE SOFT PARTS. SLOPE VALUES ARE TAKEN FROM REGRESSIONS FITTED BY THE EQUATION $\log_{10}$ CONCENTRATION $= b \log_{10}$ WEIGHT $+ \log_{10} a$, WHERE b IS THE SLOPE. (AFTER BRYAN *et al.* (1977).)

Metal	Whole soft parts		Viscera		Foot	
	Slope	Significance	Slope	Significance	Slope	Significance
Cadmium	0·086	<0·05	0·167	<0·01	−0·052	NS
Copper	−0·062	NS	0·142	<0·02	−0·210	<0·01
Iron	−0·392	<0·001	−0·336	<0·001	−0·330	<0·001
Lead	−0·183	<0·05	−0·096	NS	0·202	NS
Manganese	−0·260	<0·001	−0·183	<0·01	−0·338	<0·001
Nickel	−0·179	<0·02	−0·135	NS	−0·148	<0·05
Silver	0·078	<0·02	0·174	<0·001	0·055	NS
Zinc	−0·204	<0·001	−0·171	<0·01	−0·086	<0·001

NS: Not significant.

individuals of the prawn, *Penaeus californiensis*, samples being derived from the Gulf of California (Table 57). Although these trends appear consistent, the sample numbers are small; further confirmatory research would be helpful. Martin (1974) analysed nine elements in whole-body samples of the crab, *Cancer irroratus*. Only one element, manganese, exhibited a significant correlation with body size, concentrations increasing with size. The author suggested that manganese was concentrated progressively more actively during successive intermoult cycles, although no reasons for this phenomenon were given. Walker and his co-workers have published data concerning the use of barnacles as indicators of trace

TABLE 57

MEAN CONCENTRATIONS (μg/g DRY WEIGHT) OF TRACE METALS IN WHOLE PRAWNS, *Penaeus californiensis*, OF DIFFERENT SIZES. ALL SAMPLES ARE JUVENILES FROM THE GULF OF CALIFORNIA; ADULTS MEASURE 70 mm OR GREATER. (AFTER GARCIA AND FOWLER (1972).)

Total length (mm)	Number analysed	Cobalt	Copper	Chromium	Manganese	Zinc
39	3	50·4	368	263	22·0	977
46	3	58·8	364	223	16·0	685
50	2	42·7	272	89	17·8	552
62	2	25·8	288	30	17·9	451

metal pollution, and these studies have included some elegant work on the subcellular distribution of metals in *Balanus balanoides* (Walker *et al.* 1975*a, b*; Walker, 1977). Although no data could be found to support the notion of age dependence of metal levels in barnacles, Walker (1977) quotes concentrations of 170 and 370 µg/g dry weight for copper in *B. balanoides* of 1- and 2-years old, respectively, from environments with similar ambient copper concentrations (1·4 µg/litre cf. 1·3–1·7 µg/litre; see original author). This would suggest an age-dependent increase in copper levels of this species, although caution is necessary, especially because of the known tendency of this element to undergo complexation in seawater and hence vary in biological availability (Mantoura *et al.*, 1978).

In *Nereis diversicolor*, Bryan and Hummerstone (1973*b*) have reported that zinc concentrations vary with size. Data from several estuaries in the south-west of England are shown in Fig. 69; it is clear that the relationship is complex and location dependent. Zinc is effectively regulated in this species (see Chapter 14), whereas cadmium is not. A weight normalisation method was employed by these authors during comparisons of zinc levels in *N. diversicolor* from different areas.

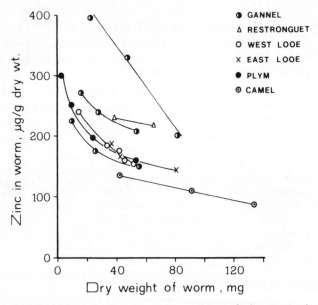

FIG. 69.   Relationship between the concentrations of zinc (µg/g dry weight) present in the polychaete worm, *Nereis diversicolor*, and the dry weight of the worm. (After Bryan and Hummerstone (1973*b*).)

Amongst finfish, considerable amounts of data are available concerning the variation in metal concentrations with size. The data for mercury, reviewed in Section A above, reveal that general increases in concentration occur with size. By contrast, most other metals either decrease in concentration or remain unchanged with increases in fish size, although a few exceptions are once again known.

Concerning freshwater species of finfish, Lovett *et al.* (1972) surveyed 29 species (406 individuals total) from New York State waters for their cadmium content. Eviscerated samples in general varied little in concentration of this element, but occasional species differences were found. Few species were studied in sufficient detail to establish the relationship between age (weight) and cadmium levels, although lake trout, *Salvelinus namaycush*, from Cayuga Lake were found to exhibit no change in cadmium concentration with age from 1 to 12 years; this may be compared with the data of Bache *et al.* (1971), cited in Section A above, for mercury in the same fish samples. A later set of samples, taken in 1972, of *S. namaycush* from Cayuga Lake, were analysed by Tong *et al.* (1974) for 37 metals; decapitated, eviscerated fish were used. The results showed that 33 of the metals (including cadmium) did not vary consistently in concentration with age of the fish. Of the other four elements, levels of chromium were found to increase with age, whilst concentrations of molybdenum and tin decreased with age (Table 58); rubidium may also have been age dependent, although the decrease was consistent only after age 7.

Kelso and Frank (1974), in studies of three species of finfish from Lake Erie, found age-dependent increases in mercury concentrations (Section A above), but could find no such changes for cadmium or copper levels. A similar independence of metal concentrations and age in whole bodies of bluegills, *Lepomis macrochirus*, was noted for cadmium, lead and zinc by Atchison *et al.* (1977), using samples from two lakes in Indiana. Pagenkopf and Neuman (1974) found that lead concentrations in the gills of brook trout, *Salvelinus fontinalis*, increased with age, although levels in the liver apparently equilibrated at least by age 1–2, and changes in whole fish were minimal. Holcombe *et al.* (1976) also noted the slow equilibration of lead in gills of this species when exposed to lead in the laboratory. Finally, Giesy and Wiener (1977), in an interesting study on frequency distributions of trace metal concentrations in five species of freshwater finfish, reported a negative correlation between zinc concentrations in whole chain pickerel, *Esox niger*, and fish length. Concentrations of cadmium, chromium, copper and iron were independent of length in this species however.

TABLE 58

MEAN CONCENTRATIONS (μg/kg WET WEIGHTS) OF CHROMIUM, MOLYB-
DENUM, RUBIDIUM AND TIN IN LAKE TROUT, *Salvelinus namaycush*, OF
DIFFERENT AGES. ALL SAMPLES WERE FROM LAKE CAYUGA, NEW YORK
STATE; THREE FISH WERE USED FOR EACH AGE GROUP. (AFTER TONG *et al.*
(1974).)

Fish age (years)	Chromium	Molybdenum	Rubidium	Tin
1	5·2	8·5	670	150
2	2·3	8·2	670	210
3	3·2	4·5	1 400	210
4	4·1	6·1	700	110
5	12	5·4	670	230
6	2·8	4·5	1 400	92
7	11	4·5	1 400	96
8	5·2	3·4	400	36
9	10	4·5	600	96
10	11	3·5	520	67
11	32	2·2	58	77
12	90	2·8	37	44

Marine species of finfish have been rather more extensively studied and more information on the size dependence of trace metals is available. As noted for freshwater species, in many cases size has no apparent effect on the concentration of trace metals found. Thus Havre *et al.* (1973) could find no difference in cadmium concentrations in muscle of several species of freshwater or saltwater finfish from southern Norway with weight of the fish. Eustace (1974), in extensive studies of 39 species of finfish and shellfish from the Derwent Estuary, Tasmania, Australia, analysing for four metals, found little inter-species or intra-species variation in muscle of the finfish. However, a positive length–concentration correlation was found for zinc in muscle of the dogfish, *Squalus* sp., and negative correlations were noted for zinc in four species and copper levels in two species. In all cases the regression slopes were close to zero, and in the opinion of the author the correlations were 'of no practical significance'. Mackay *et al.* (1975*b*), whose positive correlations between mercury or selenium and weight, length or girth of black marlin, *Makaira indica*, were discussed in Section A above, found no such size-dependent correlations for five other metals in muscle of the same species.

The elucidation of size-dependent variation in the concentrations of trace metals present in finfish depends on occasion on the tissue studied. Thus, whilst variation due to other parameters may obscure size dependence in samples of whole fish or fish muscle, significant changes may occur in some organs. For example, Stevens and Brown (1974) found zinc and copper concentrations to decrease with increasing weight of the blue shark, *Prionace glauca*, when liver and epigonal organs were considered, whilst this profile was not found in muscle tissues, where concentrations were independent of size. The reports linking zinc concentrations to fish size in cleithrum bones of the cod, *Gadus morhua* (Scott, 1977) and in otoliths of mackerel, *Scomber japonicus colias*, (Papadopoulou *et al.*, 1978) were referred to in Section A above. However, Pentreath (1976*a*) attempted to correlate zinc or manganese concentrations in individual organs of the plaice, *Pleuronectes platessa*, to fish age, and the relationships were not significant in liver, muscle or bone tissues. Clearly, no generalisations can be made for any species, tissue or metal. Occasional reports have also occurred in which authors have attempted to correlate metal excretion rates to fish size; for example, Hoss *et al.* (1978) could find no effect of body size on ^{65}Zn excretion rates in pinfish, *Lagodon rhomboides*, or black sea bass, *Centropristis striata*. It should be realised that such negative reports are probably representative of a good deal more research than is apparent from their number; the tendency of authors to fail to discuss the independence of parameters—and of journals to fail to accept such reports for publication—must give rise to many examples which remain unpublished.

However, size dependence is established in some instances and these should be considered as indicative of possible interference of size in monitoring programmes which use finfish as indicators. Eisler and his co-workers have quite extensively investigated the effects of fish size on their trace metal content. Eisler and Edmunds (1966) and Eisler (1967*a*) found adult northern puffer, *Sphaeroides maculatus*, to exhibit higher zinc concentrations in liver tissues of smaller fish. A similar inverse correlation of zinc and iron concentrations to size was noted for vertebrae of sandbar sharks, *Carcharinus milberti* (Eisler, 1967*b*). By contrast, unpublished data of Eisler was cited in Eisler and LaRoche (1972), which showed that the concentrations of cadmium in viscera of the tautog, *Tautoga onitis*, increased with age. A later publication (Mears and Eisler, 1977) included data for this species as well as for two others; the tilefish, *Lopholatilus chamaeleonticeps*, and the bluefish, *Pomatomus saltatrix*. Livers only were analysed in this study and the concentrations of several metals were found to vary with length of the fish, but in a sex-dependent fashion. This study will be further considered in terms of sex-dependence in Chapter 9, but here

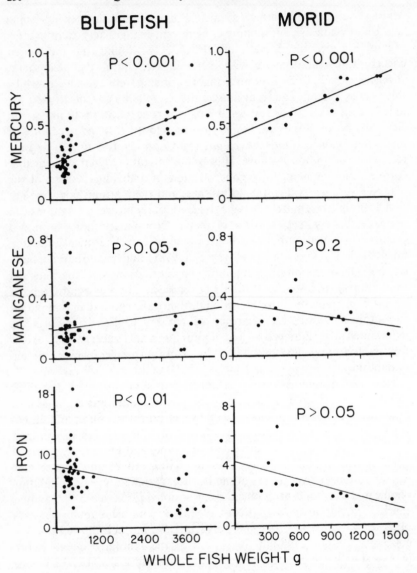

Fɪɢ. 70.   Relationships between total body weight and the concentrations of trace metals (µg/g wet weight) present in white muscle of the bluefish, *Pomatomus saltatrix* (left), and the morid, *Antimora rostrata* (right). Each point represents analysis of one individual; significance of the regression generated is shown on each plot. (After Cross *et al.* (1973).)

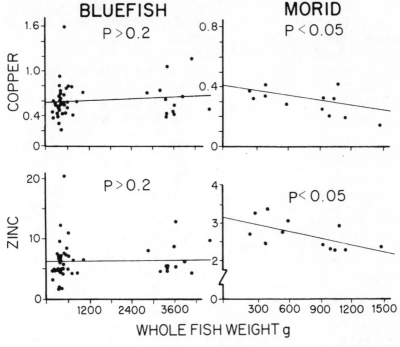

FIG. 70.—*contd.*

it can be stated that both sexes of the tautog exhibited decreased nickel levels in liver with body length increases, whereas male and female tilefish livers contained greater concentrations of cadmium, copper and iron with increased fish length.

The extensive data of Cross *et al.* (1973) concerning the concentrations of copper, iron, manganese, mercury and zinc in white muscle of the bluefish, *Pomatomus saltatrix*, and the bathyal-demersal morid, *Antimora rostrata*, were cited in Section A above. These studies serve as an example of the common differences noted both between species and between metals in any one species; results are shown in Fig. 70. Mercury concentrations in muscle increased significantly with body length in each species. In morids, the other four metals all decreased in concentration with body length, although significant regressions were evident only for copper and zinc. In bluefish, only iron was significantly affected by body weight, exhibiting an inverse relationship. Whilst fish weight is obviously a dominant factor in determining muscle mercury levels, clearly the scatter observed for other metals (which tends to decrease the chances of statistical significance) indicates that body weight is but one of several factors involved in the determination of individual metal concentrations.

Brooks and Rumsey (1974) also studied the effects of fish size on the trace metal concentrations found in muscle tissues, using 20 individuals of each of eight species. Significant relationships were found in only six cases, involving five of the eight species (Table 59). It will be noted that three of these cases involve negative correlation coefficients (elements decrease in concentration with size) and three involve positive coefficients (elements relate directly to size).

TABLE 59

CORRELATION COEFFICIENTS (r) FOR THE RELATIONSHIP BETWEEN FISH SIZE (TOTAL LENGTH) AND THE CONCENTRATIONS OF TRACE METALS IN MUSCLE TISSUE. ALL SAMPLES WERE FROM THE EAST COAST OF NORTH ISLAND, NEW ZEALAND; 20 INDIVIDUALS OF EACH SPECIES WERE ANALYSED. (AFTER BROOKS AND RUMSEY (1974).)

Species	Common name	Copper	Iron	Manganese	Zinc
Cheilodactylis macropterus	Tarakihi	—	—	—	0·46*
Chrysophrys auratus	Snapper	−0·53*	—	—	—
Polyprion oxygeneios	Hapuku	—	0·46*	—	—
Seriola grandis	Kingfish	−0·51*	—	—	−0·64**
Trigla kumu	Gurnard	—	—	0·57**	—

* $p < 0.05$.
** $p < 0.01$.

Bohn and McElroy (1976) studied arsenic, cadmium, copper, iron and zinc in Arctic cod, *Boreogadus saida*, from Baffin Island. In whole fish, arsenic and zinc correlated in a positive fashion to body weight, whilst copper and iron were negatively correlated and cadmium levels were unrelated to body weight. Correlations of the metal concentrations in muscle or liver to body weight were less common; only arsenic was correlated (positively) in muscle, and copper decreased in liver, with increased whole fish weight. Pentreath (1977a) suggested that cadmium concentrations in livers of plaice, *Pleuronectes platessa*, from the North Sea correlated with age of the fish; no correlation of significance was found with fish weight, however. Cutshall *et al.* (1977a, b) have observed weight dependence of zinc and cadmium in the hake, *Merluccius productus*. Both metals increased in concentration in either whole fish or muscle tissues with increases in whole fish weights. It is interesting that [65]Zn was found to be taken up faster by smaller hake than by larger individuals (Cutshall *et al.*, 1977*a*); possibly the weight dependence of the stable elements reflects the migration of the fish from a metal-rich water mass into a relatively less contaminated area and small fish respond to this difference faster than do larger fish.

Finally, a certain amount of information is available from the polluted Severn Estuary and Bristol Channel area of the United Kingdom. Hardisty *et al.* (1974*a*, *b*) have found that whole flounder, *Platichthyes flesus*, exhibit age-dependent increases in cadmium and lead concentrations, although profiles for zinc are less consistent and may vary between locations. Interestingly, similar results were later reported for whiting, *Merlangus merlangus*, from the same area (Badsha and Sainsbury, 1977). Both groups of authors suggest that such data may be reflections of dietary changes with age, or of migratory habits of the two species.

In marine mammals, metals other than mercury may also exhibit changes in concentration with age, at least in some tissues. Most data concern seals, principally the common harbour seal, *Phoca vitulina*, from western European coasts. Heppleston and French (1973) found the concentrations of cadmium in kidneys of this species to increase with age of the individual. Later authors have confirmed this pattern and have also shown age-dependent increases in cadmium in livers of *P. vitulina* from both British coasts (Roberts *et al.*, 1976) and German North Sea coasts (Drescher *et al.*, 1977). By contrast, concentrations of copper, lead and zinc in seal livers exhibit no relation to age (Drescher *et al.*, 1977). In addition, Heppleston and French (1973) reported interesting age-dependent profiles for trace metals in teeth of this species. Apparently, the concentrations of cadmium, chromium and lead in teeth decrease with age, whereas those of zinc increase with age. The authors correlated these changes to the variation in the development of teeth with age; initially, enamel, cement and dentine are all laid down together, but after the age of about 5 years only cement is deposited. The supposition from this is that cement has high concentrations of zinc, but low concentrations of the other metals, relative to the tooth itself at age 5.

C. CONCLUSIONS AND RECOMMENDATIONS

We have seen that whilst data are abundant concerning the effects of size on the trace metal concentrations present in aquatic biota, no generalisations of any practical use can be made. It is certainly more common to encounter increases of mercury concentrations with age or size in organisms (especially finfish) than to find such profiles for other trace metals; however, the other metals may increase, decrease, or remain unchanged with differences in animal size. Clearly, a simple physiological explanation is not tenable; the changes in metal concentration are not simply due to altered surface area/volume ratios or metabolic rates of animals with size, as all metals are affected differently.

Because of this inconsistency, it is difficult to devise a sampling programme which will effectively eliminate the influence of animal size on the results of monitoring surveys. Changes in the size–concentration relationships with location (or season) of sampling are particularly difficult to deal with, as individual populations may differ in slope functions and even weight-normalisation procedures are subject to criticism. The ideal indicator, of course, exhibits no size dependence of trace metal concentrations, at any location or season. Unfortunately, this is extremely rare and may never be encountered. The 'second best' situation is that if size dependence of trace metal concentrations exists, it is constant with location and season, i.e. regressions of concentration against size are always of the same slope, regardless of the degree of contamination (absolute height of the regression on the concentration axis). In this situation, weight normalisation would be possible and would give rise to accurate inter-sample comparisons if the regression slope were precisely known. However, as we learn more about the size dependence of trace metals in biota, the *a priori* belief in constancy of regression slopes becomes less tenable. In addition, it is clear that even if several metals exhibit slope constancy, the variation of slopes for any one metal will necessitate extra thought and effort in sampling and analysis if accurate inter-sample (inter-location) differences are sought for that metal.

The alternatives during sampling are as follows:

(i)   The effects of size are ignored.
(ii) Animals of the same, or similar, sizes are taken from each location studied.
(iii) Animals of a large range of sizes are selected and analysed in bulk.
(iv) Animals of a large range of sizes are selected and analysed individually to generate a size–concentration regression for each metal.

Concerning the first alternative, it has been shown that the effects of size may be extremely significant, i.e. regressions relating size to metal concentration can exhibit very steep slopes. It is therefore considered unwise to ignore size effects, as even small differences in the mean sizes of samples from different study locations could cause completely spurious conclusions with respect to the extent of contamination of each location.

Most authors using bivalves for monitoring purposes attempt to restrict samples to a given size range (alternative (ii) above). For example, Goldberg *et al.* (1978) report the use of mussels of shell lengths between 50 and 80 mm for their surveys of pollutants in coastal waters of the United States. Application of the data of Boyden (1974, 1977) to such a size range suggests that tissue weights would vary over almost one logarithmic cycle for mussels and would vary over greater than one logarithmic cycle for oysters. If we assume a regression slope of -0.25 relating (log) concentration of a metal to (log) tissue weight in such samples, the differences between metal concentrations of a 50 mm individual and an 80 mm individual would approximate 100 per cent, i.e. the small individual would contain twice the metal concentration of the large individual. Obviously, if the regression coefficient were increased (to a higher negative value), the differences between the two extremes of the size range would become even greater. This range of acceptable sizes may therefore be considered too large by some authors and should preferably be decreased. The decrease to a range of, for example, 60–70 mm would certainly place extra restraints on sampling of the bivalves; not only would sampling procedures take longer, but some locations might not support bivalves within this restricted range. Although transplantation techniques could be used to overcome this last problem, this alternative is expensive and considerable time is needed for transplants to equilibrate to new conditions of ambient metal availability.

The third alternative noted above may be preferable in some cases. The deliberate selection of a large range of sizes, followed by bulk analysis, is in some ways comparable to the process of weight normalisation of data using weight–concentration regressions generated from individual analysis. In this case, no data have been excluded (in case (ii), data from either end of the size distribution were excluded), and the results obtained may therefore be considered representative of the populations studied. However, unless the mean sizes (weights) of all samples are closely similar, residual size-based differences will be present and no allowance for this can be made.

The final alternative is the deliberate selection of a large range of sizes at all locations, followed by individual analysis. In this way a size–concentration regression describing each sample may be generated. The metal contents of samples may then be compared either directly, using the regressions themselves, or after weight-normalisation to a chosen weight (preferably a weight which is included in the range of each sample, so that regressions need not be extrapolated beyond the empirical data). Although perhaps more cumbersome, the comparison of the regressions themselves is preferable, as, if the size–concentration relationships differ in slope, the inter-sample differences will depend on the weight used for normalisation purposes (see discussion of Fig. 59 in Section A above). However, whilst this alternative undoubtedly gives rise to the most accurate and meaningful size-independent comparisons, the extra effort involved in analysing samples individually to produce size–concentration regressions is by no means negligible; the inherent variability of results necessitates the study of large numbers of individuals at each location.

There is therefore no simple answer concerning the elimination of the size or age parameter from monitoring surveys. Perhaps the best alternative is selection of a restricted size range of individuals for study; however, this range must be as small as possible and it is important to realise that a complete understanding of the overall picture of metal contamination in each population studied cannot be attained using this method.

CHAPTER 8

The Effects of Age (Size, Weight) on Organochlorines in Aquatic Biota

A. CONSIDERATION OF THE PUBLISHED DATA

The changes found in concentrations of organochlorines present in aquatic organisms with age, size or weight are rather more simple than those for trace metals discussed in Chapter 7. Thus, whilst trace metals may increase, decrease or remain unchanged in concentration with age of any species, and both qualitative and quantitative differences exist between each metal, organochlorines generally all follow the same pattern of age dependence in any one species. In addition, whereas the reasons for age dependence of trace metal levels are obscure, the mechanism producing age dependence of organochlorines is commonly found to be the change in lipid content which accompanies ageing in some species.

It must be understood that less data are available concerning changes in the concentrations of organochlorines in biota with age than are published for similar changes in trace metal levels. This is because age dependence of organochlorines is neither as common, nor as marked in effect, as are trace metal variations with age. This parameter is therefore more important in determining trace metal levels in aquatic biota than its influence on organochlorine contents of these organisms. However, organochlorine concentrations are age dependent in some species, and studies of these species for monitoring purposes should take account of this factor.

The dependence of organochlorine accumulation by an organism on its lipid content was discussed at length in Chapter 3. Undoubtedly, the amount of lipid present in an organism is the most important extraneous parameter determining the uptake and retention of organochlorines; the only parameter of greater importance is the actual availability of these compounds in the ambient environment. Thus, if an organism exhibits age-dependent variations in total lipid content, concomitant changes in organochlorine levels may be expected. As noted in Chapter 3, lipid chemistry may also be important in some cases; thus it is possible that changes in the relative amounts of different lipid types with age could also lead to altered affinities of the total lipid pool for organochlorines. However, the current lack of understanding of the biochemical basis of organochlorine sequestration by lipids of aquatic biota permits no accurate determination of the importance of such effects *in vivo*. This is clearly an important area for future research.

Changes in the total lipid content of biota with age are best documented for finfish, particularly salmonids. Thus, most salmonids appear to exhibit increases in total body lipid with increased age; this may be related to the greater fecundity of older fish—and hence to the increased need for storage of lipid reserves. Clearly, the changes in total lipids with age are superimposed on the seasonal lipid variation (see Chapter 6); age dependence must be studied using individuals which are in the same condition relative to the sexual cycle, or seasonal effects will interfere with attempts to define age-related differences. Other finfish which exhibit increases in total lipid with age include the eel, *Anguilla anguilla* (Lovern, 1938), the carp, *Cyprinus carpio*, (Mann, 1961), the cod, *Gadus morhua* (Jangaard *et al.*, 1967a, b), the sardine, *Sardinella longiceps* (Hornell and Nayuda, 1923) and the horse mackerel, *Trachurus trachurus* (Arevalo, 1948). In addition, some elasmobranchs exhibit increases in total lipids of the liver with age. In each of these cases, we might expect increases of organochlorine content to occur concomitant to the increased body lipids at any given exposure level. This will be reflected in an age-dependent increase in the concentration of organochlorines based on wet weights, whilst concentrations based on lipid weights would be expected not to change. It will be seen below that in most of the documented cases of age-dependent increases in organochlorine levels in finfish, the basing of concentrations on lipid weights abolishes the effect of age. In a few cases reported to date, this is not entirely so, and variations in organochlorine concentrations with fish age still exist when these are based on lipid weights; here both lipid and some other factor must be responsible for the profiles seen. Finally, in rare instances, species exhibit a decrease in total body lipid with age (e.g. see Hattula *et al.*, 1978a below), and here organochlorine contents decrease with fish weight.

Very little information exists concerning the variation in concentrations of organochlorines with age (or age-dependent parameters) in organisms other than finfish. Bivalve molluscs, which have been quite extensively studied as indicators of organochlorines, do not appear to exhibit age-dependent changes in lipid contents (Galtstoff, 1964; Giese, 1969; Bayne,

1976) and the same is true for gastropod and cephalopod molluscs (Giese, 1969). The lipid contents of these organisms do vary considerably with season, however, and this has already been discussed in relation to its effects on organochlorine levels (Chapter 6). The seasonal variations certainly far outweigh any effects of age as such, and it would be most difficult to accurately assess the effects of age on organochlorine levels whilst eliminating seasonal influences. No study to date is known in which convincing data have shown age dependence of organochlorines in molluscs; if such effects exist, they are certainly not quantitatively important compared with the effects of seasonal variation which, of course, is based not only on lipid seasonality but also on the episodic nature of organochlorine contamination of aquatic environments. The remainder of this chapter is therefore devoted almost exclusively to consideration of the published data for finfish.

Various studies have been reported which include data peripheral to the subject of age dependence of organochlorines in finfish and these will be discussed briefly here. Several authors have found that the toxicity of pesticides is size dependent in fish. Hemphill (1954) and Fukano and Hooper (1958) found that toxaphene concentrations of 5 μg/litre in a natural lake system caused mortalities amongst small individuals of some species only, large individuals being unaffected. Pickering *et al.* (1962) found a similar inverse relationship between toxicity and individual size for several species of freshwater finfish on exposure to organophosphate compounds. Mount (1962) noted that endrin was generally more toxic to young than to adults of the guppy, *Lebistes reticulatus*, and the bluntnose minnow, *Pimephales notatus*, and Tooby and Durbin (1975) reported similar data for lindane toxicity to fry and yearling trout, *Salmo gairdneri*. These and similar reports which generally indicate that pesticides in solution are more toxic to small than to large individuals of a given species, may be related to reports describing uptake studies of organochlorines using freshwater finfish species. Weiss (1965) cited an unpublished study of Gakstatter and Weiss in which the uptake of ^{14}C-dieldrin into an unnamed fish species was studied in the laboratory. Unfortunately, although the data suggest size dependence in uptake rates of the compound, no quantitation of the effect is possible because of differing exposure concentrations for fish of different sizes; these data could not be traced in any later publication. More reliable data are available from the studies of Murphy and his co-workers. The data of Murphy (1971) concerning the uptake of ^{14}C-DDT by mosquito fish, *Gambusia affinis*, from solution during an exposure period of 48 h are shown in Fig. 71. The concentrations attained by these fish were

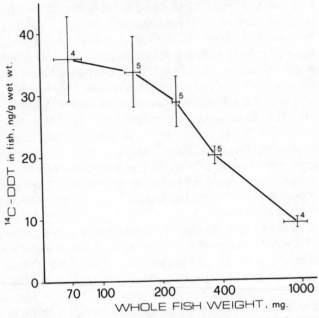

FIG. 71.   Mean concentrations of ¹⁴C-DDT (ng/g wet weight) in mosquitofish, *Gambusia affinis*, of different weight classes after 48 h exposure to ¹⁴C-DDT in solution. Initial exposure concentration was 41 ng/litre; numerals indicate the number of fish in each weight class. (After Murphy (1971).)

TABLE 60

CONCENTRATIONS OF ¹⁴C-DDT ATTAINED BY MOSQUITOFISH, *Gambusia affinis*, OF FIVE DIFFERENT SIZE CLASSES DURING A 48-H EXPOSURE TO ¹⁴C-DDT IN WATER WITH AN INITIAL CONCENTRATION OF 41 ng/LITRE. CALCULATED BY THE PRESENT AUTHOR BY GRAPHICAL INTERPOLATION FROM THE DATA OF MURPHY (1971); ALSO SHOWN ARE CALCULATED ABSOLUTE AMOUNTS OF DDT TAKEN UP AND THE MEAN RATE OF UPTAKE

Mean weight (g)	Concentration attained (ng/g)	Amount taken up (ng)	Mean uptake rate (ng/h)
70	36·0	2 520	52·5
145	33·6	4 872	101·5
270	28·7	7 749	161·4
370	20·1	7 437	154·9
945	9·3	8 788	183·1

inversely related to fish size. Graphical interpolation (present author) yields the data shown in Table 60 for absolute amounts of ^{14}C-DDT taken up, and the mean rates of uptake, for each size class. It is seen that whilst *absolute* uptake was faster by the larger fish, the weight-related uptake was obviously greater in smaller fish. A later paper (Murphy and Murphy, 1971) related the size dependence of uptake rates for DDT in the same species to metabolic rates of the fish. The regressions relating DDT uptake to fish weight and oxygen uptake to fish weight were of almost identical slope, suggesting that differences in the rate of DDT uptake with size were associated with the faster metabolism of smaller fish. Smaller fish also have a higher surface area/volume ratio, which may influence the weight-related rate of net uptake of DDT when this occurs primarily from solution. The faster increase of whole-body concentrations of organochlorines in smaller fish than in larger individuals may well explain the differences in toxicity with fish size noted above. It might be noted that faster uptake of organochlorines in smaller individuals compared with larger animals is not restricted to freshwater finfish; Armstrong *et al.* (1976) reported a similar tendency for the uptake of methoxychlor by the marine crab, *Cancer magister*.

It is interesting that the body weight of fish also affects their rate of organochlorine uptake from food. Buhler *et al.* (1969) and Buhler and Shanks (1970) have found that the toxicity of dietary DDT is also greater to smaller individuals; this pattern was noted for both juvenile chinook salmon, *Oncorhynchus tshawytscha*, and coho salmon, *O. kisutch*. The increase in median survival time of these species with age was ascribed to two factors. First, smaller fish consumed greater amounts of food as a percentage of body weight and therefore received a higher dosage of DDT on a mg/kg basis (note that this also is metabolism associated). Secondly, the smaller fish died at lower cumulative doses of DDT, and this was ascribed to a smaller lipid pool in these fish than in larger individuals—and hence to a decreased ability to sequester DDT in body lipid in a relatively non-toxic fashion.

The relationship of such studies to the field situation should be briefly discussed here, as the inverse relationship of DDT uptake rates and fish size must be seen in perspective. Murphy (1971), in addition to the uptake studies mentioned above, published data for the amounts of DDT present in field samples of mosquitofish. The results (Fig. 72) contrast dramatically with the uptake data in that higher concentrations were found in larger fish. At first sight these data are contradictory; however, it must be understood that two separate processes are being studied. The uptake data show events

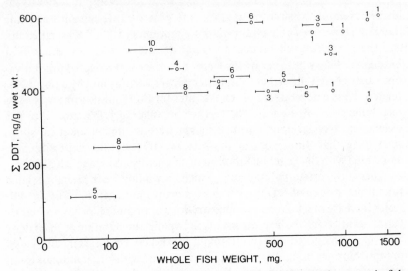

FIG. 72. Concentrations of ΣDDT (ng/g wet weight) in whole mosquitofish, *Gambusia affinis*, from a single location in Salinas, California, and their variation with fish weight. Numerals near the means indicate the numbers of fish pooled for analysis. (After Murphy (1971).)

occurring during an episodic exposure of fish to high levels of DDT, whereas the field data show the amounts of DDT present in fish *at equilibrium* with chronic exposure levels. The most likely hypothesis to explain the weight dependence of DDT seen in Fig. 72 is that larger fish contain greater amounts of body lipid. They therefore appear to contain more DDT if concentrations are based on wet weights, but if concentrations were based on lipid weights this profile would disappear. Thus, although small fish may accumulate DDT more rapidly (per unit weight) than larger individuals, at equilibrium the larger individuals may exhibit a higher concentration of DDT (based on wet weights) because of their greater lipid pools.

The final report of interest which will be discussed prior to consideration of field data concerns the effects of body lipid on the metabolism of DDT in finfish. Addison and Zinck (1977) performed experiments on brook trout, *Salvelinus fontinalis*, in which fingerlings were injected with DDT or its metabolites, and the rate of dehydrochlorination of a subsequent injection of ^{14}C-DDT was followed. The aim of these studies was to elucidate the effects of pretreatment on the subsequent metabolic breakdown of DDT. Whilst no effect of pretreatment was demonstrated (suggesting that the enzymes responsible for dehydrochlorination of DDT in this species were not induced by the pretreatment used), it was noted that the breakdown of DDT was influenced by both the weight of the fish and its lipid content. Thus, smaller fish, which exhibited low lipid contents, metabolised DDT much faster than did larger individuals of relatively high lipid content. These results are compatible with the ideas of Swedish authors, who have observed higher ratios of DDE to DDT in fish which have relatively low lipid content. In Swedish waters, the ratio of DDT to DDE approximates 1:1 in axial muscle of fish such as pike, *Esox lucius*, or cod, *Gadus morhua*, both of which contain about 1 per cent lipid in muscle tissues (Jensen *et al.*, 1972, 1975). By contrast, eels, *Anguilla anguilla*, which commonly contain 10–20 per cent lipids in muscle, exhibit much higher ratios of DDT to DDE, approximating 2:1 in most samples (Jensen *et al.*, 1975). The authors suggested that fish with relatively low lipid contents turn over the lipid pool much faster than those with high amounts of lipid, thus freeing sequestered DDT for possible dehydrochlorination. By contrast, DDT in the muscle lipids of eels will remain undisturbed for longer, as a smaller percentage of the total lipid pool is catabolised per unit time. This effect of the lipid content on the rate of DDT dehydrochlorination to more polar metabolites can be extended to single species, as found by Addison and Zinck (1977); older fish, which generally contain greater amounts of lipid, should metabolise DDT at slower rates. This may have a bearing on the retention of DDT or its metabolites, as it is known that each compound is retained with a unique half-life in fish (e.g. see Sanborn *et al.*, 1975). Although no data are available concerning other parent compound–metabolite pairs, a similar situation may be expected; thus, the retention of heptachlor and its epoxide, and aldrin and dieldrin, may vary according to the amount of lipid (and hence to age in some cases) present in fish.

As noted above, field reports of age dependence of organochlorines in finfish mainly concern freshwater species, particularly salmonids. However, many of the early reports relating age or size to organochlorine concentrations failed to include studies of the lipid contents of samples; thus, the quantitative contribution of variations in lipids to the observed changes in organochlorine concentrations with age cannot be estimated. For example, Hunt and Bischoff (1960) found increases of DDD concentrations (wet weight basis) in axial muscle of samples of the white catfish, *Ictalurus catus*, and the largemouth bass, *Micropterus salmoides*, with age of the fish, all samples being derived from the highly contaminated Clear Lake, California. Whilst isolated values for total lipids of these fish were included in this publication, data were not extensive enough to permit estimation of the contribution of lipids to the age dependence found for

DDD. Mount (1968) related concentrations of organochlorines in salmonids from Lake Michigan to fish age and Macek and Korn (1970) noted that whole-body levels of ΣDDT increased from 1 mg/kg in yearling salmonids (unnamed species) to 10 mg/kg or greater with age in Lake Michigan. Later, more detailed, studies of salmonids in this lake are discussed below (Reinert, 1970; Reinert and Bergman, 1974). Morris and Johnson (1971) found length-related increases in dieldrin concentrations in muscle of an unnamed catfish species from Iowa streams; again, a more detailed study is available from later authors (Kellog and Bulkley, 1976; Bulkley *et al.*, 1976). Samples of eviscerated lake trout, *Salvelinus namaycush*, aged between 1 and 12 years, from Lake Cayuga, New York State, were studied by both Youngs *et al.* (1972) for ΣDDT and Bache *et al.* (1972) for PCBs. The results of both groups (Fig. 73) indicated significant age–concentration and length–concentration regressions. Unfortunately, no data for lipid contents of these fish were ever published, although Youngs *et al.* (1972) stated that lipids increased significantly with age of the fish sampled. The data of Youngs *et al.* (1972) were later used by Eberhardt (1975) in attempts to fit kinetic models to the uptake and retention of pollutants by aquatic biota. The results of Bache *et al.* (1971, 1972) for mercury and PCBs were also considered in this theoretical study. Finally, Norstrom *et al.* (1976) also published model studies of pollutant accumulation by finfish and this report included real data showing an increase of PCB concentrations (by wet weight) with weight of yellow perch, *Perca flavescens*; no data for lipids were included.

The above studies, whilst all indicating significant increases of organochlorine concentrations with age of finfish in either whole fish or their tissues, do not include sufficient data to relate this profile to changes in the lipid contents of fish with age. By contrast, several published studies claim that age of the fish sampled has no apparent effect on its concentration of organochlorines. Thus, Lyman *et al.* (1968) could find no length- or weight-based variation of significance in the DDT concentrations observed for either yellow perch, *Perca flavescens*, or pumpkinseed, *Lepomis gibbosus*, samples being taken from a landlocked pond in Massachusetts. This is interesting, particularly in view of the result of Norstrom *et al.* (1976) noted for *Perca flavescens*, where PCB concentrations were dependent on fish weight. The sample sizes of Lyman *et al.* (1968) appeared more than sufficient to show weight dependence of DDT if such existed; perhaps these data suggest location-based differences in the lipid–age relationships of populations of this species (*cf.* Reinert 1970). By contrast, the inability of Henderson *et al.* (1969, 1971) to correlate

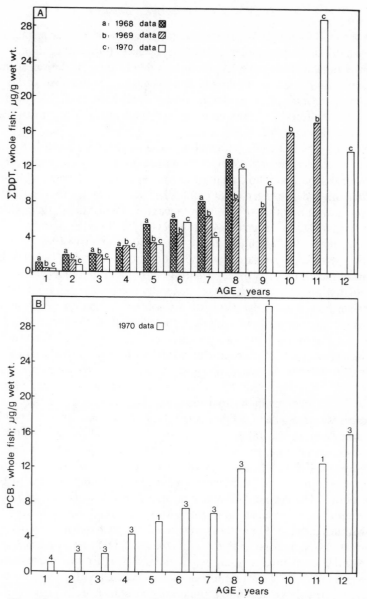

Fig. 73. Mean concentrations of (A) ΣDDT and (B) PCBs (both for whole eviscerated fish, μg/g wet weight) in lake trout, *Salvelinus namaycush*, taken from Cayuga Lake, New York State, and their variation with age. Digits above the columns in (B) indicate the number of individuals analysed for each year-class. (After Youngs *et al.* (1972) and Bache *et al.* (1972), respectively.)

age or size of fish to the observed organochlorine levels was due primarily to the small numbers of individuals of any species studied at each location. Survey data such as these have limited value in the elucidation of inter-location differences in pollutant abundance as the number of species examined in multiple locations is too few, and little attempt is made to exclude the effects of extraneous parameters such as variations in lipid, size, or sex of fish samples.

Reports which include information on the lipid contents of freshwater fish, as well as their organochlorine concentrations, permit some estimate of the contribution of lipid changes to age dependence of organochlorines. Anderson and Everhart (1966) published extensive studies of salmon, *Salmo salar*, and other species from Sebago Lake in Maine; these studies were initiated to investigate possible effects of DDT on the sport fishery for salmon which had declined in the late 1950s and early 1960s. Further studies were reported later by Anderson and Fenderson (1970). Whilst some of these data show that concentrations of DDT and/or its metabolites, calculated on a wet weight basis, generally increase with age of salmon between 2 and 6 years, age was certainly not the only parameter involved in the determination of ΣDDT levels in these fish. Both the condition of the fish (i.e. the amount of body fat present) and the sex of the fish thus appeared to alter ΣDDT accumulation and both gave rise to a large amount of variation between individuals of any given year-class. Superimposed on this within-class variation, the effects of age were at least partly due to concomitant changes in the lipid contents of fish. However, the interference of other variables affecting DDT contents of the samples permitted no clear quantitation of the relationship between the lipid variation and the organochlorine changes with age. The later paper (Anderson and Fenderson, 1970) eliminated sex effects by studying only male salmon; a clearer picture of the interdependence of age and lipid content in their effects on DDT accumulation was produced in this work, although even here variation between the lipid contents of individuals of similar ages was sometimes extreme. The authors concluded that such individual variability made it almost impossible to elucidate the real ΣDDT levels present in the population using random sampling methods. They therefore suggested that selective sampling according to fish age, fat content and sex was far more likely to provide an accurate estimate of the ΣDDT levels present in this species. Whilst *S. salar* may be more variable than most other species in terms of individual lipid contents, this suggestion has definite merit, especially when samples from different locations are to be compared.

Hannon *et al.* (1970) studied organochlorines in the ecosystem components of Lake Poinsett, South Dakota. Fourteen species of finfish were studied and levels of all organochlorines studied (ΣDDT, aldrin + dieldrin, heptachlor and its epoxide and lindane) correlated significantly to lipid contents of individuals within each species. Lipid contents tended to increase with fish age within each species also, and this gave rise to a significant rise in organochlorine levels with age. The effects of age and lipid content on the organochlorine concentrations (based on wet weights) could not be distinguished and this is powerful evidence for their interdependence. Unfortunately, no data for the lipid or organochlorine contents of individual fish were given and concentrations of organochlorines cannot therefore be based on wet and lipid weights to check for age dependence of the profiles.

Reinert (1970) also found a very close relationship between age, lipid contents and organochlorine concentrations in finfish from the Great Lakes; more than 3800 individuals of 28 species were studied. Significant increases in wet weight-based concentrations of both ΣDDT and dieldrin occurred with fish length in lake trout, *Salvelinus namaycush*, and walleye,

TABLE 61

MEAN CONCENTRATIONS OF ΣDDT AND DIELDRIN ($\mu g/g$ WET OR LIPID WEIGHTS, WHOLE FISH SAMPLES) IN DIFFERENT SIZE-CLASSES OF LAKE TROUT, *Salvelinus namaycush*, FROM LAKES MICHIGAN OR SUPERIOR AND WALLEYE, *Stizostedion vitreum vitreum*, FROM LAKE ERIE. (ALL DATA AFTER REINERT (1970).)

| Species | Lake | Length (cm) | ΣDDT | | Dieldrin | |
			Wet	Lipid	Wet	Lipid
Lake trout	Michigan	5·1–15·0	0·89	—	0·03	—
		15·2–25·1	2·38	—	0·12	—
		25·4–40·4	3·79	—	0·15	—
		40·6–55·6	6·96	—	0·20	—
Lake trout	Michigan	7·6–15·0	1·07	26·3	0·02	0·49
		15·2–25·1	2·99	34·9	0·11	1·28
		25·4–40·4	4·31	39·9	0·13	1·19
		40·6–53·1	6·61	35·6	0·21	1·13
Lake trout	Superior	5·1–15·0	0·21	—	0·03	—
		15·2–25·1	0·63	—	—	—
		25·4–40·4	0·97	—	0·02	—
		40·6–55·6	2·84	—	0·05	—
		55·9–68·3	3·99	—	0·05	—
		68·6–83·6	7·44	—	0·05	—
Walleye	Erie	30·5–40·4	1·08	—	0·06	—
		40·6–48·0	1·12	—	0·13	—

Stizostedion vitreum vitreum, all analyses involving whole fish samples. The data for *Salvelinus namaycush* may be compared with those of Youngs *et al.* (1972) for Cayuga Lake samples of the same species, discussed above (text and Fig. 73(A)). The results of Reinert (1970) are shown in Table 61, values being quoted by both wet and lipid weights where possible. Clearly, the length-related increase in organochlorine concentrations is much less on a lipid weight basis than on a wet weight basis. Figure 74 shows data for both lipid contents and ΣDDT in whole lake trout from Lakes Michigan and Superior; this plot is taken directly from Reinert (1970). The parallelism of

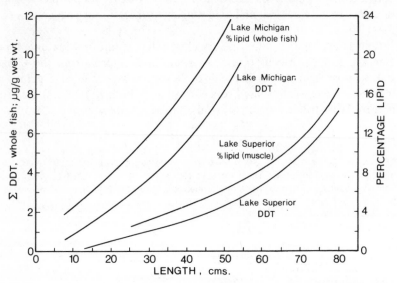

FIG. 74.   Concentrations of ΣDDT (μg/g wet weights, whole fish) and percentage lipid and their variation with length in lake trout, *Salvelinus namaycush*, from Lakes Michigan and Superior. Data for lipids in Lake Superior fish are from Eschmeyer and Phillips (1965); all other data from Reinert (1970).

the lipid and organochlorine data suggest that basing ΣDDT concentrations on lipid weights should completely eliminate any age dependence or length dependence of the data. However, perhaps other influences also affect this pattern, as data for whole trout of the same species in a later publication (Reinert and Bergman, 1974), also dealing with Lakes Michigan and Superior, show residual increases in ΣDDT levels with length even when concentrations are based on lipid weights (Table 62). Nevertheless, it is clear that age-dependent variations in lipid contents of

TABLE 62

MEAN CONCENTRATIONS OF ΣDDT (μg/g WET OR LIPID WEIGHTS, WHOLE FISH) AND
LIPID CONTENTS IN LAKE TROUT, *Salvelinus namaycush*, OF DIFFERENT LENGTH-
CLASSES. FISH WERE COLLECTED IN 1966–1970 IN LAKE MICHIGAN AND 1968–1969 IN
LAKE SUPERIOR. (AFTER REINERT AND BERGMAN (1974).) DATA FOR ΣDDT BY LIPID
WEIGHTS CALCULATED BY THE PRESENT AUTHOR

Collection site	Length (mm)	Number of fish	ΣDDT (wet weight)	Lipid (per cent)	ΣDDT (lipid weight)
Lake Michigan, northern region[a]	50–150	18	0·8	3·7	21·6
	151–252	35	1·9	8·4	22·6
	253–404	31	2·6	11·0	23·6
	405–557	26	6·1	17·4	35·1
	558–684	28	12·9	21·8	59·2
Lake Michigan, southern region[a]	50–150	3	1·3	4·2	30·9
	151–252	63	2·6	7·3	35·6
	253–404	45	5·2	10·2	51·0
	405–557	37	9·7	19·2	50·5
	558–684	14	18·1	21·0	86·2
Lake Superior, Michigan waters[b]	253–404	13	1·0	5·5	18·2
	405–557	10	1·4	12·8	10·9
	558–684	9	4·4	19·0	23·2
	685–810	31	6·4	17·0	37·6

[a] The northern and southern regions of Lake Michigan were divided by a line
extending from Ludington, Michigan, to Kewaunee, Wisconsin.
[b] Concentrations of DDT and lipid content were both much higher in siscowets
(oily, deep-bodied lake trout sometimes classified as a sub-species, *Salvelinus
namaycush siscowet*) collected in Michigan waters of Lake Superior in 1969 than in
'lean' lake trout for which data are shown here. In six siscowets 615–725 mm long,
lipid content was 45·1 per cent and DDT residues were 11·7 ppm by wet weight or
25·9 ppm by lipid weight.

these fish are responsible for most, if not all, the changes observed in
organochlorine concentrations with fish length. The other important
observation in these studies is that size–lipid relationships (and hence
size–organochlorine relationships also) may vary for a species between
locations. Thus, the slopes of the relationships describing ΣDDT–length
and lipid content–length relationships in lake trout in Fig. 74 are different
for each lake. This is equivalent to the situation for trace metals where
age–concentration regressions vary in slope with location. The result of
such location-dependent variation of the relationship is to eliminate the
possibility of size-normalisation of levels using a 'master-slope', i.e. in all

locations a range of fish sizes must be studied to elucidate the exact length–concentration relationship before size-normalisation to a standard size (length, weight, age) may be attempted.

This influence of location on the length–organochlorine concentration relationship has also been noted during the extensive monitoring studies of Frank *et al.* (1974) in Ontario freshwater ecosystems. Length–concentration relationships were reported (using both wet and lipid weight bases for concentrations) for ΣDDT and dieldrin in 21 species, many from more than one location. Within species, the general trend was toward higher ΣDDT concentrations in larger fish, and the same was commonly also true for dieldrin. However, the length–concentration relationships were not consistent between areas in most of the species studied, or between species in any one area. In addition, unusual exceptions were noted in which organochlorine concentrations actually *decreased* with increases in body weight of a species. This profile was noted for pumpkinseed, *Lepomis gibbosus*, at one location only (at other locations this species exhibited length independence of concentrations) and for golden shiners, *Notemigonus crysoleucas*, at one location; when such an inverse relationship was noted, basing concentrations on lipid weights generally made little difference to the pattern and both ΣDDT and dieldrin were involved. The mechanism involved in this length-dependent change does not therefore appear to include lipid changes; conceivably exposure changes with length in these species, by migration or by diet changes being size or age dependent. Frank *et al.* (1974) noted that length -concentration relationships were most marked amongst piscivorous fish, at least where dieldrin was concerned; by contrast, species feeding on benthic invertebrates or plankton exhibited weak or no dependence of dieldrin levels on fish length. This is interesting in view of the possible effects of a change in diet in some species as they grow; piscivorous fish such as bass eat more—and larger—fish as they grow and will be exposed as a result to higher concentrations of organochlorines in the diet. This is clearly one method whereby weight dependence of organochlorines may be produced independently of changes in body lipid. Another parameter is migration, which is important in all cases of indicator use (see discussion in Chapter 6). The example of Smith and Cole (1970) has already been referred to with respect to its effect on seasonality of organochlorines in some finfish. Briefly, the winter flounder *Pseudopleuronectes americanus* was found to spawn in the Weweantic River Estuary, and whilst juveniles resided in the estuary until age III, adults of ages III and older migrated seasonally between the estuary and offshore waters. Such behaviour, which is not uncommon amongst coastal species of finfish, many of which spawn in estuaries, obviously affects not only seasonality of organochlorines but also the profiles of organochlorine accumulation with age of the fish (see Table 41 in Chapter 6).

The dependence of concentrations of ΣDDT and PCBs on age of three species of finfish studied by Kelso and Frank (1974) was also ascribed to variations in the lipid content of these fish with age. The species studied were yellow perch, *Perca flavescens*, white bass, *Morone chrysops*, and smallmouth bass, *Micropterus dolomieui*, all from Lake Erie. Once again, however, variation between individuals of any one species was quite marked, and other factors such as diet or migration may have been implicated in determining organochlorine levels in each fish. Hattula *et al.* (1978*a*) reported extensive studies of organochlorines in fish from Lake Päijänne in Finland; more than 1700 individuals representing 12 species were analysed during 5 years of study. The most extensive data reported by these authors concerned pike, *Esox lucius*, perch, *Perca fluviatilis*, and bream, *Abramis brama*, as these were the most common fish caught. Pike and bream both exhibited a direct dependence of lipid contents on fish length and ΣDDT and PCB concentrations were also length dependent as a result of the lipid changes. Interestingly, in perch the lipid content in some cases decreased with increases in fish length; thus, organochlorines were often more concentrated in smaller specimens and both ΣDDT and PCBs correlated significantly to lipid contents in this species. Some differences were also observed in absolute levels of organochlorines in fish from different parts of the lake; a similar effect of location was earlier reported for Lake Michigan by Reinert and Bergman (1974).

It has been noted above that the age–concentration or size–concentration relationships found for organochlorines in finfish may be location dependent. However, other factors, too, may affect these relationships; one of these is season, and here the data of Kellog and Bulkley (1976) and Bulkley *et al.* (1976) must be discussed. These authors reported data for dieldrin concentrations in the ecosystem components of the Des Moines River in Iowa; the levels of dieldrin in muscle of the channel catfish *Ictalurus punctatus* received special investigation, as previous reports had indicated gross contamination (see Morris and Johnson, 1971, cited above). Studies of water samples showed that in each of the three years 1971–1973 a seasonal maximum in dieldrin levels occurred in June and July. This was correlated to spring application of aldrin in the catchment and subsequent heavy rainfall (cf. Chapter 6). During 1973, small fish of four species exhibited highest levels of dieldrin in June, which decreased through

August; these small fish thus responded rapidly to the seasonal changes in dieldrin availability (Fig. 75(A)). The muscle tissue of catfish, however, exhibited dieldrin levels which were length dependent in their seasonality (Fig. 75(B)). In addition, the seasonal variation noted in the 1973 samples did not match that of the 1971 samples of catfish. Clearly, this example illustrates the difficulty involved in sampling even a single species of fish if the aim is to produce representative data of the contamination of the water mass. The lack of complete data for lipid contents of these fish makes the erection of any hypothesis to explain the data almost impossible; differences in both lipid metabolism and diet in catfish of different lengths may be involved. Length dependence of organochlorine concentrations in finfish may therefore vary not only with location sampled, but also with season at a single location. Evidently, no general pattern of the dependence of organochlorines on finfish size can be discerned for any species studied to date; information may be considered representative of the situation occurring in only one point in time and space. This lability of the size–concentration relationship obviously makes the elimination of the effects of sample ages or sizes in monitoring surveys extremely taxing. The number of individuals studied even at a single point in time and space must be considerable if samples are to be considered representative. Such a conclusion is reminiscent of the difficulties encountered by Anderson and Everhart (1966) and Anderson and Fenderson (1970) in studies of salmon in Sebago Lake; their suggestion that sampling should be rigidly controlled as to age, condition and sex of the fish is obviously supported by the above data.

Reports concerning the variation in organochlorine concentrations with age or size of marine or estuarine finfish are much less common than are those concerning freshwater species considered above. However, the data available suggest that saltwater species may also exhibit age dependence in organochlorine levels and, once again, these may often be attributed to the covariance of lipid levels of the fish with age.

Butler (1969b) mentioned an increase in the concentrations of ΣDDT in pinfish, *Lagodon rhomboides*, from 'a Florida estuary' with fish age. These results are believed to be those of Hansen and Wilson (1970), and, in the later publication, data are given for both pinfish and pigfish, *Orthopristis chrysopterus*; the study site was Escambia Bay in Florida. Both species exhibited higher concentrations of ΣDDT (based on wet weights) amongst individuals ascribed to year-class 1 than amongst those of year-class 0. Butler (1969b) ascribed this to the length of time spent in the estuary, but the effects of lipid are uncertain, as no information is available for the

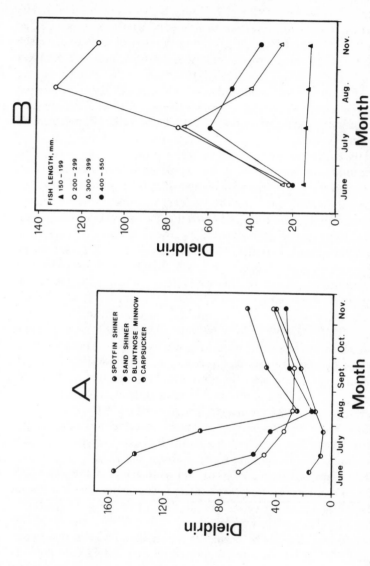

Fig. 75. (A) Mean concentrations of dieldrin (μg/kg wet weights) in four species of small fish from the Des Moines River, June–November, 1973. (B) Mean concentrations of dieldrin (μg/kg wet weights) in dorsal muscle tissue of channel catfish, *Ictalurus punctatus*, of various lengths from the Des Moines River, June–September, 1973. (After Kellog and Bulkley (1976).)

variation in lipid contents of these species. It seems unlikely that ΣDDT was accumulating with length of time spent in the estuary over a scale of years, as implied by Butler, as finfish normally equilibrate to ambient levels quite rapidly (in days or weeks). Zitko (1971) found higher levels of DDT and its metabolites, PCBs and hexachlorobenzene in whole herring, *Clupea harengus*, with increased fish weight for samples taken off Canadian coasts. However, no lipid contents were reported and sample sizes and numbers were small; further data are needed to confirm this pattern of age dependence. In more extensive studies of this species, as well as of cod, *Gadus morhua*, from the coasts of Sweden, Jensen *et al.* (1972) published interesting data for age dependence of ΣDDT and PCBs. Populations of herring and cod from sixteen areas were studied, the areas involved including the Gulf of Bothnia, the Baltic Sea, Kattegat and Skagerrak. This area of Scandinavia, besides being severely polluted by organochlorines, affords an interesting opportunity to compare fish from the brackish waters of the eastern Swedish coast with those from the more typically marine waters off western Sweden. It may be noted that the lipid chemistries of individuals of any one species are likely to differ between those two regions due to the effects of variations in salinity and diet (see Chapter 3). Cod exhibited no strong age dependence of concentrations of ΣDDT or PCBs and this is probably a result of the small differences in fat content with age of this species; most samples contain between 0·5 and 1·0 per cent lipids in muscle tissues regardless of age. However, in herring, concentrations of both ΣDDT and PCBs tended to increase with age, and this was apparent whether concentrations were based on wet weights or lipid weights. Nevertheless, age–concentration correlations were not consistent between locations on either weight basis for concentrations, and other factors may have been instrumental in defining such profiles. Both diet and migration of these herring probably change in age dependent fashion in these waters and separation of the various possible mechanisms involved in the production of age dependence of organochlorines is impossible on the basis of present data. It is interesting that a later report (Olsson and Jensen, 1975) which included data for ΣDDT and PCBs (as well as for DDT, DDE and DDD separately) in brackish-water pike, *Esox lucius*, from the Stockholm archipelago also noted occasional weight dependence of organochlorine concentrations. These data were all reported by lipid weights only, and whilst age dependence was by no means the rule (and was, in fact, never found for PCBs), some locations supported pike exhibiting such profiles. Clearly, in these cases, age dependence of ΣDDT or its components was not caused by lipid variations but by some other (location dependent) parameter, as yet unknown. Differences in organochlorine accumulation by pike of different sexes were also observed in this study, and will be considered in the next chapter. It might be noted that such differences in pike cannot be ascribed to migration, as this species is territorial, enhancing its quality as an indicator of conditions local to the site in which it is caught.

Bjerk (1973) also studied cod, *Gadus morhua*—in this case from Norwegian fjords. Concentrations of ΣDDT in muscle were low and not obviously dependent on the length or weight of the fish, agreeing with the results of Jensen *et al.* (1972) above. However, attempts to correlate wet weight-based concentrations of ΣDDT in cod livers to fish length or weight were successful on some occasions, although the data suggested a possible seasonal effect (see also Stenersen and Kvalvag, 1972). In addition, it was stated that correlations were poor when lipid weight-based concentrations were used. It therefore seems probable that during the reserve storage season, the amounts of lipid in cod livers increase in a size-dependent fashion, giving rise to size dependence in liver ΣDDT concentrations if these are based on wet weights. Utilisation of the lipid reserves during gametogenesis presumably liberates the liver ΣDDT; perhaps at this time, gonad concentrations of the organochlorine will become size dependent (as bigger fish exhibit greater fecundity and will consequently have higher amounts of lipids in gonads), although direct observations to support this are unknown. The possibility of size dependence varying between individual tissues of a fish according to their exact lipid metabolism should, in any event, be kept in mind.

Ten Berge and Hillebrand (1974) studied several marine organisms in the North Sea and Dutch Wadden Sea. Their report included data for 0-group and 3-group herring, *Clupea harengus*, and plaice, *Pleuronectes platessa*. The 0-group fish were taken from tidal waters of the western Wadden Sea, whilst 3-group fish came from commercial catches offshore in the North Sea. Both species exhibited moderate increases in mean lipid content with age, herring from 3·5 to 6·5 per cent and plaice from 1·7 to 2·2 per cent. Table 63 presents data for DDT and its metabolites in these samples. In herring, the increase in concentrations of any one component or of ΣDDT with age noted when concentrations were based on wet weights is abolished when lipid weights are used. In this species therefore, age dependence of organochlorines of the DDT group appears to be caused by changes in lipid contents of the fish with age. By contrast, the higher concentrations of any one component in 3-group plaice compared with the 0-group year-class are affected very little by changing the concentration basis from wet weights to lipid weights. It can be seen that, in the 0-group fish, herring exhibited

TABLE 63

MEAN CONCENTRATIONS (μg/kg, WET OR LIPID WEIGHT BASES) OF DDT AND ITS METABOLITES OR ΣDDT IN MUSCLE OF HERRING, *Clupea harengus*, AND PLAICE, *Pleuronectes platessa*, OF DIFFERENT YEAR-CLASSES. ALL SAMPLES WERE DERIVED FROM THE NORTH SEA AND THE DUTCH WADDEN SEA. (AFTER TEN BERGE AND HILLEBRAND (1974).)

Organochlorine	Basis	Herring		Plaice	
		0-Group	3-Group	0-Group	3-Group
DDT	Wet	9·9	28·8	1·5	14·1
	Lipid	280	450	90	1070
DDE	Wet	13·1	26·0	4·4	15·3
	Lipid	430	410	260	1100
DDD	Wet	22·7	21·6	5·1	14·0
	Lipid	640	340	310	720
ΣDDT	Wet	45·7	76·4	11·0	43·4
	Lipid	1350	1200	660	2890

higher concentrations of all compounds (on either weight basis) than did plaice, whereas the reverse is true for 3-group fish, at least on a lipid weight basis. The changes in concentrations of DDT and its metabolites in plaice with age are certainly not lipid dependent; perhaps they are caused by changes in exposure levels as these fish migrate offshore. Changes in diet may be particularly important, as it seems unlikely that uptake directly from solution would be greater in offshore areas of the North Sea than in the coastal region of the Wadden Sea.

Finally, the report of Ernst *et al.* (1976) concerning DDT and its metabolites and PCBs in organisms from the English Channel deserves mention. Finfish studied included the plaice, *Pleuronectes platessa*, and the yellow gurnard, *Trigla lucerna*. Only three individuals of the former species were studied; hence conclusions concerning the effects of size on organochlorine content of plaice cannot be considered possible. However, studies on the gurnard were more extensive and involved analysing muscle, liver and visceral adipose tissues separately from individuals varying in whole-body wet weight from 14 to 808 g. The strongest correlations of organochlorine concentrations to animal weight were noted for visceral adipose tissue and the weakest for muscle tissues; results for liver and visceral adipose tissue are shown in Table 64. Significant correlations were in all cases, positive, indicating increases of organochlorine levels with size; it can be seen that although the correlations were stronger when concentrations were based on wet weights, the levels of some of the compounds

TABLE 64

COEFFICIENT *r* OF CORRELATION BETWEEN CONCENTRATIONS OF ORGANOCHLORINES BY
WET OR LIPID WEIGHTS AND ANIMAL WEIGHT, FOR LIVER AND VISCERAL ADIPOSE TISSUE
OF THE YELLOW GURNARD, *Trigla lucerna*. ALL SAMPLES WERE FROM THE ENGLISH
CHANNEL; *p* IS THE LEVEL OF SIGNIFICANCE OF THE CORRELATION, ns REPRESENTS NOT
SIGNIFICANT. (AFTER ERNST *et al.* (1976).)

| | Liver | | | | Visceral adipose tissue | | | |
| | Wet weight basis | | Lipid weight basis | | Wet weight basis | | Lipid weight basis | |
	r	*p*	*r*	*p*	*r*	*p*	*r*	*p*
PCB[a]	0·65	ns	0·43	ns	0·81	<0·05	0·69	ns
DDT	0·85	<0·01	0·71	<0·05	−0·53	ns	−0·59	ns
DDE	0·73	<0·05	0·58	ns	0·92	<0·01	0·88	<0·01
DDD	0·87	<0·01	0·75	<0·02	0·41	ns	0·28	ns
ΣDDT	0·85	<0·01	0·75	<0·02	0·70	ns	0·51	ns

[a] PCB calculated as Clophen A60.

nevertheless increased significantly by lipid weights also. This indicates that
whilst increases in lipid contents of the tissues with age were responsible for
part of the age dependence of organochlorines, other effects were also
implicated, at least in some cases. Studies of the scallop, *Chlamys
opercularis*, by Ernst *et al.* (1976), by contrast, revealed no weight
dependence of organochlorine concentrations; as noted earlier in this
chapter, bivalve molluscs exhibit no significant increase of lipid contents
with age. Muscle of the squid, *Loligo forbesi*, was also analysed; whilst both
ΣDDT and PCB concentrations tended to show a negative correlation to
body weight when based on wet weights, these effects were not statistically
significant. As only five individuals were studied, strong conclusions are
impossible. Clearly, however, our knowledge of the size–organochlorine
concentration relationships in marine or estuarine biota is in its infancy.
Further studies are urgently required to establish the possible effect of the
size or age parameter on the results of indicator surveys for organochlorines. Such studies should employ large numbers of individuals covering
as large a size range as possible, and attention must be paid to the effects of
other parameters such as location (including organism migration), season,
sex and diet of the studied species, so that these may be minimised.

The situation concerning age dependence of organochlorines in large
marine mammals is somewhat distinct from that concerning finfish.
Whereas most finfish would be expected to be at equilibrium, or
approaching such a state, with ambient residue levels, seals may well not
reach equilibrium. A parallel may therefore be drawn between the

behaviour of mercury in high-ranking predators and that of organochlorines in seals; if uptake rates exceed the capability of the organism for
excretion, compounds may accumulate progressively throughout the
lifetime of the organism. However, in seals we shall note that the capacity of
any species for excretion of organochlorines varies with sex of the animal, as
parturition and lactation in females represent a significant contribution to
overall excretion rates and these are, of course, not present in male seals.
Because of the profound influence of sex on the age dependence of
organochlorines in seals, these data are discussed in the following chapter.

B.   CONCLUSIONS

As noted at the beginning of this chapter, the available data concerning the
effects of age or age-related parameters such as size or weight on the concentrations of organochlorines present in aquatic biota are in reasonable agreement.
In many cases, age dependence of organochlorines is caused partly or wholly
by concomitant changes in the total lipid contents of organisms as they
increase in age or size. Thus, many finfish exhibit considerable increases in
average whole-body or tissue contents of lipids with age, which may be
related to the general increase in fecundity of these species as they become
older, and hence to the increased need for storage of lipids. The increases in
size of the total lipid pool (as a percentage of tissue weights) in older animals
affords a sequestration site for greater amounts of organochlorines; hence
concentrations of these compounds calculated on the basis of wet weights
increase. This effect may be considered as a 'passive' effect of age on the
whole-body content of these compounds; any aquatic contaminant which
depends for its biological affinity on its lipophilic and hydrophobic nature
may be expected to exhibit similar age dependence.

In some cases, however, covariance of lipids is not sufficient to explain the
effects of age on the accumulation of organochlorines. Thus, basing
concentrations of these compounds on lipid weights rather than wet weights
does not always entirely eliminate age- or size-related changes. In these
instances, factors other than lipids may be involved, although conceivably
some of these instances might be explained by a change in lipid *chemistries*
as well as total amounts, which could lead to altered affinities of
organochlorines for sequestration sites in the organism. Parameters which
may be involved in the production of age dependence all involve changes in
the time-integrated exposure level of the organism to organochlorines.
Thus, if organisms exhibit age dependent migration (as seen in many

coastal finfish), the time-integrated exposure concentration of organo-chlorines may be expected to change. If migration occurs from contaminated waters to relatively clean waters, an inverse relationship between organochlorine concentration and organism age would be expected. If such migration is seasonal, the age dependence of levels would be expected to alter with season and the severity of the alteration would depend on the extent of time-integration of ambient levels of organochlorines and the rate of equilibration of organisms to new conditions. Alternatively, the diet of a species may change as the individual grows and matures (as well as with migration). The example noted above from the studies of Frank *et al.* (1974) concerned species of freshwater bass. These fish are known to become more piscivorous in nature with age, i.e. a higher proportion of the diet is represented by fish. If the fish eaten contain greater concentrations of organochlorines than other components of the diet (as would be expected in most cases), the dietary intake becomes progressively more contaminated with age of the predator and an age dependent increase in levels of organochlorines would be expected which would not relate to lipid content of the predator. It is interesting to note here that this effect would be passed on to the next step in the food web also; as the preferred size of fish prey increases with size of the predator, an age dependence of organochlorine levels in the prey would also be reflected by organisms of the next trophic level. Obviously, such an effect could give rise to inverse relationships between age (size, weight) of a species and its organochlorine concentration as well as direct relationships, depending on whether the change in diet elicits a decrease or increase in organochlorine uptake.

Whatever the mechanism producing age- or size-related changes in organochlorine concentrations present in a species may be, the implications for monitoring surveys are clear. If samples are biased for age or size, this parameter will interfere in inter-sample comparisons and may give rise to totally incorrect assumptions concerning the ambient availability of organochlorines in a study area. Whilst the use of lipid weights as a basis for organochlorine concentrations may not be expected to entirely eradicate such an influence of organism age or size, in many cases the interfering effects will be at least partly reduced. The use of lipid weights is therefore recommended as a partial answer to attempts to eliminate the effects of age or size of samples on the interpretation of analytical results.

The inability of lipid weight-based comparisons to completely eradicate size dependence of organochlorine concentrations in some instances necessitates care at sampling to ensure that organisms of any one species from all study locations are as similar as possible in terms of age or size. This naturally places further restraints on sampling and requires additional effort during this phase of monitoring; however, such effort is well spent if spurious conclusions are avoided as a result. Researchers should make a decision as to whether they require the maximum possible size range at each location for each species (attempting to characterise the mean organo-chlorine concentration in the entire population, perhaps), or whether a restricted range of sizes, available at each study location, is preferable. In most cases local availability of organisms will determine the size of organisms studied, although the feasibility of transplantation of samples from one site to another should be considered if populations are particularly impoverished with respect to the required size or year-class of species at some desired study locations.

CHAPTER 9

The Influence of Organism Sex on Accumulation of Trace Metals or Organochlorines

A. INTRODUCTION

Few authors have reported data for the variation of pollutant concentrations between males and females of any species. In some cases, of course, sex determination is not a simple matter and requires microscopical or histological examination; as Love (1970) states concerning the cod, *Gadus morhua* '...the two sexes seem to be identical in appearance, and...it is a matter of some wonder that the fish themselves know the difference...'.

However, the fish apparently can differentiate between the sexes, and in some instances the analytical chemist has also achieved this. Several instances of sex dependence of either trace metals or organochlorines have already been cited in previous chapters dealing with pollutant seasonality or variations with age, and some comment is needed here as to the mechanisms producing sex-based differences in pollutant accumulation.

It is to be expected that sexually immature individuals of a species will exhibit little or no difference between the concentrations of pollutants in males and females, as gonads are not fully developed and the existing tissue differences between the sexes will be insufficient to significantly affect whole-body levels of pollutants. However, when sexual maturity is attained, the gonads become fully differentiated and generally represent a greater percentage of total body weight. In addition, the cyclic (usually annual) variation of gonad tissues begins, and here the influence of the gonads on whole-body weights can be extremely significant. Thus, for example, in oysters such as *Crassostrea virginica* the ripe gonad may account for greater than 40 per cent of the total weight of the whole soft parts (Galtstoff, 1964) and similar percentages may be noted in finfish, reaching the extreme in species exhibiting spawning death (Love, 1970). These examples are discussed in more detail in Chapter 5, Section B. If the gonads do not contain similar concentrations of pollutants to those found in the rest of the soft tissues, changes will occur in the whole-body concentrations of pollutants which can be ascribed to gametogenesis and spawning. It is clear that if differences exist between the capacity of the male and female gonads (or gametes) to accumulate pollutants, whole-body levels of pollutants in the two sexes will differ most significantly in the period just prior to spawning when the gonads are fully ripe and represent the greatest percentage of body weight. After spawning, residual differences between the sexes may exist but are likely to be very much smaller and may be obscured by individual differences in pollutant levels caused by other factors which are not sex dependent.

In addition to the physiological and biochemical changes which surround gonad maturation, certain sex-linked differences exist in some species which may affect the accumulation of trace metals or organo-chlorines independently of gonad changes. Thus, Love (1970), reviewing the literature on both freshwater and marine species of finfish, noted that in many species females grow faster than males; in any particular year-class, therefore, the larger fish tend to be female and the smaller fish are most commonly male. Whilst several authors have suggested that this is due to the earlier sexual maturation of the male slowing its growth, castration studies indicate that hormonal control may also be involved. It was noted in Chapters 5 and 7 that growth and size may be important in some cases in determining the concentration of trace metals present in an organism, and the organochlorines also commonly exhibit size-dependent changes in concentration, as seen in Chapter 8. In some instances, therefore, differences in pollutant accumulation between fish of different sexes could occur because of the variation in growth rates between the sexes. In species which exhibit the most common pattern of faster growth in females, one would suspect this to elicit decreased pollutant levels in females compared with males, at least if the pollutant quantities ingested are similar. In a few species, however, it should be noted that the reverse trend is present. Thus, in fathead minnows (Pimephalinae), for example, the male grows faster than the female. This unusual phenomenon appears only in species in which the male has protective or nest-building duties, however, and must be considered atypical.

By contrast, no simple comparison of the growth rates of different sexes in the molluscs can be made. Many bivalve and gastropod molluscs in fact exhibit either functional or successive hermaphroditism. Thus limpets, for example, commonly exist as males in early maturity and change sex after one or more spawnings; the larger and older individuals in any one population are therefore likely to be female. Bivalve molluscs exhibit what Choquet (1970) refers to quaintly as 'more unsettled' sexuality; often rhythmical changes in sex are apparent and several changes of sex may occur during the lifetime of one individual (see also Galtstoff, 1964). One important point arises out of this tendency of some molluscs to exhibit age-dependent sex change. If populations in different locations grow at different rates, and the change in sex is a function of age (number of previous spawnings) rather than of size, a monitoring survey selecting individuals in a restricted size range from all study locations could select samples which were entirely male in one location and entirely female in another location. This possibility is obviously of some import if the species exhibits sex dependence of pollutant levels, as the inter-location comparison is confounded by the sex-based differences and the two cannot be adequately separated for correct interpretation.

Data concerning the differences in trace metal or organochlorine concentrations between sexes of various species will be considered in the various types of possible indicator organism in turn, and in each case attempts will be made to distinguish the mechanism(s) involved in the effect.

B. MOLLUSCS

Very little information concerning possible sex-based differences in the accumulation of either trace elements or organochlorines exists for either gastropod or cephalopod molluscs; as usual, bivalves have been more extensively studied. Mullin and Riley (1956) noted higher levels of cadmium in male gonads than in female gonads for both the whelk, *Buccinum undatum*, and the scallop, *Pecten maximus*. These differences were more emphasised in the bivalve (fivefold difference) than in the gastropod (approximately twofold difference), but the authors did not mention whether such variations could be noted|if whole animals—as opposed to their tissues—were analysed.

Alexander and Young (1976) analysed pooled samples of separate tissues (digestive gland, gonad and muscle) from three individuals of each sex for the mussel, *Mytilus californianus*, from coastal waters of California. Whilst no differences could be found for the concentrations of any metal in digestive glands or muscle from males and females, data for the gonads were different for copper, lead and zinc (but not for chromium, nickel or silver). Gonads of male mussels contained relatively more lead, but less copper and zinc compared with gonads of females; male:female concentration ratios were 0·5, 1·7 and 0·6 for copper, lead and zinc, respectively. In studies of the same species from the California Bight, Gordon *et al.* (1978) confirmed the differences for copper and zinc. These authors reported male:female concentration ratios for copper and zinc in gonads of 0·36 and 0·17, respectively, and could find no significant differences for concentrations of cadmium, chromium, iron, lead or nickel in gonads of the two sexes. The differences between these two studies may well be a function of the degree in gonad maturity in the samples taken; the chemistry of male and female mussel gonads changes dramatically during gametogenesis and the exact differences between the sexes no doubt depend markedly on the season of sampling. Nevertheless, it is obvious that a difference of 1·7-fold to almost sixfold in metal concentrations between the sexes is quite sufficient to severely affect the results of monitoring surveys if each sex is not adequately represented in all samples. Whilst the differences in the metal levels of whole soft parts are not likely to be nearly as pronounced as those in the gonads, because of the large amounts of metal in the digestive gland (with concentrations independent of sex), these differences between gonad levels are nevertheless a source of possible interference in indicator surveys. Watling and Watling (1976*b*) later reported similar differences between the sexes for several metals in the South African Mytilid, *Choromytilus meridionalis* (Table 65). Unfortunately, although these mussels were analysed individually, no statistical comparison of males and females can be made on the basis of the mean concentrations reported. However, the differences (for whole soft parts) are probably significant for copper, manganese and zinc, and it is interesting that lead tended to be present at higher levels in male mussels (cf. data for *Mytilus californianus* above). As no differences in growth or other parameters between the sexes were noted, and as the observed differences cannot be explained by size dependence, this appears to be a *bona fide* example of sex-based difference; unfortunately, the authors did not investigate the effect of season or report the state of gonad maturity in the samples. The most recent report concerning sexual differences in the accumulation of trace elements in bivalves is that of Greig *et al.* (1978), involving the scallop, *Placopecten magellanicus*. Extensive analyses of gonads from both males and females showed that zinc was always more concentrated in female reproductive tissues than in those of males, although large size-dependent variation was encountered with respect to the magnitude of this difference. The greatest difference recorded gave a male:female concentration ratio of 0·10, and the least, 0·90. Copper was also commonly present in greater concentration in female gonads than in males, although

TABLE 65

MEAN CONCENTRATIONS (μg/g DRY WEIGHT) OF ELEVEN TRACE METALS IN THE WHOLE SOFT PARTS OF MALE AND FEMALE MUSSELS, *Choromytilus meridionalis*, FROM SALDANHA BAY IN SOUTH AFRICA. NUMBERS OF INDIVIDUALS STUDIED WERE 41 FOR MALES AND 37 FOR FEMALES. (AFTER WATLING AND WATLING (1976*b*).)

Parameter	Male	Female
Dry tissue weights: mean (g)	3·40	3·15
range (g)	2·1–4·8	1·2–5·2
Bismuth	4·0	3·4
Cadmium	0·9	0·9
Cobalt	1·0	0·9
Copper	5·9	7·7
Chromium	1·4	1·4
Iron	54·0	66·0
Lead	2·1	1·8
Manganese	6·0	12·0
Nickel	5·7	5·2
Silver	0·3	0·3
Zinc	54·0	97·0

occasional samples revealed the inverse profile. Cadmium was highly variable, extending from a male:female concentration ratio of 0·28 to one result of 2·69; levels of silver varied similarly. Whether such variations are due wholly to differences in the reproductive state of the animals analysed is uncertain, but at least part of the variation must be ascribed to this parameter.

The effects of sex on the accumulation of organochlorines by molluscs have been almost completely ignored to date, even for bivalve species. However, Young *et al.* (1976) studied the accumulation of ΣDDT and PCBs by the mussel, *Mytilus californianus*, after its transplantation to the contaminated Palos Verdes Peninsula area of Los Angeles, California. The authors stated that no significant difference existed between the accumulation of DDT and its metabolites or PCBs by male and female mussels. However, consideration of their results for the transplanted samples suggests a tendency for the females to accumulate greater amounts of both groups of organochlorines. This difference was not observed in control animals and these data may therefore indicate a location-dependent sex difference in the accumulation of organochlorines by *M. californianus*, although the results require confirmation.

C. CRUSTACEANS

Some indirect data are available for crustaceans which suggest that
both trace metals and organochlorines could be sex dependent in
concentrations. Modin (1969) reported high concentrations of DDE in ova
of Dungeness crabs, *Cancer magister*, compared with stripped females
(Table 66), and these levels might be considered high enough to produce
significant mortality of larvae; the decline of the San Francisco based
fishery for *C. magister* may well be partly due to these high levels. The loss

TABLE 66

CONCENTRATIONS OF DDE (μg/kg WET WEIGHT) IN STRIPPED FEMALES AND OVA OF THE
DUNGENESS CRAB, *Cancer magister*, FROM THE COAST OF NORTHERN CALIFORNIA. DATA
ARE RELATED TO THE DISTANCE OF SAMPLING SITES FROM SAN FRANCISCO BAY, AS THIS IS
THE MAJOR SOURCE OF DDT COMPOUNDS FROM AGRICULTURAL USAGE IN THE AREA.
(AFTER MODIN (1969).)

Site	Distance from Bay entrance (km)	Month sampled[a]	DDE in stripped female	DDE in ova
Point Bonita	0	October	62	430
Fourfathom bank	3	January	130	220
Double Point	27	October	54	210
Drakes Bay	40	January	110	190
Bodega Bay	69	October	40	54

[a] October, 1967 or January, 1968.

of ova at spawning will also affect ΣDDT levels of the parent female quite
dramatically. Differences in the parent:ova ratio of residue concentrations
may be caused by non-synchronous spawning of these populations, as
Sheridan (1975) has shown that DDT levels in the gonads of the blue crab,
Callinectes sapidus, vary according to developmental stage, probably because
of the covariance of lipid levels. It is not known whether male crabs also
exhibit such high concentrations of organochlorines in gametes, but most
authors consider that females lose relatively greater proportions of the total
body load of these compounds at spawning than do males. Direct studies
would be worth while, as such effects have a bearing both on sex-based
differences and seasonality of organochlorines in aquatic organisms.

The toxicity of organochlorines may, in some cases, differ according to
sex of the test animal. Vernberg *et al.* (1978) investigated the effects of the
commercial PCBs Aroclor 1016 and Aroclor 1254 on the respiratory

metabolism of the fiddler crab, *Uca pugilator*. At 25°C ambient temperature, both Aroclor preparations elicited increased respiration in male and female fiddler crabs; however, at 15°C both compounds depressed respiration of female crabs but did not affect the male of the species. Whether such effects are uptake related is uncertain.

Some data are also available for the effect of mercury on *U. pugilator*, and here again interesting differences between the sexes are apparent. Vernberg and Vernberg (1972) found that no differences existed between the uptake of mercury from solution by male and female fiddler crabs. However, when the crabs were stressed by sub-optimal salinity/temperature regimes in the presence or absence of added mercury, males died faster than females. In addition, at optimal salinities of 30‰ and temperatures of 25°C, mercury depressed the metabolic rate of males more than that of females. These effects may well be purely physiological and may not reflect differences in the rates of net uptake of mercury by the two species, although clearly a biochemical difference in tolerance at least must exist between the sexes. More recently, Cunningham and Grosch (1978) found, by using reciprocal crossing techniques, that female brine shrimps, *Artemia salina*, were more stressed physiologically than were males of the same species on exposure to 1·0 or 2·0 mg/litre of methylmercuric chloride in solution. Once again, no conclusion is possible concerning the relationship of this observation to the uptake of methylmercury by each sex, as no uptake data were reported.

D. FINFISH

More direct information is fortunately available concerning the sex dependence of concentrations of organochlorines and trace metals in species of freshwater and marine finfish. Although some authors have failed to observe differences in the organochlorine levels accumulated by each sex of a species (e.g. see Henderson *et al.*, 1969, 1971; Hannon *et al.*, 1970), this may often be due either to inadequate sample sizes or to the masking of such effects by other parameters such as individual variation in lipid contents. Burdick *et al.* (1964) have shown that female lake trout, *Salvelinus namaycush*, lose appreciable amounts of ΣDDT in eggs; males, by contrast, are believed to lose much less ΣDDT in milt, although direct data do not appear to be available. Bulkley *et al.* (1976) recognised this difference in excretion routes of males and females but could find no marked effect of sex on the concentrations of dieldrin present in catfish, *Ictalurus punctatus*, from the Des Moines River, Iowa. Differences with size of fish and season were quite severe in these studies, however, and could easily have masked any sex-based influence on dieldrin levels. Anderson and Everhart (1966) noted quite severe differences between the concentrations of ΣDDT or its components in male and female salmon, *Salmo salar*, from Sebago Lake, but quantification of the differences was difficult owing to interactive effects of condition and age of the fish sampled, both of which also influenced ΣDDT levels. However, some of the data for older fish (age groups IV to VI) suggested that female salmon contained less DDT than males, and this may be due to the relatively greater organochlorine loss by females in the ova.

Amongst laboratory studies, some authors have found organochlorine toxicity to vary between the sexes. Macek (1968a) found a dietary intake of DDT to reduce the growth rates of male yearling brook trout, *Salvelinus fontinalis*, whilst females did not exhibit dose-dependent growth decreases in similar treatments. The author suggested that females could avoid the effects of DDT on growth because relatively greater amounts of the total DDT absorbed could be translocated to developing ova. In a later study (Macek, 1968b) on the same species, survival was similarly affected. However, such data require careful interpretation, as the sexes are stressed differently during maturation of sex products and may also take up differing amounts of organochlorines because of differences in lipid contents. The latter possibility was confirmed in a recent report by Defoe *et al.* (1978), in studies of the uptake and toxicity of Aroclor 1248 and Aroclor 1260 using the fathead minnow, *Pimephales promelas*. Males of this species were observed to take up much less of either PCB mixture than did females when data were calculated on a wet weight basis (e.g. see Fig. 76(A)). Thus, concentration factors for the uptake of Aròclors 1248 and 1260 by males were approximately 60 000 and 160 000, respectively, whilst the corresponding factors for females were 120 000 and 270 000. However, these differences between the sexes were almost completely abolished by considering data based on lipid weights rather than wet weights (Fig. 76(B)), although the higher-chlorinated mixture was, of course, still absorbed more rapidly than that of lower chlorination by either sex. This example of sex-dependent differences in organochlorine kinetics is therefore based on sex-linked differences in lipid contents; such effects may be seasonally dependent in the field if the lipid profiles differ through the year for male and female fish.

Differences also exist between male and female finfish of certain species for trace metal accumulation. Several authors have noted a greater toxicity of cadmium in solution to males than to females; this has been found for flagfish, *Jordanella floridae* (Spehar, 1974, 1976), brook trout, *Salvelinus*

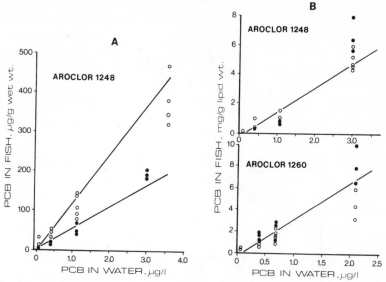

FIG. 76. (A) The uptake of Aroclor 1248 by male (closed circles) and female (open circles) fathead minnows, *Pimephales promelas*, exposed to various concentrations of this PCB mixture in solution. Note wet weight basis for concentrations in fish. (B) The uptake of Aroclor 1248 and Aroclor 1260 by male (closed circles) and female (open circles) fathead minnows, using lipid weights of the fish as a basis for concentrations. Note difference in scale of horizontal axes and greater uptake of Aroclor 1260. (All data after Defoe *et al.* (1978).)

fontinalis (Benoit *et al.*, 1976) and fathead minnows, *Pimephales promelas* (Pickering, unpublished; cited in Benoit *et al.*, 1976). However, no difference between the sexes was found for cadmium toxicity to bluegills, *Lepomis macrochirus* (Eaton, 1974) or this species and largemouth bass (Cearley and Coleman, 1974). Whether such effects are uptake related or depend on differences in tolerance between the sexes remains obscure, although no reports could be found claiming differences between the sexes for the accumulation of trace metals (other than mercury) by freshwater species of fish. Lovett *et al.* (1972) specifically stated that cadmium contents of the fish studied were not sex dependent; however, sample sizes were woefully inadequate to overcome the effects of individual variation, and such conclusions cannot be considered significant where authors study 406 individuals comprising 29 species from 49 locations.

Studies on the northern pike, *Esox lucius*, from either fresh or brackish waters have indicated that mercury concentrations differ between males

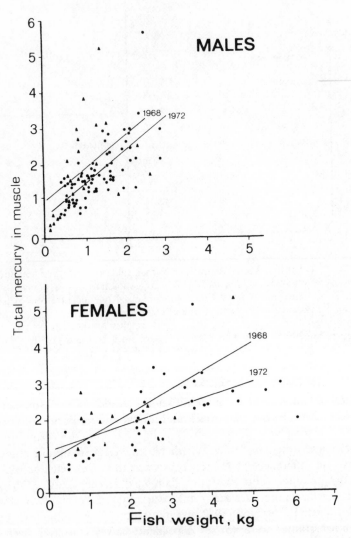

FIG. 77. Concentrations of total mercury (μg/g wet weight) in muscle of male and female pike *Esox lucius*, from Lake Marmen in Sweden, and their relationship to fish weight. Data for 1968 (triangles) and 1972 (circles) are plotted separately and regressions were calculated for each separately. (After Olsson (1974).)

and females. Olsson (1974) studied the weight-dependent profiles for total mercury in muscle samples of pike taken in Lake Marmen in Sweden during 1968 and 1972. Male pike exhibited faster accumulation of total mercury in muscle with weight than did female pike, i.e. plots of mercury concentration in muscle against fish weight were of greater positive slope in males (Fig. 77). These fish were unfortunately not aged; it would be most interesting to compare age–concentration profiles with those in Fig. 77, as the data suggest that differences are due to the differential growth rates of males and females (see below). Thus, while weight–concentration plots differ in slope between the sexes, age–concentration relationships might not show such differences. Olsson and Jensen (1975) in later studies of pike from the Stockholm archipelago, reported weight-normalised data for total mercury in muscle tissues of fish from 17 different regions (Table 67). Where five or more individuals of each sex were available for any one region, the data were also broken down into sexes. In each case, mercury levels in the male

TABLE 67

CALCULATED CONCENTRATIONS OF TOTAL MERCURY (MEANS ± 95 PER CENT CONFIDENCE INTERVALS, μg/g WET WEIGHTS) IN MUSCLE OF PIKE, *Esox lucius*, OF STANDARD WEIGHT 1 kg. SAMPLES WERE TAKEN FROM 17 REGIONS IN THE STOCKHOLM ARCHIPELAGO. VALUES FOR EACH SEX SEPARATELY HAVE BEEN CALCULATED WHERE $n \geq 5$, n BEING THE NUMBER OF INDIVIDUALS STUDIED. FOR THREE FISH IN REGION I, THE SEX WAS NOT DETERMINED. (AFTER OLSSON AND JENSEN (1975).)

Region	Both sexes		Females		Males	
	n	Mercury	n	Mercury	n	Mercury
I	27	1·16 ± 0·28	15	0·80 ± 0·68	9	1·34 ± 0·29
II	17	1·03 ± 0·19	14	1·08 ± 0·25		
III	5	0·67 ± 0·17				
IV	20	0·52 ± 0·07	17	0·52 ± 0·07		
V	14	0·57 ± 0·09	7	0·53 ± 0·21	7	0·60 ± 0·16
VI	5	0·81 ± 0·21				
VII	5	0·69 ± 0·30				
VIII	20	0·81 ± 0·17	10	0·78 ± 0·37	10	0·85 ± 0·13
IX	30	0·75 ± 0·09	16	0·74 ± 0·14	14	0·77 ± 0·12
X	5	0·68 ± 0·18				
XI	5	1·95 ± 1·93				
XII	15	0·85 ± 0·11	10	0·84 ± 0·18	5	0·86 ± 0·22
XIII	15	0·57 ± 0·16	10	0·54 ± 0·32	5	0·60 ± 0·29
XIV	5	0·82 ± 0·23				
XV	5	0·50 ± 0·20				
XVI	10	0·30 ± 0·05				
XVII	8	0·44 ± 0·16				

fish tended to exceed those in females, although whether these differences are significant statistically is debatable. However, the profile agrees with the previous observations of Olsson cited above, and it might be noted that the differences could well have attained significance if a greater standard weight had been chosen for normalisation. These pike also exhibited weight dependence of DDT and its metabolites in some samples, even though data were based on lipid weights; such correlations were exhibited more frequently by males than females, and possibly the DDT–lipid–weight relationships are also affected by sex-based differences in growth rates. The differences between the DDT, DDD or ΣDDT concentrations in fish from the regions where five or more fish of each sex were studied are shown in Table 68; it is not clear whether these differences are real or are due to the residual effects of weight, as data have not been weight normalised. However, samples from regions I and IX exhibited some evidence of higher concentrations of organochlorines in female fish; as these data are based on

TABLE 68

CONCENTRATIONS OF DDT AND ITS METABOLITES AND PCBs (MEANS ±95 PER CENT CONFIDENCE INTERVALS, $\mu g/g$ LIPID WEIGHTS) IN MUSCLE OF PIKE OF DIFFERENT SEXES FROM SIX REGIONS OF THE STOCKHOLM ARCHIPELAGO. n REPRESENTS THE NUMBER OF INDIVIDUALS STUDIED. SIGNIFICANT DIFFERENCES BETWEEN THE SEXES ARE REPRESENTED BY + ($p < 0.05$); − INDICATES NO SIGNIFICANT DIFFERENCE. (AFTER OLSSON AND JENSEN (1975).)

Region	Sex	n	DDT	DDE	DDD	ΣDDT	PCB
I	Female	16	6·6 ± 2·8	11 ± 6	2·8 ± 0·9	22 ± 9	19 ± 8
	Male	9	2·6 ± 0·8	6·1 ± 1·4	1·4 ± 0·4	11 ± 2	16 ± 5
			+	−	+	+	−
V	Female	7	4·4 ± 2·4	3·2 ± 1·5	1·1 ± 0·7	9·2 ± 4·8	4·7 ± 2·1
	Male	8	5·9 ± 3·5	5·4 ± 2·5	1·3 ± 0·7	13 ± 7	6·1 ± 2·6
			−	−	−	−	−
VIII	Female	10	5·8 ± 2·6	7·8 ± 2·7	2·6 ± 1·1	17 ± 6	7·7 ± 2·5
	Male	10	4·2 ± 1·9	7·3 ± 3·1	1·9 ± 0·7	14 ± 6	11 ± 3
			−	−	−	−	−
IX	Female	16	4·9 ± 1·3	6·1 ± 1·5	1·9 ± 0·6	14 ± 3	9·8 ± 2·7
	Male	14	5·2 ± 1·1	5·4 ± 1·3	1·2 ± 0·4	13 ± 3	9·1 ± 2·4
			−	−	+	−	−
XII	Female	10	3·9 ± 1·5	5·8 ± 2·1	1·5 ± 0·7	12 ± 4	6·5 ± 1·7
	Male	5	5·1 ± 4·6	8·7 ± 5·9	1·7 ± 0·9	17 ± 11	17 ± 11
			−	−	−	−	−
XIII	Female	10	6·4 ± 3·4	4·4 ± 1·6	1·3 ± 0·6	13 ± 6	5·8 ± 3·0
	Male	5	6·7 ± 3·1	4·8 ± 3·6	1·4 ± 0·8	14 ± 8	6·7 ± 2·9
			−	−	−	−	−

TABLE 69

REGRESSION EQUATIONS DESCRIBING THE EFFECT OF BODY LENGTH ON THE CONCENTRATIONS (mg/kg ASH WEIGHTS) OF TRACE ELEMENTS IN LIVER TISSUES OF THE BLUEFISH, *Pomatomus saltatrix*, THE TAUTOG, *Tautoga onitis*, AND THE TILEFISH, *Lopholatilus chamaeleonticeps*. ALL SAMPLES WERE DERIVED FROM THE COAST OF NEW JERSEY, USA. Y = ELEMENT CONCENTRATION, X = BODY LENGTH IN mm, r = REGRESSION COEFFICIENT AND p = LEVEL OF SIGNIFICANCE. ONLY REGRESSIONS OF $p < 0.05$ ARE SHOWN. (AFTER MEARS AND EISLER (1977).)

Element	Increase (i) or decrease (d) with body length	Sex	Regression equation	r	p
			Bluefish		
Cr	d	Female	$Y = 210 - 0.10\,X$	-0.35	0.05
Fe	i	Male	$Y = -51\,000 + 120\,X$	0.60	0.05
			Tautog		
Cr	d	Male	$Y = 680 - 1.50\,X$	-0.74	0.01
Cu	d	Male	$Y = 1\,300 - 1.20\,X$	-0.49	0.05
Ni	d	Male	$Y = 710 - 1.50\,X$	-0.77	0.01
Ni	d	Female	$Y = 660 - 1.60\,X$	-0.61	0.01
			Tilefish		
Cd	i	Male	$Y = -300 + 0.40\,X$	0.81	0.01
Cd	i	Female	$Y = -270 + 0.50\,X$	0.59	0.05
Cu	i	Male	$Y = -580 + 0.80\,X$	0.65	0.05
Cu	i	Female	$Y = -710 + 1.40\,X$	0.80	0.01
Fe	i	Male	$Y = -74\,000 + 100\,X$	0.72	0.05
Fe	i	Female	$Y = -14\,000 + 40\,X$	0.72	0.01
Mn	d	Female	$Y = 300 - 0.30\,X$	-0.83	0.01
Zn	d	Female	$Y = 4\,400 - 3.30\,X$	-0.59	0.05

lipid weights, this clearly cannot be ascribed to lipid effects such as those noted by Defoe *et al.* (1978), cited above. Conceivably, the preferred diets of pike of each sex differ, or possibly the differences between the sexes noted for both mercury and organochlorines are based on physiological differences in pollutant kinetics.

Amongst marine species, the report of Mears and Eisler (1977) may be noted. These studies of the tautog *Tautoga onitis*, tilefish, *Lopholatilus chamaeleonticeps*, and bluefish, *Pomatomus saltatix*, all refer to fish from the coast of New Jersey and involve trace metal concentrations found in the liver only; no data for any other tissue were reported. The results are shown in Table 69, where regressions for each metal in each species are given. It can be seen that in the tautog, all significant relationships indicated decreased metal concentrations with length increases of the fish, whilst in bluefish and tilefish both direct and inverse relationships were noted, depending on the metal involved. Evidently, quite severe differences were found between the different sexes in all species studied, although nickel in the tautog and cadmium, copper and iron in tilefish behave similarly in each sex at least qualitatively. As noted in Chapter 14, liver tissues may be suitable for monitoring of at least some trace metals in finfish; however, sex-based differences such as these should be noted by authors designing such studies and sufficient samples should be taken at each study site to eliminate this variation.

Sex-based differences also occur in the accumulation of mercury by elasmobranchs. Forrester *et al.* (1972), in extensive and careful studies of total mercury in the spiny dogfish, *Squalus acanthias*, from the Strait of Georgia, British Columbia, found that concentrations of this element in muscle tissues varied in a sex-dependent fashion in animals of total length greater than 65 cm (Fig. 78). Thus, above this threshold, male dogfish exhibited higher concentrations of mercury than did females. This difference was observed whether data were compared without reference to location or whether dogfish from Point Grey were considered separately to those from other areas. The Point Grey population exhibited somewhat higher total mercury levels (throughout all weights) than did other populations, and this may be considered to reflect true differences between the mercury availability in the different locations. The sex-based difference was considered by the authors to be due to differences in growth rates between males and females; male dogfish were considered to grow at slower rates than females, as seen in various teleost species (see above) as well as predators such as tuna (e.g. see Peterson *et al.*, 1973). The inability of Childs and Gaffke (1973) to confirm the differences in mercury contents of male and female dogfish of the same species from Oregon coasts cannot be taken to be indicative of location dependence, as the individuals studied by the latter authors varied very little in total length. A certain amount of variation between individuals of either sex must be expected; although this species is not considered migratory, even small ranges in such coastal populations could cover areas with widely differing ambient mercury concentrations.

The data of Forrester *et al.* (1972) are very similar to those in the later excellent study of school shark, *Galeorhinus australis*, and gummy shark, *Mustelus antarcticus*, published by Walker (1976). This latter report, concerning south-east Australian waters, used analysis of variance on extensive data to investigate the individual and interactive effects of species, location, length, and sex on the mercury concentrations found in shark

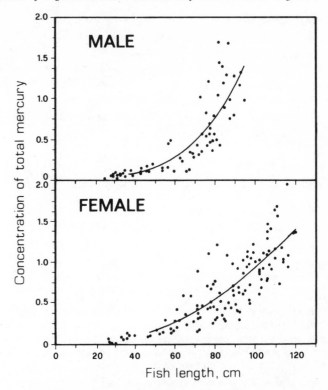

FIG. 78. Relationship between concentrations of total mercury (μg/g wet weights) in the dorsal musculature of male and female dogfish, *Squalus acanthias*, and total body length. All samples were from the Strait of Georgia, British Columbia. (After Forrester *et al.* (1972).)

musculature. Large amounts of informative data and intelligent speculation are included, and the study is an ideal example of the care needed to correctly interpret field data for monitoring purposes. Figure 79 presents the data showing the effects of sex on mercury accumulation by each species; the similarity to the data of Forrester *et al.* (1972) in Fig. 78 is immediately evident, as are the differences in absolute levels of mercury accumulated by each species. The effect of species was considered to relate to differences in diet; school sharks feed on pelagic fish and cephalopods, whilst gummy sharks feed mainly on benthic invertebrates. It is therefore to be expected that school sharks would ingest greater quantities of mercury; however, a possible species-dependent difference in growth rates (providing

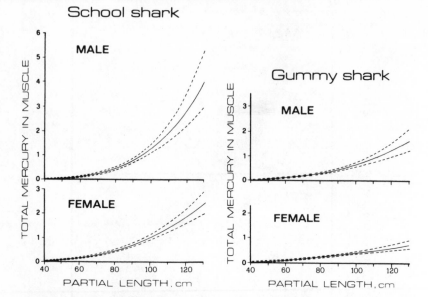

FIG. 79.   Relationships between the concentrations of total mercury in muscle
(μg/g wet weight) of the school shark, *Galeorhinus australis*, and the gummy shark,
Mustelus antarcticus, and their partial lengths. All data refer to shark taken from
coastal waters of south-east Australia; means ±95 per cent confidence limits are
given in each case. (After Walker (1976).)

different dilution rates for ingested elements) cannot be ruled out. The sex-
based differences may similarly be due to differences in the preferred diets of
males and females, but this seems unlikely, particularly in view of the
similarity between the species. Unpublished results from tagging studies of
school shark were cited by the author to support the alternative hypothesis
of greater growth rates in females than in males. It is indeed unfortunate
that such studies are unavailable; it would be most interesting to relate the
data to age and search for residual variation which could be ascribed to the
loss of residues by females to the developing embryo. It is interesting in
this respect to speculate on the possible differences between viviparous
species and oviparous species of elasmobranchs in terms of the possible
loss of pollutants during reproduction. It might be expected that viviparous
species, producing live young (and often with large litter sizes, although in
some species cannibalism *in utero* occurs) would be presented with greater
opportunity for pollutant loss from the female parent compared with
species which are oviparous in nature. Perhaps, therefore, sex-based

differences in mercury concentration will be found to be more extreme in viviparous species.

E. MARINE MAMMALS

Finally in this chapter, some discussion is needed concerning the differences found between the sexes in species of marine mammals with respect to their accumulation of pollutants. It was noted in Chapter 8 that the variation in organochlorine concentrations with age in seals is profoundly influenced by sex of the individual; for this reason, discussion of age dependence of organochlorine concentrations was held over until the present chapter. The reason for the extreme effect of sex on age dependence of organochlorines in mammals is connected to the speculation above concerning viviparous and oviparous elasmobranchs; females may lose significant amounts of these compounds to the foetus during pregnancy. Furthermore, mammals suckle their young; hence further losses may occur by lactation. It will be seen below that such effects can give rise to completely different profiles of organochlorine accumulation with age in seals, and possibly in other marine mammals also. In complete contrast, the age dependence of trace metals in seals or other mammals appears totally unaffected by the sex of the individual. No reports could be found suggesting that sex-based differences in trace metal levels occur in any marine mammal. At first sight this is surprising, as (by comparison with terrestrial mammals, including humans) mercury at least would be expected to cross the placental barrier from parent to the developing foetus. However, it will be remembered (see Chapter 7) that seals exhibit rather low amounts of methylmercury compared with total mercury, probably because of their capacity to demethylate ingested methylmercury in the liver. It therefore appears that marine mammals do not lose significant amounts of metals to the foetus, either directly or through lactation; hence differences between the concentrations of elements found in males and females do not occur.

The variation in concentrations of organochlorines in seals with age appears similar to that of mercury in predatory fish, in that increases seem to occur at least in males throughout the lifetime of the individual. Anas and Wilson (1970*a*, *b*) found that in the northern fur seal, *Callorhinus ursinus*, from the Pribiloff Islands in Alaska, DDT and its metabolites occurred at very low levels in unborn foetuses. DDT, DDD, PCBs and dieldrin could not be detected in any foetal samples (i.e. concentrations were all less than 0·01 mg/kg dry weight), whereas DDE was found in livers at concentrations up to 0·10 mg/kg wet weight. Where data were available, ratios of DDE concentrations in the livers of mothers and foetuses averaged about fivefold. Residues in nursing seal pups, 4 months of age, were higher than those of foetuses and the difference is obviously due to the residues accumulated during the later stages of pregnancy and post-parturition from the mother's milk. Samples of ingested milk were directly analysed by Anas and Wilson (1970b) and were found to contain up to 5 mg/kg ΣDDT by wet weight, mainly as DDE. Whilst samples were not particularly extensive, it is clear that the newborn pup probably contains rather less organochlorine amounts than its parent but may accumulate these compounds from the milk rapidly at suckling. Comparisons of the ΣDDT levels in the tissues of mothers and pups for common seals, *Phoca vitulina*, and grey seals, *Halichoerus grypus*, have revealed similar tendencies concerning populations around the coasts of Great Britain (Holden and Marsden, 1967; Holden 1972a). There is no suggestion in any of these data that a difference exists between the sexes amongst suckling pups, and such a difference appears most unlikely on theoretical grounds.

Addison *et al.* (1973) examined blubber samples of 18 harp seals, *Pagophilus groenlandicus*, from the Gulf of St. Lawrence for DDT and its metabolites, PCBs, and dieldrin. ΣDDT and PCB levels were similar, ranging from 3·1 to 22·6 μg/g wet weight and 2 to 22 μg/g wet weight, respectively; by contrast, dieldrin concentrations were much lower (0·1–0·3 μg/g wet weight). ΣDDT and PCB variations between individuals (without reference to sex) correlated significantly to age, as did DDE levels. Concentrations of DDT, DDD and dieldrin were not significantly age dependent. Of the 18 individuals studied, 14 were males aged 1 to 18 years and only four were females, aged 1 to 6 years. Consequently, conclusions concerning differences between the sexes were limited, although the oldest female exhibited consistently lower concentrations of the DDT group compounds and PCBs compared with males of similar age. Re-examination of the data of Holden (1972a) and of Anas and Wilson (1970a) by these authors failed to confirm sex dependence of the age profile, as the studies of the former author included mainly female seals and those of the latter authors involved liver samples rather than blubber. However, Frank *et al.* (1973) reported studies of 78 individual harp seals from the Gulf of St. Lawrence and the Newfoundland and Labrador coasts of eastern Canada. The greater number of individuals permitted stronger conclusions concerning sex dependence of the age–ΣDDT concentration profiles and these authors claimed that ΣDDT levels in the blubber of female *P. groenlandicus* levelled off at about 6·5 μg/g wet weight on reaching the breeding age, whereas concentrations in males increased throughout their lifetimes.

A similar conclusion was reached by Addison and Smith (1974) concerning DDT, DDE and PCB concentrations in the blubber of ringed seals, *Pusa hispida*, from the Canadian Arctic. Concentrations of each compound (and ΣDDT) increased significantly in blubber samples with age in male seals, but no such increase could be seen for females, despite similar numbers of individuals and age ranges. More recently, the situation in *Pusa hispida* has been confirmed by studies of Helle *et al.* (1976*a*, *b*) on the populations present in the Bothnian Bay, north of the Baltic Sea. Seals from Simo in the extreme north of this area contain about a hundred times the concentration of ΣDDT and 25–50 times that of PCB in blubber lipids compared with the same species in the Canadian Arctic, and this extraordinary level of contamination has been correlated to the extremely low breeding success of the Bothnian Bay population. The data of Helle *et al.* (1976*b*) have already been tabulated (see Table 38 in Chapter 6), and it is clear from this pattern that the differences between the sexes in *Pusa hispida* correlates perfectly to parturition and lactation in the female. Thus females suffering from occlusion of the uterine horns—and hence unable to become pregnant—exhibit similar concentrations of ΣDDT and PCBs to those of males. Non-pregnant females retaining the capacity to reproduce contain lower levels (correlated to previous pregnancies), whilst pregnant females exhibit the lowest concentrations of both ΣDDT and PCBs, and the amounts of each compound lost by these female parents are clearly observed in the foetuses.

The results of other authors concerning either seals or other species of marine mammals in general confirm the above picture of age dependence and sex dependence of organochlorines. Gaskin *et al.* (1971, 1973) have found low levels of ΣDDT and PCBs in post-parturient females of both porpoises, *Phocoena phocoena*, and harbour seals, *Phoca vitulina*, compared with males of each species. Anas and Worlund (1975) could find no age dependence in 51 adult female northern fur seals, *Callorhinus ursinus*, ranging in age from 8 to 13 years. Finally, the effects seen by Helle *et al.* (1976*a*, *b*) on the ringed seal populations of the Bothnian Bay may have a counterpart in premature pupping amongst Californian sea-lions, *Zalophus californianus californianus*. Both ΣDDT and PCBs were significantly more concentrated in tissues of female sea-lions and their pups which suffered premature deliveries compared with normal full-term pups and their mothers (Delong *et al.*, 1973). In addition, the organochlorine and trace metal insult to these sea-lion populations may give rise to greater susceptibility to diseases such as leptospirosis (Buhler *et al.*, 1975). The most elegant recent study is that of Addison and Brodie (1977) dealing with the grey seals, *Halichoerus grypus*, from Sable Island, Nova Scotia. These authors found that concentrations of ΣDDT and PCBs, based on lipid weights, were higher in the blubber of parent female seals than in the milk. Thus, ΣDDT concentrations in the milk lipid were 60 per cent of those in parent blubber lipids, whilst PCB levels in milk were 30 per cent of the corresponding values for blubber. A partial barrier evidently exists in the transfer of organochlorines via milk to the progeny or conceivably the residues are diluted by new lipids synthesised *in situ* in mammary tissue. Young pups contained approximately similar levels of ΣDDT and PCBs in blubber lipids to those in the ingested milk. Calculations involving estimates of the total organochlorine loss in milk and the amounts of ingested organochlorines in the (mainly fish) diet suggested figures of about 340 mg ΣDDT loss, cf. 425 mg ΣDDT ingestion, compared with 200 mg PCB loss, cf. 300 mg PCB ingestion, annually for a lactating female seal. These figures convert to represent the loss of about 30 per cent and 15 per cent of total body loads of ΣDDT and PCBs, respectively per annum in a lactating female, which is balanced roughly by intake. The lack of any notable increase in organochlorine concentrations with age in female seals is thus explained.

F. CONCLUSIONS

The effects of the sex of an organism on its accumulation of trace metals or organochlorines have been seen to be due mainly to either of two mechanisms.

(a) The amounts of pollutant lost during spawning or reproduction may differ between the sexes. Such differences may be caused by differing gonad or gamete chemistries affecting the affinity of pollutants for the sex products, or by simple differences in the total amounts of sperm and ova shed (e.g. some finfish), or by loss of pollutants from females to progeny maintained *in utero* and during lactation after birth of the young. As might be expected, the more highly evolved organisms which exhibit birth of live young and suckling after birth (mammals) tend to also exhibit the greatest sex dependence of residues, at least for organochlorines.

(b) Male and female individuals of a species may differ in age–length relationships. Hence the faster growing sex (generally the female) may be expected to exhibit lower concentrations of a pollutant which is age dependent for net accumulation (e.g. mercury in finfish). This tendency is a function of differences in the dilution of accumulated pollutants by tissue growth. Alternatively, a sex-based difference may exist between the lipid contents of male and female individuals of a species and this may affect the apparent accumulation of organochlorines if data are based on wet weights.

The elimination of the effects of sex on results of monitoring surveys is apparently a simple matter of cognisance of this factor at sampling, effort being expended where necessary to select organisms of the desired mixture or ratio of sexes at each study site. If this is impossible because of either severe restrictions on sampling time or effort, or complete lack of one sex of animals in one or a few study sites (e.g. for some molluscs which are successive hermaphrodites), the effects of sex on the ensuing data should be recognised and some attempt should be made to study the likely qualitative interference from this parameter. It might be worth emphasising, in conclusion, that the amount of currently available data concerning the influence of organism sex on pollutant accumulation is not great, and that further examples will no doubt be discovered in the future. The lack of current data to positively identify sex-based variation in pollutant accumulation in any given species should not, therefore, be interpreted as a reason for ignoring this parameter in future studies.

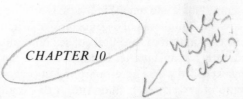

CHAPTER 10

The Effects of Shore Level or Depth of Sampling

In some instances, the results of monitoring surveys may be affected by the vertical position of sampling of organisms, either intertidally or sublittorally at the shore line, or in the water column away from the shore. These effects merit consideration in that they may, on occasions, be substantial enough to introduce significant within-site variability into monitoring surveys designed to investigate between-site variations. Thus if, for example, differences in pollutant concentrations are found with vertical position of sampling on the shore line, all samples should be taken from the same vertical position (relative to tide levels) to avoid interference of this effect with conclusions concerning inter-site differences in pollutant availability.

Such variation in pollutant levels with vertical sampling has been noted mainly in estuarine areas or in regions (e.g. embayments) where vertical mixing is reduced compared with open oceans. Most examples known to date concern water bodies with known vertical stratification and the differences may be explained on the basis of such stratification. Data concerning trace metals are more abundant than is information for organochlorines, and the former will thus be considered first.

A. TRACE METALS

It is obvious that for differences to exist between the pollutant levels of an organism found in a given vertical zone, samples of the organism must be representative of ambient conditions at the point of sampling. With reference to variations within the intertidal zone at the shore line, this basically means that organisms must be sessile, as even limited migrations will be sufficient to eliminate the vertical differences in pollutant

282

availability. Thus, almost all data to date concern macroalgae, bivalve molluscs or barnacles, which are probably the most commonly studied sessile estuarine indicator organisms. The only exceptions to this are reports involving the limpet, *Patella vulgata*; this species, whilst not exactly sessile, nevertheless grazes within a limited area close to its point of attachment. In situations with marked stratification of pollutant availability, the restricted movement is clearly insufficient to eliminate such stratification and as a result the concentrations of a pollutant may vary in limpets with habitat on the shore line.

Macroalgae

Concerning macroalgae, Nickless *et al.* (1972) first noted the influence of vertical position of sampling on trace metals in *Fucus vesiculosus* from the

TABLE 70

MEAN CONCENTRATIONS (μg/g DRY WEIGHT) OF CAD-
MIUM, LEAD AND ZINC IN MACROALGAE, *Fucus vesi-
culosus*, TAKEN FROM DIFFERENT PARTS OF ITS VERTICAL
RANGE ON THE SHORE LINE AT ABERAVON, BRISTOL
CHANNEL. (AFTER NICKLESS *et al.* (1972).)

Sampling position	Cadmium	Lead	Zinc
Upper limit	7	13	230
Mid-range	10	ND[a]	370
Lower limit	11	6	290

[a] ND: not detectable (no detection limits quoted).

Bristol Channel. These results, shown in Table 70, reveal that each metal exhibited its own characteristic profile; concentrations of cadmium were highest in algae from the lowest limit of the range, those of lead from the upper limit and zinc concentrations were greatest in the middle of the vertical range of the species. Unfortunately, only mean concentrations were quoted with no information concerning intra-sample variability; it is therefore difficult to know which of the observed differences are significant. However, Fuge and James (1973, 1974) also observed variations in the concentrations of several trace metals in *F. vesiculosus* from sites in the Bristol Channel and it will be seen below that limpets also exhibit such fluctuations here. Bryan and Hummerstone (1973a) compared seasonally averaged data for metals in the thallus of *F. vesiculosus* in the Tamar Estuary for the effect of shore position. Unfortunately, these data were not fully reported, although it was stated that copper and zinc did not vary with vertical level of the weed on the shore (cf. Table 70). However, lead concentrations were always higher in algae taken from the lower part of the distribution and similar tendencies were observed for manganese, iron and aluminium. The magnitude of these differences varied from site to site in the estuary, but exceeded a factor of two, in some cases at least, for lead and manganese. The tendency for some metals to be present at highest concentration in algae from the lower end of the distribution of *F. vesiculosus* is probably due to the less frequent exposure of algae in this position to air compared with samples from higher sites on the shore. It could be argued that the greater amount of time spent immersed in water would give rise to greater contamination of the algae. However, this is clearly not always the case, and it should be remembered that weed from the lower levels probably also grows faster because of its more frequent submergence. Finally, it is interesting that whilst Bryan and Hummerstone (1973a) encountered higher levels of lead in samples lower down the shore in the Tamar Estuary, Nickless *et al.* (1972) observed the opposite profile in algae from the Bristol Channel. In this case, the deposition of metal-rich particulates from the air may be significant, as industrialised or heavily populated areas would be expected to contain elevated airborne lead concentrations (Morris and Bale, 1975). Avoidance of the effects of the deposition of airborne particulates in surveys which employ algae would appear to be worth while, at least in some areas, as algae are particularly difficult to clean prior to analysis. Perhaps the solution in these cases is to sample in the subtidal zone at each study site, at a given depth below the spring low-water mark. This naturally entails more effort at sampling, but may be expected to produce results which are of greater consistency and which are more meaningful in terms of comparative water quality at the various study locations.

Bivalve Molluscs

Nielsen (1974) investigated the concentrations of metals in the cultured mussel, *Perna canaliculus*, from New Zealand waters. In this case, samples were taken from ropes which were suspended vertically from floating rafts; this situation is thus rather different to those discussed above as the mussels are maintained at the same depth, regardless of tide. Two study locations were selected, one (Kenepuru Sound) a sheltered estuarine region in the South Island and the other (Waiheke Island) a more exposed ocean location off the North Island. As might be expected, mussels from the latter site exhibited no change in metal concentration with depth, suggesting that vertical mixing was sufficient to eliminate any such differences which might tend to form in the water column. By contrast, the estuarine site was found to exhibit quite marked stratification of metals in the mussels (Fig. 80). Concentrations of zinc tended to decrease with depth whereas those of cadmium, iron and lead increased. As the growth rates of these mussels varied little with depth, such profiles cannot be ascribed to differences in

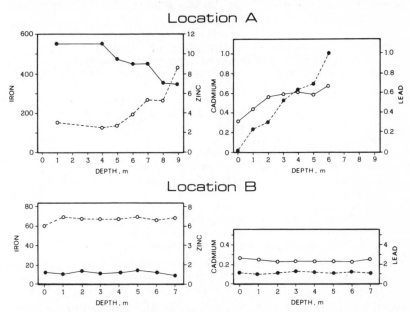

FIG. 80.   The variation in concentrations (μg/g wet weight) of cadmium, iron, lead and zinc in mussels, *Perna canaliculus*, taken at various depths in the water column from (A) Kenepuru Sound, a sheltered estuarine site in South Island, New Zealand, and (B) Waiheke Island, a more open and better flushed location in North Island, New Zealand. (After Nielsen (1974).) ——●—— Zn, ——○—— Cd, ——○—— Fe, ——●—— Pb.

growth dilution of accumulated elements, and are unlikely to be caused by variations in available food with depth. However, it is possible that the uptake of metals was dominated in some cases by elements in the underlying sediments (cf. Ayling, 1974, and see discussion on organochlorine availability below), and it may be significant that iron and lead (which exhibited the most marked increases in concentration with depth) commonly associate with inorganic particulates (Raymont, 1972; Preston *et al.*, 1972).

De Wolf (1975) found that the concentrations of total mercury present in mussels, *Mytilus edulis* and *M. galloprovincialis*, were generally greater in intertidal samples than in subtidal animals from a given location (Table 71). Although the degree of difference seems to vary with location, the consistency of the profiles suggests that depth dependence of mercury levels may be present in all populations. Although De Wolf also noted significant effects of size on mercury concentrations present in some mussel populations (see Chapter 7), he did not state whether the comparison

TABLE 71

MEAN CONCENTRATIONS OF MERCURY (ng/g WET WEIGHT) IN MUSSELS, *Mytilus edulis* OR *M. galloprovincialis*, FROM INTERTIDAL OR SUBTIDAL ZONES OF SEVERAL LOCATIONS IN WESTERN EUROPEAN WATERS. (AFTER DE WOLF (1975).)

Sampling area	Month of sampling[a]	Mean concentration (ng/g)	
		Subtidal	Intertidal
Eastern Scheldt	November	88	110
Eastern Scheldt	January	95	121
West coast of Holland	March	157	186
Western Wadden Sea	March	137	218
Eastern Wadden Sea	December	106	135
Eems Dollard Estuary	November	146	300

[a] 1971 (November, December) or 1972 (January, March).

between intertidal and subtidal mussel was based on animals of the same size. If the mussels were indeed of the same size, it is probable that the intertidal samples were of greater mean age than the subtidal populations at each location, as it is known that intertidal individuals exhibit slower growth than do subtidal mussels (see Seed, 1976). Possibly, then, this difference is based on age-dependent increases in the mercury concentrations present in mussels, although this theory would require confirmation, especially as the studies of Bourget and Cossa (1976) reached no definite conclusions as to the effects of shore level on the concentrations of mercury found in *M. edulis* from the Gulf of St. Lawrence in Canada. Davies and Pirie (1978) also made no mention of this factor in their studies of the mercury contents of *M. edulis* from the Firth of Clyde in Scotland, but in this case it appears that the possible influence of this parameter was not studied.

Phillips (1976a) reported further data for the effect of sampling depth on the concentrations of metals in *M. edulis*. In this instance the sampling site was a vertical pile in the estuary of the Yarra River, to the north of Port

Phillip Bay, Australia. The location was of great interest, as in winter the water column was highly stratified with metal-rich low-salinity water from the river overlaying relatively uncontaminated seawater of high salinity. In summer, when run-off was much reduced, no salinity stratification was present and the metal content of the waters probably varied little with depth. Results of studies conducted in late winter and late summer are shown in Table 72. Clearly, the dependence of metal levels on

TABLE 72
CONCENTRATIONS (MEANS $\pm$ STANDARD DEVIATIONS, $\mu g/g$ WET WEIGHT) OF CADMIUM, LEAD AND ZINC IN WINTER SAMPLES AND CADMIUM AND ZINC IN SUMMER SAMPLES OF MUSSELS, *Mytilus edulis*, FROM DIFFERENT DEPTHS IN THE WATER COLUMN AT AN ESTUARINE LOCATION IN THE NORTH OF PORT PHILLIP BAY, AUSTRALIA. ALL DATA REFER TO MUSSELS OF SIMILAR SIZE AND TISSUE WEIGHTS; TEN INDIVIDUALS WERE ANALYSED IN EACH SAMPLE. (AFTER PHILLIPS (1976a).)

| Depth | Winter samples | | | Summer samples | |
(m)[a]	Cadmium	Lead	Zinc	Cadmium	Zinc
0·5	1·81 $\pm$ 0·52	2·37 $\pm$ 1·11	97·1 $\pm$ 67·0	0·35 $\pm$ 0·10	19·3 $\pm$ 6·5
1·5	1·31 $\pm$ 0·28	2·29 $\pm$ 0·64	44·2 $\pm$ 12·5	0·31 $\pm$ 0·06	19·9 $\pm$ 8·1
3·5	1·06 $\pm$ 0·18	1·35 $\pm$ 0·44	29·9 $\pm$ 6·4	0·36 $\pm$ 0·07	18·0 $\pm$ 5·7
6·5	1·14 $\pm$ 0·24	1·22 $\pm$ 0·15	31·7 $\pm$ 9·6	0·51 $\pm$ 0·12	17·8 $\pm$ 7·2
9·5	0·85 $\pm$ 0·20	1·15 $\pm$ 0·21	20·6 $\pm$ 4·1	0·41 $\pm$ 0·18	15·5 $\pm$ 6·1

[a] All depths refer to metres below spring high-water mark.

depth of sampling was marked in winter studies, especially for zinc, whereas in summer the effect was statistically absent, at least for cadmium and zinc. It is notable that the extreme differences observed for zinc in winter samples compared with those for the other metals agree with the conclusions of the survey data reported later (Phillips, 1976b); the Yarra River was a major source of zinc, whilst cadmium and lead discharge was not nearly so great. These data show that variation of trace metal levels in mussels with depth may be seasonally dependent in areas where contaminated discharges vary in volume seasonally, causing differences in vertical stratification of the water column throughout the year. Such effects will be most important in estuaries which exhibit significant layering of fresh and salt waters, and it might be worth emphasising that a difference of only one metre in sampling position in the intertidal zone altered zinc levels in mussels by a factor of 2·2; such effects could be significant if introduced by accident into monitoring programmes. Similar conclusions were reached by Stephenson *et al.* (1978) in studies of *M. californianus* from the coast of California.

Finally, the burrowing bivalve, *Scrobicularia plana*, is also known to exhibit significant differences in trace metal content according to its vertical position on the shore. Bryan and Uysal (1978) analysed both *S. plana* and the alga *Fucus vesiculosus* from three shore levels at one site in the Tamar Estuary in southwestern England. Concentrations of the ten trace metals studied were similar in *S. plana* from the middle and lower shore samples, but all metals other than manganese and zinc were present at higher concentrations (difference of one-and-a-half to twofold) in samples of the bivalve taken from the upper shore. By contrast, *Fucus vesiculosus* exhibited decreases in metal levels with increased height on the shore, and sediment samples also displayed this pattern. No explanation of these differences was suggested and the indicator ability of this bivalve seems far from proven, especially for some metals which interact at uptake (see Chapter 11).

Gastropod Molluscs

A certain amount of information exists to suggest that the limpet, *Patella vulgata*, contains differing concentrations of trace metals according to its vertical habitat. Whilst Nickless *et al.* (1972) published some data concerning these effects for cadmium in *P. vulgata*, conclusions are difficult on the basis of this information because of the covariance of size of the limpets studied, which also influences the levels of cadmium accumulated (see Chapter 7). More extensive studies were performed by Peden *et al.* (1973), again in the polluted British Channel. Limpets of similar size were taken from six levels on the shore at Watchet and analysed for six elements

TABLE 73

MEAN CONCENTRATIONS (μg/g WET WEIGHTS) OF SIX TRACE ELEMENTS IN LIMPETS, *Patella vulgata*, OF COMPARABLE SIZE TAKEN FROM SIX VERTICAL LEVELS ON THE SHORE AT WATCHET IN THE BRISTOL CHANNEL ON 3 FEBRUARY, 1972. LEVEL 1 IS AT THE MEAN LOW WATER MARK, LEVELS 2–5 ASCENDING THE SHORE TO LEVEL 6 AT THE MEAN HIGH WATER MARK. (AFTER PEDEN *et al.* (1973).)

Level	Arsenic	Cadmium	Copper	Lead	Mercury	Zinc
1 (MLWM)	4·7	93·0	4·5	0·28	0·06	83·5
2	1·3	100·5	6·5	0·20	0·05	137·0
3	3·5	116·5	4·1	0·28	0·05	68·0
4	3·2	75·0	4·8	0·18	0·05	152·0
5	2·6	81·0	4·1	0·42	0·05	260·0
6 (MHWM)	1·4	69·5	4·7	0·18	0·06	143·0

(Table 73). Once again, no data for element variability within each sample are quoted, and it is therefore difficult to reach strong conclusions. However, mercury at least varied very little between samples from different vertical habitats and the differences for copper and lead were not particularly marked. Variations noted for arsenic, cadmium and zinc, were not always consistent. Nevertheless, cadmium appeared to be accumulated to higher levels in mid-tidal populations, whereas zinc was more concentrated in animals from near the high tide mark. It may be that movement of the limpets at feeding affected these results somewhat and the inconsistencies evident in these profiles do not lend confidence to the use of such species as indicators of trace metals.

Other Organisms

As noted above, the most reliable data concerning the variation in trace metal concentrations in biota with vertical position on the shore involve macroalgae and bivalve molluscs. It might be expected that any sessile organism which accumulates metals in proportion to the ambient environmental concentrations would exhibit such variation, at least in stratified estuaries. However, data are hard to find, perhaps because the differences due to vertical habitat are commonly obscured by the effects of other parameters such as size or growth rates of the organisms studied. Although Stenner and Nickless (1975) found rather higher concentrations of cadmium, copper and zinc in the barnacle, *Balanus amphitrite*, with higher position on the shore, only one location was involved and the studies were insufficient to lend any substance to such comparisons. Later studies on the same species in lagoons of the North Adriatic (Barbaro *et al.*, 1978) noted much higher levels of copper and mercury in barnacles from the bottom of the water column compared with the surface. The exact reason for this difference is unclear, as unfiltered water samples revealed no such difference for copper at least, whilst mercury concentrations in the water collected were below the limits of detection. Concentrations of fluoride in these barnacles did not vary with position in the water column. Further studies are needed to clarify the importance of sampling position in the water column as a determinant for trace metal levels in barnacles.

B.   ORGANOCHLORINES

Very little information is available concerning the variation in organo-chlorine concentrations of organisms with depth or position on the shore line.

Studies such as those cited above for trace metals have not apparently been performed. However, organochlorines may be stratified in the water column under some circumstances. For example, it is known that these hydrophobic compounds may be concentrated in the surface microlayer which also contains high amounts of microbiota or natural hydrocarbons (e.g. see Seba and Corcoron, 1969; Bidleman and Olney, 1974). Organisms which are sessile and live intertidally may thus be exposed to the high concentrations of organochlorines associated with the surface microlayer and this could give rise to increased levels of such compounds in intertidal individuals of a species compared with those living subtidally.

Apart from the effects of organochlorines in the surface microlayer, the tendency of these compounds to exist in association with particulates may also give rise to stratification of total organochlorine amounts in the water column. In cases where haloclines are formed in estuaries during high run-off conditions, the amounts of particulates may be greater in the surface waters of lower salinity, which bring organochlorines into the marine ecosystem attached to silt particles. Once again, such effects could give rise to increased levels of these pollutants in organisms from the top of the water column.

However, a third situation is possible in which the opposite profile would be produced, and data for organochlorines in mussels supports this as a practical problem in monitoring. Thus, if a situation exists where most of the organochlorines are present in bottom sediments, filter-feeding organisms may respond to an input from particulates stirred off the bottom by wave action. In this case the concentrations accumulated by the organisms would increase from the bottom of the water column to the top, as greater turbidity would be present with increased depth. Organochlorines bound (probably by adsorption in most cases) to bottom sediments are known to be available to benthic infauna such as polychaetes (Courtney and Langston, 1978; Elder et al., 1979; Fowler et al., 1978b), as well as to animals, including both crustaceans and finfish, living on top of the sediments (e.g. see Odum et al., 1969; Nimmo et al., 1971b, 1974; Young et al., 1977). It is thus reasonable to assume that these compounds would be available to at least some organisms in the water column if the sediment is stirred off the bottom. This suggestion is supported at least by the studies of Young et al. (1976) using mussels, *Mytilus californianus*, suspended at various depths on a taut-line buoy system designed specifically for these experiments. These results were presented previously in Chapter 6 (Fig. 54); they show that both ΣDDT and PCBs were accumulated to a much higher degree by mussels living near the bottom sediments. Admittedly, these experiments were performed off Palos Verdes where the concentrations of organochlorines are very high in the sediments as a result of the industrial discharges, mainly from the Hyperion outfall (see also MacGregor, 1974); nevertheless, organochlorines may be made available in resuspended bottom sediment particles in many coastal areas. Further study is needed to investigate how widespread this phenomenon is; if this route of uptake is indeed prevalent in bivalves and other organisms, the depth of sampling (or the position relative to the bottom sediments) will be an important parameter which should be standardised in monitoring programmes.

CHAPTER 11

Pollutant Interactions as a Source of Error in Monitoring Studies

It is now well known that the toxicities of some pollutants can be altered by the co-presence of other contaminants. Thus, although some mixtures of pollutants exhibit simple additivity of toxic action, many exhibit antagonism or less-than additive effects and some may interact in a synergistic or more-than-additive fashion. Whilst instances of non-additive interaction between toxicants may not always be due to alterations in the net uptake of one of the components by the other, some cases can certainly be ascribed to alterations in the net accumulation of toxicants. Whether such alterations are due to enhancement or depression of uptake or to similar changes in the excretion of pollutants is uncertain in most cases. However, interference in the uptake or retention of a contaminant caused by the co-presence of a different element or compound is perhaps the most potentially damaging effect which can interfere in the use of biological organisms to monitor pollutants. Most effects of other parameters on the results of monitoring surveys such as those due to age or size, season, sex and so on, may be eliminated by the researcher at sampling in many cases; however, the effects due to pollutant interaction cannot be allowed for. Indeed, in many cases such effects will not even be suspected and spurious conclusions may be reached as a result with respect to the relative abundance of contaminants at different study locations.

Little information exists as to the precise manner of accumulation of either trace metals or organochlorines by aquatic biota. It appears likely that different types of indicator organism accumulate these contaminants by rather different processes. Thus, most authors consider the binding of trace metals to macroalgae as an ion-exchange type of process; indeed, macroalgae appear most similar of all aquatic biota to an inert ion-exchange medium. In such cases, the process of metal accumulation probably involves adsorption to alginates on the plant surfaces (Haug,

1961) and it appears possible that the different affinities of alginate binding sites for different metals could give rise to displacement effects which might be involved in metal–metal interactions. Much less is known concerning the uptake of organochlorines by macroalgae and little work has been done to attempt to develop any species as an indicator of organochlorines, although basic surveys have occasionally been attempted (e.g. see Parker and Wilson, 1975). The accumulation of trace metals by phytoplankton may also be dominated by adsorption of the elements to the cell wall rather than by true absorption and transport into the cytoplasm, and organochlorines probably also concentrate at the lipoprotein cell membrane of phytoplankters. However, in higher organisms of greater size, although adsorption to external surfaces must occur, in most cases such binding is non-specific and readily reversible, at least for trace metals. The pollutants of importance are thus translocated to internal tissues subsequent to real absorption across the body surface. In the case of organochlorines, translocation across a limiting membrane should be no problem, as the lipophilic nature of these compounds would allow simple dissolution into lipoprotein membranes and specific binding sites are probably unnecessary. For trace metals, however, specific transport processes may exist and may depend on a supply of metabolic energy (ATP). Although examples of the biochemical basis of trace metal uptake into aquatic biota are few, some studies are known. For instance, Goodbody (1974), in reviewing the uptake of vanadium by ascidians, notes that this process is both temperature sensitive and partially inhibited by ouabain (Fig. 81). Vanadium is concentrated extremely efficiently by many ascidian species (although certain species apparently prefer iron, niobium, tantalum, titanium or other elements), and element uptake is thought to occur mainly from solution across the single-cell epithelium of the branchial wall, the metal being transferred finally into specialised amoebocytes. The effects of the glycoside ouabain (Strophanthin G) suggest that the transport of vanadium, into *Ciona intestinalis* at least, is linked to the Na^+/K^+-dependent ATPase activity of the limiting membrane, as ouabain inhibits this activity. Whether the transport system is specific for vanadium is uncertain, but the differences in the affinity of ascidian species for this and other metals suggest no little specificity occurring either at uptake or excretion. Unfortunately, very few studies of this type are known and our knowledge of the mechanisms involved in the uptake of trace elements by aquatic biota is thus almost non-existent. Studies such as those of George *et al.* (1976) and of George and Coombs (1977*a, b*) on the mussel, *Mytilus edulis*, and of Wrench (1978) on the oyster, *Ostrea edulis*, are notable exceptions, although it is clear even

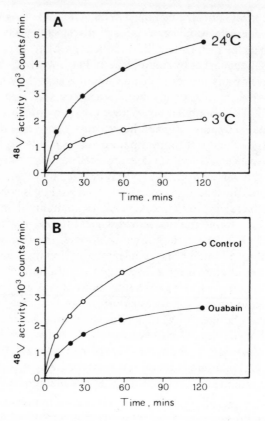

Fig. 81. The net uptake of ^{48}V in the branchial sac of the ascidian, *Ciona intestinalis*, and the effects of (A) temperature, and (B) the addition of ouabain. (After Rummel *et al.* (1966), cited by Goodbody (1974).)

from these limited data that the processes involved are not simple and are likely to differ between species and between metals in any one species. Thus, cadmium uptake by the mussel may involve prior complexation with a carrier ligand before translocation of the complex across the gill (or intestinal?) membrane can take place (Fig. 82); the increased net uptake of this element in the presence of added complexing or chelating agents may then be explained by the independence of the complex from the (rate limiting) process of cadmium complexation to the specialised carrier ligand (George and Coombs, 1977b). Complexation of lead also influences the uptake and retention of this element in *M. edulis* (Coombs, 1977), but these data have not been fully published to date. The uptake of iron, whilst being affected by prior complexation of the metal, is somewhat different from that of cadmium, as it apparently occurs by pinocytosis in *M. edulis*. In addition, the increased rates of uptake for iron complexes compared with the element itself are balanced by their higher excretion, giving rise to an almost constant residence time for the element, regardless of form (George *et al.*, 1976; George and Coombs, 1977a). Unfortunately, these authors do not include any studies on the metabolic requirements for element uptake in

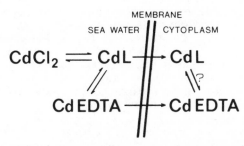

FIG. 82. Hypothetical mechanisms of cadmium uptake at the gills of the mussel, *Mytilus edulis*. L represents a carrier ligand, necessary for the uptake of cadmium unless the element is complexed by other materials such as EDTA. (After George and Coombs (1977b).)

their interesting work. However, Wrench (1978), in attempts to correlate the tissue distribution of mercury in the oyster, *Ostrea edulis*, to the amounts of soluble protein in the tissues (*cf.* Wolfe, 1970b; Coombs, 1974), found that inorganic mercury uptake by isolated gill tissues required a metabolisable substrate (dextrose) and was inhibited by 2,4-dinitrophenol; thus ATP again appears necessary. Furthermore, the presence of potassium ions also inhibited mercury uptake and this leads to a satisfying hypothesis that mercury uptake occurs using the metabolically necessary Na^+/K^+ ATPase system and mercury competes with potassium for transport. Unfortunately, the hypothesis is short lived, as ouabain, which inhibits the transport of K^+ by this system specifically, enhances mercury uptake. The author is drawn to the conclusion that the effects of potassium are probably mediated via its secondary influence on ATP levels. Thus, ouabain tends to increase ATP levels in the membrane by inhibiting Na^+/K^+ ATPase activity. If K^+ were to stimulate ATPase activity, as seems likely, it could give rise to decreased mercury transport by this effect alone rather than by out-competing Hg^{2+} ions at uptake. The most likely explanation is, therefore, that mercury uptake requires ATP (and hence is affected by any event which causes decreased ATP levels in the membrane), but that it is taken up by a system other than the Na^+/K^+ ATPase. Finally in this section, the report of Sheppard (1977) may be mentioned. This author correlated the concentrations of major ions (Ca^{2+}, K^+, Mg^{2+}, Na^+) with those of the trace metals copper, lead, nickel and zinc in two

TABLE 74

CORRELATIONS OF THE CONCENTRATIONS OF THE MAJOR IONS, CALCIUM, POTASSIUM, SODIUM AND MAGNESIUM WITH THOSE OF THE TRACE METALS, LEAD, COPPER, NICKEL AND ZINC IN THE URCHINS, *Paracentrotus lividus* AND *Arbacia lixula*, AND THE LIMPET, *Patella vulgata*. DATA FOR URCHINS REFER TO A POLLUTION GRADIENT ON THE ITALIAN COAST; THOSE FOR THE LIMPET REFER TO A POLLUTION GRADIENT IN THE NORTH SEA. ALL SIGNIFICANT ($p < 0.05$) COEFFICIENTS ARE SHOWN IN FIGURES; THE SIGNS OF NON-SIGNIFICANT CORRELATIONS ARE SHOWN IN BRACKETS. (AFTER SHEPPARD (1977).)

	P. lividus	*A. lixula*	*P. vulgata*
Ca with Pb	0·496	0·490	0·282
Cu	0·450	0·690	0·273
Ni	0·823	0·671	0·426
Zn	0·618	(+)	0·506
K with Pb	−0·755	−0·650	(−)
Cu	−0·527	−0·837	(−)
Ni	−0·620	(−)	(−)
Zn	−0·755	−0·480	−0·314
Na with Pb	−0·746	−0·420	0·420
Cu	−0·500	(−)	0·424
Ni	(−)	(−)	0·286
Zn	−0·673	−0·371	0·424
Mg with Pb	(+)	0·502	0·229
Cu	(+)	(+)	(+)
Ni	0·674	0·476	0·286
Zn	(+)	(+)	0·325

urchin species (*Arbacia lixula* and *Paracentrotus lividus*) and the limpet, *Patella vulgata*. Along 'pollution gradients' on either Italian or English coasts, several suggestive correlations were noted (Table 74). All correlations between calcium or magnesium with trace elements were positive, but potassium exhibited negative correlations throughout, and sodium was positively correlated to trace metal levels in the limpet but negatively related in the two urchin species. Interpretation of these data as either causal or cause–effect relationships is not possible at the present time. Conceivably, as Sheppard suggests, the toxic trace metals affect membrane integrity to give rise to leakage of major ions. Conversely, the presence of major ions may elicit changes in the net uptake of trace metals. Further research concerning the relationships between the major and minor elements present in aquatic biota appears worth while, especially in the light of reports linking cadmium uptake to calcium availability (Phillips, 1976a; Wright, 1977a, b, c). The uptake of a host of major and minor ions by more or less specific carrier mechanisms certainly affords real chances for ion competition and interaction, and perhaps some of the examples which follow may be explained by such effects. However, effects are theoretically just as possible at storage sites or excretion, and similar efforts must be made to identify toxicant interactions at all three points if a full understanding is to be achieved. Although very little is known of interactions between pollutants which might occur at excretion, some limited data are available concerning interactions at storage, at least for trace metals. Recent work has identified the existence of specific binding proteins in both invertebrates (e.g. the mussel, *Mytilus edulis*) and vertebrates; these compounds had been suspected in aquatic organisms since their discovery in terrestrial mammals. Such specific binding proteins are known by the blanket term of metallothioneins; they probably differ somewhat between species, but are commonly present in storage organs (liver, hepatopancreas, kidney) and may exhibit inducible synthesis. Because most metallothioneins may bind several metals, but exhibit different affinities for different metals, one element may displace another. Hence in a situation where episodic uptake of one element after another occurs, ion displacement from specific binding sites on metallothioneins may result; such an effect will present as a metal–metal interaction if the displaced ion is lost to other tissues or excreted.

It must be clearly kept in mind during the discussion presented below that, regardless of mechanism, the mere existence of interactions between contaminants in an indicator species severely limits the potential of that species for successful monitoring of the affected component(s). It is worth restating that such effects cannot be simply accounted for or eliminated in monitoring surveys and are thus of the greatest potential interference. Published data will be considered by indicator type, commencing with primary producers and dealing sequentially with molluscs, polychaetes, crustaceans, finfish and mammals; trace metals and organochlorines will be considered together in each case.

A. PHYTOPLANKTON

The information available for phytoplankton is scattered and inadequate. However, Braek *et al.* (1976) noted significant interaction of copper and zinc toxicity for four species of marine phytoplankton and similar toxicity interactions have also been observed for freshwater green algae (Bartlett *et al.*, 1974; Hutchinson, 1974; Wong *et al.*, 1978). Interestingly, Braek *et al.*, (1976) found that whilst copper and zinc acted synergistically (more than additively) in three species, the fourth (*Phaeodactylum tricornutum*) exhibited antagonistic (less than additive) response. Thus, in *P. tricornutum*, addition of zinc ions reduced the growth inhibition caused by copper. In addition, an interaction between zinc and magnesium was observed in *P. tricornutum*, low magnesium concentrations serving to increase toxicity. Whether such interactions between major ions and trace metals reflect a specific action on a transport system in the membrane or an overall effect of the metal on membrane integrity (e.g. see Overnell, 1975; Riisgård, 1979) is uncertain. The relationship of toxicity interaction to the interaction of metals at uptake was studied by DeFilippis and Pallaghy (1976) for mercury and zinc in *Chlorella*. After exposure to mercury, this freshwater species exhibited depressed uptake of ^{65}Zn. Presumably mercury affected some part of the membrane transport system for ^{65}Zn and such effects could give rise to metal tolerance amongst phytoplankters.

Toxicity interactions of organochlorines are also known amongst certain phytoplankters. For example, Mosser *et al.* (1974) found that the toxicity interactions of DDT and PCB, and DDE and PCB, to the marine diatom, *Thalassiosira pseudonana*, differed greatly. Whereas DDT tended to counteract the toxicity of PCBs (Aroclor 1254) to this species, DDE and PCBs acted synergistically. Interactions between DDT and DDE were minimal. These authors also found that the antagonistic effect of DDT on PCB toxicity did not depend on the removal of PCBs from solution, i.e. was not based on a mechanism prior to uptake. Thus, DDT exhibited such antagonism even when added after PCB was taken up by the diatom, indicating an effect at a cellular site. Unfortunately, very little information is available concerning the uptake of either trace metals or organochlorines by phytoplankton; hence mechanisms to explain such interactions of pollutant toxicity as those described above are necessarily speculative.

B. MACROALGAE

Amongst macroalgae, no reports are known concerning interactions of organochlorines; as noted above, macroalgae have been little used as indicators of these compounds. By contrast their use as indicators of trace metals has been quite extensive and they are perhaps second only to bivalve molluscs in their conformation to indicator requirements (Phillips, 1977*b*). However, significant metal–metal interactions have been noted for each of the three species (*Laminaria digitata*, *Fucus vesiculosus* and *Ascophyllum nodosum*) in common use as indicators of trace metals. Bryan (1969) performed extensive laboratory studies on the effects of metals on ^{65}Zn uptake by *Laminaria digitata*. It was observed that additions of 20 μg/litre or more of cadmium, copper or manganese to a solution containing

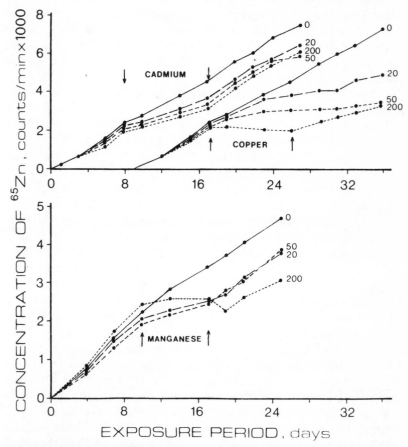

FIG. 83. Effects of the addition of different concentrations of cadmium, copper or manganese on the net uptake of ^{65}Zn by growing algae, *Laminaria digitata*. Vertical arrows indicate the periods of exposure to metals other than zinc; numerals on each line show the amount of metal added, as μg/litre. (After Bryan (1969).)

6 μg/litre [65]Zn inhibited the uptake of the radionuclide (Fig. 83). Whilst the effects of cadmium and manganese appeared largely reversible (i.e. [65]Zn uptake returned to normal rates on removal of the interacting ions), those due to copper were not completely reversible and residual effects on the uptake of [65]Zn were noted even after the removal of copper ions from the ambient seawater. These differences were suggested to be due to the severity of copper toxicity to the plant; at the highest concentration (200 μg/litre), extensive weed death was noted. The growth inhibition caused by copper was probably sufficient to explain the copper–[65]Zn interaction, but cadmium and manganese may have competed for binding sites on the weed rather than influencing the growth of the plant. Whatever the mechanism, it appeared from these studies that, in polluted situations, the co-existence of several metals would give rise to idiosyncrasies in metal uptake rates and the plant would no longer reflect the ambient availability of each metal in isolation.

A later report by Foster (1976) produced data from field observations which support these ideas of Bryan (1969). A comparison of the concentrations of seven trace metals in water and in the algae *Fucus vesiculosus* and *Ascophyllum nodosum* from the relatively clean area of Menai Straits and the polluted Dulas Bay was involved. Metal levels in the water samples were known with some certainty to be accurate mean levels, as studies had been carried out over a period of almost two years. Dulas Bay receives a contaminated inflow of freshwater from Afon Goch, a river draining a highly mineralised area. Calculations of river and tidal flows indicated maximal dilutions of river water in Dulas Bay (at high tide) to be 120:1; thus minimum concentrations of metals can be calculated for Dulas Bay water, as shown in Table 75. Clearly the Afon Goch inflow gives rise to marked contamination of Dulas Bay by copper, zinc and manganese, although concentrations of the other four elements are only moderately elevated here compared with the Menai Straits. Consideration of the data for the macroalgae shows that *Fucus vesiculosus* responds to the higher levels of copper and zinc in the water at Dulas Bay, but not to the higher levels of each of the other five metals. *Ascophyllum nodosum* exhibits a similar pattern except that differentiation of the zinc levels in the two regions is rather poor. Whilst these data could be explained by an unusually high particulate:soluble ratio of most of the metals in Dulas Bay compared with the Menai Straits (giving rise to a lower percentage of total metal in forms available to the alga in the former location compared with the latter), the existence of such an effect for five metals simultaneously appears unlikely. It is more likely that the excessive copper and zinc pollution causes

TABLE 75

COMPARISON OF THE CONCENTRATIONS OF SEVEN TRACE METALS IN WATER AND TWO SPECIES OF ALGAE FROM THE RELATIVELY UNPOLLUTED MENAI STRAITS AND THE CONTAMINATED AFON GOCH AND DULAS BAY, NORTH WALES. DATA FOR WATER ARE MEANS, QUOTED IN μg/litre; DATA FOR ALGAE ARE MEANS OR MEANS $\pm$ STANDARD DEVIATIONS, QUOTED IN μg/g DRY WEIGHT. (AFTER FOSTER (1976).)

Metal	Water			*Fucus vesiculosus*		*Ascophyllum nodosum*	
	Menai	Afon	Dulas[a]	Menai	Dulas	Menai	Dulas
Copper	1·4	2 850	24·5+	9 ± 1	71 ± 11	12 ± 4	68 ± 14
Zinc	11·3	5 580	56·7+	116 ± 11	306 ± 46	149 ± 40	199 ± 43
Manganese	5·3	2 150	23·0+	103 ± 13	71 ± 10	21 ± 6	16 ± 5
Nickel	1·2	10	1·27+	8·1 ± 1	6·0 ± 1	5·5 ± 1	4·6 ± 1
Cadmium[b]	0·2	3·9	0·23+	2·1	1·8	1·8	1·5
Chromium[b]	0·4	3·1	0·42+	4·5	3·8	2·8	2·2
Lead[b]	1·1	2·0	1·11+	3·2	2·3	2·6	2·2

[a] Calculated minimum values; see text.
[b] Algae less extensively studied; hence no standard deviations.

saturation of binding sites on the algal surface by these metals and that other metals are thus taken up less efficiently in the Dulas Bay populations. The high levels of copper may also lead to growth inhibition, altering the relationship between metal uptake and growth dilution of accumulated metals. These data are in some ways reminiscent of the inability of Morris and Bale (1975) to prove a link between manganese concentrations in waters of the Bristol Channel and those in *Fucus vesiculosus*; perhaps metal interactions were also involved in this case. The results of Bryan and Hummerstone (1973a) for manganese in *F. vesiculosus* from the highly polluted Restronguet Creek afford a third example. An understanding of such effects is clearly of great importance if erroneous conclusions regarding the degree of contamination of study sites are to be avoided. In some situations at least it appears that macroalgae are not accurate indicators of ambient metal availability. Such effects appear most prevalent in highly contaminated regions; it could be argued that it is in these regions that accurate data are most vital.

C. MOLLUSCS

Amongst molluscs, most information concerning pollutant interactions involves bivalve molluscs, which have been more extensively studied than either gastropods or cephalopods. In addition, almost all the available data concerns trace metals. No report of interactions between one organochlorine and another at uptake in any mollusc is known. However, one paper exists claiming an interaction between trace metals and the organochlorine methoxychlor. Eisler and Weinstein (1967) found that neither the organophosphate insecticide malathion nor the organochlorine methoxychlor elicited toxic symptoms in quahog clams, *Mercenaria mercenaria*, during a 96-h exposure to concentrations of 3·7 mg/litre and 1·1 mg/litre of the respective compounds. However, consistent dose-dependent changes in the concentrations of both major ions (Ca^{2+}, K^+, Na^+, Mg^{2+}) and trace metals (iron and zinc) in tissues of the clams were found to occur during pesticide exposure. The effects on trace metals were most evident for zinc in the mantle of the clams; animals exposed to either pesticide exhibited consistent increases in concentration of zinc in the mantle. Similar increases in muscle zinc were also noted on treatment with methoxychlor, but not in clams exposed to malathion. Iron concentrations were relatively unaffected by methoxychlor, but were decreased in clam muscle by exposure to malathion. The mechanisms of such effects were unknown to the authors and remain speculative to date. However, bivalves living in estuaries in particular will be commonly exposed to a wide range of pollutants which will, in some cases, include both pesticides and trace metals; such interactive effects on pollutant kinetics are therefore of obvious import in these cases. A later report (B. A. Fowler, *et al.*, 1975) concerning the same species established marked interaction between mercury and iron in epithelial cells of the quahog mantle. Inorganic mercury taken up from solution by the experimental animals was located by electron microscopy in cytosomes of epithelial cells of mantle tentacles. Energy dispersive X-ray microanalysis revealed high levels of both iron and mercury in these cytosomes, which are similar morphologically to metal-rich lysosomes found in mammalian tissues after exposure to metals. Atomic absorption spectrophotometric studies of mantle fringes of the clams produced the results shown in Table 76; mercury apparently caused decreases in iron levels of this tissue at low dosage, but not at high dosage. The co-presence of the two metals in the same cytoplasmic organelle is of most interest; clearly, such systems require further study as they appear different in some respects to the granular sequestration of zinc and copper in barnacles *Balanus balanoides*, for example (see Walker *et al.*, 1975b; Walker, 1977). The use of ultrastructural techniques of analysis such as those reported here should be encouraged, as our current knowledge of metal storage subcellularly is certainly inadequate.

TABLE 76

CONCENTRATIONS (μg/g WET WEIGHT; MEANS $\pm$ STANDARD ERRORS) OF MERCURY AND IRON IN THE MANTLE FRINGES OF QUAHOG CLAMS, *Mercenaria mercenaria*, EXPOSED TO MERCURIC CHLORIDE IN SEAWATER FOR FIVE DAYS AT CONCENTRATIONS OF 0·1, 1 AND 10 mg/litre. (AFTER B. A. FOWLER *et al.* (1975).)

Metal	Exposure concentration of mercury (mg/litre)			
	0	0·1	1·0	10
Mercury	0.90 ± 0.32	1.99 ± 0.57	3.90 ± 1.91^a	6.59 ± 3.70^a
Iron	16.69 ± 2.76	9.61 ± 2.87^a	6.00 ± 1.97^a	15.28 ± 0.91
Fe: Hg ratio[b]	51.45 ± 22.35	6.56 ± 1.82^a	3.22 ± 1.62^a	4.73 ± 1.32^a

[a] Significantly different from respective control value ($p < 0.05$).
[b] Calculated on the basis of individual animal ratios.

Some species of oyster also exhibit significant metal–metal interactions. Brooks and Rumsby (1967) exposed the oyster, *Ostrea sinuata*, to very high concentrations of cadmium in solution, and noted a loss of manganese, lead, silver and vanadium from the visceral mass. However, this probably does not reflect displacement of these ions by cadmium, but rather a loss of intestinal contents containing the contaminants. Hence this report cannot be considered as an example of interaction; it is however, worth noting that ingested food may interfere with analytical results. Most authors using bivalves for monitoring purposes include a 24- or 48-h period of maintenance of samples in clean seawater to permit defecation of gut contents. A later report by Romeril (1971*a*) involved the uptake of ^{65}Zn by *Ostrea edulis*. Uptake of the radionuclide by whole soft parts of this oyster was significantly depressed over the entire 40-day exposure by the addition of very low concentrations (1 μg/litre) of ferric chloride or cobaltous chloride; cobalt depressed uptake rather more than iron. By contrast, both elements increased the uptake of ^{65}Zn into the shell of this species, although the kinetics of ^{65}Zn uptake were different in the presence and absence of the interfering ions (Fig. 84). The author suggested that equilibrium concentrations would be similar in whole soft parts for ^{65}Zn in all three cases and that ^{65}Zn levels would be greater at equilibrium in the shell in the absence of interfering ions. However, the data support these suggestions poorly at best, and the conclusions are based on extrapolation of curves beyond the limits of the experiment. Whatever the equilibrium levels, such effects will be important in the environment where a constantly changing ambient mixture of trace metals will be present. This example is particularly important in that the interfering ions were present at very low

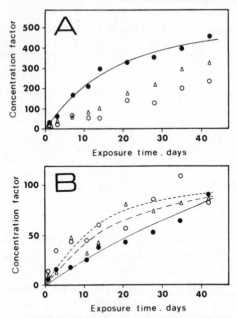

FIG. 84.   Concentration factors describing the net uptake of ^{65}Zn by (A) whole soft parts and (B) shells of the oyster, *Ostrea edulis*. Oysters were exposed to 1 μg/litre of zinc, with or without the addition of either 1 μg/litre iron (as ferric chloride) or 1 μg/litre cobalt (as cobaltous chloride). (After Romeril (1971a).) ——●—— ^{65}Zn, --○-- ^{65}Zn + Co, —△— ^{65}Zn + Fe.

concentrations which bivalves would be expected to encounter in the field. It might be noted here that Coombs (1974) reported investigations of the biochemistry of zinc and copper complexes in this oyster species. Some metal was reversibly bound to amino acids and other small molecules, but about 60 per cent of the total was present in at least two complexes which were associated with cell debris rather than any soluble components. A later comment by Bryan (1976) suggested that Coombs was having some success isolating specific metallothioneins from *Ostrea edulis*, but no published report has been traced to date.

Scallops have been relatively little studied as indicator organisms compared to other bivalves. However, Young and Jan (1976) analysed *Hinites multirugosus* from several sites on the California coast in attempts to define contamination by trace metals in effluent from the Palos Verdes sewage outfall, which receives domestic and industrial waste from Los Angeles. Concentrations of cadmium in tissues of this scallop (and in the

Dover sole; see McDermott and Young, 1974, below) were lower in the outfall zone compared to offshore island sites. In view of the extreme pollution of the outfall site by zinc (with which cadmium is generally found in nature; see Schroeder *et al.*, 1967) as well as other metals such as chromium and copper, this finding was surprising. The authors speculated that cadmium uptake into the scallop may have been depressed by high ambient levels of DDT and its metabolites, also discharged from the Palos Verdes sewage outfalls. As will be seen below, methoxychlor and cadmium are known to interact in the shrimp, *Penaeus duorarum* (Nimmo and Bahner, 1976), the organochlorine depressing cadmium uptake. More recent data from this group have failed to prove this hypothesis (Young, pers. comm.), and laboratory studies are perhaps needed to elucidate the basis of the unusual cadmium profiles in the area.

Mussels have probably been the most widely used indicator types to date, at least for trace metals. In addition, laboratory studies of the uptake of trace metals have been reported by several authors. For many metals, species such as *Mytilus edulis* appear to be ideal indicators; however, exceptions

TABLE 77

CONCENTRATIONS OF CADMIUM, COPPER, LEAD AND ZINC (μg/g WET WEIGHT; MEANS $\pm$ STANDARD DEVIATIONS) IN WHOLE SOFT PARTS OF MUSSELS, *Mytilus edulis*, EXPOSED FOR 35 DAYS TO VARIOUS COMBINATIONS OF METALS (AS CHLORIDES) IN SOLUTION. DATA HAVE BEEN WEIGHT-NORMALISED WHERE APPROPRIATE. (AFTER PHILLIPS (1976a).)

Tank	Exposure concentration (μg/litre)[a]				Concentrations in mussels (μg/g wet weight)			
	Cd	Cu	Pb	Zn	Cadmium	Copper	Lead	Zinc
Control	0	0	0	0	0·47 ± 0·13	<0·12	1·80 ± 0·68	21·2 ± 5·8
1	10	10	10	100	3·11 ± 0·57	0·22 ± 0·09	10·7 ± 1·9	33·0 ± 13·4
2	20	20	20	200	6·13 ± 1·21	1·24 ± 0·47	13·7 ± 3·5	56·4 ± 21·8
3	20	40	40	200	6·02 ± 1·08	7·42 ± 2·31	20·1 ± 7·6	52·3 ± 15·0
4	40	20	20	400	6·68 ± 2·50	0·53 ± 0·15	11·1 ± 4·0	73·7 ± 38·7

[a] Refers to added concentrations of metals.

exist and metal interactions are known. Phillips (1976a) found the uptake of copper by *M. edulis* from solution to be extremely erratic. Mussels exposed to mixtures of four metals in solution were studied, using an exposure period of 35 days (Table 77). Whilst the uptake of cadmium, lead and zinc appeared to be unaffected by the presence of other metals, that of copper bore little relation to the exposure concentration and was certainly affected by alterations in the exposure concentrations of cadmium and zinc (compare tanks 2 and 4 in Table 77). Data from a monitoring survey (Phillips, 1976b) tended to confirm the inability of this species to respond simply to the ambient level of copper contamination; the relationship of copper in mussel samples to that discharged by industry to Port Phillip Bay was obscure. Similar results were noted in the monitoring data of Stenner and Nickless (1974) for Skjerstadfjord in Norway, and other authors have also cast doubts on the monitoring ability of *M. edulis* for copper (Scott and Major, 1972; Davenport, 1977; Davenport and Manley, 1978). Both Phillips (1976a, b) and Davenport and Manley (1978) have considered the effects of interfering parameters on copper uptake by this species of sufficient severity to give rise to insurmountable problems in monitoring surveys. In a later report concerning the uptake of ^{109}Cd by *M. edulis* and three other bivalve species, Jackim *et al.* (1977) found an interference by zinc. Both *M. edulis* and *Mulinia lateralis* exhibited depressed uptake of

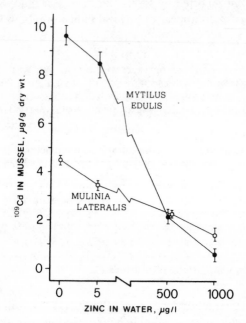

Fig. 85.   Concentrations of ^{109}Cd (μg/g dry weight, means $\pm$ one standard error) attained by whole soft parts of the bivalves *Mytilus edulis* and *Mulinia lateralis*, on exposure to 5 μg/litre cadmium in solution in the presence of 0, 5, 500 or 1000 μg/litre zinc. The exposure period was 7 days at 10 °C and a salinity of 28‰; each point represents results from 10 individuals. (After Jackim *et al.* (1977).)

cadmium in the presence of zinc, in a dose-dependent fashion (Fig. 85). The earlier results in Table 77 may support this effect for *Mytilus edulis*, at least at high concentrations of zinc, but the data are difficult to interpret, as the ratio between the exposure concentrations of cadmium and zinc in the studies of Phillips (1976a) was constant. By contrast, Fowler and Benayoun (1974) found no evidence that zinc influenced the uptake of [109]Cd by the closely related mussel, *Mytilus galloprovincialis*, and further studies would appear necessary to confirm cadmium–zinc interactions in these (and other) bivalves. It may be noted that the effects found by Jackim *et al.* (1977) for *M. edulis* were marked only at high ambient levels of zinc; perhaps this explains the lack of a noticeable effect in field samples (Phillips, 1976b, 1977c). A further report for Mytilids concerns the uptake of selenium by *Mytilus galloprovincialis;* Fowler and Benayoun (1976c) could find no significant effect of added mercury on the net uptake of tetravalent ^{75}Se from solution by this mussel, although a consistent trend towards decreased uptake of the nuclide was present with increased ambient mercury levels. The excretion of ^{75}Se was apparently completely unaffected by the concentrations of mercury present in the mussels. This inability to establish a mercury–selenium interaction is interesting in view of the co-presence of the two elements in marine mammals (see below). Finally, with respect to Mytilids, it might be noted that Brown *et al.* (1977) have observed a peak (peak III) on the eluate from a Sephadex G-75 column which they claim to represent metallothionein and which apparently contains a range of metals including cadmium, copper and zinc. Compounds of this type were noted in a range of samples including the mussel, *Mytilus edulis*, a clam, and the livers of rats and the duck, *Aythya marila*. The authors suggest that the toxic effects of metals may be caused by spillover of metals from metallothioneins into the high molecular weight protein pool; such evidence will be further considered below. The probable existence of metallothionein(s) in bivalve molluscs, however, affords opportunities for metal–metal interaction at storage sites, although the types of interaction possible remain unknown until further information on the specificity of such metallothioneins becomes available.

Finally concerning bivalves, the most interesting report of Luoma and Bryan (1978) merits discussion. This paper concerns the deposit-feeding bivalve, *Scrobicularia plana*; other data on metal uptake by this species in relation to ambient levels of elements may be found in Bryan and Hummerstone (1978) and Bryan and Uysal (1978). The uptake of metals by *S. plana* occurs mainly from sediments, and a simple relationship between the metal concentration in the bivalve and that extractable from the sediment in a dilute acid leach is commonly observed. However, for lead, the correlation between amounts in the sediment and the soft parts of the bivalve was not particularly strong and appeared to vary between locations (see Table 78). Thus, for example, amounts of extractable lead in sediments of the Looe Estuary, Restronguet Creek and the Gannel Estuary were all in the same range, but *S. plana* from the Restronguet Creek contained much

TABLE 78

CONCENTRATIONS OF LEAD IN WHOLE SOFT PARTS OF THE BIVALVE, *Scrobicularia plana*, FROM 14 ESTUARIES IN SOUTH-WESTERN ENGLAND, AND THEIR COMPARISON TO ACID-EXTRACTABLE LEAD IN THE SEDIMENTS OF EACH LOCATION. ACID EXTRACTION OF SEDIMENT WAS PERFORMED USING 1N HYDROCHLORIC ACID. (AFTER LUOMA AND BRYAN (1978).)

Estuary	Concentration of lead ($\mu g/g$ dry weight)	
	Sediment	*S. plana*
Torridge	22–26	35–40
Erme	22–42	47–60
Fowey	33–44	20–42
Camel	41	14
Beaulieu	42	17
Plym	46–60	27–44
Bristol Channel	80–83	49–54
Poole	103	40
Hayle	111	26
Southampton	78–193	44–132
Tamar/Tavy	139–162	40–88
Looe	52–326	120–428
Restronguet Creek (Fal)	210–401	58–72
Gannel	264–1 134	309–1 016

less lead than those from the other estuaries. Clearly, an additional factor (or factors) was present which influenced the availability of lead to *S. plana*. Whilst particle size, organic carbon content and salinity varied significantly between study sites and may have partially influenced the lead availability, none of these parameters was paramount in explaining the observed inter-site differences. However, the amounts of iron present in the sediments were found to be of over-riding importance; thus linear plots of the Pb:Fe ratios for acid extractions of the sediments against the concentrations of lead in *S. plana* gave an excellent fit, with a highly significant correlation coefficient

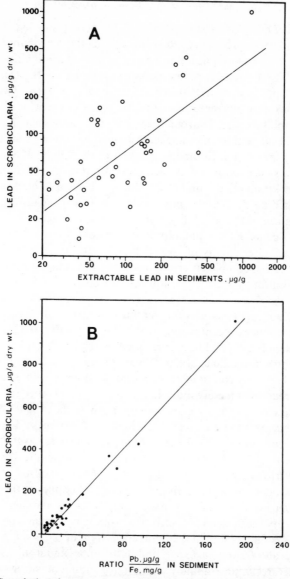

FIG. 86. Correlations between the concentrations of lead in whole soft parts of the bivalve, *Scrobicularia plana*, and (A) concentrations of lead extracted from sediments by 1N hydrochloric acid, or (B) the ratio of lead:iron concentrations extracted from sediments by 1N hydrochloric acid. 37 data points are present in each case, representing results from 14 estuaries in south-west England. For (A), correlation coefficient $r = 0.69$; for (B), $r = 0.99$. (After Luoma and Bryan (1978).)

($r = 0.99$). This plot is shown in Fig. 86 and a log–log plot of the relationship between lead in *S. plana* and extractable lead in the sediment is shown for comparison. The influence of iron on lead availability accounted for some 78–94 per cent of the variance observed in the lead levels of *S. plana*, depending on the statistical method employed. Two possible explanations were advanced to explain this dependence of lead uptake on iron availability. First, hydrous oxides of iron present in the sediments could bind lead, making it biologically unavailable; hence lead availability would vary inversely with the iron content of the sediment. Secondly, the two elements may compete with each other for uptake in the digestive tract after the ingestion of contaminated sediment. These alternatives cannot be distinguished on the basis of present data, but their inclusion is useful in that it emphasises the possibility of metal–metal interaction *exterior* to the animal as well as in the animal itself at uptake. It is also clear from these studies that observations of the lead concentration present in *S. plana* would give rise to completely erroneous data concerning the contamination of study locations by this element unless the effects of iron are taken into account.

To conclude reports concerning molluscs, Martin and Flegal (1975) have noted high copper concentrations (up to 15 000 μg/g dry weight) in livers of three species of squid and have correlated these to high levels of cadmium, silver and zinc in the same organ. Whether such correlations (examples of which are relatively common in the literature) are representative of actual metal interaction or merely show that each metal is absorbed from the same major source which has a definite ion–ion ratio, is uncertain. However, the copper concentrations are exceedingly high, and are worthy of note in their own right; conceivably this element is concentrated in the liver to be used in the synthesis of haemocyanin. More recently, Schipp and Hevert (1978) analysed various organs of the squid, *Sepia officinalis*, from French waters for both copper and iron. With the exception of copper in the blood, the highest concentrations of each metal were found in the hepatopancreas (liver). Histochemical and electron microscopical techniques identified cytolysosome-like bodies in the basal epithelium of the hepatopancreas of this species and *Octopus vulgaris*, and both copper and iron were stored in these structures. Unfortunately, no data for cadmium, silver or zinc were included, and the suggestions of Martin and Flegal (1975) above cannot therefore be assessed by reference to data for storage sites of these metals. However, it appears possible that a wide range of metals are stored in these cytoplasmic inclusions; if this is so, interactions between the metals may occur at storage.

D. POLYCHAETES

The only data available concerning pollutant interactions in polychaetes are those of Bryan and Hummerstone (1973*b*) for zinc and cadmium in *Nereis diversicolor*. Zinc concentrations in this worm are well regulated, varying little with external variation in sediment zinc levels. By contrast, cadmium is regulated little, if at all; surveys of cadmium in the sediments of 26 rivers in southwestern England revealed concentrations of 0·2–9·3 µg/g dry weight (a factor of 46 between least and most contaminated), whilst the polychaetes varied in concentration by a factor of 45 (0·08–3·6 µg/g dry weight). Despite the obvious differences in element kinetics, ambient zinc concentrations were found to influence the rate of cadmium uptake into the species (Fig. 87). Thus increasing the ambient concentration of zinc

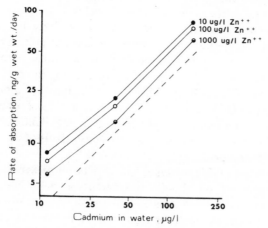

Fig. 87. The effect of zinc on the relationship between cadmium uptake by the polychaete, *Nereis diversicolor*, and cadmium levels in the ambient seawater. Each point is a mean of four individuals; test salinity was 17·5‰. The line of direct proportionality is shown as dashes. (After Bryan and Hummerstone (1973*b*).)

decreased the rate of uptake of cadmium and this effect was observed over a wide range of cadmium exposure levels. The rate of cadmium uptake at 10 µg/litre ambient zinc levels was depressed an average of 9 per cent by elevation of zinc levels to 100 µg/litre, and of 37 per cent by use of 1000 µg/litre zinc. Such effects, although statistically significant, are unlikely to be important in the field except under excessively contaminated conditions. The mechanism of the interaction is unknown.

E. CRUSTACEANS

Crustaceans have also been observed to exhibit metal–metal and metal–organochlorine interactions in some cases. Interactions between the toxic effects of metals have been noted for zinc and cadmium in the freshwater shrimp, *Paratya tasmaniensis* (Thorp and Lake, 1974) and for mercury and cadmium in crabs of the genus *Uca* (Weis, 1976, 1978). The report of Weis (1978) is of particular interest. The fiddler crabs, *Uca pugilator*, *U. pugnax* and *U. minax*, were used, and the effects of methyl mercury and cadmium on regeneration of limbs after multiple autotomy were studied at both 30‰ and 15‰ salinity. Methylmercury and cadmium both retarded limb regeneration and ecdysis at a salinity of 30‰, and were additive in effect when present simultaneously. However, at a salinity of 15‰, the effects of cadmium were intensified greatly, indicating that salinity decreases potentiate the toxic effects of this element. When methylmercury was present in addition to cadmium at the lower salinity, the effects of the latter element were partially ameliorated; thus, the metals are antagonistic in this case. Similar effects were observed if calcium was added at low-salinity exposures to cadmium, tending to confirm the hypothesis of a calcium–cadmium competition. The effects of salinity are almost certainly uptake-related, as O'Hara (1973a, b) has reported increases of both toxicity and uptake of cadmium in *Uca pugilator* at lower salinities. In addition, mercury and cadmium are known to interact in terms of uptake into the tissues of *U. pugilator*, as will be discussed below.

Vernberg *et al.* (1974) analysed gill and hepatopancreas samples of *U. pugilator* exposed to cadmium and mercury alone or in combination; experiments were performed at several salinity–temperature combinations. These data are difficult to interpret, as both salinity and temperature alter whole-body uptake and the transport of metal from gills to the hepatopancreas (see Vernberg and O'Hara, 1972; Vernberg and Vernberg, 1972). However, cadmium was found to cause a general decrease in mercury transport from uptake sites at the gills to storage sites in the hepatopancreas, and this would be expected to give rise to potentiation of mercury toxicity. The addition of mercury may have caused a slight decrease in uptake rates of cadmium also, although whole-body data would be needed to confirm this profile. Clearly, effects such as these serve to emphasise the caution necessary in attempts to use single tissues as indicators of trace metal exposure.

Metal–metal interaction has also been reported recently for copper and lead in the isopod crustacean, *Asellus meridianus* (Brown, 1978). Two

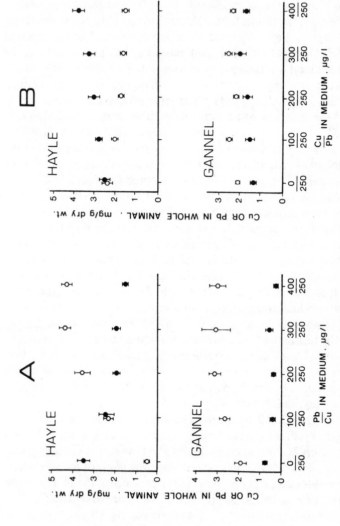

FIG. 88.   The net uptake of copper and lead by isopods, *Asellus meridianus*, from the River Hayle and the River Gannel. In (A), effects of lead on the uptake of copper are plotted; in (B), effects of copper on the uptake of lead are shown. In both cases an exposure period of 14 days was used, at 15 ± 1°C. Each point represents the mean and standard error values for copper (filled circles) or lead (open circles) in four samples of 5 pooled individuals. (After Brown (1978).)

'metal-tolerant' populations of this isopod were studied, the first from the River Hayle, exhibiting tolerance to both copper and lead, and the second from the River Gannel, exhibiting lead tolerance only. Samples from both populations were exposed to constant concentrations of 250 μg/litre of one element with incremental additions of 0, 100, 200, 300 and 400 μg/litre of the second element; the results for uptake are shown in Fig. 88. In the Hayle population, the uptake of both metals was proportional to the external exposure level. However, at a constant exposure level of 250 μg/litre, the uptake of each metal was reduced by increases in the concentration of the second element. In complete contrast, individuals from the Gannel population took up small amounts of copper in all cases and the amounts accumulated were affected little by changes in either copper or lead levels of the medium. Whilst the uptake of lead by Gannel animals was somewhat greater and showed a moderate response to external concentrations of the element, uptake was little affected by the co-presence of copper. The author also demonstrated that lead and copper were stored together in cells of the hepatopancreas; X-ray microanalysis revealed both metals in so-called 'cuprosomes'—membrane-bound vesicles similar to lysosomes but extremely rich in trace elements. It was suggested that the Gannel isopods were tolerant of lead because of their ability to sequester this metal in the hepatopancreas without overt effects. In the Hayle population, however, lead and copper compete for storage sites and the observed interactions between the metals are a function of the ratio of element concentrations at the storage site. Whilst competition at uptake has not been excluded, such data represent an interesting example of metal interactions and further research on the biochemical mechanisms of uptake, storage and excretion could be most illuminating. Furthermore, these studies show that interaction between metals may occur in some populations, but not in others, of a species. Clearly, the potential of such effects for interference in monitoring surveys is substantial.

Nimmo and Bahner (1976) reported an interesting case of interaction between methoxychlor and cadmium in the pink shrimp, *Penaeus duorarum*. The uptake of cadmium by muscle tissues of this shrimp was significantly depressed in the presence of quite low levels of methoxychlor (Table 79), but this effect was not found in the presence of the PCB mixture Aroclor 1254 alone, or in the co-presence of all three toxicants. This last observation suggests that Aroclor 1254 eliminates the effect of methoxychlor on cadmium uptake. As noted previously, interactions of organochlorines and metals are probably of greatest importance in estuaries, particularly those draining agricultural catchments, or mixed agricultural/

TABLE 79
CONCENTRATIONS OF CADMIUM (μg/g WET WEIGHT $\pm$ 2 STANDARD ERRORS OF THE
MEAN) ATTAINED BY MUSCLE OF THE PINK SHRIMP, *Penaeus duorarum*, EXPOSED TO
MIXTURES OF CADMIUM CHLORIDE, METHOXYCHLOR AND THE POLYCHLORINATED
BIPHENYL, AROCLOR 1254. ALL DATA REFER TO 10-DAY FLOW-THROUGH BIOASSAYS AT
25 °C AND A SALINITY OF 20‰. (AFTER NIMMO AND BAHNER (1976).)

Measured toxicant concentration (μg/litre)			Cadmium in muscle (mean $\pm$2 SEM)	Concentration factor
Cadmium	Aroclor 1254	Methoxychlor		
640	BG^a	BG^a	15·58 $\pm$ 2·90	24
774	BG^a	1·1	9·90 $\pm$ 2·79	13
746	0·9	BG^a	13·99 $\pm$ 3·05	19
829	0·9	0·8	16·28 $\pm$ 5·44	20
BG^a	BG^a	BG^a	0·25 $\pm$ 0·10	—
BG^a	BG^a	1·0	0·25 $\pm$ 0·05	—
BG^a	0·7	BG^a	0·28 $\pm$ 0·10	—
BG^a	1·1	1·0	0·26 $\pm$ 0·07	—

^{a} BG: Background concentrations only present (no addition).

industrial areas. It might be noted here also that the loss of trace metals
in cast moults amongst crustaceans (see Chapter 5) may also afford
possibilities for organochlorine–trace metal interactions. Armstrong *et al.*
(1976) have shown that exposure of the Dungeness crab, *Cancer magister*,
to methoxychlor in solution reduced the incidence of moulting in juvenile
individuals. Such an effect, which is not restricted to this compound–species
pair (e.g. see Sharp *et al.*, 1979 on the effects of Kelthane on moulting of the
shrimp, *Crangon franciscorum*) will give rise not only to increases in
organochlorine retention (81 per cent of the total body load of
methoxychlor was associated with the exoskeleton of *C. magister*) but also
to increased retention of trace metals adsorbed to the carapace. Whether
this may be significant for the rest of the tissues is uncertain, as transport of
either organochlorines or trace metals through the cuticle to internal tissues
has not been demonstrated. However, studies which include the carapace of
crustaceans in analysis should be properly cognisant of the effects of
moulting on whole-body levels of trace metals or organochlorines.

F.   FINFISH

Finfish are no exception to the other groups discussed above; both
freshwater and marine species have been reported to exhibit significant

pollutant interaction. Data for the interaction of the toxicity of different pollutants is reasonably plentiful, but will not be considered in detail here, as the effects of pollutant interaction are important in monitoring surveys only if uptake is affected. However, the report of Sprague (1964) may be mentioned as a classical early example; here, the toxicity of copper and zinc to immature Atlantic salmon, *Salmo salar*, was studied. Mixtures of the two toxicants apparently elicited more-than-additive effects, although the linear relationship joining but two experimental points in the figure describing interactive effects might excite some editorial comment in a modern publication. More recently, Weis and Weis (1978) have performed experiments on fin regeneration in the estuarine species *Mugil cephalus* and *Fundulus confluentus* with results somewhat similar to those concerning limb regeneration and ecdysis in crabs noted above. Both methylmercury and cadmium retarded the regeneration of amputated caudal fins in these species when present alone; however, their presence in combination did not significantly influence growth rates of the fins compared with control fish exposed to no added toxicants. Salinity was also significant in its direct effects on regeneration as well as in interactions with the toxicants. Amongst reports concerning organochlorine toxicities, the paper of Macek (1975) is worth mentioning for its breadth of study; bluegills, *Lepomis macrochirus*, were exposed to 29 two-chemical combinations involving a total of 19 pesticides, which included organochlorines, organophosphates and other types of pesticide as well as copper sulphate. Of these 29 pairs of toxicants, 17 pairs were additive in their action, 11 were greater than additive and only one (malathion-copper sulphate) exhibited less-than-additive interaction. Studies of six of the combinations using rainbow trout, *Salmo gairdneri*, revealed little species differences in response. Such studies, which are relatively rapid and easy to perform, are valuable as an initial screening of chemicals for interaction; research in this area should be encouraged, preferably with a follow-up phase to investigate the uptake of compounds used. More recently, Leatherland and Sonstegard (1978) reported interactive effects of dietary mirex and PCBs on serum thyroxine and triiodothyronine levels in yearling coho salmon, *Oncorhynchus kisutch*; the effects of organochlorines on fish hormones have been much neglected to date and may become increasingly important in the future if we are to understand the biochemical basis of action of these compounds.

Instances of pollutant interaction at uptake (or retention) in finfish are perhaps more numerous than those for any other class of organism. This probably reflects a greater research emphasis on commercially important species rather than a greater incidence of such interactions amongst finfish compared with other organisms. Correlations between total mercury and selenium concentrations in black marlin, *Makaira indica*, were noted by Mackay *et al.* (1975*b*) for both muscle and liver tissues; several other metal pairs also exhibited significant correlations in one or other of the tissues, although only mercury and selenium were also significantly related to fish size (weight, length or girth). This finding is reminiscent of the situation in mammals (see below), and whilst no other reports of mercury and selenium correlations in finfish are known, it would not be surprising to discover further instances, at least in long-lived species occupying high positions in the food web. The mechanisms of sequestration of mercury and selenium in such species promises to be an interesting area for future research.

Eisler and Gardner (1973) observed interaction of both toxicity and uptake of cadmium, copper and zinc using the estuarine mummichog, *Fundulus heteroclitus*. The data for uptake are shown in Fig. 89, and are plotted to show the effects of the addition of cadmium at 0, 1 or 10 mg/litre (sublethal levels when cadmium is present alone) on the concentrations of cadmium, copper and zinc found in fish surviving the 96-h exposure period. It is unfortunate that no statistical tests can be performed to investigate the significance of some of the alterations in whole-body uptake noted, and it should also be remembered that the analysis of survivors only represents a bias in sampling, as mortalities differed between treatments. However, dead fish could not be used for analysis, as metal accumulation by adsorption after death is rapid. Notwithstanding these deficiencies, tentative conclusions may be drawn from the data. Cadmium uptake may have been increased somewhat by high ambient levels of copper, whereas high levels of zinc decreased uptake (and gave rise to loss of cadmium in controls; perhaps this is an effect at excretion), although moderately high zinc appeared to increase uptake of cadmium. The accumulation of copper may have been increased at high cadmium levels in the absence of zinc. The uptake of zinc is most interesting; copper appeared to have little effect, and zinc uptake was unaffected by either element, or by increases in ambient concentrations of zinc itself, up to and including 6 mg/litre. However, at concentrations of 12 mg/litre zinc and above, the element was significantly absorbed by mummichogs, and cadmium depressed this effect consistently. Evidently, the interactions between the elements were complex in this study; investigations of this nature are of great importance concerning the use of finfish as indicators (see Chapter 14). It should be realised that the levels of metals to which these fish were exposed are far in excess of any expected to occur in even polluted estuaries; such acute exposure may not be completely representative of field conditions, but certainly produces

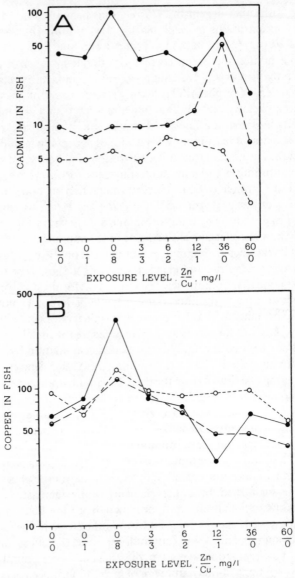

FIG. 89.　The effects of 0, 1 and 10 mg/litre cadmium on the net uptake of (A) cadmium, (B) copper and (C) zinc by mummichogs, *Fundulus heteroclitus*, surviving a 96-h exposure to various mixtures of the three metals in solution. All uptake axes are shown as milligrammes of metal per kilogramme whole-body ash. (After Eisler and Gardner (1973).)

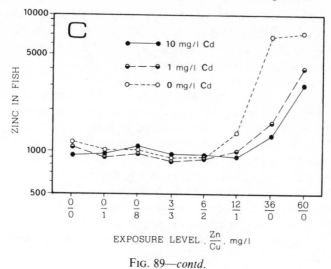

EXPOSURE LEVEL, $\frac{Zn}{Cu}$, mg/l

FIG. 89—*contd.*

interesting results in terms of the regulatory ability of finfish for trace metals.

It is interesting to speculate on the basis of metal–metal interactions in finfish. Reports of the existence of metallothionein-like compounds are becoming more numerous for finfish and, as noted previously, the binding of several metals at one such sequestration point presents possibilities for interaction. Considerable time elapsed subsequent to the first suggestion by Piscator (1964) that metallothioneins might serve to detoxify trace metals in terrestrial animals before researchers discovered such compounds in aquatic biota. However, Olafson and Thompson (1974) reported the isolation of cadmium-binding proteins of a metallothionein-like nature in the copper rock fish, *Sebastodes caurinus*, and showed, furthermore, that exposure of this fish to cadmium chloride elicited an increase in hepatic levels of the protein, the molecular weight of which was 11 000. Similar cadmium-binding proteins were found in livers of the grey seal, *Halichoerus grypus*, and the fur seal, *Callorhinus ursinus*, by the same authors who speculated that the differences in amounts isolated from the two seals might be age related. More recent data concerning cadmium in seal livers supports the idea of an age-related increase in levels of the element (see Chapter 7), but the idea of an age specific increase in metallothionein levels to keep pace with the trace metal concentrations has not been confirmed to date. As different metals exhibit different age dependence in seal tissues, an interesting possibility might be presented for the study of metallothionein specificities or affinities for different metals, simply by comparison of the profiles present in seals of different ages. If the synthesis of these compounds in the liver (and other organs?) is inducible, as it appears to be at least in terrestrial mammals, induction of synthesis by the exposure of an organism to one metal might also protect the organism from the toxic effects of a second metal. The relationship of such a hypothesis to the observed mercury–selenium relationships in some teleosts and marine mammals (Koeman *et al.*, 1973, 1975) is speculative but fascinating. Sheline and Schmidt-Nielsen (1977) found, in a study of methylmercury–selenium interaction in the killifish (mummichog) *Fundulus heteroclitus*, that although selenium pretreatment did not alter whole-body retention of mercury, the distribution of mercury amongst the tissues was influenced by selenium. This again tends to suggest the possibility of interaction at element storage sites subcellularly, and metallothioneins might be expected to be involved.

Amongst other reports concerning metallothioneins in finfish, those of Brown and his co-workers deserve especial consideration. Brown (1977) studied the biochemical distribution of zinc and cadmium in livers of flounders, *Parophrys vetulus*, suffering from tumours in comparison to a normal control group. He observed no significant differences between the zinc and cadmium concentrations bound to metallothioneins in the two groups of fish, but both metals were present at increased concentration in the high molecular weight proteins of livers from tumour-bearing flounders compared with control fish without tumours. Concentrations of cadmium in high molecular weight proteins were elevated by a factor of 3·3 over controls, whilst zinc levels were 2·1-fold higher in the tumour-bearing fish. The hypothesis from these data was bold indeed; that spillover of cadmium from metallothioneins gave rise to a higher competition ratio of cadmium to zinc for binding in zinc-requiring enzymes involved in the metabolism of nucleic acid, and was thus central to the carcinogenetic process. It is a curious fact that almost all the enzymes known to be involved in the transcription of replication of DNA are dependent on zinc for their action. If cadmium were to replace this zinc (because of inadequate sequestration of the former element by metallothioneins), enzyme function would be impaired, with the result that DNA and RNA metabolism would be affected. The changes or mutations involved in the production of carcinogenetic tissue may thus be produced. The existence of metallothioneins in humans—and their function in the reduction of metal toxicity—may lead us to similar hypotheses concerning some forms of tumour production in man (Brown, pers. comm.); whilst this is speculative, it is nevertheless exciting in its far-reaching possibilities. For example, tobacco contains significant amounts of cadmium and the cadmium insult caused by smoking has been documented (Friberg *et al.*, 1974); it should not be necessary to point out that hypertension and cancer are both related to the smoking of cigarettes.

Whatever the eventual outcome of this research on metallothioneins, the fact of their presence in finfish organs which store much of the body burden of elements may suggest that metal–metal interactions could occur in these organs. If one metal displaces another on metallothionein, the displaced element would presumably be more readily excreted; such effects would be noted by the researcher as an interaction between metal levels. In addition, it should be kept in mind that a wide range of elements are probably stored and detoxified by binding to metallothioneins; Brown and Parsons (1978) have shown that mercury will displace copper and zinc from hepatic metallothioneins in chum salmon, *Oncorhynchus keta*, exposed to mercury in the CEPEX (controlled ecosystem pollution experiment) facility of Saanich Inlet. In zooplankton, however, no displacement occurred, although metallothioneins from zooplankton bound mercury as well as zinc and copper. Olson *et al.* (1978) have found metallothionein in liver of the rainbow trout, *Salmo gairdneri*, and suggest that mercury binds to this protein by displacement of zinc. This informative report also shows the existence of metallothionein in gill tissue of the trout and includes speculation on the capacity of this species for the demethylation of mercury. Other species of freshwater finfish also contain metallothionein-like proteins capable of binding several metals. For example, Marafante *et al.* (1972) found such a protein in the liver of the goldfish, *Carassius auratus*, and a later report by Marafante (1976) showed that the protein was also present in kidneys of this species. Once again, its specificity was not great—cadmium, mercury and zinc could all be bound with differing affinities. Clearly, there is much still to learn concerning the biochemical interactions between metals in finfish and in marine mammals. Research to date has but scratched the surface of this interesting field; no doubt the mechanisms evolved in higher organisms for the detoxification of trace elements will be intensively studied in the future.

Some authors have also observed interactions between organochlorines and trace metals in finfish. Eisler and Edmunds (1966) found that exposure of adult northern puffers, *Sphaeroides maculatus*, to endrin at 1 μg/litre for 96 h caused decreases in the zinc content of livers and gills; changes in major ions were also observed. Treated fish exhibited 32 per cent less zinc in gills and 88 per cent less zinc in livers compared with control animals which were not exposed to endrin. In a later study, Eisler (1967a) used the same species exposed for up to 45 days to methoxychlor and methylparathion either individually or in combination. Methoxychlor, present at 30 µg/litre, did not affect feeding, activity or mortality of the test fish; in addition, no effects of the organochlorine were observed on tissue levels of major ions (Na^+, K^+, Ca^{2+}, Mg^{2+}) or trace metals (iron and zinc). By contrast, the organophosphate caused decreased feeding and activity and increased mortality when present alone at 20 200 µg/litre or with methoxychlor at 10 100 µg/litre and 15 µg/litre, respectively. Sublethal effects of methyl-parathion included reductions of the haematocrit, erythrocytes and haemo-globin, complete inhibition of serum esterases, and this compound also reduced magnesium and zinc levels in liver and lowered zinc concentrations in gill filaments. It should be noted that the exposure concentrations involved in this study were exceedingly high, and some at least of the changes observed in the animals exposed to the organophosphate could have been due to starvation induced by the pesticide. Whether similar effects occur in the field is, therefore, uncertain. These data were discussed further in a later paper (see Eisler, 1972).

McDermott and Young (1974) produced data which showed that the elevations in ambient DDT and its metabolites around the Palos Verdes outfall in California may have interfered with the uptake of cadmium in locally caught Dover sole, *Microstomus pacifus*. Although the connection was not made at this time, the similarity of the pollutant profiles for this species and for scallops, *Hinites multirugosus*, was noted by Young and Jan (1976) after further research; these data were discussed above. No conclusion as to the veracity of the suggestion has been possible to date, and the higher cadmium levels found in livers of offshore samples of the sole may, in fact, reflect a greater availability of cadmium from upwelling in offshore regions. The connection between organochlorine exposure and methylmercury concentrations in finfish is also speculative; Goldberg (1975a) has suggested that DDT or PCBs may inactivate or inhibit enzymes involved in the methylation of inorganic mercury in finfish. However, Preston (see discussion section in Goldberg, 1975a) could not agree and it appears just possible from more recent data that demethylation may be affected. If such effects occur, they are more likely to be found in seals or other long-lived marine mammals, as the body burdens of several contaminants reach much higher levels in these animals than in most teleosts.

To conclude this chapter, four papers of note exist concerning interactions between different organochlorines in finfish species. Two of these involve positive findings, whilst the authors of the other two reports could find no significant interactions. Dealing with the latter first, Frederick (1975) exposed white suckers, *Catastomus commersoni*, to dieldrin and to Aroclor 1232 in solution. No differences could be found in the uptake of each compound, whether present alone or in combination, and interaction of these two organochlorines was therefore deemed to be absent. It might be noted, incidentally, that the fish had not attained equilibrium conditions; thus although the rates of uptake may not be affected, the final concentration attained could have varied. This author also noted interesting differences in the relative ability of different organs to metabolise components of the PCB used; whereas peak profiles in gill and intestinal tissues were similar to those of the exposure mixture, liver, brain and kidney tissues all contained components which were not present in the original Aroclor 1232 mixture. Addison *et al.* (1976) injected fry of the Atlantic salmon (*Salmo salar*) intramuscularly with ^{3}H–DDT or ^{14}C–aldrin, as well as with mixtures of the two organochlorines. Clearance of DDT was slow, only 40 per cent being lost in 8 weeks, whereas 45 per cent of the injected aldrin was lost in one day. Both compounds were metabolised, although again the rates varied widely; the half-time of DDT conversion to DDE was 60 days, whereas 50 per cent of the aldrin residues were converted to dieldrin within two days. The processes of excretion and metabolism were unaffected by the presence or absence of the other compound (or its metabolites) in each case.

By contrast to these negative reports, rainbow trout, *Salmo gairdneri*, are known to exhibit interactions between DDT, dieldrin and methoxychlor. Mayer *et al.* (1970) analysed only visceral fat bodies from fish receiving each of these three compounds in food at one of three dosage levels. All concentrations were reported on the basis of lipid weights, thus eliminating any effect of lipid variations on the results. Dieldrin tended to increase the accumulation of DDT and DDE in visceral fat bodies, whereas methoxychlor had the opposite effect and the co-presence of both dieldrin and methoxychlor also gave rise to depression of DDT and DDE levels in this tissue. The accumulation of dieldrin was reduced by either of the other two compounds. Methoxychlor storage was increased by dieldrin, decreased by DDT and decreased by the simultaneous presence of dieldrin and DDT. These effects may be compared to those observed in the studies of Macek *et al.* (1970) on the same species, using DDT and dieldrin labelled with ^{14}C and introduced to the trout in food. In the pyloric caecae, dieldrin increased the uptake of DDT, whereas DDT decreased the accumulation of dieldrin (Fig. 90). This profile, similar qualitatively to that noted by

Mayer *et al.* (1970) for visceral fat bodies, was suggested to be due to the inhibition of DDT excretion by dieldrin, whereas DDT apparently partially blocked the uptake of dieldrin into the tissue. As interaction effects on a whole fish basis were minimal, such changes appear suggestive of alterations in tissue distributions of the compounds rather than gross changes in organochlorine uptake. The contribution of metabolic

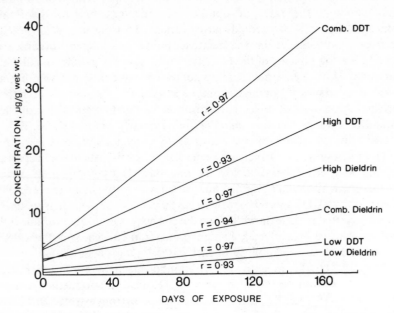

FIG. 90. Regressions and their correlation coefficients (*r*) describing the accumulation of DDT and dieldrin in pyloric caecae of rainbow trout, *Salmo gairdneri*, exposed to low or high doses of individual organochlorines (0·2 or 1·0 mg/kg/week, respectively) in food, or to a combination of the two organochlorines at high dosage. (After Macek *et al.* (1970).)

alterations of each compound due to catabolic enzyme activity in the liver (which is probably inducible) is uncertain. However, if the hepatic microsomal enzymes in fish are relatively non-specific for substrates (as they are in humans at least for some drugs), some interaction between organochlorines at least may be ascribed to the induction of these enzymes. Once again, we must conclude that there is much yet to learn concerning interactions between organochlorines and many of the answers will be produced from studies at the biochemical level.

G. CONCLUSIONS

To summarise, interactions can occur between different trace metals, between different organochlorines and even between trace metals and organochlorines or other pesticides in some species of aquatic organisms. In most cases the basis for the interaction is uncertain. As trace metals are probably taken up (either from solution or food) at specific sites, interaction is possible at uptake for these pollutants; it may be noted that trace metals may also interact with major ions at this stage. In addition, trace metals may interact with each other at storage or sequestration sites by competition for specific binding sites, or at excretion. Organochlorines, if they are taken up by simple diffusion across membranes, are unlikely to interact at uptake, but may do so at storage either by competition or by indirect effects elicited by the induction of hepatic (or other?) microsomal enzymes which metabolise a range of contaminants. In most cases, increases in biotransformation of organochlorines absorbed by biota will yield higher proportions of metabolites of generally shorter half-life, i.e. the overall excretion rate will tend to be increased. It may be noted that discussion in this chapter has been restricted exclusively to what may be termed endogenous interactions, i.e. interactions between contaminants occurring within the organism or at uptake into the organism. Some pollutants may, of course, also interact exogenously before being taken up into organisms. For example, Bartha (1969) cites an example in which two herbicides present together in soil underwent transformation to a hybrid compound which contained one molecule of each parent compound. The hybrid product naturally will have different properties (ecosystem cycling, bioavailability, etc.) to those of either parent compound. More recently, Maugh (1973) speculated on the possible routes of transformation of DDT to specific polychlorinated biphenyls, which might take place by irradiation with ultraviolet light from sunlight. Such chemical transformations of pollutants, whilst they may, in a few cases, be important in determining the environmental insult elicited by a contaminant, are considered outside the scope of this chapter.

CHAPTER 12

The Use of Shells as Indicators

At several points in this book it has been noted that the shells of molluscs and crustaceans may contain significant amounts of pollutants. In the case of trace metals, these may be either adsorbed on to the surface of the shell relatively non-specifically, or may be integrated into the shell structure. Organochlorines, however, are almost all adsorbed on to shells, as very little lipid exists in any shell material. Adsorbed pollutants generally exhibit reversible binding and are lost rapidly on return of the organism to relatively unpolluted water. However, trace metals which are integrated into shells are very firmly bound and are often non-exchangeable with ambient elements. In certain cases, authors have suggested that the accumulation of trace elements in shells affords possibilities for the use of these materials as indicator tissues. This chapter presents a brief discussion of our current knowledge of trace metals in shells and concentrates on molluscs and crustaceans. It is clear that for shells to be used as an indicator of ambient element availability, they must contain metals in simple relation to those in seawater. This basic pre-requisite of an indicator may be satisfied in some instances, and present data are reviewed in an attempt to discover whether shells have advantages over soft tissues as indicator materials for monitoring trace metals.

A. CRUSTACEANS

Stable Isotopes of Trace Metals and Artificial Radionuclides
Current knowledge of non-radioactive isotopes of trace metals in the exoskeletons of crustaceans is quite limited, although some studies have been reported on decapod crustaceans and on barnacles. Studies on decapod crustaceans do not suggest that the exoskeleton is of any particular

use as an indicator of most trace metals. For example, exposure of the lobster, *Homarus vulgaris*, to zinc in seawater elicited only moderate increases in the zinc concentrations in the shell (Bryan, 1964) and the same was true when zinc was introduced by injection into the animal. Later studies by the same author (Bryan, 1966, 1967) and a review paper (Bryan, 1968) failed to show any benefit in the use of the shell as an indicator of zinc or copper in any species of decapod crustacean, although these studies were extensive and included both freshwater and marine species. Both metals were quite strictly regulated in all tissues of the species studied, although the hepatopancreas showed some evidence of acting as a temporary storage organ; both this tissue and blood exhibited high concentrations of each metal. Species differences were noted in the concentrations of zinc in shells of 13 species; the range in zinc levels was from $3 \mu g/g$ to $28 \mu g/g$ by wet weights (Bryan, 1968). The author suggested that these differences might be associated with moulting, as new shells might contain metalloenzymes not present in old shells. However, much of the zinc found in exoskeletons was considered to be adsorbed non-specifically on the shell surface. Concentrations of copper in shells of these species were lower than those of zinc, ranging from 'trace' ($< 0.5 \mu g/g$) to $9.5 \mu g/g$ wet weight; no data were presented to indicate the proportion of copper which was adsorbed and that which was integrated into the shell.

By contrast, studies of manganese in the lobster, *Homarus vulgaris*, revealed a completely different pattern of tissue distribution (Bryan and Ward, 1965). About 98 per cent of the total body load of this element was present in the exoskeleton and mean concentrations of manganese exceeded $200 \mu g/g$ by wet weight (Table 80). Exposure of these animals to concentrations of up to 1 mg/litre manganese in solution elicited no great increase in tissue levels of the element, and absorption was obviously very slow from solution. The uptake of manganese from food must predominate in the field, but again it would appear that this element is regulated and that shells are not useful as indicators of ambient concentrations of the metal. Studies of the distribution of manganese in the shell showed that dorsal and lateral surfaces of the carapace contained similar concentrations. In addition, the inner layer of the shell, which is uncalcified, contained very little manganese, and in the calcified part of the shell, concentrations of the element increased towards the outer surface. This is probably not due to surface adsorption of manganese, which appears minimal (see Table 80) except in cases where decomposition of what may have been manganese dioxide occurred in pits on the shell surface of animals exposed to very high concentrations of the metal in solution. The authors suggested that

TABLE 80

MEAN CONCENTRATIONS (μg/g WET WEIGHT) OF MANGANESE IN TISSUES OF THE LOBSTER,
Homarus vulgaris, AND THE EFFECTS OF ELEVATIONS IN AMBIENT EXPOSURE
CONCENTRATIONS OF MANGANESE. BOTH MALE AND FEMALE LOBSTERS OF WEIGHTS
200–350 g WERE USED. (AFTER BRYAN AND WARD (1965).)

Tissue	Fresh lobster	Exposure concentration and period		
		50 μg/litre for 20 days	100 μg/litre for 23 days	1 000 μg/litre for 15 days
Whole blood	2·4	1·0	1·1	3·9
Abdominal muscle	0·8	0·6	0·5	0·8
Hepatopancreas	4·8	4·5	4·1	4·1
Gills	20·8	8·4	8·9	26·9
Shell (dorsal carapace)	225	268	236	207
Ossicles/teeth of gastric mill	155	136	118	106
Stomach fluid	2·8	1·2	—	1·6
Hindgut and rectum	10·5	2·0	2·8	3·4
Excretory organs	3·7	2·8	3·9	5·1
Ovary	1·6	—	3·2	3·3

manganese was present at such high levels in calcareous tissues (shell, ossicles and teeth of gastric mill) because of its substitution for calcium in calcium carbonate. Finally, it is worth noting that moulting was accompanied by a large decrease in concentrations of manganese in the exoskeleton (i.e. the new shell contained only about a quarter of the manganese levels present in the cast shell) even when the cast moult was eaten by the animal.

Cadmium kinetics in decapod crustaceans appear different again. Wright (1977a) published quite extensive data for the uptake of this element by the shore crab, *Carcinus maenas*. He found that concentrations of cadmium in the carapace were exceeded only by those in haemolymph, and both these tissues responded to increases in the ambient cadmium level in solution. Salinity was found to affect cadmium uptake by the carapace, this being greater in more dilute seawater (similar effects are known for the soft tissues of other species; see Chapter 5). The carapace was also important in cadmium loss when animals were returned to clean seawater and this suggests that bound cadmium may have been mostly adsorbed rather than integrated into the shell. These data compare well with a more recent study of the kinetics of [109]Cd uptake and loss in the same species (Jennings and Rainbow, 1979). The exoskeleton contained between 59 and 80 per cent of the total body load of the radionuclide after exposure of *C. maenas* to 0·1, 1 or 10 mg/litre labelled cadmium in solution. By contrast, after uptake of [109]Cd from labelled food, only 22 per cent of the total body load of the nuclide was found in the exoskeleton. This suggests that the exposure of crustaceans to metals in solution may, in some cases, lead to overestimation of the importance of the carapace in element accumulation (compared with that in field situations), presumably because non-specific adsorption of some metals to this tissue may occur. The rapid loss of [109]Cd associated with the exoskeleton of *C. maenas* when animals previously exposed to the nuclide in solution were maintained in clean water (Jennings and Rainbow, 1979) supports this hypothesis. However, even for a single element the amount of surface adsorption which occurs may be species-dependent, as the carapace of the shrimp, *Lysmata seticaudata*, is apparently somewhat less important than that of *C. maenas* in determining whole-body accumulation of [109]Cd from solution (Fowler and Benayoun, 1974).

The importance of the route of uptake of an element in determining the amounts in crustacean exoskeletons has also been emphasised by Amiard (1978*a, b*). Thus, on exposure of *Carcinus maenas* to [110m]Ag in solution, the exoskeleton and gills accumulated 40 and 38 per cent respectively of the total body load of the nuclide, and subsequent moulting of these animals served as an important route of excretion for [110m]Ag. By contrast, [110m]Ag accumulated from food was found mainly in internal organs, particularly the hepatopancreas, with levels in the carapace being much lower (Amiard, 1978*a*). The surface-adsorbed metals derived from solution were rapidly lost to clean seawater, whereas those in the carapace derived from labelled food were presumably integrated into the skeletal matrix (Amiard, 1978*b*). Similar data were reported by Fowler and Benayoun (1976*b*) for the uptake of ^{75}Se by the shrimp, *Lysmata seticaudata*; again, the shell exhibited greater importance in determining whole-body levels of the isotope when uptake was from solution. These profiles are reminiscent of the suggestions of Hannerz (1968) that the ratio of mercury concentrations in gill and liver tissues of finfish could be used to elucidate the predominant route of uptake of the element. Certainly, the use of shells as indicators of ambient availability would suffer from such differences, as a high concentration of an element in shells could be due to either moderate ambient levels of that metal in solution or to the ingestion of severely contaminated food. If the importance of the two uptake routes differs in different populations of an organism, monitoring data concerning levels in shells alone will be impossible to interpret accurately.

A certain amount of published data also exists concerning trace elements in the shells of barnacles. Gordon *et al.* (1970) analysed the shells of several species of *Balanus* from Chesapeake Bay for sodium and manganese. Whilst changes in sodium content were ascribed to the effects of salinity, those of manganese were considered to relate to the level of manganese in the ambient water. However, the ambient manganese may also be correlated to salinity (e.g. see Graham *et al.*, 1976), and it is probably impossible under field conditions to separate salinity effects from availability effects. Bourget (1974) studied a wider range of both major and minor elements in five species of barnacles from the coasts of Wales. The concentrations of manganese in shells correlated to the amount of organic matter present in the shell matrix and this could have had a bearing on species differences in manganese levels. A general agreement between manganese concentrations in shells and (estimated) levels of this element in the ambient water was noted, concentrations being higher in the shells of barnacles from estuarine conditions; the above comments concerning salinity pertain here also. Whilst zinc and aluminium were also detected in these studies, no quantitative data were quoted. Walker *et al.* (1975a) attempted to prove indicator ability in the barnacle, *Balanus balanoides*, by relating the concentrations of zinc in soft tissues and the shell to estimated ambient concentrations of the element at four locations in Wales. Whilst this is not to be recommended because of the uncertainties involved in estimating the average concentrations of zinc in seawater, data for the soft parts suggested that the barnacle responded to zinc contamination of its environment (Table 81). Thus, raising the ambient zinc levels by an estimated factor of 8 caused elevation in the concentrations of zinc in whole soft parts by a factor of 3·34. By contrast, the amounts of zinc present in the

TABLE 81

MEAN CONCENTRATIONS OF ZINC (μg/g DRY WEIGHT) IN THE WHOLE SOFT PARTS AND SHELLS OF THE BARNACLES, *Lepas antifera*, FROM THE NORTH ATLANTIC AND *Balanus balanoides* FROM FOUR LOCATIONS IN WALES. ALSO GIVEN ARE ESTIMATES OF THE MEAN AMBIENT CONCENTRATION OF ZINC IN WATER (μg/LITRE) AT EACH LOCATION. (CALCULATED FROM WALKER *et al.* (1975a).)

Species	Location	Estimated ambient zinc	Zinc in soft parts	Zinc in shell
Lepas antifera	North Atlantic	3·0	691·4	49·6
Balanus balanoides	Menai Strait	12·5	5 139	64·6
Balanus balanoides	Alltwen	50·0	8 850	55·8
Balanus balanoides	Castle Point	50·0	10 515	108·5
Balanus balanoides	River Ystwyth	100·0	17 188	125·7

shell increased by a factor of only 1·95. More importantly, shells of the sample from Alltwen in Cardigan Bay (known to be severely polluted by zinc; see Ireland, 1973, 1974) contained less zinc than those of the samples from the Menai Strait, although the soft parts (and estimated water levels of zinc) exhibited the opposite profile. Clearly, the shells were not particularly efficient indicators of the ambient zinc concentrations in seawater in this instance. It is possible that certain parameters may interfere with the accumulation of metals by the shells of barnacles, but not with that by the soft parts (or that the qualitative or quantitative effects of interfering parameters differ in the two cases). For example, both salinity and position in the intertidal zone affect the accumulation of manganese by barnacle shells (Pilkley and Goodell, 1963; Pilkley and Harriss, 1966) whereas the effects of these parameters on manganese uptake into whole soft parts may be different. Alternatively, it is possible that the differences discussed above may be instrumental, i.e. that shells respond mainly to metals in solution, whereas elements in the soft parts are accumulated from both solution and ingested food. Whatever the explanation, there is certainly no evidence that any advantage accrues from the use of crustacean shells to monitor trace metals, compared with the use of the soft parts.

Naturally Radioactive Elements
There may be an advantage to the use of shells of crustaceans rather than their soft parts for the biological indication of at least some of the naturally occurring radionuclides. These elements, which include polonium, radon, radium, actinium, thorium, protoactinium and uranium, are considered here with the trans-uranics, which are elements with atomic numbers greater than that of uranium and are produced by nuclear reactions. Some of these radioactive isotopes may exhibit selective accumulation in calcareous materials, i.e. some of them may be present in higher concentrations in the shells of crustaceans (and other organisms) than in the soft parts of these species. However, there is a certain amount of doubt about the predominance of the carapace in determining concentrations of such isotopes in crustaceans; as will be seen below, different authors have reached opposite conclusions with respect to this matter. In any event, it must be emphasised here that preferential accumulation of isotopes in shells, rather than soft parts, of crustaceans is of analytical significance only; there are no grounds whatever for supposing that an organism or tissue which exhibits unusually high concentrations of a pollutant is an ideal indicator of that pollutant (*cf.* Papadopoulou and Kanias, 1977). The indicator ability of an organism thus depends on the conformity of the

organism to indicator pre-requisites discussed in Chapter 2, and on its response to variables discussed in the different chapters of this book. However, a great capacity for accumulation of one or more pollutants is nevertheless helpful to the analytical chemist. In certain circumstances biological indication is the only method available for study of pollutants because the concentrations of these pollutants in abiotic components of the ecosystem are impossible to determine analytically. This may be the case for some of the artificial radionuclides (e.g. see Folsom *et al.* 1963; Folsom and Young, 1965), for hydrocarbons or organochlorines (e.g. see Goldberg *et al.*, 1978), and for many of the naturally radioactive elements discussed in this section. In these instances, no choice is available; the indicator method must be used and the decisions made by nature and evolutionary adaptation accepted by the researcher. However, the pitfalls inherent in this approach are obvious; if the available indicator tissue or organism responds to unknown variables and no supportive analysis of the ambient concentrations of the pollutant in water can be made, the results based on the biotic component may be totally misleading as an index of the relative contamination of different study areas. Research into pollutants present in an organism but which cannot currently be analytically determined in the ambient environment of the organism is thus one of the most difficult and challenging areas of biological indication. Given this warning, we may now examine the data available concerning the use of exoskeletons of crustaceans as indicators of the naturally occurring radioactive elements. It should perhaps be emphasised that the present text does not attempt to fully review the subject of radionuclides in aquatic biota; rather, examples will be selected in an attempt to show whether such elements may be usefully monitored by biological indicators or their tissues. The conclusions in some cases also have a bearing on the use of shells to monitor stable isotopes of the more abundant trace metals.

Pillai *et al.* (1964) first showed that plutonium could be measured in biota of the oceans, using organisms taken from areas off southern California; several isotopes of plutonium were noted but no data on tissue distributions of the isotopes were given. Ward (1966) undertook experiments designed to study the uptake of ^{239}Pu from solution by the lobster, *Homarus vulgaris*. She found that cast moults contain greater amounts of activity than the intermoult carapace and the new shell accumulated ^{239}Pu rapidly during calcification. A total of 89·5 per cent of the total body load of ^{239}Pu was present in the exoskeleton of a lobster prior to ecdysis (Fig. 91) which comprised only 43 per cent of the total weight of the animal. By contrast, the hepatopancreas and muscle contained only 4·6 and 1·2 per cent,

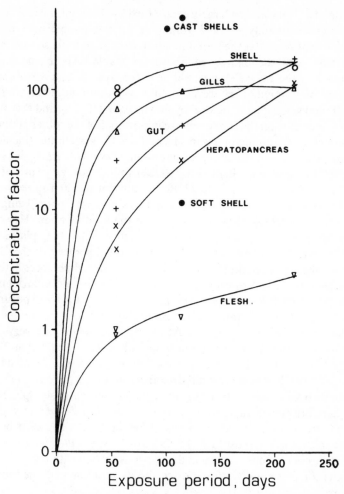

FIG. 91. The net uptake of ^{239}Pu by tissues of the lobster, *Homarus vulgaris*, exposed to the radionuclide in solution at $6·5 \times 10^{-2}$ μCi/litre. Data refer to inter-moult specimens; ^{239}Pu levels in cast moults and new shells are shown as solid symbols for comparison. (After Ward (1966).)

respectively of the total body load of ^{239}Pu. Similar results were reported for ^{237}Pu uptake by the shrimp, *Lysmata seticaudata*, by Fowler *et al.* (1975*b*) during a 27-day exposure period to this isotope in solution. Moulting of these shrimp severely affected whole-body accumulation profiles and cast moults lost little of their radioactivity to water. The retention of ^{237}Pu was also largely determined by the moulting rates of the animals. Unfortunately, no data were given for the tissue distribution of plutonium isotopes after their accumulation from food in these studies; by comparison with the data cited above for stable trace elements, the importance of the exoskeleton would be expected to be less when uptake from food predominates. However, uptake of plutonium in shrimp from ingested food was found to be slow by Fowler *et al.* (1975*b*), and this might lead to speculation on the actual relative importance of the routes of uptake for isotopes of plutonium in organisms in the field. Vertebrates (including fish) are also known to absorb plutonium very inefficiently in some instances. For example, Pentreath (1978*a*) found that exposure of the plaice, *Pleuronectes platessa*, to ^{237}Pu in solution resulted in very little uptake. Accumulation from labelled food was also very poor, being less than 0·0012 per cent of the concentration in the food ingested. However, species differences certainly exist; by contrast to the plaice the elasmobranch, *Raja clavata*, accumulated up to 0·2 per cent of the ^{237}Pu given in a single labelled meal (Pentreath, 1978*b*). Such differences between species seem to extend to crustaceans as well. Fowler and Guary (1977) labelled the polychaete, *Nereis diversicolor*, with ^{237}Pu by exposure in solution and fed the contaminated worms to shore crabs, *Carcinus maenas*, or edible crabs, *Cancer pagurus*. Absorption efficiency was very high compared with vertebrates or elasmobranchs and was estimated as 20–60 per cent. Of the ^{237}Pu accumulated, 43–85 per cent was found in the hepatopancreas, 8–43 per cent in the carapace and 5–10 per cent in muscle and gill, with lesser amounts in the stomach, gut and haemolymph. These crabs therefore appear superior to *Lysmata seticaudata* in their absorption of ^{237}Pu from food. In addition, the differences in tissue distribution between this study and those of Ward (1966) or Fowler *et al.* (1975*b*) tend to confirm the conclusions reached in the previous section with respect to the accumulation of metals by the carapace and its variation with the route of exposure.

Further data for organisms from the field may help to clarify the real possibilities for the use of crustacean exoskeletons as indicators of radionuclides. Such studies are relatively rare because of the difficulties associated with the analysis of plutonium in organisms which are exposed only to small amounts of this element from nuclear fallout sources. However, nuclear fuel reprocessing also produces significant quantities of plutonium, and close to reprocessing plants the ambient levels may be much higher. Guary *et al.* (1976) studied the levels of plutonium in *Cancer pagurus* and *Pleuronectes platessa* from coastal waters near La Hague reprocessing facility in France. In the plaice, only gut tissues accumulated significant amounts of plutonium (agreeing with the findings of Pentreath, 1978a, above). However, in the edible crab, the gills showed the highest specific activity by far (Table 82), followed by the hepatopancreas, the gastrointestinal tract and the carapace. At least in this instance it appears that surface adsorption to the carapace is relatively minimal, although the high levels in the gills are almost certainly due to adsorption and are somewhat surprising in view of the results of Ward (1966), who found less in this tissue than in the exoskeleton of lobsters (Fig. 91).

TABLE 82

DISTRIBUTION OF PLUTONIUM IN THE TISSUES OF THE EDIBLE CRAB, *Cancer pagurus*. DATA ARE SHOWN FOR SPECIFIC ACTIVITIES IN EACH TISSUE (BY SEX IN SOME CASES) AND ARE CONVERTED TO CONCENTRATION FACTORS USING A MEAN VALUE FOR THE SPECIFIC ACTIVITY OF PLUTONIUM IN AMBIENT SEA WATER OF 0.013 pCi/LITRE (AFTER GUARY *et al.* (1976).)

Tissue	Sex[a]	Specific activity (pCi/kg wet weight)	Concentration factor
Gills	M + F	102·00	7 846
Exoskeleton	M + F	2·23	172
Muscle	M + F	0·52	40
Gonads	M + F	0·56	43
Remainder	M + F	0·39	30
Whole organism	M + F	3·50	269
Hepatopancreas	M	0·97	75
Hepatopancreas	F	2·89	222
Gastrointestinal tract	M	2·30	177
Gastrointestinal tract	F	2·14	165
Haemolymph	M	0·23	18
Haemolymph	F	0·44	34

[a] M = male, F = female; note large difference for hepatopancreas and *cf.* Chapter 9.

The distribution of elements other than plutonium in the tissues of crustaceans are less well documented. However, some indication of differences between different isotopes exists in the literature. For example, Heyraud *et al.* (1976), in detailed studies of polonium in the euphausiid, *Meganyctiphanes norvegica*, found ^{210}Po concentrations to be size dependent (levels were higher in smaller individuals) and to be highest in the internal organs, particularly the hepatopancreas and the alimentary tract (Table 83). A dynamic model of the flux of ^{210}Po suggested that food was

TABLE 83

CONCENTRATIONS OF ^{210}Po (MEANS ± ONE STANDARD DEVIATION) IN THE TISSUES OF THE EUPHAUSIID, *Meganyctiphanes norvegica*, FROM THE NORTH-WESTERN MEDITERRANEAN SEA AND THE CONTRIBUTION OF EACH TISSUE TO THE TOTAL ACTIVITY OF THE ORGANISM. (AFTER HEYRAUD *et al.* (1976).)

Tissues and organs	pCi/g dry material	Wet:dry weight ratio	pCi/kg wet weight	Per cent total wet weight[a]	Contribution to total activity of euphausiid (pCi/kg wet weight)	Per cent of total activity
Alimentary tract	9·9 ± 1·1	4·08	2 426 ± 267	0·98	24 ± 3	8·3
Eyes	0·8 ± 0·3	3·73	214 ± 80	2·08	5 ± 2	1·7
Hepatopancreas	23·6 ± 1·8	3·51	6 724 ± 513	2·24	151 ± 12	52·1
Muscle	0·24 ± 0·02	4·74	51 ± 4	43·0	22 ± 2	7·6
Exoskeleton	1·04 ± 0·07	4·25	245 ± 16	35·5	87 ± 6	30·1

[a] The values in this column do not add up to 100 per cent but to 83·8 per cent; the deficiency of 16·2 per cent represents interstitial fluid lost during the dissection process.

the major source of this isotope and faecal pellets the major excretion route. This isotope is therefore not preferentially concentrated in shells of at least this species of euphausiid. More recently, Guary and Fowler (1978) found neptunium (^{237}Np) to be taken up by the shrimp, *Lysmata seticaudata*, and the crab, *Cancer pagurus*, mostly into shells, but again exposure was in solution only and the relevance of these studies to the situation in the field is uncertain.

Conclusions on the Use of Crustacean Shells as Indicators

Three major problems exist concerning the use of crustacean exoskeletons to monitor trace metals or radionuclides in the aquatic environment. The first of these is the dichotomy between adsorbed and absorbed metals. It is clear from the above examples that some elements are (either specifically or non-specifically) readily adsorbed to the outer surface of the carapace of crustaceans. In addition, elements may be integrated into the matrix of the shell as calcification occurs. Because of these two very different modes of element accumulation, interpretation of data will be extremely difficult. If we assume that two populations exhibit differences in their concentrations of an element in the carapace material, this might be ascribed to either long-term (meaningful) differences in the degree of contamination of available food or, alternatively, to short-term differences in the availability of metals in solution, which may be transient and atypical. Thus, it is possible that shells will provide an atypical result for metal availabilities in two regions because of transient changes in the amounts of metals adsorbed to the exoskeleton. By contrast, soft parts respond in a much more buffered or time-integrated fashion (assuming that elements are not regulated to within definite limits). Whilst it might be theoretically possible to overcome the influence of adsorbed metals on the results (for example, by subjecting all samples to dilute acid wash prior to analysis) such procedures would be difficult to regulate in that it would be extremely difficult to remove only the adsorbed metals without disturbing the metals integrated into the calcareous material (which itself is highly acid-soluble).

Secondly, the problem of moulting must be overcome. The results of most authors indicate that metal levels are unusually low in new, soft shells of crustaceans immediately after ecdysis; during the intermoult period, concentrations typically increase concomitant to shell thickening and calcification. Elements attain their maximal levels just prior to shedding of the exoskeleton and cast moults exhibit the greatest concentrations of elements as a result. Even if cast moults are eaten, as is commonly observed in some species, the concentrations of trace metals in the new shell take some time to increase once more. This regular variation in element levels with the moulting cycle will influence attempts to monitor such pollutants using the exoskeletons. Thus variations in the metal concentrations of samples from different areas could be caused by the different stages of intermoult in the animals selected rather than by any divergence in the abundance of metals at each location. Clearly, the samples selected must be at equivalent stages in the moult–intermoult cycle if this parameter is not to influence results. If metals are laid down in the exoskeleton throughout the intermoult cycle with varying efficiencies (so that, for example, the surface and inner layers of the exoskeleton vary in element concentration; see Bryan and Ward, 1965, above, for an example), the stage of the animals with respect to moulting will be particularly important. For some cases at least it would appear that selection of hard-shelled individuals would not be sufficient to eliminate the effects of moulting on the results obtained from survey samples.

Finally, it must be recognised that research into the trace element content of shells of crustaceans is in its infancy, and even less is known of metal kinetics in the exoskeleton than of those in the soft parts. In particular, very little information exists concerning the effect of external variables on the element accumulation in the carapace. Although variables such as salinity and position in the water column have been implicated as significant in the accumulation of elements such as manganese in barnacles, no data exist as to how widespread such phenomena are. It might be expected that metals are laid down in the exoskeleton of crustaceans in proportion to the degree of contamination of the soft parts. At least in the case of manganese in the lobster, *Homarus vulgaris* (Bryan and Ward, 1965), this appears to be partially the case. If this is so, any variable (season, size, salinity, and so on) which influences the trace metal levels found in the soft tissues will have a secondary effect on the amounts of metals present in the shell. Furthermore, these parameters may also influence the direct adsorption process and the effects on this process may differ both qualitatively and quantitatively from those on the accumulation of elements by the soft tissues.

The multiplicity and complexity of the parameters which may influence the accumulation of trace elements (either stable or radioactive) by the exoskeleton tissues of crustaceans must lead us to conclude that a great deal more information is needed before such tissues can be employed with confidence as indicators of the ambient availability or abundance of trace elements in aquatic environments. The regulation of some elements to a defined range of concentration in crustaceans (above and see Chapter 14) may suggest that such elements cannot be usefully monitored in either shells or soft parts of these species. However, other metals (often those of less, or no, importance physiologically) appear not to be regulated; further studies concerned with the prospects of using crustaceans as indicator organisms should be concentrated on these elements.

B. MOLLUSCS

Gastropod Species

Much less information is available concerning pollutants in the shells of gastropod molluscs than has been published for crustaceans. Because of this relative paucity of data, all trace elements, whether stable isotopes or radionuclides, will be considered in one section.

Mullin and Riley (1956) found that cadmium was present at much higher concentration in the soft parts of gastropods than in their shells (Table 84).

TABLE 84

MEAN CONCENTRATIONS OF CADMIUM ($\mu g/g$ DRY WEIGHT) IN WHOLE SOFT PARTS AND SHELLS OF SEVEN SPECIES OF GASTROPOD MOLLUSCS FROM THE IRISH SEA. ALSO SHOWN IS THE RATIO OF CONCENTRATIONS OF THE ELEMENT IN SOFT PARTS TO THOSE IN THE SHELL. (AFTER MULLIN AND RILEY (1956).)

Species	Cadmium in whole soft parts	Cadmium in shell	Ratio $\dfrac{\text{whole soft parts}}{\text{shell}}$
Buccinum undatum	31·80	0·018	1 767
Calliostoma zizyphinum	3·05	0·049	62
Gibbula umbilicalis	0·83	0·029	29
Littorina littoralis	3·54	No data	—
Littorina littorea	1·84	0·012	153
Nucella (= *Thais*) *lapillus*	37·90	0·082	462
Patella vulgata	16·40	No data	—

Thus the ratio of concentrations in the soft tissues to those in shells varied from 29 to almost 1800, depending on the species concerned. The levels of cadmium in the shells would present much greater analytical problems, not only because they are very low relative to the soft parts, but also because of possible matrix interference effects. Three of these species were also studied by Segar *et al.* (1971), as was the limpet, *Crepidula fornicata*; these data are shown in Table 85. Data for cadmium reveal ratios for the concentration in

TABLE 85

MEAN CONCENTRATIONS OF TRACE ELEMENTS (μg/g DRY WEIGHT) IN WHOLE SOFT PARTS AND SHELLS OF THE GASTROPOD MOLLUSCS, *Buccinum undatum*, *Nucella* (= *Thais*) *lapillus*, *Crepidula fornicata* AND *Patella vulgata*. *N. lapillus* and *P. vulgata* WERE SAMPLED IN THE IRISH SEA WHEREAS THE OTHER TWO SPECIES WERE TAKEN FROM THE SOLENT. (AFTER SEGAR *et al.* (1971).)

Element	*Buccinum undatum*		*Nucella lapillus*		*Crepidula fornicata*		*Patella vulgata*	
	Soft parts	Shells	Soft parts	Shells	Soft parts	Shells	Soft parts	Shells
Aluminium	300	83	160	170	150	80	240	470
Cadmium	2·2	0·05	73	1·64	3·9	2·4	31	2·0
Chromium	ND	ND	ND	ND	2·0	ND	ND	ND
Cobalt	0·76	0·16	0·30	0·25	17	0·15	0·4	0·80
Copper	180	9·1	150	0·29	270	1·8	7·7	42
Iron	110	476	65	4·5	2000	1600	150	330
Lead	5·4	0·45	4·9	0·45	3·9	0·42	32	46
Manganese	1·7	1·2	12	1·1	17	2·1	13	8·6
Nickel	0·6	0·12	2·4	0·25	850	1·6	2·5	0·54
Silver	0·58	0·11	ND	ND	0·97	0·10	ND	ND
Zinc	620	13·0	860	0·59	940	1·1	84	51

ND: not determined.

soft parts to that in shells of about 44 for both *Buccinum undatum* and *Nucella lapillus*; both results differ considerably from those of Mullin and Riley (1956) and it is not clear whether this represents a real difference or whether it is indicative of problems with analytical methodologies. The species differences shown in the data of Table 85 are particularly noteworthy, e.g. the unusual accumulative ability of the limpet *Crepidula fornicata* for nickel and, to some extent, iron. It is seen that the ratio of levels of elements in soft parts to those in shells is highly species dependent; clearly, this indicates either differences in the processes of shell calcification and synthesis between species, or perhaps differences in the capacity of the shells of the various species to adsorb metals from the ambient seawater.

This mass of data, whilst interesting in terms of its indication of which elements may be found in large quantities in the shells of gastropods, does not afford any possibility for estimation of the indicator ability of shells for trace elements. However, two surveys have been reported which permit a comparison of contamination profiles for metals in shells and soft parts. The first of these was published by Navrot *et al.* (1974) and concerns a survey of eight elements in the limpet *Patella vulgata* from the Mediterranean coast of Israel. Data for six elements are shown in Fig. 92, where profiles of metal contamination are plotted with distance from the major sewage outfall at Tel Aviv. In the cases of silver and strontium, results for the soft tissues indicated a consistent and marked contamination profile; silver concentrations declined with distance from Tel Aviv, whilst strontium levels increased. By contrast, levels of each element in shells exhibited very little variation and we must conclude that elements are not therefore integrated into the shell matrix in proportion to their concentration in the soft tissues. Consideration of the data for the other elements confirms this conclusion; contamination profiles for the soft parts and the shell were in no case similar, and generally the shell exhibited less variability in element concentrations than did the soft parts. Clearly, the shell is responding to ambient metals in a completely different manner to the soft tissues. The second survey of note is that of Ireland and Wootton (1977); these authors studied metals in the marine gastropods *Thais lapillus* and *Littorina littorea* from nine sites on the coast of Wales. Results for the soft parts have already been discussed in Chapter 2 (see text and Fig. 3). Comparison of metal profiles in the shells and soft parts is possible at four of the sites, and these data are shown in Table 86. It is notable that the concentrations of metals in the shells of the two species were similar, notwithstanding differences in the accumulation of elements in the soft parts; *L. littorea* accumulated greater amounts of manganese but

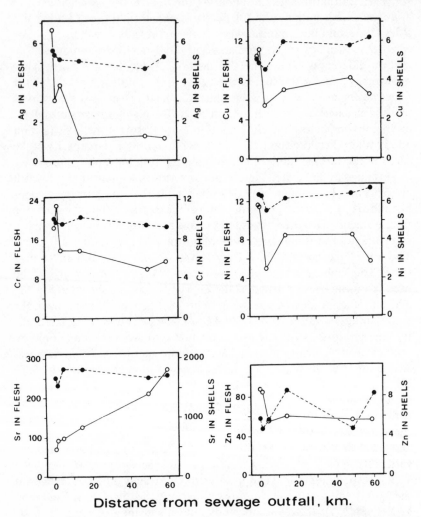

Fig. 92. Mean concentrations (μg/g dry weight) of silver, copper, chromium, nickel, strontium and zinc in whole soft parts (continuous line, left-hand axis) and shells (dotted line, right-hand axis) of limpets, *Patella vulgata*, from six sites on the Mediterranean coast of Israel. Data are plotted as a function of distance from Tel Aviv sewage outfall, which is believed to be a source of some elements. (After tabulated data in Navrot *et al.* (1974).)

TABLE 86

CONCENTRATIONS (MEANS ± STANDARD ERRORS, µg/g DRY WEIGHT) OF COPPER, LEAD, MANGANESE AND ZINC IN WHOLE SOFT PARTS AND IN SHELLS OF THE GASTROPODS, *Thais lapillus* AND *Littorina littorea*, FROM FOUR SITES ON THE COASTS OF WALES. EACH SAMPLE WAS MADE UP OF SIX INDIVIDUALS. (AFTER IRELAND AND WOOTTON (1977).)

Species	Site	Copper		Lead		Manganese		Zinc	
		Soft parts	Shell	Soft parts	Shell	Soft parts	Shell	Soft parts	Shell
Thais lapillus	Llandudno	223 ± 18	2·6 ± 0·2	3·9 ± 0·4	44·9 ± 2·1	12·6 ± 0·6	4·2 ± 0·3	889 ± 67	3·1 ± 0·2
	Barmouth	166 ± 6	3·6 ± 0·1	9·6 ± 1·0	30·0 ± 0·3	8·3 ± 0·3	3·2 ± 0·1	562 ± 25	3·0 ± 0·1
	New Quay	223 ± 10	3·6 ± 0·1	6·4 ± 0·3	28·4 ± 0·4	5·9 ± 0·2	2·8 ± 0·1	564 ± 41	2·7 ± 0·1
	Tenby	168 ± 13	2·8 ± 0·2	11·8 ± 0·5	30·6 ± 0·8	12·3 ± 0·5	2·8 ± 0·2	492 ± 28	3·0 ± 0·2
Littorina littorea	Llandudno	79 ± 5	2·1 ± 0·1	7·1 ± 0·5	41·5 ± 1·4	34·0 ± 2·8	8·2 ± 0·4	129 ± 6	3·0 ± 0·3
	Barmouth	95 ± 7	3·6 ± 0·1	7·6 ± 1·0	29·7 ± 0·3	34·9 ± 4·4	8·3 ± 0·2	96 ± 2	3·0 ± 0·1
	New Quay	96 ± 9	3·5 ± 0·1	9·9 ± 0·6	28·8 ± 0·4	21·6 ± 1·8	5·5 ± 0·2	133 ± 4	2·6 ± 0·1
	Tenby	73 ± 8	2·8 ± 0·2	5·8 ± 0·4	28·8 ± 0·4	18·6 ± 1·7	5·8 ± 0·2	98 ± 3	2·8 ± 0·2

less copper and zinc in its soft tissues compared with *T. lapillus*. In addition to this similarity between the absolute concentrations of metals in the shells of the two species, the location-based differences in metal levels in the shells were extremely similar for each species. However, the trends shown by the shell do not match those of the soft parts for either organism. This observation confirms the conclusion above—that the soft parts and shells of gastropods respond to different portions of the total ambient metal load. It is tempting to suggest that metal accumulation by the shell is dominated by the adsorption of elements from solution, whilst the soft parts probably accumulate most of their total load from food. However, this is probably only partly true. It is certainly clear that in the cases of these two surveys, the amounts of metal found in shells of the gastropods studied bore little obvious relationship to ambient metal availability or to anthropogenic contamination of the study areas. The use of shells of these species cannot therefore be recommended as indicator materials, at least for the elements studied by these authors. It may be noted that the lack of obvious indicator ability in shells is valid whether elements preferentially accumulate in the shells or in the soft parts. Thus, for example, there is no evidence to suggest that the shells of gastropods such as those in Table 86 are better indicators of lead than of copper, even though the former element is present mostly in shells, whereas the latter metal is found mainly in the soft tissues. This phenomenon serves to remind us that indicator ability has little relationship to the ability of an organism or a tissue to accumulate unusually large amounts of metals (see discussion on radionuclides in crustaceans, above).

Much less information concerning naturally radioactive elements is available for gastropod molluscs compared with that published for crustaceans or bivalve molluscs. However, elements such as plutonium are found in the shells of gastropods, and in some cases it would appear that concentrations in the shell exceed those in the soft parts. Thus Guary and Fraizier (1977) observed high levels of plutonium in gastropods from the western coast of France, particularly near the nuclear fuel reprocessing plant at Ecalgrain, La Hague (Table 87). These data will be discussed in more detail in the section dealing with bivalve molluscs below; although it might be noted here in passing that the ratio of the concentrations of plutonium in shells and soft tissues of the gastropods studied appears to be location dependent, and that the location dependence of these data is different for soft tissues and for shells.

For the sake of completeness, it is worth mentioning that the accumulation of trace elements by the shells of gastropods is also apparently sensitive to perturbation by environmental factors, at least in

TABLE 87

CONCENTRATIONS OF PLUTONIUM (MEANS ± STANDARD DEVIATIONS, pCi/kg WET WEIGHT) IN THE SOFT TISSUES AND SHELLS OF FOUR SPECIES OF GASTROPOD MOLLUSCS TAKEN FROM TWO LOCATIONS CLOSE TO THE NUCLEAR FUEL REPROCESSING PLANT AT LA HAGUE IN FRANCE. (AFTER GUARY AND FRAIZIER (1977).)

Location	Species	Plutonium in soft tissues	Plutonium in shells
St. Vaast-la-Hougue	*Littorina littoralis*	0·82 ± 0·23	1·0 ± 0·4
	Nucella lapillus	0·58 ± 0·18	5·3 ± 1·9
	Patella vulgata	0·60 ± 0·18	2·1 ± 0·7
	Crepidula fornicata	0·33 ± 0·10	26·7 ± 6·6
Ecalgrain	*Littorina littoralis*	13·3 ± 3·5	7·1 ± 2·3
	Nucella lapillus	3·4 ± 1·0	2·7 ± 0·9
	Patella vulgata	2·2 ± 0·7	1·7 ± 0·6

some instances. Thus, Pilkley and Goodell (1963) have found that both water temperature and salinity may influence the ionic composition of the shells of gastropods. Such effects will only serve to compound the problems associated with the use of these tissues to monitor trace elements in aquatic ecosystems.

Bivalves and Stable Trace Metals or Artificial Radionuclides

The processes of shell synthesis and calcification in bivalve molluscs are quite well understood; data for oysters may be found in Galtstoff (1964) and mussels are dealt with in the excellent review book of Bayne (1976). These data will not be discussed here and interested readers should refer to the two reviews.

Several authors have published data concerning the amounts of metals found in the soft parts and shells of bivalves; these data serve to show the relative accumulative abilities of the two tissues which are, of course, metal dependent to a large extent and also depend somewhat on the species considered. Mullin and Riley (1956) observed much greater concentrations of cadmium in soft tissues of the bivalves, *Mytilus edulis, Chlamys opercularis* and *Pecten maximus*, than in their respective shells; for *M. edulis* the whole soft parts contained 3·21 µg/g dry weight, compared with 0·003 µg/g in the shell. Brooks and Rumsby (1965) studied several elements in the soft parts and shells of the mussel, *Mytilus edulis aoteanus*, the oyster, *Ostrea sinuata*, and the scallop, *Pecten novae-zelandiae*, all samples being derived from Tasman Bay in New Zealand. Mean levels of each element in the two tissues are shown in Table 88. Several elements (Cd, Cr, Pb, Ni, Ag,

Zn) were below the limits of detection in shells from all three species and little can be said of these apart from noting that their concentrations in shells were generally less than in the soft tissues. However, two surprising results were obtained in that vanadium was found to be accumulated in the shells of all species in much greater amounts than in the soft parts; in addition, the shell of the mussel was observed to accumulate appreciable amounts of molybdenum. Similar survey data were published by Segar *et*

TABLE 88

MEAN CONCENTRATIONS OF ELEVEN TRACE ELEMENTS (μg/g DRY WEIGHTS) IN THE WHOLE SOFT PARTS AND SHELLS OF A MUSSEL, AN OYSTER AND A SCALLOP FROM TASMAN BAY, NEW ZEALAND. (AFTER BROOKS AND RUMSBY (1965).)

Element	*Mytilus edulis aoteanus*		*Ostrea sinuata*		*Pecten novae-zelandiae*	
	Soft parts	Shells	Soft parts	Shells	Soft parts	Shells
Cadmium	< 10	< 20	35	< 20	249	< 20
Chromium	16	< 3	3	< 3	10	< 3
Copper	9	3	41	< 1	9	2
Iron	1 960	< 10	682	570	2 915	2 000
Lead	12	< 5	10	< 5	16	< 5
Molybdenum	0·6	11	0·3	< 0·1	0·9	< 0·1
Manganese	27	< 1	8	1	111	1
Nickel	7	< 2	2	< 2	6	< 2
Silver	0·1	< 0·1	5·6	< 0·1	0·7	< 0·1
Vanadium	5	110	3	49	9	130
Zinc	91	< 100	1 103	< 100	283	< 100

al. (1971) for eleven trace elements in six marine species and one freshwater species of bivalve (Table 89). It is seen that the relative concentrations of any one metal in the soft parts and shells of these animals vary with the species considered, as noted previously for gastropods. It is interesting that the high accumulative power of the gastropod shell for lead, seen at least for some species (Tables 85 and 86 above) is not matched in any species of bivalve (*cf.* Talbot *et al.*, 1976). Differences between the freshwater *Anodonta* sp. and marine species are not consistent for most metals, although the freshwater species accumulates larger amounts of manganese in both soft parts and shells than any of the marine bivalves. As manganese concentrations are salinity dependent this probably reflects the higher availability of this element in freshwater environments.

A certain amount of survey data also exists in which authors have

TABLE 89

MEAN CONCENTRATIONS (μg/g DRY WEIGHT) OF ELEVEN TRACE ELEMENTS IN THE WHOLE SOFT PARTS AND SHELLS OF SIX MARINE SPECIES AND ONE FRESHWATER SPECIES OF BIVALVE. MARINE SPECIES WERE DERIVED FROM THE IRISH SEA OR THE SOLENT; THE FRESHWATER SPECIES, *Anodonta*, WAS TAKEN FROM A LAKE AT ABERFFRAW, ANGLESEY. (AFTER SEGAR *et al.* (1971).)

Species	Tissue	Aluminium	Cadmium	Chromium	Cobalt	Copper	Iron	Lead	Manganese	Nickel	Silver	Zinc
Cardium edule[a]	Soft parts	2700	1·5	ND	7·1	11	590	0·76	6·3	7·9	0·04	130
	Shell	84	0·34	ND	0·16	3·0	1600	0·44	2·0	0·11	0·11	6·8
Glycymeris glycymeris	Soft parts	110	3·3	ND	0·92	5·7	68	3·5	34	1·4	ND	120
	Shell	420	0·03	ND	0·20	0·1	47	0·60	1·5	0·16	ND	160
Mercenaria mercenaria	Soft parts	615	2·1	0·79	4·3	25	5400	18	18	11	1·3	94
	Shell	71	0·80	0·37	1·2	1·7	1600	0·43	1·5	2·4	0·21	3·4
Modiolus modiolus	Soft parts	260	7·1	ND	5·5	10	350	1·9	47	133	ND	530
	Shell	150	0·03	ND	0·30	1·9	15	1·9	20	0·20	ND	6·2
Mytilus edulis	Soft parts	1230	5·1	1·50	1·6	9·6	1700	9·1	3·5	3·7	0·03	91
	Shell	76	0·95	ND	0·15	2·0	290	0·4	3·6	2·1	0·10	0·04
Pecten maximus	Soft parts	610	13·0	ND	8·5	3·3	170	8·3	140	49	ND	230
	Mixed shell	190	0·04	ND	0·31	1·1	30	2·0	16	0·21	ND	6·6
	Upper valve	230	0·04	ND	0·20	0·1	37	0·62	12	1·2	ND	4·1
	Lower valve	230	0·04	ND	0·20	0·1	49	0·60	4·9	2·4	ND	6·1
Anodonta sp.	Soft parts	107	1·2	0·84	0·42	3·0	5500	1·2	2100	0·35	0·28	120
	Shell	173	0·43	0·45	0·22	7·6	2600	0·60	560	1·2	0·15	6·4

[a] = *Cerastoderma edule*.
ND: not determined.

reported the concentrations of trace metals in both soft parts and shells of bivalves taken from several sites. For example, Windom and Smith (1972) studied the concentrations of iron, manganese and zinc in tissues of the oyster, *Crassostrea virginica*, from ten locations on the coast of Georgia. Results are shown in Fig. 93. It is clear that in no case do profiles for metal levels in the shells match those for the same metal in the soft parts. However, this does not appear to be due to the regulation of metal levels in the shells; significant differences occurred between element concentrations in the shells of different samples. The most probable explanation is that the soft parts and the shell of *C. virginica* respond to different portions of the total trace metal load on the ecosystem. Thus, for example, the uptake of trace

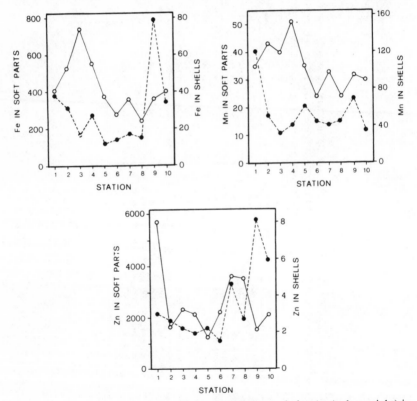

FIG. 93.   Mean concentrations of iron, manganese and zinc (μg/g dry weight) in whole soft parts (continuous lines, left axes) and shells (dashed lines, right axes) of oysters, *Crassostrea virginica*, from ten sites along the coast of Georgia. (After tabulated data in Windom and Smith (1972).)

elements by shells may occur by adsorption from solution, whereas that by soft parts is probably dominated in most cases by metals ingested with food. If the solution and food (phytoplankton, seston) components exhibit different relative concentrations at different locations, the profiles produced from shells and soft parts will necessarily differ also. However, this explanation relies on the assumption that trace elements in the shell are derived mainly by surface adsorption from solution. In some cases at least this may not be the case, and metals may actually be integrated into the matrix during the synthesis of the shell by the mantle.

In addition, it is significant that manganese concentrations are generally greater in the shell of *C. virginica* than in the soft parts (compare the scales of the vertical axes in the profile for manganese in Fig. 93), although, as the profiles do not match, the actual ratio of manganese in shells and soft tissues varies with location. Frazier (1975) correlated the levels of iron and manganese in the soft parts of *C. virginica* with shell deposition. Thus, from studies of the levels of elements in both shells and soft parts of oysters from Chesapeake Bay, this author showed that the amounts of iron and manganese incorporated into the shell during the season of rapid shell growth were large compared with the total body load of each element in the soft parts (see Table 28 in Chapter 5). This was particularly marked in the case of manganese, and calculations showed that about 20 μg of manganese was deposited in the shell each day during the shell growth season (about 150 days in length), compared with an average body load in the soft parts of 10 μg of manganese. Clearly, manganese flux in the soft parts was very high in periods of active shell synthesis and the possibility is remote that either soft parts or shells of this species could be used to indicate the environmental abundance of this element. Whilst the turnover of iron was somewhat less, it is similarly improbable that these oysters could accurately indicate the ambient iron levels in the environment during seasonal shell growth. It is interesting that the levels of manganese present in shells of the oysters studied by Frazier were typically about 500 μg/g dry weight, compared with a seasonal range of about 2 to 30 μg/g dry weight in the soft parts. If these are compared to the concentrations shown in Fig. 93 for the same species from Georgia coasts, it is seen that the Chesapeake Bay oysters exhibited unusually high amounts of manganese in their shells and rather low amounts in their soft parts. One would therefore expect the Georgia oysters to exhibit a somewhat lesser turnover of manganese in the soft parts during the period of shell growth, although the amounts of the element lost to the shell will nevertheless be significant. Perhaps this difference is a function of salinity; it will be remembered from the discussion of crustaceans and gastropod molluscs earlier in this chapter that manganese is commonly highly concentrated in shells compared with soft tissues of organisms and may be dependent on the ambient salinity for its persistence in seawater. Survey data are available also from the recent studies of Bryan and Uysal (1978) on the burrowing bivalve, *Scrobicularia plana*, in the Tamar Estuary. Gross comparison of the profiles by these authors for copper, iron, manganese and zinc in whole soft parts and shells of *S. plana* involved eight samples taken at distances of 1 to 18 km from the mouth of the estuary.

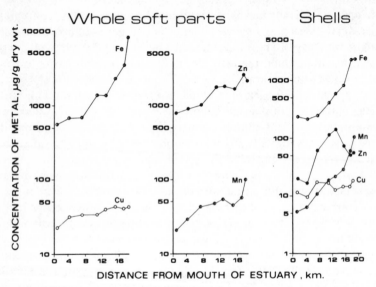

FIG. 94. Mean concentrations (μg/g dry weight) of copper, iron, manganese and zinc in whole soft parts and shells of the bivalve, *Scrobicularia plana*, from eight sites in the Tamar Estuary, UK. All data refer to 1969–1970; shells were washed but not scrubbed. Note different vertical scale for shells compared with soft parts. (After Bryan and Uysal (1978).)

Agreement between the contamination profiles was qualitatively quite good for copper, iron and manganese in whole soft parts and shells (Fig. 94), although quantitative differences between the response of the two tissues were present at least for some of these metals. In addition, significant differences were noted in the profiles obtained from shells according to whether these were merely washed to remove adhering sediment or scrubbed to remove what the authors referred to only as 'a more firmly attached coating'. The differences observed according to the preparative technique used for shells were extensive; for example, shells of animals at the 11 km station lost 50 per cent of their copper, 60 per cent of their iron, 20 per cent of their manganese and 70 per cent of their zinc by scrubbing compared with simple washing. It is impossible to know from the report whether such metals are part of the outer shell matrix or periostracum, or whether they are present in fine particulates attached to the shell surface. However, this source of variation must represent a real problem in the use of shells as indicator materials. Additional variation in the metal levels present in shells was noted with both shell size and part of the shell sampled in these studies. The extreme dependence of zinc concentrations on the pre-analysis preparative techniques used to clean the shell may have been partly to blame for the disagreement between the profiles for zinc in soft parts and shells of *S. plana* from the Tamar. Despite the poor agreement for zinc and the above-noted effects of washing techniques, however, these results are certainly indicative of better agreement between contaminant profiles derived from whole soft parts and shells than the results of Windom and Smith (1972) discussed previously. Perhaps the reason for this is the relative constancy of the trace metal load in each exposure route for *S. plana*, i.e. although shells and soft parts may respond to different portions of the total load of a metal in the ambient environment, both these load parameters may be dominated by estuarine dilution and may therefore change in a similar fashion with distance towards the mouth of the estuary. It is commonly much easier to obtain qualitative agreement from different indicator types in estuaries which are dominated by oceanographic influences (dilution of metals by freshwater–saltwater mixing, tidal effects, etc.) than in open coasts, where simple gradients of metal abundance or availability with distance from a point source may not exist.

Occasional reports are available in which authors have studied the uptake of metals by shells of bivalves in laboratory experiments or in model ecosystems. Some of these studies involve stable isotopes and others involve artificial radionuclides. Kameda *et al.* (1968) observed appreciable uptake of ^{65}Zn by the shell of *Mytilus edulis* when mussels were exposed to this radionuclide in solution and similar results for *Tapes japonica* were also quoted. By comparison to the soft tissues, shells appeared to respond faster to additions of ^{65}Zn in the ambient seawater and this might suggest different types of metal binding occurred in the tissues. A later study by the same group (Shimizu *et al.*, 1971) included some interesting data for ^{58}Co uptake, which was grossly similar to that of ^{65}Zn. Intrigued by the high capacity of the shell to take up metals, the authors studied ^{58}Co accumulation by empty shells and by the shells of live animals. The results showed concentration factors for ^{58}Co of similar magnitude in each case, and the authors concluded that this was evidence for uptake by surface adsorption rather than incorporation of the nuclide into the shell during the synthesis of new shell by the mantle. Experiments involving coating the surfaces of the shells with molten paraffin suggested that most ^{58}Co was adsorbed on to the outer surface of each valve, little adsorption occurring on to the inner surfaces; the periostracum may be involved in this process.

It was emphasised in previous sections of this chapter that conclusions concerning the uptake of trace elements by shells could not be based solely on experiments involving metal accumulation from solution only. Thus, the shells of crustaceans in particular were found to contain the majority of the body load of metals when animals were exposed to metals in solution, whilst much less metal was present in shells if exposure were via contaminated food. The difference involved here is clearly one of metal adsorption on to the shell from solution and metal integration into the shell matrix by the mantle after its absorption from food. Such differences would also be expected in bivalves. However, current evidence suggests that the adsorptive capacity of the shells of bivalves is not as great as that of crustaceans (although it must be remembered that each group of species also exhibits differing adsorptive capacities for different elements). These differences are best exhibited in the comparative studies of Fowler and his co-workers, using the mussel, *Mytilus galloprovincialis*, and the shrimp, *Lysmata seticaudata*. For ^{109}Cd, Fowler and Benayoun (1974) found that shells of the mussel contained only 5·5 per cent of the total body load accumulated from solution, whilst the exoskeleton of the shrimp contained 23·2 per cent. ^{75}Se (tetravalent) was also taken up better by the shrimp exoskeleton than by the shell of the mussel (Fowler and Benayoun, 1976*b*) and ^{203}Hg followed a similar pattern (Fowler *et al.*, 1978*a*). The relatively poor uptake of radionuclides from solution by the shells of mussels compared with the response of the soft parts was also noted by Pentreath (1973*a*) in studies of the accumulation of ^{58}Co, ^{59}Fe, ^{54}Mn and ^{65}Zn by *Mytilus edulis*. The shell of bivalves may therefore be expected to be of even less importance in determining the whole-body loads of most elements when uptake occurs from food and the studies of Amiard (1978*a*, *b*) on the kinetics of ^{110m}Ag in *Scrobicularia plana* support this concept. Perhaps the most interesting study is that of Saward *et al.* (1975), in which copper was added to a model marine ecosystem including a food chain consisting of phytoplankton, the bivalve *Tellina tenuis* and 0-group plaice, *Pleuronectes platessa*. Figure 95 shows comparative data for the uptake of copper by the shell and soft parts of the bivalve at four exposure concentrations (added nominal copper levels

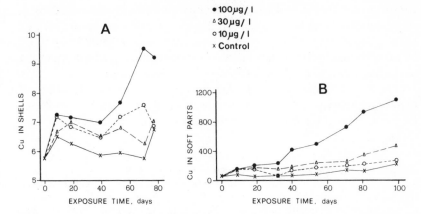

FIG. 95. The accumulation of copper by (A) shells and (B) whole soft parts of the bivalve, *Tellina tenuis*, exposed to nominal concentrations of 0, 10, 30 and 100 μg/litre added copper in a model ecosystem containing a food chain of mixed phytoplankton, *T. tenuis* and 0-group plaice, *Pleuronectes platessa*. All data for copper in shells and soft parts expressed as μg/g dry weight. (After Saward *et al.* (1975).)

of 0, 10, 30 and 100 μg/litre; mean measured concentrations in solution were 4·93, 8·83, 17·78 and 47·58 μg/litre, respectively). It is seen that whilst the shells accumulated very little copper (concentrations increasing by a factor of only about 1·6 even in the highest exposure level), the whole soft parts accumulated the element rapidly in proportion to the external concentration; animals in the highest concentration exhibited increases in soft tissue levels of copper of a factor of about 20 during the same period.

Such data do not lend confidence to any suggestion of using the shells of bivalve molluscs as indicators of trace metal abundance in marine or estuarine environments. Certainly, trace elements may accumulate in the shells of these species under certain conditions; however, it is also known that some elements at least can accumulate significantly in the soft parts of bivalves without influencing the levels present in shells. However, mussel shells have been suggested as indicators by some authors (e.g. see Sturesson, 1976, 1978), and no doubt limited work will continue in attempts to improve their status as meaningful indicator materials.

Bivalves and Naturally Radioactive Elements

Fowler *et al.* (1975*b*), in experimental studies on the uptake of ^{237}Pu by the mussel, *Mytilus galloprovincialis*, found that uptake by the shell constituted 65–89 per cent of the total body load of the radionuclide when [237]Pu was available from solution only. This plutonium accumulated by the shell was strongly bound; the biological half-life of whole-body [237]Pu (+6) was found to be 776 days (slow component only). In addition, rinsing of the shell with dilute acid released little of the activity.

Guary and Fraizier (1977) reported data for the distribution of plutonium activity in the soft parts and shells of several bivalve molluscs from the region of La Hague, the site of the French nuclear fuel

TABLE 90

CONCENTRATIONS OF PLUTONIUM (MEANS ± STANDARD DEVIATIONS, pCi/kg WET WEIGHT) IN THE SOFT TISSUES AND SHELLS OF BIVALVE MOLLUSCS FROM SEVERAL LOCATIONS ON THE WEST COAST OF FRANCE. ST. VAAST-LA-HOUGUE IS CLOSEST TO THE NUCLEAR FUEL REPROCESSING PLANT; CANCALE, ILE DE RÉ AND ARCACHON ARE SUCCESSIVELY FURTHER SOUTH. (AFTER GUARY AND FRAIZIER (1977).)

Location	Species	Plutonium in soft tissues	Plutonium in shells
St. Vaast-la-Hougue	*Crassostrea gigas*	0·38 ± 0·14	2·5 ± 0·9
	Ensis ensis	0·27 ± 0·08	1·3 ± 0·4
	Ostrea edulis	0·47 ± 0·14	3·5 ± 1·1
	Mytilus edulis	0·44 ± 0·14	4·0 ± 1·5
	Venerupis decussata	0·60 ± 0·18	1·9 ± 0·7
Cancale	*Crassostrea gigas*	0·31 ± 0·09	1·4 ± 0·4
Ile de Ré	*Crassostrea gigas*	0·11 ± 0·03	3·3 ± 1·0
Arcachon	*Crassostrea gigas*	Not detected	2·1 ± 0·7
	Mytilus edulis	0·14 ± 0·05	No data

reprocessing plant. These data are shown in Table 90 and may be compared with the results for gastropods cited previously (Table 87). Concentrations of plutonium in whole soft parts of the oyster, *Crassostrea gigas*, decreased consistently with distance away from the reprocessing plant and the soft tissues of *Mytilus edulis* exhibited a similar tendency. By contrast, plutonium activities in the shells bore no simple relationship to the supposed discharge point of the element; activities in the shells of *C. gigas* first decreased, then increased, and finally decreased once again in successive southerly samples. The authors noted that both gastropods and bivalves taken from sites other than the Bay of Ecalgrain (which receives effluent from the reprocessing plant) consistently exhibited higher plutonium activities in shells than in soft parts. By contrast, the gastropods from Ecalgrain (Table 87) exhibited the inverse profile, soft parts containing greater activities than shells. It was suggested that such a profile was possibly due to different physico-chemical forms of the isotope at the various locations. However, the difference may also be due to some extent to the effects of unknown parameters on the availability of plutonium to the shells of the species studied; it is clear that the contamination profile is most strange at least in shells of *C. gigas*, and the shells certainly do not indicate the relative abundance of plutonium in the study sites as the soft parts appear to. Perhaps some form of regulation of plutonium levels in shells occurs.

TABLE 91
^{210}Po ACTIVITIES (MEANS ± STANDARD ERRORS, pCi/kg WET WEIGHT) IN TISSUES OF THE HORSE CLAM, *Tresus nuttallii*, FROM TWO LOCATIONS OFF THE COAST OF CALIFORNIA. THE SAMPLE AT SAN ONOFRE WAS TAKEN FROM A SANDY BEACH IN DECEMBER, 1971; THAT FROM TIJUANA SLOUGH WAS FROM A MUDDY INLET SAMPLED IN JANUARY, 1972. (AFTER FOLSOM *et al.* (1972).)

Tissue	San Onofre	Tijuana Slough
Outer shell layer[a]	6 200 ± 700	810 ± 130
Inner shell[a]	75 ± 15	67 ± 15
Siphon valve (cap only)	590 ± 60	440 ± 30
Siphon tube (skin only)	320 ± 30	720 ± 40
Muscle	—	960 ± 180
Viscera	—	2 800 ± 50

[a] Outer layer less than 1 mm; inner shell that below 1 mm.

A few studies involving naturally radioactive elements other than plutonium have been reported. Folsom *et al.* (1972), in a little-known but somewhat prophetic paper concerning the difficulties involved in sampling organisms correctly for monitoring studies, reported data for ^{210}Po in the shell of the horse clam, *Tresus nuttallii* (Table 91). It is seen that the sample from San Onofre exhibited much greater activity in the shell than the soft parts. It is perhaps meaningful that whilst the outer shell layer differed considerably in activity between the two sites, the inner shells contained similar activities. Perhaps the differences may be ascribed, at least in part, to adsorbed ^{210}Po in the shell of the San Onofre animals. Such differences in the ratios of the amounts of radionuclides in the soft parts and shells of bivalves were not observed by Goldberg *et al.* (1978) in their monitoring studies of transuranics in mussels (*Mytilus edulis* and *Mytilus californianus*) from the coasts of the United States. These authors found that the ratio of ^{241}Am to ^{239,240}Pu in the shell and soft parts of the mussels studied rarely varied by more than a factor of two and suggested that the variation observed could be related to the different time-integration capacities of the hard and soft tissues. By comparison with the results reported for stable trace metals and plutonium in bivalves from the French coasts cited above, this finding is surprising. Further study is obviously needed to clarify whether this observed agreement between contamination profiles in shells and soft parts of mussels extends to more polluted locations. It might be noted here that these and other studies have observed a large incorporation of radionuclides into the byssal threads of mussels; clearly, inadequate removal of the byssus may lead to highly variable results in monitoring surveys of soft parts or whole animals. The same may be true of iron and lead amongst stable metal isotopes; iron in particular is known to be excreted via its incorporation into the byssus (Pentreath, 1973a; George *et al.*, 1976; George and Coombs, 1977a).

Finally, Guary and Fowler (1978) exposed mussels, *Mytilus galloprovincialis*, to ^{237}Np in seawater. As noted previously for crabs and shrimp studied in the same experiment, almost all the accumulated activity (averaging about 91 per cent of the total body load) was found in the shell. These experiments did not distinguish between adsorbed and absorbed amounts of ^{237}Np however, and the result may well be different if the isotope is introduced via food into the mussels.

Conclusions on the Use of Mollusc Shells as Indicators
Whilst the use of the shells of molluscs as indicators of the environmental abundance of trace elements does not suffer from the problems associated with moulting (as experienced by crustaceans), the other problems discussed previously with reference to crustaceans apply equally to molluscs. Thus the distinction between elements adsorbed to the shell surface and those integrated into the shell matrix exists once again for mollusc species, and the kinetics governing these accumulative routes are not well understood. If the adsorption of metals were non-existent, one would suspect that the integration of elements into shells during their synthesis by the mantle would occur in simple proportion to the amounts of the contaminants in the soft parts. If this were so, contamination gradients produced by studies of the shells and the soft parts would be expected to agree substantially although, as Goldberg *et al.* (1978) pointed out, different time-integration capacities would be likely (*cf.* Young and Folsom, 1967; Keckes *et al.*, 1968). In addition, shell synthesis occurs during only part of the year in most temperate bivalve species and the

elements integrated into shells by this route would therefore be proportional to the load in the soft parts through this portion of the seasonal cycle only. However, even given these possible differences, some qualitative agreement would be expected between the contamination profiles obtained from hard and soft tissues. The fact that many authors have not obtained such agreement suggests that the adsorption of metals, either specifically or non-specifically, to exposed shell surfaces is a highly significant parameter in determining the levels of elements in shells but not in soft parts. The few studies of metal distribution in shells tend to confirm the importance of surface adsorption of elements, which are commonly found in greater concentrations in surface layers (and perhaps the periostracum) of bivalve shells. The existence of surface adsorption of metals gives rise to uncertainty in the interpretation of differences between element abundance in shells of different samples, as surface-adsorbed contaminants cannot be simply separated from elements integrated into the shell matrix. Both these contaminants are significant, but represent different portions of the total metal load on an ecosystem; as a result, interpretation of the element levels found in shells may be very complex and, in some cases, impossible.

In addition to these problems of interpretation, it must be understood that shells are extremely difficult to work with. It is not always easy to fully clean the shell surface of epibiota or particulates; insufficient cleaning will cause the inclusion of metals in components other than the shell and too vigorous cleaning may strip metals from the shell surface. The latter possibility is particularly well illustrated in the studies of Bryan and Uysal (1978) on *Scrobicularia plana*, where contamination profiles produced by the analysis of shells varied according to the cleaning procedure. Not least amongst the problems associated with the use of shells as indicator materials is the difficulty experienced in analysis; elements such as lead would be particularly difficult to analyse successfully because of the large amounts of calcium present in samples.

Finally, many parameters may interfere with the accumulation of trace elements in the shells of molluscs, and most of these effects have been insufficiently investigated to date. For example, metal levels vary in different parts of the shell, commonly being greater in the region of the umbo than in the edge of the shell (Table 92); this may be related to age of the different areas, and is additional to the variation in metal levels in the surface and inner layers of the shell. The differences shown for *S. plana* in Table 92 were also observed for *Mytilus edulis* after exposure to ^{58}Co in solution (Shimizu *et al.*, 1971, see Table 93) and, once again, the umbonal

TABLE 92

MEAN CONCENTRATIONS (μg/g DRY WEIGHT) OF FOUR TRACE METALS IN DIFFERENT REGIONS OF THE SHELL OF *Scrobicularia plana* TAKEN FROM THE TAMAR ESTUARY IN 1974. (AFTER BRYAN AND UYSAL (1978).)

Part of shell	Per cent total weight	Copper	Iron	Manganese	Zinc
Umbo region	31·2	29·0	153	19·3	91
Intermediate region	28·9	5·5	130	18·3	74
Edge region	39·9	5·0	150	13·0	29
Whole shell	100·0	12·6	145	16·5	61

region was found to contain greater amounts of the metal. In this case, uptake was predominantly by adsorption (see discussion above) and it therefore seems likely that binding sites for metals may be more numerous in the umbo region than in the shell edge. The size of the shell may also be important; Bryan and Uysal (1978) found increases in the concentrations of both copper and zinc in shells of *S. plana* with increasing length, although iron and manganese levels were unaffected by size in the same samples. Amongst other variables we may include shore position (Pilkley and Harriss, 1966) and ambient salinity (Rucker and Valentine, 1961; Roberts, 1976). Temperature may also be expected to alter at least the time integration capacity of shells, as shell synthesis will be controlled metabolically by temperature-sensitive processes. Finally, it was noted in Chapter 11 (see

TABLE 93

MEAN CONCENTRATION FACTORS (BASED ON DRY WEIGHT CONCENTRATIONS) DESCRIBING THE ACCUMULATION OF [58]Co BY DIFFERENT REGIONS OF THE SHELL OF THE MUSSEL, *Mytilus edulis*, AFTER EXPOSURE OF MUSSELS TO [58]Co IN SOLUTION FOR 34 DAYS. REGION 1 IS THE SHELL EDGE MOST DISTANT FROM THE UMBO; REGIONS 2, 3 AND 4 ARE SUCCESSIVELY CLOSER TO THE UMBO AND REGION 5 IS THE UMBONAL REGION ITSELF. (AFTER SHIMIZU *et al.* (1971).)

Part of shell	Concentration factor for [58]Co	
	Left shell	Right shell
1. Abdominal margin	101	100
2. Intermediate/edge	89	95
3. Intermediate/edge	117	99
4. Intermediate/umbo	202	137
5. Umbonal region	268	251

text and Fig. 84) that metal–metal interaction may also occur in the accumulation of trace elements by shells. In this example, Romeril (1971a) found that additions of cobalt and iron in solution enhanced the rate of uptake of ^{65}Zn by shells of the oyster, *Ostrea edulis*, although these metals depressed uptake rates into the soft tissues. We may expect that any variable which alters the uptake of trace metals into soft tissues of bivalves will also quantitatively affect at least that portion of the total metal content of shells which is present in absorbed form, i.e. which is derived from the mantle. The adsorption of elements to the shell surface may also be influenced by some parameters such as salinity or metal interactions, particularly if competition for surface binding sites occurs between elements. These multivarious effects will give rise to extreme difficulty in interpreting any but gross differences in the amounts of stable or radioactive elements present in bivalve shells and on the basis of present data these tissues cannot therefore be recommended for indicator purposes.

C. BIVALVE MOLLUSCS AND AGEING METHODS

At first sight it may appear somewhat unlikely that methods of ageing bivalves should be discussed in a chapter devoted to consideration of the use of shells as indicator materials. However, very recent evidence, much of it as yet unpublished, suggests that chemical methods of ageing bivalves may be developed in the near future and some of these methods depend on contaminants present in the shells of these organisms. As these methods are presently still in the experimental stage, they will be referred to only briefly here.

Goldberg *et al.* (1978) have pointed out that if a contaminant present in the soft parts or shell of an organism possesses an unusually long half-life compared with the lifespan of the organism itself, the levels of the contaminant will increase with age (assuming that rates of uptake exceed rates of growth). Whilst this is probably not the case for most stable trace metal isotopes in bivalves (with the possible exception of mercury; see data in Chapter 7), some of the transuranic elements may follow such a profile, as may ^{210}Pb. The continued accumulation of such isotopes may then be used as an index of the age of the organism.

It is well known that age determination in bivalves is a difficult task. Some temperate species (particularly oysters) may exhibit more or less well-defined growth rings caused by differences in growth rates between different seasons; however, such rings commonly permit only approximation of the age of the organism and occasionally the use of rings produces incorrect estimates of age. This is because rings may be produced by several stimuli apart from seasonal changes in growth rate; for example, violent wave action or physical disturbance have been implicated in ring formation (Wilbur and Owen, 1964). In addition, species which have extended spawning periods can be aged only as belonging to a certain year-class in some cases, as it is difficult to define the time of spawning from the shell. Finally, some temperate and many tropical species of bivalves do not lay down rings or annuli seasonally and cannot therefore be aged by this method. Other methods of ageing bivalves include the use of the shell dimensions, size–frequency distributions and so on (Wilbur and Owen, 1964) but no simple method is available in many instances. Shell dimensions are exceedingly variable in some species (e.g. see Seed, 1976) and may vary in relation to age both between and within populations according to food availability, salinity and temperate, microhabitat and other factors.

Studies currently in progress at Scripps Institute of Oceanography, alluded to briefly in Goldberg *et al.* (1978) but otherwise unpublished, have

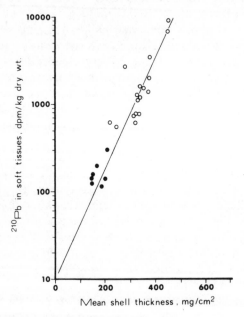

FIG. 96. Relationship between the ^{210}Pb activity in whole soft parts of the mussels, *Mytilus edulis* (filled circles) and *M. californianus* (open circles), and the mean shell thickness of the mussels. (After Goldberg *et al.* (1978).)

investigated alternative methods of age determination. One of these is mean shell thickness, measured in terms of weight per unit area. Bertine (pers. comm.) considers shell thickness as a far superior parameter to shell length as a measure of age in the mussel, *Mytilus edulis*. However, some authors consider that bivalves stressed by salinity fluctuations or high concentrations of pollutants may exhibit unusually thin shells (Frazier, 1976; Boyden, pers. comm.). I have observed unusually thin shells of *M. edulis* on two occasions. The first of these was in samples from Corio Bay in the western part of Port Phillip in Australia; these mussels exhibited thin, brittle shells and were found to contain very large amounts of cadmium (up to a mean of $18 \cdot 12 \, \mu g/g$ wet weight; see Phillips, 1976*b*) in their soft tissues. The second instance was in Scandinavia; samples taken from areas in the northern Baltic Sea typically exhibited much thinner shells than did those from areas to the west of Sweden in Kattegat or Skagerrak. Whether this was due to the lower salinity—or the higher metal contents—of mussels in the former region remains unknown (Phillips, 1977*c*, 1978*a*).

Finally, the amounts of long-lived radionuclides present in either the soft tissues or the shells of *Mytilus* species may be indicative of the age of the bivalve. Goldberg *et al.* (1978) related ^{210}Pb activities in the soft parts of mussels to shell thickness to produce a reasonable correlation (Fig. 96), and an unpublished manuscript by Griffin *et al.* (1978) has extended this work to ^{210}Po and to several populations. If the relationship between isotope accumulation in the shell and/or soft tissues and age is similar in all locations, such techniques have real promise as a method of ageing bivalves. However, more work is clearly needed and it will be some time before such methods can be considered to be universally applicable.

CHAPTER 13

Behavioural Alterations which may Affect Indicator Ability

Most studies published to date on the toxicity of pollutants involve the elucidation of acute lethal levels of toxicants, with much less emphasis on the possible sublethal effects. However, this situation is slowly changing and researchers are making greater efforts to understand the effects of pollutants such as trace metals and organochlorines on the behaviour of organisms. In some instances, behavioural changes caused by a given pollutant may be important in determining the accumulation of that pollutant either by the organism affected, or by its predator(s). For example, some finfish are known to avoid sublethal concentrations of metals such as copper by moving away from the contaminated area; clearly, this will alter their exposure to metals. Alternatively, certain pollutants may interfere with the escape reflex in crustaceans and this phenomenon could lead to selective predation of affected individuals containing high toxicant levels—and hence to a 'food chain overamplification' of the toxicant.

In addition, some naturally variable parameters such as salinity or temperature may affect the behaviour or physiology of organisms in such a way as to decrease the monitoring ability of the affected species. For example, the filtration rates of bivalves are influenced by several natural parameters and this may considerably affect the uptake rate of pollutants.

These effects of pollutants themselves and naturally variable water quality parameters will be discussed in terms of their possible influence on the monitoring ability of crustaceans, polychaetes, molluscs and finfish. Emphasis will be placed on the exposure levels at which such effects occur as in some cases the concentrations of toxicants employed in laboratory studies of such effects far exceed those in the natural environment. Trace metals and organochlorines will be considered together in each section.

A. CRUSTACEANS

Most of the information concerning the sublethal effects of pollutants on crustacean species involves organochlorines rather than trace metals, as these animals are rather more sensitive to the former compounds, perhaps because of their evolutionary proximity to insects. However, some data on trace metals are of note, all of which refer to the possible effects of metals on the predation rate of crabs or shrimp. Barthalmus (1977) investigated the effects of mercuric chloride on the shock response of the shrimp,

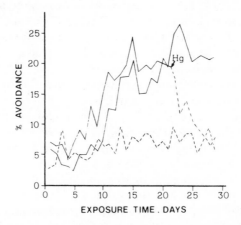

FIG. 97.   Acquisition of a conditioned response by shrimp, *Palaemonetes pugio*. Shrimp were conditioned to avoid an electric shock by exhibiting negative phototaxis. Control shrimp (solid line throughout) were not exposed to mercury at any time; treated animals (dashed line throughout) were exposed to 0·5 mg/litre mercuric chloride in solution throughout the experiment and control/treated shrimp (solid line and dashes) were exposed to the same concentration of the element only after day 20. (After Barthalmus (1977).)

Palaemonetes pugio. Shrimp were conditioned to avoid an electric shock by moving away from the illuminated part of the test tank at the onset of illumination following a dark period. Untreated shrimp were conditioned quite readily (Fig. 97). By contrast, shrimp exposed to mercuric chloride in solution at 0·5 mg/litre exhibited almost no learning ability. Furthermore, untreated animals lost the ability to respond to the stimulus at the onset of exposure to mercury. Whilst the stimulus for conditioning in these experiments is artificial, the results nevertheless suggest that mercury may alter the acquisition of conditioned response in *P. pugio*, presumably via an effect on the central nervous system. Such an effect may be important in, for example, the avoidance of predators by this species. Weis (1976, 1978) reported a different type of effect of trace metals, involving mercury and cadmium and the fiddler crab, *Uca pugilator*, or its close relatives, *U. pugnax* and *U. minax*. Both elements retarded the regeneration of autotomised limbs and ecdysis in these species and these effects were subject to both metal–metal interaction and metal–salinity interaction (see Chapter 11). In cases of multiple autotomy of limbs, such effects may give rise to increased predation of crabs exposed to metals in the field. However, multiple autotomy of limbs is probably rare in the natural environment and the significance of such observations is therefore doubtful. If such effects do occur, one would expect that predators would selectively take crabs with the highest levels of accumulated metals and this would lead to both an 'overamplification' of metals at this step of the food chain and to a bias in the mean levels of metals in the surviving crab population. It might be noted that, in some cases, the methods of collection of organisms for use as indicators of pollutants could also preferentially select individuals which exhibit behavioural abnormalities such as impaired avoidance; in a sense, the trawler and the natural predator may often cull the same part of a population.

Most of the effects of organochlorines on the behaviour or physiology of crustaceans are similar to those of trace metals. However, it is interesting to note that, by contrast to the depression of limb regeneration and ecdysis in *Uca pugilator* and *U. pugnax* noted above for mercury and cadmium, DDT accelerates these processes (Weis and Mantel, 1976), perhaps via an effect on neuro-endocrine secretion. Sevin, malathion and parathion had no effect on regeneration or moulting in *Uca*, although moulting, at least, is retarded in *Cancer magister* by Sevin (Buchanan *et al.*, 1970).

Crustaceans have been found to exhibit avoidance of some pesticides by Hansen *et al.* (1973, 1974). The grass shrimp, *Palaemonetes pugio*, did not avoid DDT and endrin, or the organophosphates Dursban and malathion, or the carbamate, Sevin. However, the herbicide 2,4-D elicited a strong avoidance response at concentrations of 1 mg/litre and above; finfish also avoid 2,4-D more readily than other pesticides (see below). The commercial PCB preparation, Aroclor 1254, was avoided by *P. pugio* when concentrations in solution were 5–10 mg/litre, but not at 0·5–1·0 mg/litre; the pink shrimp, *Penaeus duorarum*, did not avoid Aroclor 1254 even at 5–10 mg/litre exposure. It was noted by Phillips (1978*b*) that such effects occur only at extremely high exposure concentrations, commonly in the milligrammes per litre range, and that such concentrations would rarely, if ever, be encountered in the natural environment. Whilst it is conceivable that a massive accidental spill of organochlorine could produce such concentrations in restricted coastal waters of poor circulation, in the absence of such an event it seems unlikely that avoidance reactions are of significance in the natural environment.

Interference of predator–prey relationships, however, may occur when crustaceans are exposed to much lower levels of organochlorines and Phillips (1978b) suggested that such effects were of greater environmental significance than was avoidance, and might also lead to biased sampling of highly contaminated individuals. Krebs *et al.* (1974) exposed field populations of fiddler crabs, *Uca pugnax*, to fertiliser manufactured from sewage sludge and containing high levels of aldrin, dieldrin and other organochlorines. Locomotor activity of crabs in the treated areas was drastically impaired due to the uptake of organochlorines from the sediments containing added fertiliser. This impairment of movement would give rise not only to greater predation but also to higher winter mortalities from freezing. Similar results were reported for the same species in field populations treated with the organophosphate, Temefos (Ward and Busch, 1976; Ward *et al.*, 1976). As pointed out by Ward and Busch (1976), the effective acute toxicity of a toxicant to field populations of species such as *Uca pugnax* depends on the concentration needed to impair the escape reflex rather than that necessary to actually elicit mortality. Several authors believe that the use of organochlorines as pesticides has been responsible for drastic reductions in field populations of both fiddler crabs (Odum *et al.*, 1969) and blue crabs, *Callinectes sapidus* (Leffler, 1975). If this is so, the use of such species in indicator surveys would be open to some criticism, as the field effects of the measured pollutant(s) dominate the sampling process. The effects of organochlorines on the predator–prey interaction may not only involve the direct changes in escape reflex caused by toxic events at the central nervous system; autotomy impairment, regeneration changes and other factors may also be involved. At higher concentrations, PCBs at least will also cause changes in the colour of *Uca pugilator* (Fingerman and Fingerman, 1978) because of its interference in the release of the melanin-dispersing hormone from eyestalk neuroendocrine cells. Shrimp are also known to exhibit impairment of escape behaviour on exposure to some pesticides (e.g. see Tagatz, 1976; Farr, 1977 and Sharp *et al.*, 1979) and it is conceivable that field populations of these organisms are also affected—or even limited—by organochlorines in some areas (Butler, 1969a; Nimmo *et al.*, 1970).

B. POLYCHAETES

Little information is available concerning the behavioural effects of either trace metals or organochlorines on polychaete species. Only one reference is considered worth mentioning; Schoor and Newman (1976) found the fire ant toxicant, mirex, to decrease burrowing and feeding activity of the lugworm, *Arenicola cristata*. Such decreases in activity would presumably give rise to increased predation if present in field populations; again, this would have repercussions for the accumulation of mirex in populations of both the lugworm itself and of its predators.

C. MOLLUSCS

Most bivalve and gastropod molluscs are either sedentary or sessile. This is, of course, an enormous advantage to the researcher intent on performing monitoring surveys for trace metals or organochlorines and bivalve molluscs in particular have received much attention to date. As discussed in Chapter 2, the ideal indicator is the biological counterpart of an ion-exchange medium, responding throughout its life in a constant and predictable fashion to the ambient concentration of pollutants. However, just as mobile organisms have in some cases developed the ability to detect and avoid toxicants in solution, molluscs may also be able to avoid contact with some contaminants. Because most species are immobile—or at least capable of only slow movement—evolution has provided an alternative method of isolating the tissue from the environment. Thus, bivalve molluscs may adduct the valves tightly in unfavourable conditions, whereas gastropods withdraw into the shell and tightly close the operculum. This phenomenon of the isolation of tissues from ambient conditions may be elicited by changes in the concentrations of certain pollutants or by rapid fluctuations in water quality parameters such as salinity or temperature. Although the literature concerning the effects of natural parameters (salinity, temperature, turbidity, food concentration, water current, and so on) on the filtration and feeding rates of bivalves is spectacularly abundant (see review by Bayne, 1976, for example), very few authors have attempted to tackle these aspects of bivalve physiology or behaviour in terms of their influence on indicator ability. The only notable exceptions have been the reports of Phillips (1977a), Davenport (1977) and Davenport and Manley (1978). Phillips (1977a) investigated the uptake of zinc from solution by the mussel, *Mytilus edulis*. Although a previous report (Phillips, 1976a) had observed that salinity did not affect the net uptake of zinc from solution by this species, these earlier studies had employed mussels which were pre-acclimated to salinity for 21 days before the addition of the metal. By contrast, it was found in the later studies that mussels exposed to rapid fluctuations of salinity *in the co-presence of zinc* exhibited unusually fast net uptake of the metal compared with animals exposed to the same concentrations of zinc in relatively stable salinity conditions. However, this was only true if the particular salinity regime employed precluded valve closure. If mussels could adduct the valves (for periods up to 96 h in this species), the animals would obviously take up less metal than those individuals exposed to stable salinities which did not, therefore, exhibit valve closure. Two possibilities thus exist in which the uptake of zinc by *M. edulis* can be affected by salinity.

(i) Valve closure may occur, typically in periods of rapidly decreasing salinity, effectively isolating the internal tissues from the ambient environment and eliminating metal uptake for the duration of the adduction period.

(ii) Where valve closure cannot occur—for example, in periods of increasing salinity which closely follow a salinity decrease—the mussel is highly stressed and, as a result, exhibits a greater net accumulation of zinc.

It is evident that these phenomena operate in opposite directions with respect to the uptake of zinc and will therefore tend to cancel each other out. Nevertheless, such effects are of importance in determining the true indicator ability of bivalves. Davenport (1977) and Davenport and Manley (1978) have investigated the valve closure mechanism of *M. edulis* on exposure both to fluctuating salinities and to copper sulphate in solution. This example is rather more complex, as the metal itself can also elicit valve closure at low concentrations, whereas zinc levels must be much higher to do so (Phillips, unpublished data); this is perhaps an adaptive phenomenon caused by the much greater toxicity of copper than of zinc to *M. edulis*. Valve closure elicited by copper was suggested in the later paper (Davenport and Manley, 1978) to be a three-part process:

(i) On elevation of the ambient copper concentration to 21 μg/litre the valves are sharply adducted.

(ii) 'Testing' behaviour occurs between 21 and 200 μg/litre ambient copper concentrations, during which the mussel intermittently opens the valves to test the surrounding water quality.

(iii)   If the copper levels in solution exceed 200 μg/litre, complete valve closure occurs and the internal tissues are completely isolated from the ambient water.

It is significant that mussels which have been previously exposed to 20 μg/litre copper in solution for 10 days exhibit the initial valve adduction (described in (i) above) only when copper levels in solution exceed 160 μg/litre. This suggests that mussels in polluted locations are more tolerant of small fluctuations in the copper concentrations of the water and would therefore theoretically be reasonably efficient indicators of the metal until the higher concentrations of 160–200 μg/litre were reached; these latter concentrations would be unusual even in severely polluted locations.

TABLE 94

THE ACUTE LETHAL TOXICITY, MEASURED AS 96-h LC_{50} VALUES, OF SIX POLLUTANTS TO THE MUSSEL, *Mytilus edulis*, AND ITS COMPARISON TO THE CONCENTRATIONS NEEDED TO REDUCE THE FILTRATION RATE OF THE MUSSEL BY 50 PER CENT (EC_{50} FILTRATION). (AFTER ABEL (1976).)

Toxicant added	96-h LC_{50} (mg/litre)	EC_{50} filtration (mg/litre)[a]
Copper sulphate	0·28	0·08–0·23
Mercuric chloride	Not determined	0·04
Potassium cyanide	36·0	0·25–0·33
Potassium thiocyanate	> 200·0	84·0
Sodium sulphide	> 50·0	1·9
Zinc sulphate	7·8	1·2–1·9

[a] Means or ranges; ranges are for three replicate experiments (KCN) or four replicate experiments ($CuSO_4$, $ZnSO_4$).

M. edulis is also known to be sensitive to pollutants other than copper. Abel (1976) measured the changes in filtration rates of mussels (by clearance of the dye Neutral Red from test solutions) due to the addition of various toxicants. The results (Table 94) showed that filtration rates were impaired by concentrations of each toxicant significantly less than the LC_{50} levels. However, most such effects nevertheless occur at toxicant concentrations much greater than those expected, even in polluted regions and the same is probably also true for methylmercury which Dorn (1976) found to depress the feeding rate of *M. edulis*. Such effects of pollutants on the filtration or feeding rates of mussels may be distinct from the valve adduction phenomenon; at least in some cases filtration rates appear to be influenced at lower levels of toxicants than those eliciting valve closure.

Other behavioural effects are also known. For example, copper and phenol were both found to depress the normal burrowing of the bivalve *Tellina tenuis* (Stirling, 1975) but, here again, the effects were evident only at high exposure levels (250 μg/litre for copper, and 5 mg/litre for phenol). Burrowing is also responsive to some organochlorines in certain bivalve species (see below).

Reports concerning gastropods are less common. However, Shore *et al.* (1975) tentatively correlated cadmium levels in *Patella vulgata* from the Bristol Channel to the ability of these limpets to utilise glucose. Such effects may be due to non-specific binding of cadmium (accumulated to exceedingly high levels in limpets; see Tables 84 and 85 in Chapter 12) to glycolytic enzymes, although this remains hypothetical and it is unclear as to how these effects might influence behaviour of the animals. More recently, Saliba and Vella (1977) found the trochid snail, *Monodonta articulata*, to retract into its shell on exposure to 800 μg/litre mercury and to exhibit reduced activity at exposure levels of greater than 250 μg/litre mercury. Oxygen consumption was also affected and may have caused the observed effects on the frequency of immersion of this species.

The sublethal effects of organochlorines on bivalve molluscs are similar to those of trace metals. Roberts (1972) studied the effects of the acaricide

TABLE 95

PERCENTAGE CHANGES IN THE SHELL DEPOSITION OF OYSTERS, *Crassostrea virginica*, EXPOSED TO DIFFERENT CONCENTRATIONS OF INDIVIDUAL PESTICIDES IN SOLUTION, COMPARED WITH CONTROL ANIMALS MAINTAINED IN CLEAN SEAWATER. THE TEST PERIOD WAS 96 h; DEPRESSION OF SHELL DEPOSITION IS SHOWN BY A NEGATIVE SIGN AND ENHANCEMENT BY A POSITIVE SIGN. (AFTER BUTLER (1966).)

Pesticide	Exposure concentration of pesticide in solution (μg/litre)				
	1 000	100	10	1	0·1
Aldrin	−100	−86	−43	−36	−11
Endrin	−70	−40	−20	0	
DDT	No data	−100	−52	0	
DEF	−100	−50	0		
Baytex	−91	+4	0	+14	
Dibrom	−76	−12	+15	+20	

Endosulfan on the mussel, *Mytilus edulis*, and pointed out that estimates of the acute LC_{50} of such compounds could be underestimated because of the valve closure (avoidance) of the test animal. DDT, dieldrin and endrin were also found to affect the oxygen consumption and heart rates of several bivalves in a later study (Roberts, 1975) and burrowing behaviour of the cockle, *Cerastoderma edule*, was altered by Endosulfan. However, such effects were evident only at the mg/litre exposure level, or at least at concentrations above 50–200 μg/litre (DDT and Endosulfan on heart beat). Butler (1966) found shell growth in the oyster, *Crassostrea virginica*, to be depressed significantly by much lower exposure concentrations of DDT and other organochlorines in solution (Table 95) and ascribed these effects to inhibition of filtration or pumping activity in the oysters. By contrast, organophosphate pesticides such as Baytex may have promoted shell deposition at low concentrations. Although effects were observed for aldrin at ambient concentrations as low as 0·1 μg/litre, the effective concentrations of the other organochlorines studied would be encountered only in severely polluted locations close to application areas or after accidental spillage of organochlorines, and the general applicability of these observations to most natural environments cannot be accepted (see Portmann, 1975).

D. FINFISH

A certain amount of information is available concerning the behavioural effects of sublethal levels of trace metals on finfish. For example, copper sulphate is known to influence the selection of preferred water temperatures by the fathead minnow, *Pimephales promelas* (Opuszýnski, 1971). This effect may either drive the fish away from a polluted area or induce it to enter a polluted area, depending on the relationship between the temperature profile and the contamination profile of the waters. By contrast, Peterson (1976) could find no significant effect of cadmium, copper or zinc (added as sulphates) on the temperature selection of juvenile Atlantic salmon, *Salmo salar*. Trace metals appear to influence temperature selection in finfish far less than do organochlorines (see below). Other sublethal effects of metals on finfish include inhibition of fin regeneration in *Mugil cephalus* or *Fundulus confluentus* by methylmercury and cadmium (Weis and Weis, 1978) and elimination of the ability of female zebrafish, *Brachydanio rerio*, to respond to an attractant pheromone (Bloom *et al.*, 1978). However, the field significance of such effects with respect to the indicator ability of finfish is obscure.

Of more importance are the possible changes in predator–prey relationships elicited by trace metals. Kania and O'Hara (1974) used mosquitofish, *Gambusia affinis*, as prey animals and compared the behaviour of untreated fish with those of fish exposed for 24 h to 5, 10, 50 or 100 µg/litre mercury in solution. All fish exposed to 10 µg/litre mercury or greater concentrations exhibited impaired escape behaviour and were therefore preyed upon more efficiently by the bass, *Micropterus salmoides*. Concentrations of mercury in whole bodies of the mosquitofish were 0·39 µg/g and 0·67 µg/g by wet weight in fish exposed to 5 and 10 µg/litre, respectively. A whole-body concentration of 0·67 µg/g wet weight is not unusually high compared with levels found in freshwater finfish in some parts of the world such as Sweden or Canada; it is therefore possible that the behavioural effects of mercury on field populations of some finfish species cause selective culling of the most sensitive or most contaminated individuals from the population by predators. If this is so, the residual part of the population will exhibit mercury levels which are controlled by predation at a given level; furthermore, the transfer of mercury through the food chain will be unusually efficient compared with less polluted locations where behavioural effects are not evident. Similar results were reported by Sullivan *et al.* (1978) in studies of cadmium influence on the predation of fathead minnows, *Pimephales promelas*, by the same predator (*M. salmoides*). Exposure of minnows was either acute (24 h) or sub-acute (21 days). Prey vulnerability was increased by 375 µg/litre cadmium in acute exposure tests, and by 25 µg/litre of the metal when the prey were exposed in sub-acute experiments. Clearly, if exposure had been truly chronic (as in field populations), the effective concentration might have been even lower. The exact effect elicited by cadmium may, in this case, have been an alteration of schooling behaviour as well as impairment of the escape reflex; both these effects may be assumed to be mediated by metal toxicity at the central nervous system.

Organochlorines are also effective in changing behaviour in some species of finfish. Hansen *et al.* (1974) found that both mosquitofish, *Gambusia affinis*, and pinfish, *Lagodon rhomboides*, could detect and avoid the PCB Aroclor 1254, although the former species was more sensitive to the toxicant than the latter. Thus, *G. affinis* avoided the PCB at concentrations above 0·05 mg/litre whereas the latter avoided 5·7 mg/litre and more concentrated solutions. The sheepshead minnow, *Cyprinodon variegatus*, was even less sensitive, failing to avoid 5·7 mg/litre Aroclor 1254. Kynard (1974) tested mosquitofish, *G. affinis*, from two populations differing in their toxicological sensitivity to pesticides. As might be expected, susceptible individuals generally avoided the toxicants tested at lower concentrations more easily than did fish from the resistant population (Table 96). However, neither susceptible nor resistant fish responded to any of the pesticides at concentrations below 0·2 mg/litre and such levels are orders of magnitude higher than those to be expected in the natural environment.

TABLE 96

THE AVOIDANCE OF FOUR PESTICIDES BY MOSQUITOFISH, *Gambusia affinis*, FROM ORGANOCHLORINE-SUSCEPTIBLE OR ORGANOCHLORINE-RESISTANT POPU-LATIONS. FORTY INDIVIDUALS WERE USED IN EACH TEST, IN A Y-MAZE. (AFTER KYNARD (1974).)

Pesticide	Population	Exposure concentration (mg/litre)	Percentage avoidance	Level of significance[a]
DDT	Susceptible	0·000 1	40·0	NS
		0·001	42·5	NS
		0·01	60·0	NS
		0·1	52·5	NS
		1·0	45·0	NS
		10·0	67·5	<0·05
DDT	Resistant	0·000 1	45·0	NS
		0·001	50·0	NS
		0·01	55·0	NS
		0·1	37·5	NS
		1·0	45·0	NS
		10·0	42·5	NS
Endrin	Susceptible	0·01	60·0	NS
		0·02	65·0	NS
		0·25	72·5	<0·01
Endrin	Resistant	0·25	57·5	NS
		1·00	72·5	<0·01
Toxaphene	Susceptible	0·01	60·0	NS
		0·05	42·5	NS
		0·25	67·5	<0·05
Toxaphene	Resistant	0·05	60·0	NS
		0·25	85·0	<0·001
		0·50	67·5	<0·05
Parathion	Susceptible	0·02	60·0	NS
		0·20	87·5	<0·001
Parathion	Resistant	0·20	57·5	NS
		1·00	82·5	<0·001

[a] NS: Not significantly different from control avoidance.

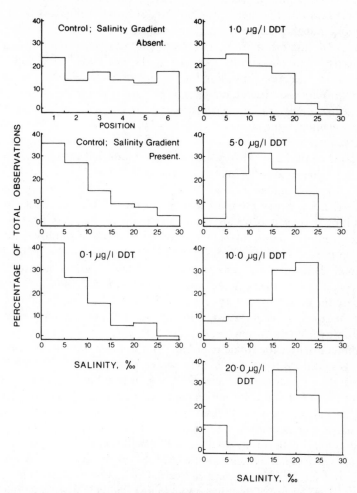

FIG. 98.   Distribution of control (not exposed to DDT) mosquitofish, *Gambusia affinis*, in a fluvarium in the absence and presence of a salinity gradient, and salinity preferences of mosquitofish exposed for 24 h to one of five different DDT concentrations in solution. Fish were previously acclimated to 15‰ salinity. Ten fish were used in all experiments except the control in the presence of a salinity gradient, where seventy fish were used. (After Hansen (1972).)

Organochlorines may also alter the temperature selection or preferred salinity of some finfish species in laboratory experiments. Anderson has published considerable amounts of information on the effects of DDT and other organochlorines on temperature selection in Atlantic salmon parr, *Salmo salar*, and brook trout, *Salvelinus fontinalis*; most of these data are summarised in his review (Anderson, 1971). DDT may influence temperature selection at quite low exposure levels (of the order of 10 μg/litre) in these species, commonly decreasing the preferred temperature at low concentrations but increasing the selected temperature when present at higher exposure levels. Peterson (1976) published further data for the effects of various pesticides on temperature selection in *S. salar* and suggested on the basis of his own, and other, results that such effects may be related to alteration in the toxicity of pollutants. Thus, chemicals which are more toxic at higher temperatures tend to decrease the preferred temperature whereas those (including several of the organochlorines) exhibiting greater toxicity at lower water temperatures may increase the selected temperature. If this is so, the process is clearly of adaptive value, as the fish moves to water regions in which the toxicity of the pollutant is minimal. Hansen (1972) has shown that DDT exposure also changes salinity selection, at least in the mosquitofish, *Gambusia affinis*, tending to increase the preferred salinity (Fig. 98). Such an effect may be adaptive in terms of exposure, as suggested by Phillips (1978*b*), as the estuarine fish will move away from the freshwater outfall which will generally be the source of the pollutant. Whether toxicity of DDT is also lower at higher salinities is uncertain but Murphy (1970) has shown that accumulation of DDT decreases with increasing salinity in *G. affinis* (see Fig. 56 in Chapter 6). Such effects of organochlorines on the behaviour of finfish can only detract from the indicator ability of these organisms if they exist in field conditions.

Finally, organochlorines and other pesticides may also increase the susceptibility of finfish to predation. Regeneration of the caudal fins of *Fundulus heteroclitus* is depressed by DDT, Sevin, malathion and parathion (Weis and Weis, 1975) at exposure levels of 10 μg/litre and this might elicit selective predation of highly contaminated individuals. Schooling behaviour is also known to be sensitive to organochlorines such as DDT (Weis and Weis, 1974*a*) and Sevin (Weis and Weis, 1974*b*), and exposure to these pollutants disrupts schools, spreading them over a larger area. This gives rise to increased energy consumption and respiration, effects on feeding (especially in obligatory schooling species) and increased susceptibility to predation.

E. CONCLUSIONS

The sublethal behavioural effects of trace metals and organochlorines may basically be divided into three types, as follows.

(i) Avoidance reactions. Many organisms possess the ability to detect high levels of these pollutants in solution in the ambient aquatic environment. Avoidance is brought about by negative chemotaxis in the case of mobile organisms such as finfish or some crustaceans, or by isolation of the soft tissues from the ambient seawater in sedentary or sessile molluscs. Either of these changes will detract from the indicator ability of the organism, as the ambient water quality will no longer be unselectively and continuously monitored by the accumulation of pollutants. However, with only a few possible exceptions (copper in *Mytilus edulis*, perhaps), avoidance reactions are elicited only at exceedingly high ambient levels of toxicants which would be most unusually encountered in even severely polluted locations. It is possible that the so-called episodic pollution event, produced by an (accidental) very large discharge of a toxicant could produce such concentrations in restricted water bodies; direct spraying of pesticides may also create these conditions. In these cases, species exhibiting efficient avoidance reactions would be poor indicators. However, such conditions are unusual and avoidance reactions of this type are unlikely to be important influences on the indicator ability of species in chronically polluted locations.

(ii) At somewhat lower levels of exposure, trace metals and/or organochlorines may elicit physiological or behavioural changes such as altered burrowing behaviour or filtration in bivalve molluscs, or shifts in the preferred temperature or salinity of mobile species such as finfish. These effects would once again be likely only in severely polluted conditions, but may conceivably occur during, for example, episodic seasonal contamination of estuaries by pesticides in run-off derived from agricultural catchments. Mobile species may be expected to move away from the affected area of the estuary for the duration of the episodic event; sedentary species may be subjected to increased predation (e.g. in bivalves which fail to burrow normally) or may respond poorly to the increased ambient concentrations of toxicants (e.g. in bivalves which exhibit lower filtration or feeding rates in the presence of high levels of pollutants). It must be emphasised that almost all the studies from which such suggestions arise were performed under laboratory conditions using very high concentrations of metal salts (in available form) in solution, or of organochlorines solubilised by an organic solvent. In polluted conditions in the natural environment such high availability may never occur.

(iii) Predator–prey relationships may be disturbed by rather lower concentrations of trace metals or organochlorines than those eliciting either of the above-mentioned effects. Unfortunately, most of these data also derive from laboratory studies and it would be extremely difficult to show such effects under field conditions unless the prey species were severely depleted. Perhaps such effects are more important for crustaceans than for other, more resistant, organisms; it may be significant that crab populations have suffered very severe depletion on both the east and west coasts of the United States, for example (although this could also be ascribed to the direct effects of pollutants on reproduction of these species, as well as to overfishing by man).

In any event, these subtle and chronic effects of pollutants may be the most important in terms of sublethal influences. If prey populations are subjected to selective culling on the basis of such effects (because of schooling changes, altered escape reactions, effects on colour and so on), both prey and predator will be affected in terms of the transfer of pollutants through the food chain and the use of either species as an indicator of local pollution will be affected. Our understanding of such phenomena is clearly rudimentary at best to date and improved knowledge is necessary not merely to permit efficient and accurate selection of indicator species but also to protect the vital food resources of coastal waters of the world's oceans.

CHAPTER 14

Biological Indicators: a Retrospective Summary

Throughout this book, emphasis has been given to individual parameters which may interfere in the use of biological indicator organisms to monitor pollution of aquatic ecosystems by trace metals or organochlorines. These interfering factors differ in the magnitude of their perturbation—and thus in their importance—in defining toxicant levels in organisms. This final chapter represents an attempt to summarise the major problems or unknowns in the use of indicator species and may be useful as a guide to the best types of indicator for monitoring aquatic contamination. Organisms will be considered by phylum or class, both trace metals and organochlorines being considered together in each section.

A. PHYTOPLANKTON

Whilst phytoplankton have attracted considerable interest in respect of their response to the toxic action of trace metals or organochlorines, they have been rarely used as true indicators for the comparison of pollutant abundance at more than one location. The principal reasons for this appear to be the difficulty in obtaining reasonable sample amounts free from other material or other organisms (zooplankton) and the acknowledged importance of species composition in the accumulation of pollutants by phytoplankton. The latter point is particularly important for trace metals; for example, Riley and Roth (1971) found great differences between the accumulation of eighteen trace metals by fifteen species of phytoplankton grown in the same medium. The trace element content of natural mixed populations no doubt varies in the same fashion; the results of Mullin and Riley (1956) for cadmium in surface waters of the English Channel and the Irish Sea may reflect these species differences in metal accumulation by phytoplankton as well as the patchiness of the distribution of each organism. It is evident that the use of phytoplankton as indicators of pollutants affords little time-integration and, unless single species are studied, the levels of pollutants observed will be a complex composite of the amounts of available metals in the water column and the species succession in the phytoplankton community. The accumulative ability of phytoplankters for organochlorines is even less well understood but data from Cox (1970, 1971), Williams and Holden (1973) and other authors tend to support the concept of high species variability, which perhaps depends at least in part on the lipids present in the outer membrane of each species.

Although the indicator ability of phytoplankton is suspect because of the effects of species composition, the uptake of pollutants from seawater by phytoplankters is extremely important in the cycling of these chemicals through the ecosphere as it represents a bioconcentration and hence dictates the amounts of each pollutant passed on to higher organisms through the food chain. The degree of bioconcentration once again depends on the species balance present and is important in determining the efficiency of pollutant transfer from the abiotic to the biotic components of the ecosystem. Phillips (1977c, 1978a) postulated that the differences in trace metal levels present in mussels, *Mytilus edulis*, from the east and west coasts of Sweden were caused by differences in the phytoplankton populations present in the two water masses, the Baltic Sea being dominated by blue–green algae adapted to the low salinities, whilst Kattegat and Skagerrak phytoplankton are more marine in nature. Such effects may operate on a smaller scale also and may not even be dependent on species variability; for example, Olsson and Jensen (1975) suggested that the accumulation of mercury and ΣDDT by pike in different parts of the Stockholm archipelago varied according to the phytoplankton biomass present in each region. Thus, a high standing crop and turnover of phytoplankton would cause greater dilution of the available pollutant load throughout the primary producers and a lower final concentration of pollutant presented to higher organisms. Bryan (1973) suggested a similar kind of effect to explain the seasonality of trace elements in the scallops *Pecten maximus* and *Chlamys opercularis* from the English Channel. Metal levels in these bivalves were lowest following the spring and summer peak phytoplankton productivity, when element contents of phytoplankton would be diluted by the high biomass present and rapid multiplication.

Finally, it should be noted that pollutants such as trace metals or organochlorines are exceedingly toxic to phytoplankton. The most toxic trace elements are copper, zinc and mercury (e.g. see Saward *et al.*, 1975;

Zingmark and Miller, 1975; Jensen *et al.*, 1974, 1976; Braek *et al.*, 1976; Thomas *et al.*, 1977). Amongst organochlorines, both DDT and PCBs are known to be highly toxic at least at the microgramme per litre exposure level, if not below (e.g. see Wurster, 1968; Moore and Harriss, 1972; Mosser *et al.*, 1972*a*; Fisher and Wurster, 1973), and the sensitivity of phytoplankters varies with species (Menzel *et al.*, 1970; Mosser *et al.*, 1972*b*; Moore and Harriss, 1974) and with geographical area (Fisher *et al.*, 1973). It is possible that either or both these pollutants may significantly inhibit primary productivity or alter the species composition of phytoplankton communities in some instances, at least in polluted coastal waters of poor circulation where pollutants may accumulate to high levels in phytoplankters. These effects are speculative at present and will be very difficult to establish in the field; however, if they occur, the transfer of pollutants through this vital first step in the food web will certainly be affected and the consequences will be seen in higher organisms which accumulate at least part of their pollutant load via the food chain.

B. MACROALGAE

Macroalgae have been commonly used as indicators of trace metals; by contrast, their use for monitoring organochlorines has been very restricted and no obvious reason can be found for this distinction. As pointed out by Phillips (1977*b*), they probably respond almost entirely to metals in solution and binding appears to occur to alginates in the cell wall. Attempts to correlate trace metal levels in algae and in the ambient water have been successful at least in some cases (Morris and Bale, 1975; Seeliger and Edwards, 1977). In addition, laboratory studies of the uptake of trace metals suggest that a linear relationship approximating direct proportionality exists between metals in the alga and those in the water, indicating little regulation of metal uptake (e.g. Bryan, 1969).

Macroalgae also satisfy many of the basic indicator requirements discussed in Chapter 2; they are sessile, hardy enough to permit laboratory studies and to live in grossly polluted areas and large enough for easy analysis. Certain species also have widespread distributions in some parts of the world, especially species of *Fucus* in temperate waters and *Sargassum* in sub-tropical and tropical areas. Species of *Ulva* are particularly hardy and are often useful indicators in areas which are severely polluted by sewage effluents, to the exclusion of other organisms.

Given these attributes, one would expect macroalgae to be amongst the

most accurate and efficient indicator organisms, at least for trace elements
—and such is indeed the case. The major variables which affect the levels of
trace metals in macroalgae (season, shore position and part of the plant
sampled) may readily be eliminated by use of a carefully designed sampling
programme. However, certain effects cannot be eliminated at sampling and
it is these which limit the ability of macroalgae as indicators. These effects
include regulation of the uptake of certain metals, metal–metal interactions
and growth inhibition by pollutants; these effects will be discussed in turn.

Regulation of Metal Uptake

Whilst it was stated above that macroalgae in general exhibit little or no
regulation of their metal content, certain exceptions to this pattern are
known. Thus, Morris and Bale (1975) have suggested that manganese is
partially regulated by the brown alga, *Fucus vesiculosus*, perhaps the algal
species most commonly used as an indicator of trace metals to date. This
suggestion arose from studies of the relationship between trace metals in
water and in *F. vesiculosus* from the Bristol Channel in Great Britain. These
data have already been alluded to (see Fig. 34 and text, Chapter 5). The
correlation between metal levels in the alga and the average concentrations
of metal in the water was found to be generally high for cadmium, copper
and zinc. However, that for manganese was poor; sites upstream in the
Bristol Channel supported algae with anomalously high contents of this
metal compared with those present in the water. This may, of course, be due
to several factors (for example, a change in available manganese with
distance upstream) and need not suggest manganese regulation by the
plant. In addition, it is possible that manganese levels in the water altered
significantly between the collection of algae (Fuge and James, 1974) and
sampling of water by Morris and Bale. However, substantial evidence of the
ability of species of *Fucus* to monitor manganese in marine or estuarine
environments is lacking and, in the absence of such evidence, the
conclusions of Morris and Bale (1975) appear valid. It may be noted that
Foster (1976) also found very poor correlations between manganese in
Fucus vesiculosus and that in water and this author extended such
conclusions to iron also, as well as to *Ascophyllum nodosum*.

We might also address here the question of the indicator ability of
macroalgae for arsenic. Arsenic has received relatively little attention in this
book, although greater interest is currently being generated concerning its
cycling in the marine ecosphere. Coulson *et al.* (1935) showed, over forty
years ago, that arsenic in shrimp existed in a form which was relatively non-
toxic (compared with inorganic arsenic) to the rat. Lunde (1969, 1973*a*, *b*)

has been instrumental in studies devoted to arsenic speciation in marine organisms, but it is not clear to date exactly what the organic species of arsenic is in biota, or whether the same organic form occurs in all organisms. Brahman and Foreback (1973) claimed to have found dimethylarsinic acid in the marine environment and McBride and Wolfe (1969) have suggested that bacteria can methylate arsenic in a similar fashion to the methylation of mercury. Wood (1974) has proposed a scheme for the biological cycle of arsenic which involves metabolic interconversion of different forms of the element by anaerobic bacteria in aquatic sediments.

Such data suggest in general that the interconversion of organic and inorganic forms of arsenic depends, to a large extent, on bacteria; the predominance of one or other form of the element in higher organisms would then be explained by their different uptake and excretion characteristics. Such a scheme is reminiscent of that for mercury which occurs in many aquatic organisms, predominantly as the methylated derivative. However, more recent data of Wrench *et al.* (1979) suggest a completely different scheme for the cycling of arsenic. These authors exposed organisms of a three-step food chain to [74]As as arsenate and used differential extraction procedures to separate the organic and inorganic forms present in the organisms. The results suggested that the phytoplankter, *Dunaliella marina*, could mobilise arsenic into the lipid fraction, whereas the shrimp, *Lysmata seticaudata*, could not do this. The brine shrimp, *Artemia salina*, showed some evidence of an ability to synthesise a lipophilic arsenic derivative, but this may have been due to intestinal microflora. Furthermore, feeding experiments suggested that the lipid-soluble arsenic derivative (presumed to be an organic species of the element) was transferred efficiently up the food chain from primary producer to secondary consumer. The authors speculated that the chemical similarity of arsenic to phosphate may permit the synthesis of arsenolipids by the same metabolic pathways which produce phospholipids.

Whilst these two hypotheses to explain the prevalence of organic forms of arsenic in marine biota are not necessarily mutually exclusive, they certainly differ radically in terms of their implications concerning the ecosystem cycling of the element. It is perhaps instructive to consider the prevalence of arsenic in marine biota. If Wrench *et al.* (1979) are correct in that organic forms of the element are synthesised by phytoplankton and passed up the food web, and if organic forms of the element predominate in marine organisms, one would expect all species ingesting phytoplankton to contain significant amounts of the organic derivative(s). This theory does not implicate macroalgae as necessarily able to synthesise organic arsenic derivatives. Several authors have shown, however, that arsenic levels are high in brown algae (e.g. see Bohn, 1975; Bryan, 1976) and Lunde (1973*b*) noted that *Laminaria digitata* contained the lowest amounts of inorganic arsenic and the greatest amounts of organic arsenic of all the species studied. Clearly, therefore, macroalgae can also synthesise organic arsenic derivatives, or perhaps these are taken up from water after their bacterial synthesis. In any event, it is evident that phytoplankton are not the only source of organic arsenic compounds in the marine ecosphere. If both bacteria and primary producers can synthesise organic arsenic derivatives, the ecosystem cycling of arsenic promises to be extremely complex. Furthermore, if arsenic does replace phosphate in the production of phospholipids, we may expect the existence of several different forms of arsenolipids and intermediate compounds.

It is clear that the cycling of arsenic is most complex and there is much yet to learn. Whilst the kinetics of inorganic arsenic accumulation by higher organisms may be relatively simple (e.g. see Ünlü and Fowler, 1979), the predominance of organic forms of the element in the field obviates the possibility of accurate monitoring of this element in any biological indicator, including macroalgae (Penrose *et al.*, 1975).

Metal–metal Interactions
It was noted in Chapter 11 that interactions between metals occur in macroalgae. Bryan (1969) found the net uptake of ^{65}Zn by the brown alga, *Laminaria digitata*, to be depressed by additions of cadmium, copper and manganese (Fig. 83). Copper effects were the most severe and may have been due to inhibition of algal growth, at least in part. The basis for the effects of cadmium and manganese are not known; perhaps direct competition between these elements and ^{65}Zn for binding sites occurred. Foster (1976) also noted metal–metal interactions—in this case in the brown algae, *Fucus vesiculosus* and *Ascophyllum nodosum*. Samples of these species from a severely polluted site failed to accurately reflect the elevated ambient metal levels compared with those in a cleaner control site; several metals were involved (see Table 75 and text in Chapter 11). Conceivably, in this case, the extreme elevation of zinc and copper levels gave rise to saturation of available binding sites on the algal surface, thereby excluding other elements. However, consideration of published data on the ion selectivity of polyanions present in the cell wall of such plants (Haug, 1961; Haug and Smidsrød, 1967; Skipnes *et al.*, 1975; Myklestad *et al.*, 1978) suggests that this may perhaps be simplistic, as the uptake of most trace metals

appears to involve preliminary binding to an extracellular site, followed by translocation of the element across the cell membrane to an intracellular binding site. Melhuus *et al.* (1978), in studies of the same species from the highly polluted Sørfjorden in Norway, also noted inconsistencies in the relationship between metal levels in the algae and those in water. Computation of concentration factors showed consistency in the accumulation of cadmium and zinc throughout the study area; by contrast, concentration factors for copper and lead decreased towards the mouth of the fjord (away from the metal source in Odda). This phenomenon could possibly be ascribed to differences in the speciation of copper and lead in the fjord but may also have been caused by interactive effects. Without further data, no concrete conclusion may be made but, once again, the indicator ability of macroalgae has been found to be suspect in a highly polluted region.

The existence of metal–metal interaction in macroalgae represents a real—and possibly insoluble—problem for the researcher intending to use these species as indicator organisms. Fortunately, current evidence suggests that interaction effects occur only at high ambient concentrations of metals, which would be encountered only in severely polluted locations. It is therefore possible that the use of macroalgae to monitor trace metals is a viable proposition in waters which do not exhibit excessive concentrations of one or more metals. However, further research is clearly needed to delineate the exact extent of metal–metal interactions in macroalgae and results from monitoring surveys (at least in highly polluted areas) should be treated with caution until satisfactory evidence is available concerning this most important variable.

Growth Inhibition by Pollutants

Growth of macroalgae depends on a great range of factors in the ambient environment, which include the presence of adequate carbon dioxide, nutrients and micronutrients (including trace elements) and light. Factors influencing growth include salinity, water temperature and turbidity and changes in the levels of the required parameters described above. These factors act and interact in a complex fashion, resulting in large variation in the growth rates of these plants, even over small areas.

It must be accepted that current evidence clearly points to a dependence of trace metal levels in macroalgae on the growth rates of the plant or its component parts. Several of the variables shown in previous chapters to be of significant influence on the accumulation of metals by macroalgae may in fact act via their effects on growth. For example, seasonal variation of the concentrations of metals present in these species may (at least in an environment with relatively stable ambient metal levels) be caused almost entirely by temporal variations in growth. Typically, temperate species exhibit their highest trace element levels in the late winter, when growth has been poor or absent for some time; new material synthesised in the spring and summer then 'dilutes' pre-existing metals, to give rise to a seasonal minimum of element concentrations in the early autumn. Variation of metal levels within individual plants is also related to growth rates, metals being impoverished in growing tips and relatively enriched in the older, slower growing tissues. Even variation based on shore position (Chapter 10) may be caused, at least partially, by the effects of growth, which varies with the time of submergence of the individual during each tidal cycle and with the depth of submergence (which dictates light availability).

If such effects are accepted, we must consider the implications for the use of macroalgae as indicators of the environmental abundance of trace elements at multiple locations. The hypothesis above suggests that the amounts of trace metals present in a given plant are a function of the balance between metal availability and plant growth, with each factor varying (independently of each other) with time. If we now consider two locations with identical levels of ambient (available) metals, but supporting a given algal species which exhibits growth rates varying by a factor of 2 between the locations, we must expect (simplistically) to find metal accumulation to be halved in the sample which grows the faster. Such differences will fail to occur only if:

(a)　the alga is continually in equilibrium with ambient concentrations of trace elements, regardless of growth

or:

(b)　the abundance of external (or, perhaps, internal) binding sites is of greatest significance in the accumulation of metals by macroalgae.

However, there is no evidence to suggest that either of these alternatives is correct; as noted previously, the evidence all points to at least partial dependence of accumulated metal levels on plant growth rates. The conclusion from this speculation is inescapable; if growth is important in determining the metal concentrations in aquatic plants, all environmental parameters which influence growth will influence the results of monitoring surveys. It may be submitted that the supportive evidence for this statement has already been cited; the results of monitoring surveys are known to depend on parameters (season, part of plant taken, shore position, etc.) which alter plant growth. The inability of researchers to date to identify the effects of other growth-perturbing parameters (salinity, turbidity, etc.) in field surveys is probably a result of a failure to attempt such correlations. Certainly, laboratory studies of metal uptake have shown such factors as light and temperature to be centrally important in determining metal accumulation by macroalgae (Gutknecht, 1961, 1963, 1965; Bryan, 1969).

It is therefore evident that differences in the growth rates of plants from different locations could be of great influence on the results of monitoring surveys which employ macroalgae as indicators of trace elements. Metals will be abnormally enriched in samples which grow slowly and unusually impoverished in fast-growing weed. In most estuarine (polluted) situations, one might expect variations in the growth rates of algal samples according to the ambient contamination, salinity, turbidity, and so on (see, for example, Burrows, 1971 and Strömgren, 1979); in these cases, profiles of contamination would probably be overemphasised in algal samples due to lowered growth rates in plants from the most contaminated areas. One might expect such effects to be of greatest importance where several contaminants are discharged together—for example, in sewage outfalls. In such cases, the effects of the non-metallic components of the discharge could well interfere with the ability of the plant to accurately monitor the relative abundance of elements in the ambient environment; studies such as that of Augier *et al.* (1978) on the marine plant, *Posidonia oceanica*, must therefore be interpreted with caution. A true profile of the ambient pollution conditions would be produced only if all samples were to exhibit identical growth rates. This hypothesis—of great importance in determining the real indicator ability of macroalgae—could be easily tested in species such as *Ascophyllum nodosum*, as growth rates are relatively easily measured in this organism because of the presence of vesicles (see Haug *et al.*, 1974; Myklestad *et al.*, 1978).

C. ASCIDIANS

Although the presence of large amounts of trace metals in ascidian species has been known for almost 70 years since the report of Henze (1911) and has been periodically confirmed (see reviews by Webb, 1939, 1956 and Goodbody, 1974), these organisms have been remarkably little used as possible indicator species for trace elements. Papadopoulou and Kanias (1977) have recently attempted to revive interest in the use of such species as *Ciona intestinalis* and *Microcosmus sulcatus*, but whilst their results reveal high accumulative abilities of these species for certain elements, this should not be interpreted necessarily as representative of indicator ability. However, *Ciona intestinalis* in particular is common and widely distributed in some waters and perhaps these organisms deserve further study in the future. Little or no information exists as to the accumulation of organochlorines by ascidians; however, the feeding mechanisms involved in ascidians might suggest that they would be quite efficient in taking up pollutants adsorbed to particulate material.

D. ANNELIDS

Most studies on annelid species have involved polychaetes and the organism most commonly used has been *Nereis diversicolor*; both trace metal and organochlorine accumulation have been studied in this species. Because of their habitat in sediments, polychaetes are exposed to high concentrations of pollutants both in their food and in the ambient milieu. Pollutants may also be enriched in the interstitial water present in sediments and infauna may thus take up unusually large amounts of trace metals and organochlorines from solution, although this is difficult to confirm experimentally.

Bryan and his co-workers have been responsible for most of the data published on trace metal kinetics in *N. diversicolor*. The earliest report (Bryan and Hummerstone, 1971) related copper concentrations in animals to those in the ambient sediments. It was concluded that copper was not (or was poorly) regulated in *N. diversicolor* and was probably taken up substantially across the body surface. Animal size and ambient salinity were significant variables and populations of this polychaete were shown to develop tolerance to copper in chronically polluted situations, the tolerance probably being genetically based. Two later reports (Bryan and Hummerstone, 1973*b*, *c*) were concerned with zinc, cadmium and manganese in the same species. Zinc is quite severely regulated in *N. diversicolor*; in sediments of estuaries in south-west England, zinc levels varied by a factor of 30 (100 to 3000 μg/g dry weights), whereas worms from these locations exhibited only a 2·7-fold variation (130 to 350 μg/g dry weight). Nevertheless, several parameters altered zinc accumulation; these included size, salinity and the acquisition of tolerance to the element. By contrast, cadmium was not well regulated; sediment concentrations of 0·2 to 9·3 μg/g (factor of 46) were reflected quite faithfully in the worms (0·08 to 3·6 μg/g dry weight, a factor of 45). However. the uptake rates of cadmium also varied between populations, suggesting the acquisition of tolerance based on the partial inhibition of metal uptake or on increased excretion of the element (see Bryan and Hummerstone, 1973*b*, Table 3). In addition, cadmium uptake was influenced by the co-presence of zinc (see Chapter 11), effectively eliminating the possibility of use of this organism as an indicator of environmental contamination by the former element. Manganese kinetics in *N. diversicolor* again appear distinct from those of other metals. This element appears to occur in two pools, with different exchange kinetics. The size of the rapidly exchanging pool is highly variable and accumulation is greatly dependent on the ambient salinity of the interstitial waters present in the sediment habitat. Such effects of salinity may be mediated by a calcium–manganese competition at uptake (Bryan and Hummerstone, 1973*c*); this hypothesis was further developed by Bryan (1976). Lastly, a certain amount of information concerning the uptake of chromium by the polychaetes *Hermione hystrix* and *Neanthes arenaceodentata* exists (Bryan, 1976; Oshida, 1976, 1977). Whilst neither species regulates chromium levels within its tissues and may therefore conceivably be useful as an indicator of the bioavailability of this element, further studies are needed to elucidate the effects of external variables on chromium accumulation.

From these data, we may conclude that *N. diversicolor*, at least, is far from an ideal indicator. Even metals which are not actually regulated to within definite limits are taken up at different rates by different populations and the existence of genetically based metal tolerance mediated by changes in element accumulation appears widespread. Evidence for *N. diversicolor* is generally confirmed by authors investigating other species also (e.g. see Cross *et al.*, 1970, Bryan, 1976), many of which restrict the amounts of metals accumulated within their tissues to definite levels. The relatively highly evolved regulation in annelid worms is perhaps of little surprise if one considers the habitat of these organisms which may, in some instances, be exceedingly rich in trace elements, even in situations where anthropogenic sources are minimal. Parameters which may interfere with the use of polychaetes as indicators (salinity, animal size, metal–metal interaction, etc.) assume great importance in some instances in defining metal uptake (e.g. the effects of salinity on manganese accumulation in *N. diversicolor*) and this may effectively eliminate the use of these organisms as monitors of the environmental abundance of elements.

Studies of the accumulation of organochlorines by polychaetes have been less common than those concerned with trace metals. However, PCBs are certainly taken up quite efficiently from both water and contaminated sediments by some species of polychaetes; once again, most research has concerned *Nereis diversicolor*. Courtney and Langston (1978) showed that both *N. diversicolor* and *Arenicola marina* took up Aroclor 1254 from solution and from contaminated sand, although *A. marina* appeared to exhibit a longer retention of the PCB mixture than did *N. diversicolor*. Elder *et al.* (1979) and Fowler *et al.* (1978*b*) studied the uptake of PCBs by *N. diversicolor* from sediments spiked with various concentrations of Phenoclor DP-5. Equilibrium was attained in about 2 months, concentration factors being 3–4 (concentration in worms: concentration in sediments). By comparison, uptake of the same mixture from water was very rapid, attaining concentration factors of 800 after 2 weeks. Despite such differences, the affinity of PCBs for particulates in the natural environment leads to much higher exposure concentrations in sediments compared with water, and sediment-associated residues probably therefore represent the greatest source of PCBs to polychaetes in the field. Because of this, it may be possible to utilise polychaetes as indicators of the bioavailability of sediment-associated organochlorines. However, the relevance of this to organisms living in the water column is somewhat obscure, and it is clearly possible that a pelagic indicator could exhibit quite different contamination profiles to those from an infaunal organism. This observation is not intended to detract from the value of sediment infauna as indicators, but is made in order to emphasise the importance of the interpretation of indicator profiles in terms of the loads or pollutant sources to which the chosen organism responds. If Fowler *et al.* (1978*b*) are correct in estimating the predominance of sediment-derived PCBs in defining the total residue load in *N. diversicolor*, these organisms may be useful indicators of the potential for organochlorine mobilisation from sediments by infauna. Residues mobilised from sediments are no doubt important sources of organochlorines even in parts of the pelagic food web, although total residues in pelagic organisms must also respond to the organochlorine load in ambient solution.

E.   ECHINODERMS

Very little information has been published to date on the possible use of echinoderm species as indicator organisms. A few studies concerned with the elucidation of the magnitude of trace metal levels present in starfish and other echinoderms are known (e.g. Riley and Segar, 1970) and limited information on the tissue distribution of metals may be found in these. As may be expected, most metals are found at rather higher amounts in the uncalcified tissues, especially the digestive organs; gonads also contain significant amounts of elements but their importance obviously varies with season. The toxicity of certain metals has also been investigated in some echinoderm species. For example, Ahsanullah (1976) found the asteroid *Patiriella exigua* to be very insensitive to cadmium and zinc. However, the exact LC_{50} values for each metal could not be determined because of difficulties in delineation of the point of death; no criterion for death could be satisfactorily elucidated. Phillips (in prep.) has found that different subtropical urchin species vary considerably in their sensitivity to metals, and it may be that the above-mentioned studies fortuitously employed a relatively tolerant species (*cf.* Eisler, 1971).

Data for organochlorines in echinoderms are similarly extremely rare and no studies of significance in determining the important variables interfering with the uptake of these pollutants are known for members of this phylum.

F. CRUSTACEANS

Most of the data pertaining to trace metal kinetics in crustaceans were discussed in Chapter 12. It was noted that the use of crustacean carapaces as indicator materials suffered from several disadvantages; one of these was ecdysis or periodic moulting. It should be understood that moulting is also of significance in determining the amounts of metals present in the soft tissues of crustaceans as at least some of the metal lost in cast moults is derived originally from the soft parts and laid down in the shell during the calcification process. This therefore represents an additional perturbation which should be considered by authors attempting to use decapod crustaceans as indicator organisms for trace elements.

However, the most serious problem associated with the study of crustaceans as environmental monitors of trace metals is that of regulation. Bryan and his co-workers have again been instrumental in elucidating the extent of regulatory processes in decapod species. In a series of important papers, Bryan (1964, 1966, 1967, 1968, 1971, 1976) has amply demonstrated that elements such as copper, manganese and zinc are all regulated in some fashion by crabs, lobsters and crayfish, as well as by amphipods and other species. Each element nevertheless has its own importance and characteristic kinetics. For example, copper is deeply involved in the physiological status of crustaceans and is needed in large amounts for the blood pigment, haemocyanin. Great variability between individuals is found for copper, and may be correlated to the moult–intermoult cycle (Zuckerkandl, 1960; Bryan, 1964, 1968; Martin, 1974). Manganese, at least in the lobster, *Homarus vulgaris*, is almost entirely associated with the shell, and levels in the soft parts are strictly regulated. Zinc concentrations are also regulated to within defined limits over a large range of ambient exposure levels; however, above a certain threshold (generally exceeding concentrations likely to be encountered in the environment), regulatory processes break down. An example is shown for the crab, *Carcinus maenas*, in Fig. 99.

The widespread existence of trace metal regulation amongst decapod crustaceans contrasts sharply with the accumulation of elements by barnacles. Studies to date suggest that barnacles resemble some of the sedentary molluscs more than the decapod crustaceans in terms of their handling of trace metals. They also have the advantage of being filter-feeders, in common with many of the molluscan species which have enjoyed widespread attention as indicators of trace metals. The regulation of trace metals is no doubt achieved by decapod crustaceans through restrictions on metal uptake and excretory adaptations; however, barnacles sequester accumulated elements in a (relatively) non-toxic form in granules (Walker *et al.*, 1975*b*; Walker, 1977). These two different evolutionary adaptations are central to the usefulness of the organisms as indicators of trace metal contamination of the environment. Unfortunately, studies to date have not fully developed the indicator capability of barnacle species; however, survey reports such as those of Ireland (1973, 1974), Navrot *et al.* (1974), Walker *et al.* (1975*a*) and Barbaro *et al.* (1978) have shown that these organisms have clear potential as indicators of trace elements in marine and estuarine environments.

Crustaceans, especially decapods, are amongst the most sensitive species to organochlorines in aquatic ecosystems. Some authors consider that certain crab and prawn species are undergoing decimation by organochlorine contamination and it has been noted that concentrations of DDT and other organochlorines in shrimp killed in laboratory experiments of acute organochlorine toxicity may be approached by individuals of the same species taken from some contaminated areas in the field. The route of uptake of organochlorines in crustaceans is not completely understood, but some species at least probably accumulate residues from detritus and bottom sediments (e.g. see Odum *et al.*, 1969). The degree of incorporation of organochlorines into the exoskeleton of crustaceans is probably quite low and moulting may therefore be somewhat less important in defining the residue levels present compared with its influence on trace metal accumulation.

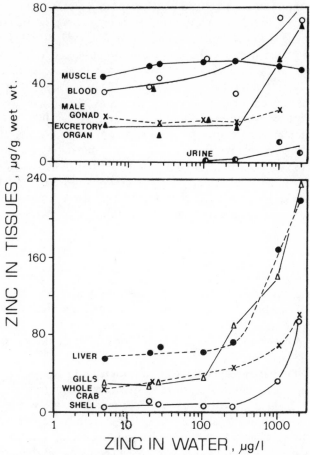

FIG. 99. Mean concentrations of zinc (μg/g wet weight) in the tissues of the crab, *Carcinus maenas*, after exposure to various levels of zinc in solution for 32 days at 13 °C. Each point represents a mean of at least two individuals. Note difference in vertical scales. (After Bryan (1966, 1976).)

Despite the possibility that crustaceans may serve as accurate indicators of environmental contamination by organochlorines, their use has been somewhat restricted to date. In particular, very few survey reports have been published which can be used to test the indicator ability of a species by its study in areas with known inputs of organochlorines. Exceptions to this rule include the studies of Modin (1969) on the Dungeness crab, *Cancer magister*, in the area surrounding San Francisco Bay and those of Burnett

(1971) on *Emerita analoga* and of Heesen and McDermott (1974) on *Cancer anthonyi*, both these latter studies encompassing the area of Palos Verdes which is known to be severely contaminated by DDT and its metabolites from industry. PCBs were also considered in the work of Heesen and McDermott (1974) and other survey data are available from Escambia Bay (Nimmo *et al.*, 1970, 1971*a, b*, 1974). These studies in general support the concept of using decapod species as indicator organisms for organochlorines. Many of the interfering variables can be overcome by careful sampling procedures (season, size, sex, etc.). Perhaps the only variable of significance which cannot easily be eliminated in such indicator surveys is the selection of a biased sample by the researcher because of the field toxicity of the organochlorines; this aspect was discussed in Chapter 13 and, whilst it remains somewhat theoretical, the effects of selective predation may nevertheless be proved significant in future studies.

G. MOLLUSCS

Molluscs have certainly been the most commonly used indicators to date, at least for trace metals; their use as monitors of organochlorines has not been as widespread as that of finfish, but it is notable that the US National Pesticide Monitoring Survey relied heavily on bivalves, at least in estuaries (Butler, 1969*a, b*, 1973).

Trace metals have been most extensively studied in bivalve molluscs, with less emphasis being given to gastropod species and least to cephalopods. Bryan (1976), in a critical review of trace elements in the marine and estuarine environments, stated: '... it has generally been found that concentrations of heavy metals in bivalve molluscs change with those in the environment...'. This statement appears unassailable to date, with the exception of iron and manganese kinetics in the oyster, *Crassostrea virginica* (Frazier, 1975, 1976; see Chapter 5) and certain other instances which involve metal–metal interaction (discussed below and in Chapter 11). Thus, bivalves exhibit very little evidence of metabolic regulation of trace elements, although a slight decrease in efficiency of removal of metals from solution may occur at high exposure levels (e.g. see Schulz-Baldes, 1972, 1974), such that direct proportionality is not fully attained. Trace elements are presumably sequestered in a relatively non-toxic form, possibly as granules, in particular organs such as the hepatopancreas and kidneys (Bryan, 1973) and in some cases the blood (George *et al.*, 1978). The amounts of pollutants which can be accumulated without overt toxic effects are very great compared with other organisms, and it is rare indeed to discover a site so polluted that bivalves cannot be found in the vicinity.

However, it should be apparent that no organism is a perfect indicator for pollutants and the use of bivalves to monitor trace elements is subject to several problems. Variables such as season, size, sampling position in the water column, and so on, may be relatively simply eliminated during the sampling procedure; a scheme for reproducible sampling has been suggested by Phillips (1976a). Parameters such as salinity and water temperature should also be considered inasmuch as they influence metal accumulation by some species; if the intention of an indicator or monitoring survey is to elucidate unusually contaminated areas, these parameters may be particularly important. Bivalve sex is a variable which has been little considered to date, but the data discussed in Chapter 9 suggest that sexing of bivalve samples may be worth while in some monitoring surveys, particularly as some species exhibit cyclic changes of sex which may bias samples greatly towards a predominance of one sex or the other.

Apart from the above parameters, all of which may be relatively simply eliminated, the major problems associated with the use of bivalve molluscs as indicators of trace elements are metal–metal interactions and discontinuity of feeding or filtration. Metal–metal interactions (and interactions of metal uptake with any co-existing pollutant) are of extreme potential in disrupting indicator surveys and in most cases cannot be allowed for. This has given rise to the suggestion that *Mytilus edulis* should not be relied upon as an accurate indicator of copper in the marine environment (Phillips, 1976a, b, 1977b). However, it might be noted that most studies in which metal–metal interaction has been observed have employed exposure of bivalves (and other organisms) to elements in solution only; if the majority of the total body load of elements is absorbed from food in the natural environment, such studies may overemphasise interactive effects (depending on whether they occur at uptake across the gill or at sequestration sites or at excretion).

Discontinuity of feeding or filtration has been little discussed in the present work, although certain aspects were considered in Chapter 13. The ideal indicator organism time-integrates pollution levels by continuous subsampling of ambient conditions, both via feeding and by passing water over the gills for respiratory purposes. Continuous feeding, of course, does not really exist, and it is sufficient if feeding occurs by the selection of prey containing a reasonable approximation of the mean pollutant level of the prey population (*cf.* selective feeding on crabs exhibiting behavioural modifications caused by pollutants; see Chapter 13). However, most or all bivalve species possess the ability to isolate the internal tissues from the ambient seawater in periods of unfavourable conditions; this phenomenon is the bivalve equivalent of the avoidance response found in more mobile organisms. If valve closure occurs in unfavourable conditions (of salinity, for example) which coincide with abnormal pollutant availability, a bivalve may not respond to the change in ambient pollutant levels in the required fashion (Davenport, 1977; Phillips, 1977a; Davenport and Manley, 1978). The same may be true if feeding or filtration rates differ according to the state of the tide or other factors which may co-vary with pollutant availability (e.g. Morton, 1970, 1977).

The valve closure mechanism varies between species both in its efficiency in isolation of the internal tissues and in its prolongation. For example, Shumway (1977) discussed species differences amongst bivalves in their response to fluctuating salinities; members of the genera *Mytilus* and *Crassostrea* may exhibit full valve closure for quite long periods (up to 96 h in *M. edulis*), whereas this behavioural adaptation is less well developed in sublittoral species such as scallops and the mussel, *Modiolus modiolus*, and is perhaps intermediate in species such as *Mya arenaria* which are incapable of siphon withdrawal or full valve closure but which close the mantle edges and the siphon tips by muscle action. Such differences may have some bearing on the *exact* relationship between the accumulation of metals by the bivalve and the time-integrated ambient levels of each element; however, this point is somewhat esoteric and the precise effects of valve closure on the ability of bivalves to time-integrate ambient pollutants have never been accurately assessed. Whilst it is possible that some species could fail to monitor episodic discharges of a pollutant occurring only during periods of valve closure, the available evidence suggests that this is a rare occurrence, if indeed it occurs at all. The possibility of the pollutant itself eliciting valve closure (or decreased filtration rates) is more likely, and may conceivably be more important in locations which are very severely polluted. For *Mytilus edulis* the most likely candidate for this type of effect is copper, whereas oysters may be influenced in this fashion by high ambient DDT levels (see Chapter 13); however, even this effect may never be significant in the environment because of the development of tolerance in highly polluted populations (Davenport and Manley, 1978).

To summarise, the excellent conformity of many bivalve species to the basic indicator pre-requisites (Chapter 2) which has been mainly responsible for the widespread monitoring research performed to date with such species, is matched by their marked ability to act as efficient and accurate monitoring organisms of a wide range of pollutants. Whilst current understanding of trace element kinetics in bivalves is rather more advanced than that of organochlorine accumulation, most authors clearly consider bivalve molluscs of great potential as indicators of either type of pollutant. However, success thus far does not imply any requirement for less research in the future, and refinement of indicator techniques using bivalves is of great importance, particularly if global monitoring is to become a reality (Goldberg, 1975*b*; Phillips 1976*a*, 1977*b*, 1979*c*).

Compared with our knowledge of the biology and pollutant kinetics of bivalves, studies on gastropod molluscs are much less common, especially with respect to organochlorines. However, some gastropod species have clear potential as indicators of trace metals at least. Like bivalves, gastropods conform well to basic indicator pre-requisites, although some species would be better termed sedentary rather than sessile and this is perhaps a disadvantage. The concentrations of trace elements present in these animals are high compared with most other aquatic organisms and there is little evidence of regulation of most metals (*cf.* Young, 1975). Limpets in particular appear to accumulate large amounts of many elements and whilst this is no guarantee of indicator ability, it is certainly useful to the analytical chemist. The similarity of the accumulative capacities of bivalve and gastropod molluscs leads one to suspect similar modes of element sequestration in the two groups, but this is perhaps simplistic and the cautious trace metal researcher quickly learns to avoid generalisations, especially as species differences within phyla or classes are common (e.g. see Hoggins and Brooks, 1973).

Most variables which have been found to affect pollutant accumulation in bivalves are also effective in this respect in gastropods, although, as noted above, studies on the latter group are rather more rare. Nevertheless, examples were cited for gastropods in many of the foregoing chapters concerning the effects of such parameters as season, size of animal, shore line position, and so on. The two major variables discussed above as of greatest potential for disruption of indicator surveys using bivalves (pollutant interactions and discontinuity of feeding or filtration) also operate in gastropod molluscs and should be considered of equal importance. The valve closure mechanism seen in bivalves has as its counterpart in gastropods a mechanism whereby the animal withdraws completely into the shell, fastening tightly to the substrate (limpets, etc.) or strongly closing the operculum to isolate the soft tissues from the ambient environment. Whilst species differences occur amongst both bivalves and gastropods concerning the efficiency of this phenomenon in isolating the internal tissues, no evidence is known to suggest that the process is more prevalent in one group rather than the other. Gastropods, however, include more carnivorous species than are found amongst the bivalves and differences in diet certainly affect indicator profiles (e.g. Ireland and Wootton, 1977; see Chapter 2 for further discussion). As noted for several other phyla, studies on organochlorine kinetics in gastropods are rare; most authors to date have been committed to the use of finfish for monitoring these and other pesticides. Perhaps research into the use of more sedentary organisms such as gastropods would be worthwhile; however, the economic aspects of such studies are less attractive, and repercussions for public health are similarly much reduced.

Finally in this section, the cephalopods must be mentioned. These organisms have attracted least attention amongst molluscs as indicators of environmental contamination and cannot therefore be considered as serious candidates for large-scale surveys. Our knowledge of the effects of external variables on the accumulation of either trace metals or organochlorines by cephalopods is sadly inadequate. Certainly, these organisms conform less well than do bivalves or gastropods to the basic indicator requirements discussed in Chapter 2; this is particularly the case in terms of availability and distribution of species as well as mobility differences. However, both squid and octopus species appear to accumulate significant amounts of trace elements and organochlorines, which is at least suggestive of a restricted ability to regulate such pollutants. Whilst it is unrealistic to envisage the use of cephalopods as particularly useful indicators of inshore, estuarine or coastal pollution, several species exist which are widely distributed in the open oceans and these organisms deserve further study. It may be noted that most research to date dealing with the monitoring of pollutants in ocean waters has employed finfish; it is becoming apparent that many species of finfish are inadequate as indicators of certain pollutants (see below) and substitutes will have to be found. The use of cephalopods is one major alternative, and research to date (such as it is) tends to support the concept that these organisms exhibit pollutant kinetics much like those of the other molluscs.

H.   FINFISH

Research into pollutant kinetics in finfish has been widespread, and the use of finfish species to monitor trace elements and organochlorines has been no less common. The major reason for this emphasis has undoubtedly been the economic importance of finfish to man, although other factors have also played a certain role. However, few finfish species conform even to the basic requirements for indicator species. For example, mobility is a ubiquitous problem in the use of these organisms as indicators. Many pelagic species have large ranges and thus exhibit, at best, some composite moving average of ambient pollutant levels over a large area. Authors have continually ignored this problem, assuming that the concentrations of pollutants present in a fish characterise the site at which the animal was caught. The problem of mobility extends to coastal species as well as including open ocean finfish; many coastal finfish migrate into estuaries or nearshore waters to spawn, returning to areas further offshore for the rest of the year. The influence of such behaviour on the accumulation of pollutants (and their seasonality and variation with fish age) was beautifully demonstrated in the studies of Smith and Cole (1970) on winter flounders, *Pseudopleuronectes americanus*, from the Weweantic Estuary in Massachusetts (see Chapters 6 and 8). This most important problem is to some extent overcome by the use of demersal—rather than pelagic—finfish species; bottom-dwelling finfish commonly migrate little between areas throughout their life, although gross exceptions (e.g. *Anguilla* species) of course exist. Species which have been of particular interest to researchers include the northern pike, *Esox lucius* (mercury and organochlorines in particular have been studied in this species), and the sand flathead, *Platycephalus bassensis* (for cadmium in liver and mercury in muscle; see Phillips, 1976*b*, 1977*b*, and Dix *et al.*, 1976). Other demersal species such as the Dover sole, *Microstomus pacificus*, have also been the subject of recent studies and may be useful as indicators of organochlorine contamination of the environment (e.g. see Young *et al.*, 1977).

Bryan (1976), in his excellent review of trace metals in marine ecosystems, stated that the evidence to that point suggested that copper, molybdenum and zinc at least were regulated over a range of ambient concentrations in finfish. Phillips (1977*b*) reached similar conclusions and suggested that such regulation of elements to within strict ranges eliminated the possibility of using at least muscle tissues of teleosts as indicator materials for any metal other than mercury. The evidence for these contentions will be reassessed here in the light of both the early reports and more recent studies; freshwater and marine species will be discussed separately.

Freshwater Finfish
Much of the early data on the accumulation of metals by freshwater finfish species concern the results of toxicity tests undertaken in the laboratory to

elucidate maximum allowable toxicant concentrations (MATC) for water quality regulation. Copper, one of the most toxic metals in either freshwater or marine environments, has been used in several studies. Brungs *et al.* (1973) exposed the brown bullhead, *Ictalurus nebulosus*, to copper sulphate at concentrations between 6·5 and 422 μg/litre. No accumulation of copper was observed in the blood or the kidneys. However, copper concentrations increased in liver and gills of fish exposed to levels greater than 27–53 μg/litre in solution, and the authors noted that the profiles suggested that some 'defence mechanism', operative at low ambient copper, was overcome by raising the copper levels in solution above the 27 μg/litre threshold. It is most unfortunate that muscle tissues were not analysed in this study. McKim and Benoit (1974) studied copper accumulation and effects on brook trout, *Salvelinus fontinalis*, at exposure concentrations between 2·7 and 9·4 μg/litre; these observations extended earlier work

TABLE 97

CONCENTRATIONS OF COPPER (MEANS AND 95 PER CENT CONFIDENCE LIMITS, μg/g DRY WEIGHTS) IN EGGS AND TISSUES OF BROOK TROUT, *Salvelinus fontinalis*, EXPOSED TO COPPER SULPHATE FOR 24 MONTHS AT FOUR DIFFERENT CONCENTRATIONS. NUMBERS IN PARENTHESES REPRESENT THE NUMBER OF SAMPLES ANALYSED. (AFTER McKIM AND BENOIT (1974).)

| Tissue | Mean exposure concentration of copper (μg/litre) | | | |
	9·4	6·1	4·5	2·7 (Control)
Gill	6·7 ± 2·2(12)	4·0 ± 1·2(12)	4·0 ± 1·0(12)	5·0 ± 3·3(6)
Liver	238·4 ± 89·5(12)	207·8 ± 67·3(11)	237·6 ± 146·4(12)	239 ± 109·1(6)
Kidney	16·5 ± 7·4(12)	12·6 ± 3·0(11)	15·2 ± 6·1(12)	19·7 ± 14·1(5)
Muscle	17·0 ± 6·6(10)	8·2 ± 2·9(11)	6·9 ± 2·7(11)	15·3 ± 6·3(4)
Eggs (from body cavity of ripe fish)	6·8 ± 2·1(5)	8·4 ± 2·1(7)	5·7 ± 0·4(3)	9·4 ± 3·6(4)

dealing with toxicity alone (McKim and Benoit, 1971). The uptake of copper in tissues of this species did not vary significantly with changes in the exposure concentration (Table 97) showing that, at least in this concentration range, regulation is perfect in each of the tissues investigated. In later studies on the bluegill, *Lepomis macrochirus*, Benoit (1975) used a greater range of copper levels in solution, from 3 to 162 μg/litre. The results (Table 98) showed significant increases in copper in gills of fish exposed to 40 μg/litre or greater concentrations, whereas livers and kidneys responded

TABLE 98

CONCENTRATIONS OF COPPER (MEANS ± STANDARD DEVIATIONS, µg/g DRY WEIGHT) IN TISSUES OF BLUEGILL, *Lepomis macrochirus*, EXPOSED FOR 24 MONTHS TO VARIOUS LEVELS OF THE ELEMENT IN SOLUTION (AS COPPER SULPHATE). NUMBERS IN PARENTHESES REPRESENT THE NUMBER OF SAMPLES ANALYSED. (AFTER BENOIT (1975).)

Tissue	Mean exposure concentration of copper in solution (μg/litre)					
	162	77	40	21	12	3 (Control)
Liver	480 ± 284·7[a](5)	57 ± 44·8(7)	61 ± 41·6(8)	10 ± 3·3(8)	8 ± 1·6(7)	7 ± 0·5(5)
Gill	13 ± 2·2[a](5)	6 ± 1·1[a](7)	5 ± 1·1[a](8)	3 ± 0·5(8)	3 ± 1·1(7)	3 ± 0·3(5)
Kidney	44 ± 17·6[a](5)	12 ± 4·7(7)	13 ± 4·2(8)	12 ± 2·7(8)	9 ± 1·8(7)	22 ± 7·7(5)

[a] Significantly greater than control ($p < 0.05$, t test).

only at the highest concentration tested. All these data therefore agree, and show that freshwater finfish regulate tissue levels of copper when exposed to a range of relatively low ambient concentrations of the element; when concentrations exceed this range (which appears to be somewhat species-dependent), tissue levels of copper begin to increase.

Cadmium uptake by *L. macrochirus* was investigated by Eaton (1974). The exposure concentrations used ranged between 31 and 2140 μg/litre, all of which are exceedingly high compared with the levels expected in the field. Accumulation of the metal was significant in all exposed fish in all tissues tested (gill, intestine and caecum, liver and kidney), but the response was only weakly dose-dependent, perhaps because mortalities interfered in the profile. Benoit *et al.* (1976) later investigated the accumulation and toxic effects of cadmium using brook trout, *Salvelinus fontinalis*, exposed at much lower concentrations which are more likely to be encountered in the environment. These data were partially discussed in Chapter 5 (text and see Fig. 28). Concentrations of cadmium of only 0·5 μg/litre were effective in increasing the cadmium concentrations present in gill, liver and kidney tissues of this species, and no evidence of regulation as such could be found in these tissues. However, cadmium kinetics in red blood cells, muscle and, to some extent, spleen, showed evidence of regulatory processes (Fig. 28), even at the higher exposure concentrations. Studies on lead accumulation by the same species (Holcombe *et al.*, 1976) indicated very similar profiles, although exposure concentrations were very high (33 to 473 μg/litre, as lead nitrate in solution). Gill, liver and kidney tissues once again exhibited dose-dependent uptake of lead; accumulation was less pronounced in red blood cells at the lower exposure levels and muscle and spleen exhibited very little uptake of the metal even at high ambient concentrations. For these metals, therefore, the situation differs compared with copper; whilst cadmium and lead are partially regulated in some organs such as muscle, they are accumulated in a dose-dependent manner in other organs, notably gills, liver and kidneys. Other tissues seem to be intermediate between these extremes, suggesting weak regulatory processes.

The picture is completed by the studies of Buhler *et al.* (1977) on the uptake of hexavalent chromium by rainbow trout, *Salmo gairdneri*. The uptake data in this report must be treated with caution, as exposure concentrations were 2·5 mg/litre which is far too high to be significant environmentally. However, data were included for fish which were reared in 'background' concentrations of 0·25 μg/litre (Naches trout) and 2–10 μg/litre (Hanford trout) and the differences between these control fish (Table 99) revealed that chromium was taken up by all tissues of the

TABLE 99

CONCENTRATIONS OF CHROMIUM (MEANS ± STANDARD ERRORS, $\mu g/g$ WET WEIGHTS) IN TISSUES OF NACHES TROUT REARED IN WATER CONTAINING $0.25\,\mu g/litre$ HEXAVALENT CHROMIUM AND THOSE OF HANFORD TROUT REARED IN EXPOSURE CONCENTRATIONS OF $2–10\,\mu g/litre$ HEXAVALENT CHROMIUM. ALL FISH WERE *Salmo gairdneri*, 2 YEARS OLD, AND HAD BEEN MAINTAINED IN THEIR RESPECTIVE CONCENTRATIONS OF THE ELEMENT THROUGHOUT THEIR LIVES. (AFTER BUHLER *et al.* (1977).)

Tissue	Naches trout[a]	Hanford trout[b]
Opercular bone	1.00 ± 0.10	4.90 ± 0.69
Gall bladder	0.56 ± 0.07	10.60 ± 3.20
Anterior kidney	0.28 ± 0.13	1.71 ± 0.01
Brain	0.22 ± 0.08	1.03 ± 0.57
Vertebral bone	0.21 ± 0.20	0.96 ± 0.22
Bile	0.17 ± 0.05	1.21 ± 0.20
Small intestine	0.17 ± 0.03	1.78 ± 0.48
Colon	0.16 ± 0.05	0.98 ± 0.17
Posterior kidney	0.13 ± 0.05	1.64 ± 0.08
Heart	0.12 ± 0.05	1.58 ± 0.48
Spleen	0.10 ± 0.06	3.57 ± 0.55
Skin	0.09 ± 0.03	0.49 ± 0.16
Fat	0.09 ± 0.03	0.69 ± 0.05
Stomach	0.06 ± 0.11	0.27 ± 0.09
Red cells	0.05 ± 0.01	0.77 ± 0.30
Gill	0.04 ± 0.01	0.65 ± 0.11
Ceca	0.04 ± 0.01	0.43 ± 0.13
Liver	0.04 ± 0.01	0.44 ± 0.05
Plasma	0.03 ± 0.01	0.40 ± 0.13
White muscle	0.01 ± 0.00	0.07 ± 0.01

[a] $N = 12$, mean whole-body weight 528 g, range 295–727 g.
[b] $N = 3$ or 6, mean whole-body weight 322 g, range 261–597 g.

Hanford trout. Thus chromium does not appear to be significantly regulated in any tissue of *S. gairdneri*, and this conclusion is similar to those reached in studies of mercury kinetics in species such as *Salmo gairdneri* (Reinert *et al.*, 1974), *Salvelinus fontinalis* (McKim *et al.*, 1976) and *Lepomis macrochirus* (Cember *et al.*, 1978).

The different behaviour of each of the elements in freshwater finfish has also been noted in field studies. Lucas *et al.* (1970) analysed whole fish (three species) or fish livers (ten species) for fifteen trace elements; the samples were derived from Lakes Erie, Michigan and Superior. Concentrations of

TABLE 100

MEAN CONCENTRATIONS OF THIRTEEN TRACE ELEMENTS (μg/kg WET WEIGHTS) IN DRESSED FISH OF TWO SPECIES, LAKE WHITEFISH, *Coregonus clupeaformis*, AND NORTHERN PIKE, *Esox lucius*. MOOSE LAKE IS CONSIDERED UNCONTAMINATED RELATIVE TO THE OTHER LAKES STUDIED. (AFTER UTHE AND BLIGH (1971).)

Species	Lake	Antimony	Arsenic	Cadmium	Chromium	Copper	Lead	Manganese	Mercury	Nickel	Selenium	Tin	Uranium	Zinc
Lake whitefish	Moose Lake	2·2	90	<50	33	500	<500	690	70	<200	240	3 570	<3 000	14 000
Lake whitefish	Lake Ontario	3·1	700	<50	<17	940	<500	660	170	<200	380	800	<2 000	12 000
Northern pike	Moose Lake	3·2	<50	<50	<35	700	<500	2980	110	<200	170	5 430	<3 000	19 000
Northern pike	Lake Erie	4·3	<50	<50	<31	700	<500	930	490	<200	190	540	<1 000	11 000
Northern pike	Lake St. Pierre	3·7	90	<50	<26	890	<500	3160	700	<200	370	670	<2 000	19 000

cobalt, copper and zinc varied little with either species or location, suggesting possible regulation; by contrast, cadmium, chromium and arsenic levels varied with species and with location. The variability of cadmium and chromium tends to support the concept developed above that these elements are not (or are poorly) regulated in livers of freshwater finfish. The authors suggested that the presence or absence of regulatory processes could be linked to whether the elements concerned were physiologically essential. Uthe and Bligh (1971) compared the concentrations of thirteen elements in dressed fish from a non-industrialised lake (Moose Lake) and from the heavily industrialised Lake Ontario, Lake St. Pierre and Lake Erie. Results for lake whitefish, *Coregonus clupeaformis*, and northern pike, *Esox lucius*, are shown in Table 100. Clearly, the detection of cadmium, chromium, lead, nickel and uranium was inadequate to support any conclusions. Of the other metals, antimony, copper, manganese and zinc do not appear to be significantly different in the samples from different locations, and the only metals which may be present at higher levels in the fish from the industrialised areas are arsenic and mercury. This is convincing evidence for the regulation of most metals in finfish.

The conclusion that some metals at least are strictly regulated in freshwater finfish is supported by the interesting work of Giesy and Wiener (1977). These authors studied the frequency distributions of trace element concentrations in five species of finfish. Frequency distributions of concentrations of copper, iron and zinc, all of which are essential elements, tended more towards normality than did those of cadmium and chromium concentrations; the latter elements commonly exhibited strong positive skewness in their distributions and this may be due to a lack of regulation. In a later paper (Wiener and Giesy, 1978) these ideas were amplified by studies of five elements in bluegills, *Lepomis macrochirus*, introduced to a new pond environment. The conclusions supported the concept of homeostatic control of copper, manganese and zinc in freshwater finfish, although changes of cadmium and lead levels in the introduced fish suggested that some organs at least were responding to alterations in the amounts of these metals available in the environment.

Further support for metal regulation in finfish from fresh waters can be found in the report of Ward (1973). The concentrations of molybdenum were investigated in three water bodies and in rainbow trout, *Salmo gairdneri* and kokanee salmon, *Oncorhynchus nerka*, from each area. The results for tissues of the rainbow trout are shown in Table 101; it is clear that some tissues did not respond at all to increases in the ambient concentration of the element, and most tissues responded only weakly. The results for the stomach and intestines should be treated with caution, as both included some contents, which may have contributed significantly to the molybdenum levels observed. Studies on *O. nerka* were less extensive but suggested a similar regulatory ability for molybdenum.

TABLE 101

CONCENTRATIONS OF MOLYBDENUM (MEANS ± STANDARD DEVIATIONS, μg/kg WET WEIGHTS) IN TISSUES OF RAINBOW TROUT, *Salmo gairdneri*, FROM WATERS WITH DIFFERING CONCENTRATIONS OF MOLYBDENUM. NUMBERS OF SAMPLES ARE IN PARENTHESES. (AFTER WARD (1973).)

| Tissue | Concentrations of molybdenum in tissues (μg/kg wet weight) | | |
	Trace ambient	6 μg/litre ambient	300 μg/litre ambient
Liver	110 ± 20(9)	41 ± 18(6)	223 ± 22(4)
Spleen	48 ± 2(9)	92 ± 15(6)	208(4)
Kidney	108 ± 34(9)	113 ± 46(6)	147 ± 12(4)
Skin	71 ± 40(4)	70 ± 45(6)	99 ± 55(4)
Bone[a]	118 ± 33(9)	146 ± 21(6)	224 ± 78(4)
Muscle	10 ± 5(9)	10 ± 3(6)	13 ± 5(4)
Intestine[b]	67 ± 14(8)	61 ± 37(6)	134 ± 102(4)
Stomach[b]	47 ± 23(8)	35 ± 12(6)	332 ± 113(4)
Brain	21 ± 9(9)	17 ± 6(5)	92(4)
Gonads	13(9)	67(1)	No data
Gills	16(5)	No data	201(4)
Fat	5 ± 1(9)	No data	24(2)

[a] Composite of skull and vertebral elements.
[b] Including contents, if any.

By contrast to the above reports, recent studies of bluegills, *Lepomis macrochirus*, and largemouth bass, *Micropterus salmoides*, from Palestine Lake and Little Center Lake in Indiana (Atchison *et al.*, 1977; Murphy *et al.*, 1978) have shown that, at least in these highly contaminated areas, whole fish and their muscle do contain greater amounts of cadmium, lead and zinc than those present in control fish from less polluted sites. However, it is notable that even in the extremely contaminated Williamson Ditch area of Palestine Lake, which receives effluent from an electroplating industry, the fish studied contained only slight elevation of zinc levels, whereas cadmium was elevated by a factor of more than 30 in whole-body samples (Table 102), and lead was similarly elevated in Little Center Lake bluegill. The later study by the same group (Murphy *et al.*, 1978) confirmed

TABLE 102

MEAN CONCENTRATIONS (RANGES IN PARENTHESES) OF CADMIUM AND ZINC IN THE DISSOLVED AND SUSPENDED FRACTIONS OF WATER, IN SEDIMENTS, AND IN WHOLE BLUEGILLS, *Lepomis macrochirus*, FROM TWO SITES IN PALESTINE LAKE, INDIANA. WILLIAMSON DITCH RECEIVES EFFLUENT FROM AN ELECTROPLATING INDUSTRY LOCATED ON THE WEST SHORE OF THE LAKE. (AFTER ATCHISON *et al.* (1977).)

ND: NOT DETECTABLE (NO LIMITS QUOTED)

Site	Metal	Water		Sediment (upper 5 cm) (μg/g dry weight)	Fish (whole body) (μg/g dry weight)
		Dissolved (μg/litre)	Suspended (μg/litre)		
Williamson Ditch	Cadmium	17·3 (3·3–43·3)	30·3 (14·4–57·7)	800 (340–1 300)	3·4 (ND–15·0)
	Zinc	293 (133–636)	270 (196–390)	12 800 (4 100–24 800)	220 (120–480)
East Palestine Lake	Cadmium	0·9 (0·6–1·1)	0·3 (ND–0·9)	4·4 (0·3–6·2)	0·1 (ND–0·4)
	Zinc	52·4 (23·0–110)	5·2 (1·6–12·5)	320 (100–790)	140 (99–240)

TABLE 103

CONCENTRATIONS OF CADMIUM AND ZINC (MEANS ± STANDARD ERRORS AND RANGES, μg/g DRY WEIGHT) IN MUSCLE OF BLUEGILL, *Lepomis macrochirus*, AND LARGEMOUTH BASS, *Micropterus salmoides*, FROM WILLIAMSON DITCH AND EAST PALESTINE LAKE. (AFTER MURPHY *et al.* (1978).) SITES ARE THE SAME AS THOSE IN TABLE 102

Site	Species	n^a	Cadmium		Zinc	
			Mean ± SEM	Range	Mean ± SEM	Range
Williamson Ditch	Bluegill	15	0·431 ± 0·087	0·06–1·31	67·8 ± 7·5	29·9–158·2
East Palestine Lake	Bluegill	14	0·076 ± 0·008	0·05–0·15	47·8 ± 2·2	35·1–64·5
Williamson Ditch	Largemouth bass	26	0·075 ± 0·017	0·01–0·31	43·3 ± 1·7	30·2–60·7
East Palestine Lake	Largemouth bass	18	0·012 ± 0·002	0·01–0·05	37·2 ± 3·0	18·2–65·8

[a] Sample number.

these differences (Table 103). Clearly, zinc is better regulated than cadmium or lead in both bluegills and largemouth bass, and this conclusion agrees with the previously cited data although, in cases of extreme contamination, it seems possible to overcome even the greater regulatory ability of fish for zinc.

We may thus conclude that the major differences in regulation of trace elements in freshwater finfish are a function of degree rather than being indicative of an absolute difference in element kinetics. Metals such as copper, iron, manganese and zinc appear to be controlled by quite severe homeostatic processes, and the ambient concentrations must be increased very considerably before regulation breaks down. Presumably at this point, influx of metals outpaces the excretory capacity of the animal, and individual tissues begin to respond to alterations in the external levels of the elements. Although this point may be attained at different ambient concentrations of a given metal for different species, this variation is quantitative, rather than qualitative, i.e. most or all species possess some homeostatic ability for these elements. Non-essential metals such as cadmium and lead, however (and perhaps chromium), are poorly regulated; this is particularly evident in the response of organs such as gills, liver and kidney to low ambient concentrations of these elements. The breakdown in homeostatic control of such metals thus occurs at lower ambient levels (or at levels which represent smaller increases over 'background' concentrations), and the indicator ability of the fish is therefore greater. Presumably this also correlates to metal toxicities; as toxic effects must occur when the regulatory ability of the animal is exceeded, elements which are less well regulated (cadmium, lead, mercury) should exhibit a toxic action at concentrations relatively close to ambient (unpolluted) levels.

Marine Finfish

In general, the conclusions which may be reached from existing reports of metal kinetics and accumulation by marine and estuarine species of finfish support those from the studies discussed above for freshwater species. Once again, both laboratory studies and field studies have been reported, although laboratory studies at low ambient concentrations have been rare. Certainly, finfish such as the mummichog, *Fundulus heteroclitus*, will take up cadmium, copper and zinc from solution when presented with ambient concentrations in the milligramme per litre range (e.g. Eisler, 1967*c*; Eisler and Gardner, 1973; Eisler, 1974), but these levels are orders of magnitude above those in the environment and such studies tell us little of the existence (or otherwise) of regulatory processes occurring in the microgramme per litre range of concentration. Similarly, studies with artificial radionuclides are not completely to be trusted in this respect, as the exposure concentrations of the nuclide itself, or the nuclide plus carrier, are often very high compared with those of the stable element in the field. Furthermore, if very low concentrations of radionuclides are used, apparent uptake may occur by exchange of the radioactive isotope with the stable element already present in the tissues (see below), and what may appear to be unregulated uptake may, in reality, be progressive isotopic exchange into a strictly regulated pool of the stable element. The excellent studies of McKim and others cited in the previous subsection thus have no counterpart where marine finfish are considered. Perhaps the most useful report concerning trace element regulation in a marine species of finfish is that of Saward *et al.* (1975), dealing with the effects of copper on an experimental marine food chain incorporating mixed phytoplankton, the bivalve, *Tellina tenuis*, and 0-group plaice, *Pleuronectes platessa*. Dosing of this artificial ecosystem with (measured) concentrations of copper of about 9, 18 and 48 μg/litre in solution gave rise to copper accumulation in almost all parts of the experimental ecosystem. The accumulation of copper in the bivalve was discussed previously (see text and Fig. 95 in Chapter 12). By contrast to the dose-dependent response of the bivalve soft parts, the muscle tissue of the plaice did not respond to copper additions to the external environment; however, viscera samples indicated some increases which were dose-dependent, although the authors did not ascribe this to any particular organ. In this case, therefore, it may be concluded that *P. platessa* actively regulates muscle levels of copper, although concentrations in visceral organs may reflect exposure levels.

Much of the data available from field studies of marine finfish support the concept of partial or complete regulation of elements, at least in muscle tissues. It may be noted here in passing that most metals are found at lowest concentration in axial muscle of finfish (e.g. see Figs. 23 and 24 in Chapter 5) and this in itself may be indicative of a regulatory process present in muscle tissue. The obvious exception is mercury (also, perhaps, selenium; see Mackay *et al.*, 1975*b*), which commonly occurs in axial muscle of finfish at concentrations approaching or exceeding those in other organs, and of course appears to be very poorly regulated (if at all) in any finfish species.

With respect to metals other than mercury, reports are numerous and only selected examples of particular interest will be noted here; further discussion may be found in Phillips (1977*b*). Cross *et al.* (1973) considered that their studies of copper, iron, manganese and zinc in muscles of bluefish,

Pomatomus saltatrix, and *Antimora rostrata*, from the Atlantic Ocean were indicative of strict metabolic regulation of the elements. Mercury, by contrast, was not regulated as such, as increased concentrations were found with age (see Chapter 5). Eustace (1974) studied 39 species of teleosts and elasmobranchs from the contaminated Derwent Estuary in Tasmania, Australia. He concluded that in no case did muscle samples reflect the presence or absence of contamination of the external environment by cadmium, copper, manganese or zinc. By contrast, whole soft parts of the bivalves, *Mytilus edulis* and *Ostrea angasi*, responded well to such contamination and the author noted that '. . . the monitoring of commercial fish species caught in the River Derwent would provide a much less sensitive index of pollution than would the monitoring of oysters or mussels . . .'. Similar data were provided more recently by Jan *et al.* (1977), who failed to show significant accumulation of metals in the muscle of six species of finfish taken close to wastewater outfalls on the California coast, compared with the same species taken from control sites. Once again, bivalve molluscs (and some crustaceans) monitored the additional contamination from the outfalls and the differences in element regulation between the samples were clear. Results for muscle, gonads and livers of Dover sole, *Microstomus pacificus*, were also indicative of the regulation of trace elements, differing very little between sites known to be polluted and those considered uncontaminated (McDermott and Young, 1974). Conclusions from other field studies of various species of finfish support this concept of element regulation, notwithstanding the significance of parameters such as species, season, age, and so on in defining the actual level of regulation (e.g. see Windom *et al.*, 1973; Hardisty *et al.*, 1974*a*, *b*; Cutshall *et al.*, 1977*b*; Greig *et al.*, 1977; Badsha and Sainsbury, 1977, 1978).

Thus, at present, there seems to be little or no justification for assuming that finfish species (either freshwater or marine) commonly accumulate metals in proportion to the concentrations present in the external environment. Many or all of the essential elements appear to be regulated to within definite limits—at least in some tissues and at least in the absence of severe contamination of the environment. Some species may also regulate —or partially regulate—non-essential elements. The only instance in which finfish appear to act as reliable indicator organisms concerns mercury, and whilst some authors have suggested that this element also is partially regulated (e.g. see Johnels *et al.*, 1967; Cross *et al.*, 1973; Bryan, 1976), the degree of homeostatic control is so poor that finfish may be used to monitor mercury availability in either freshwater or marine ecosystems; reports such as that of Gardner (1978) serve to support this contention. It is interesting to note that the phenomenon of element regulation in finfish muscle (and sometimes other tissues) does not necessarily eliminate the usefulness of these organisms as monitors of contamination of aquatic ecosystems by artificial radionuclides. As mentioned above, it is quite possible for exchange to occur between a stable isotope present in a regulated pool in the organism and an externally available radionuclide; the amount of exchange will depend on the ambient concentration of the radioactive isotope and the latter may thus be quantitated (e.g. see Cutshall *et al.*, 1977*a*). Exchange may be slow enough to afford long time-integration of the radionuclide, assuming its decay is slow also (Renfro *et al.*, 1975).

Compared with the situation for trace elements, there is very little evidence for homeostatic control of organochlorines in either marine or freshwater finfish. Hence these organisms have been very widely used to monitor contamination of the aquatic environment by such chemicals. The greatest source of interpretive error is certainly due to the marked effect of lipid on the accumulation of organochlorines; this factor is an important influence in its own right as well as being responsible for a large proportion of the effects of other variables. If authors take this into account by quantitating lipids in all samples and basing analytical results on both wet weights and lipid weights, interpretation of spatial or temporal differences between samples is much simpler. Care must nevertheless be taken to ensure that samples from different locations are normalised as to season, size, sex and other variables, discussed in previous chapters at length. It must also be remembered that the comments concerning fish migration (see above) are as important for the accurate monitoring of organochlorines as they are for trace elements; the tendency to assume that fish have small ranges and are therefore characteristic of their capture site must be avoided for most species, at least until proven. This interference of migration in the use of finfish as indicator organisms for organochlorines tends to support the concept of using more sedentary (or better yet, sessile) organisms such as the bivalve molluscs. However, our understanding of organochlorine kinetics in bivalves does not match our knowledge of trace metal kinetics in these organisms and, as a result, the monitoring of organochlorines must be envisaged as in the developmental stage as yet, whilst techniques using bivalves as indicators of trace metals are perhaps now advancing to the refinement stage. Much research is clearly needed to improve our use of indicator techniques for any pollutant; however, the field is perhaps legitimately only 10 years old and promises to be a powerful tool in the future.

I. MARINE MAMMALS

Finally, mention is required of the indicator ability of marine mammals. Almost all studies to date, either for trace metals or of organochlorines, have concentrated on seals, although some work on dolphins, sea-lions and whales has been reported. Clearly, these organisms suffer from the real problem of being far too large for their widespread use as indicators, it being somewhat difficult to organise laboratory studies. Whilst this may appear facetious, it is nevertheless a serious disadvantage, as much of our present knowledge of pollutant kinetics in molluscs, finfish or other indicator types derives from laboratory investigations.

Although data concerning the effects of age on pollutant levels in seals are available, our knowledge of such effects as those of season is poor to date. The greatest problem in the use of any marine mammal as a *bona fide* indicator organism is, once again, however, that of animal migration. This aspect was mentioned in Chapter 8, where it was noted that the concentrations of a pollutant in a migrating animal are a complex function of ambient exposure concentrations with space and time. It is probably impossible to separate the effects caused by an acute exposure to a high level of a pollutant from those due to a chronic low-level exposure. Thus contamination of a seal population with a given pollutant may have been caused by a recent acute exposure or by chronic exposure throughout the lifetime of each animal. It is usually unrealistic to sample enough individuals (e.g. of different ages) to allow separation of such effects; many populations are suffering anthropogenic decimation without the attempts of pollutant researchers. Research into the levels of pollutants found in marine mammals is thus of more importance in terms of monitoring the toxic effects of pollutants on the ecosphere than in terms of measuring the abundance of the pollutants as such. Seals and sea-lions are certainly sensitive to organochlorines such as PCBs and may, in addition, be undergoing sublethal stresses caused by their accumulation of trace elements. One is lead to the conclusion that lower organisms should be used to quantitate the degree of contamination of the aquatic ecosphere; marine mammals will hopefully inform man when it is time to stop such contamination. At least in some regions of the world's oceans, that time is clearly approaching; indicator organisms represent a powerful opportunity to elucidate the spatial and temporal variation in aquatic contamination and will at least show man where to look when he decides to stop employing the world's oceans as a sink, rather than a source.

References

Abdullah, M. I. and L. G. Royle (1974). A study of the dissolved and particulate trace elements in the Bristol Channel. *J. mar. biol. Ass. UK.* **54**: 581–97.

Abel, P. D. (1976). Effect of some pollutants on the filtration rate of *Mytilus. Mar. Pollut. Bull.* **7**(12): 228–31.

Ackefors, H. (1971). Mercury pollution in Sweden with special reference to conditions in the water habitat. *Proc. Roy. Soc. Lond. B.* **177**: 365–87.

Ackman, R. G. (1967). Characteristics of the fatty acid composition and biochemistry of some freshwater fish oils and lipids in comparison with marine oils and lipids. *Comp. Biochem. Physiol.* **22**: 907–22.

Ackman, R. G. and S. N. Hooper (1974). Long-chain monoethylenic and other fatty acids in heart, liver and blubber lipids of two harbour seals (*Phoca vitulina*) and one grey seal (*Halichoerus grypus*). *J. Fish. Res. Bd. Canada.* **31**: 333–41.

Ackman, R. G., C. A. Eaton and P. A. Jangaard (1965). Lipids of the fin whale (*Balaenoptera physalus*) from North Atlantic waters. *Can. J. Biochem.* **43**: 1513–20.

Ackman, R. G., C. A. Eaton, E. G. Bligh and A. W. Lantz (1967). Freshwater fish oils: Yields and composition of oils from reduction of sheepshead, tullibee, maria and alewife. *J. Fish. Res. Bd. Canda.* **24**: 1219–27.

Addison, R. F. and P. F. Brodie (1977). Organochlorine residues in maternal blubber, milk, and pup blubber from grey seals (*Halichoerus grypus*) from Sable Island, Nova Scotia. *J. Fish. Res. Bd. Canada.* **34**: 937–41.

Addison, R. F. and T. G. Smith (1974). Organochlorine residue levels in Arctic ringed seals: Variation with age and sex. *Oikos.* **25**: 335–37.

Addison, R. F. and M. E. Zinck (1975). The metabolism of some DDT-type compounds by brook trout (*Salvelinus fontinalis*). *Environ. Qual. Saf. (Suppl.).* **3**: 500–6.

Addison, R. F. and M. E. Zinck (1977). Rate of conversion of ^{14}C-p,p'-DDT to p,p'-DDE by brook trout (*Salvelinus fontinalis*): Absence of effect of pretreatment of fish with compounds related to p,p'-DDT. *J. Fish. Res. Bd. Canada.* **34**: 119–22.

Addison, R. F., S. R. Kerr, J. Dale and D. E. Sergeant (1973). Variation of organochlorine residue levels with age in Gulf of St Lawrence harp seals (*Pagophilus groenlandicus*). *J. Fish. Res. Bd. Canada.* **30**: 595–600.

Addison, R. F., M. E. Zinck and J. R. Leahy (1976). Metabolism of single and combined doses of ^{14}C aldrin and ^{3}H-*p,p'*-DDT by Atlantic salmon (*Salmo salar*) fry. *J. Fish. Res. Bd. Canada.* **33**: 2073–76.

Ahmed, M. (1975). Speciation in living oysters. *Advances in marine Biology.* **13**: 357–97.

Ahmed, M. and A. K. Sparks (1970). Chromosome number, structure and autosomal polymorphism in the marine mussels *Mytilus edulis* and *M. californianus. Biol. Bull. mar. biol. Lab. Woods Hole.* **138**: 1–13.

Ahsanullah, M. (1976). Acute toxicity of cadmium and zinc to seven invertebrate species from Western Port, Victoria. *Aust. J. mar. Freshwat. Res.* **27**: 187–96.

Alexander, G. V. and D. R. Young (1976). Trace metals in Southern California mussels. *Mar. Pollut. Bull.* **7**(1): 7–9.

Allison, D., B. J. Kallman, O. B. Cope and C. C. Van Valin (1963). Insecticides: Effects on cutthroat trout of repeated exposure to DDT. *Science.* **142**: 958–61.

Amiard, J. C. (1978*a*). Modalités de la contamination d'une chaine trophique marine benthique par l'argent 110 m. 3. Influence du mode de contamination sur l'organotropisme du radionucléide. *Helgoländer wiss. Meeresunters.* **31**: 444–456.

Amiard, J. C. (1978*b*). Modalités de la contamination d'une chaine trophique marine benthique par l'argent 110 m. 4. Influence du mode de contamination sur l'élimination du radionucléide. *J. exp. mar. Biol. Ecol.* **34**: 215–25.

Anas, R. E. (1970). Mercury found in fur seals. *Commer. Fish. Rev.* **32**(12): 3.

Anas, R. E. (1974). Heavy metals in the northern fur seal, *Callorhinus ursinus*, and harbour seal, *Phoca vitulina richardi. Fish. Bull.* **72**: 133–37.

Anas, R. E. and A. J. Wilson (1970*a*). Organochlorine pesticides in fur seals. *Pestic. Monit. J.* **3**(4): 198–200.

Anas, R. E. and A. J. Wilson (1970*b*). Organochlorine pesticides in nursing fur seal pups. *Pestic. Monit. J.* **4**(3): 114–16.

Anas, R. E. and D. D. Worlund (1975). Comparison between two methods of subsampling blubber of Northern fur seals for total DDT plus PCBs. *Pestic. Monit. J.* **8**(4): 261–62.

Anderson, J. M. (1971). Assessment of the effects of pollutants on physiology and behaviour. *Proc. R. Soc. Lond. B.* **177**: 307–20.

Anderson, R. B. and W. H. Everhart (1966). Concentrations of DDT in landlocked salmon (*Salmo salar*) at Sebago Lake, Maine. *Trans. Am. Fish. Soc.* **95**: 160–64.

Anderson, R. B. and O. C. Fenderson (1970). An analysis of variation of insecticide residues in landlocked Atlantic salmon (*Salmo salar*). *J. Fish. Res. Bd. Canada.* **27**: 1–11.

Andreu, B. (1963). Propagacion del copépodo parasito *Mytilicola intestinalis* en el mejillón cultivado de las rias gallegos (N.W. de Espana). *Investigación Pesquera.* **24**: 3–20.

Andreu, B. (1968). Fishery and culture of mussels and oysters in Spain. *Proc. Symp. Mollusca.* **3**: 835–46.

Arevalo, A. (1948). Study of the variation in the chemical composition of the *Trachurus trachurus* L. *Boln. Inst. esp. Oceanogr.* (8) 13 pp.

Arima, S. and S. Umemoto (1976). Mercury in aquatic organisms—II. Mercury distribution in muscles of tunas and swordfish. *Bull. Jap. Soc. sci. Fish.* **42**(8): 931–7.

Armstrong, D. A., D. V. Buchanan, M. H. Mallon, R. S. Caldwell and R. E. Milleman (1976). Toxicity of the insecticide methoxychlor to the Dungeness crab, *Cancer magister*. *Mar. Biol.* **38**: 239–52.

Atchison, G. J., B. R. Murphy, W. E. Bishop, A. W. McIntosh and R. A. Mayes (1977). Trace metal contamination of bluegill (*Lepomis macrochirus*) from two Indiana Lakes. *Trans. Amer. Fish. Soc.* **106**(6): 637–40.

Augier, H., G. Gilles and G. Ramonda (1978). Recherche sur la pollution mercurielle du milieu maritime dans la region de Marseille (Méditerranée, France): Partie 1. Degre de contamination par le mercure de la phanerogame marine *Posidonia oceanica* delile a proximité du complexe portuaire et dans la zone de rejet du grand collecteur d'égouts de la ville de Marseille. *Environ. Pollut.* **17**: 269–85.

Ayling, G. M. (1974). Uptake of cadmium, zinc, copper, lead and chromium in the Pacific oyster, *Crassostrea gigas*, grown in the Tamar River, Tasmania. *Water Res.* **8**: 729–38.

Bache, C. A., W. H. Gutenmann and D. J. Lisk (1971). Residues of total mercury and methylmercury salts in lake trout as a function of age. *Science.* **175**: 951–2.

Bache, C. A., J. W. Serum, W. D. Youngs and D. J. Lisk (1972). Polychlorinated biphenyl residues: Accumulation in Cayuga lake trout with age. *Science.* **177**: 1191–92.

Badsha, K. S. and M. Sainsbury (1977). Uptake of zinc, lead and cadmium by young whiting in the Severn Estuary. *Mar. Pollut. Bull.* **8**(7): 164–6.

Badsha, K. S. and M. Sainsbury (1978). Some aspects of the biology and heavy metal accumulation of the fish *Liparis liparis* in the Severn Estuary. *Est. cstl. mar. Sci.* **7**: 381–91.

Baird, R. H. (1966). Factors affecting the growth and condition of mussels (*Mytilus edulis*). *Fish. Invest., Min. Ag. Fish. Food, London, Ser. II.* **25**: 1–33.

Barbaro, A., A. Franceson, B. Polo and M. Bilio (1978). *Balanus amphitrite* (Cirripedia: Thoracica)—A potential indicator of fluoride, copper, lead, chromium and mercury in North Adriatic lagoons. *Mar. Biol.* **46**: 247–57.

Barber, R. T., A. Vijayakumar and F. A. Cross (1972). Mercury concentrations in recent and ninety-year-old benthopelagic fish. *Science.* **178**: 636–9.

Bartha, R. (1969). Pesticide interaction creates hybrid residue. *Science.* **166**: 1299–300.

Barthalmus, G. T. (1977). Behavioural effects of mercury on grass shrimp. *Mar. Pollut. Bull.* **8**(4): 87–90.

Bartlett, L., F. W. Rabe and W. H. Funk (1974). Effects of copper, zinc and cadmium on *Selenastrum capricornutum*. *Water Res.* **8**: 179–85.

Battle, H. (1932). Rhythmical sexual maturity and spawning of certain bivalve mollusks. *Contrib. Canadian Biol. Fish. N.S.* **7**: 257–76.

Bayne, B. L. (1964). Primary and secondary settlement in *Mytilus edulis* L. (Mollusca). *J. An. Ecol.* **33**: 513–23.

Bayne, B. L. (1976) (Ed.). *Marine mussels: Their ecology and physiology.* Cambridge University Press, Cambridge, 506 pp.

Bayne, B. L., D. L. Holland, M. N. Moore, D. M. Lowe and J. Widdows (1978). Further studies on the effects of stress in the adult on the eggs of *Mytilus edulis*. *J. mar. biol. Ass. U.K.* **58**: 825–41.

Bedford, J. W., E. W. Roelofs and M. J. Zabik (1968). The freshwater mussel as a biological monitor of pesticide concentrations in a lotic environment. *Limnol. Oceanogr.* **13**: 118–26.

Belding, D. L. (1934). The cause of the high mortality in the Atlantic salmon after spawning. *Trans. Amer. Fish. Soc.* **64**: 219–24.

Benoit, D. A. (1975). Chronic effects of copper on survival, growth and reproduction of the bluegill (*Lepomis macrochirus*). *Trans. Amer. Fish. Soc.* **104**(2): 353–8.

Benoit, D. A., E. N. Leonard, G. M. Christensen and J. T. Fiandt (1976). Toxic effects of cadmium on three generations of brook trout (*Salvelinus fontinalis*). *Trans. Amer. Fish. Soc.* **105**(4): 550–60.

Berner, L. (1935). La reproduction des moules comestibles (*Mytilus edulis* L. et *M. galloprovincialis* Lmk) et leur répartition géographique. *Bulletin de l'Institut Oceanographique, Monaco.* **680**: 1–8.

Bernhard, M. (1978). Heavy metals and chlorinated hydrocarbons in the Mediterranean. *Ocean Management.* **3**: 253–313.

Betzer, S. B. and M. E. Q. Pilson (1974). The seasonal cycle of copper concentration in *Busycon canaliculatum* L. *Biol. Bull.* **146**: 165–75.

Betzer, S. B. and M. E. Q. Pilson (1975). Copper uptake and excretion by *Busycon canaliculatum* L. *Biol. Bull.* **148**: 1–15.

Betzer, S. B. and P. P. Yevich (1975). Copper toxicity in *Busycon canaliculatum* L. *Biol. Bull.* **148**: 16–25.

Bidleman, T. F. and C. E. Olney (1974). Chlorinated hydrocarbons in the Sargasso Sea, atmosphere and surface water. *Science.* **183**: 516–18.

Biggar, J. W., L. D. Doneen and R. L. Riggs (1966). *Soil interaction with organically polluted water.* Summary report. Davis, California, Department of Water Science and Engineering University of California.

Bjerk, J. E. (1973). Residues of DDT in cod from Norwegian fjords. *Bull. environ. Contam. Toxicol.* **9**: 89–97.

Bloom, H. D., A. Perlmutter and R. J. Seeley (1978). Effect of a sublethal concentration of zinc on an aggregating pheromone system in the zebrafish, *Brachydanio rerio* (Hamilton-Buchanan). *Environ. Pollut.* **17**: 127–31.

Bøhle, B. (1965). Undersøkelser av blåskjell (*Mytilus edulis* L.) i Oslofjorden. *Fiskets Gang.* **51**: 388–94.

Bøhle, B. (1971). Settlement of mussel larvae (*Mytilus edulis*) on suspended collectors in Norwegian waters. pp. 63–69. In: D. J. Crisp, (ed.) *Fourth European Marine Biology Symposium.* Cambridge University Press, London.

Bohn, A. (1975). Arsenic in marine organisms from West Greenland. *Mar. Pollut. Bull.* **6**(6), 87–9.

Bohn, A. and R. O. McElroy (1976). Trace metals (As, Cd, Cu, Fe, and Zn) in Arctic cod, *Boreogadus saida*, and selected zooplankton from Strathcona Sound, northern Baffin Island. *J. Fish. Res. Bd. Canada.* **33**: 2836–40.

Boje, R. (1965). Die Bedeutung von Nahrungsfaktoren für das Wachstum von *Mytilus edulis* L. in der Kieler Forde und im Nord-Ostsee Kanal. *Kieler Meeresforschungen.* **21**: 81–100.

Bottino, N. R., R. D. Newman, E. R. Cox, R. Stockton, M. Hoban, R. A. Zingaro and K. J. Irgolic (1978). The effects of arsenate and arsenite on the growth and morphology of the marine unicellular algae *Tetraselmis chui* (Chlorophyta) and *Hymenomonas carterae* (Chrysophyta). *J. exp. mar. Biol. Ecol.* **33**, 153–68.

Bourcart, C. and P. Lubet (1965). Cycle sexuel et évolution des réserves chez *Mytilus galloprovincialis* Lmk (Moll. Bivalve). *Rapports et Procès-verbaux des Réunions. Conseil permanent International pour l'Exploration de la Mer.* **18**: 155–8.

Bourget, E. (1974). Environmental and structural control of trace elements in barnacle shells. *Mar. Biol.* **28**: 27–36.

Bourget, E. and D. Cossa (1976). Mercury content of mussels from the St Lawrence Estuary and northwestern Gulf of St Lawrence, Canada. *Mar. Pollut. Bull.* **7**(12): 237–39.

Bouxin, H. (1956). Observations sur le frai de *Mytilus edulis* (var. *galloprovincialis* Lmk) dates precises de frai et facteurs provoquant l'emission de produits génitaux. *Rapports et Procès-verbaux des Réunions. Conseil permanent International pour l'Exploration de la Mer.* **140**: 43–46.

Bowman, M. C., F. Acree and M. K. Corbett (1960). Solubility of ^{14}C-DDT in water. *J. agric. Fd Chem.* **8**: 406–34.

Boyce, R. and W. A. Herdman (1898). On a green leucocytosis in oysters associated with the presence of copper in leucocytes. *Proc. Roy. Soc. Lond.* **62**: 30–38.

Boyden, C. R. (1974). Trace element content and body size in molluscs. *Nature, Lond.* **251**: 311–14.

Boyden, C. R. (1975). Distribution of some trace metals in Poole Harbour, Dorset. *Mar. Pollut. Bull.* **6**(12): 180–7.

Boyden, C. R. (1977). Effect of size upon metal content of shellfish. *J. mar. biol. Ass. U.K.* **57**: 675–714.

Boyden, C. R. and M. G. Romeril (1974). A trace metal problem in pond oyster culture. *Mar. Pollut. Bull.* **5**(5): 74–8.

Braek, G. S., A. Jensen and Å. Mohus (1976). Heavy metal tolerance of marine phytoplankton. III. Combined effects of copper and zinc ions on cultures of four common species. *J. exp. mar. Biol. Ecol.* **25**: 37–50.

Brahman, R. S. and C. C. Foreback (1973). Methylated forms of arsenic in the environment. *Science.* **182**: 1247–49.

Brandes, C. H. and R. Dietrich (1953). On the distribution of fat in the body of herrings. *Veröff. Inst. Meeresforsch, Bremerh.* **2**: 109–21.

Branson, D. R., G. E. Blau, H. C. Alexander and W. B. Neely (1975). Bioconcentration of 2,2′,4,4′-tetrachlorobiphenyl in rainbow trout as measured by an accelerated test. *Trans. Amer. Fish. Soc.* **104**(4): 785–92.

Brodtmann, N. V. (1970). Studies on the assimilation of 1,1,1-trichloro-2,2-bis (*p*-chlorophenyl) ethane (DDT) by *Crassostrea virginica* Gmelin. *Bull. environ. Contam. Toxicol.* **5**: 455–62.

Brooks, R. R. and M. G. Rumsby (1965). The biogeochemistry of trace element uptake by some New Zealand bivalves. *Limnol. Oceanogr.* **10**: 521–28.

Brooks, R. R. and M. G. Rumsby (1967). Studies on the uptake of cadmium by the oyster, *Ostrea sinuata* (Lamarck). *Aust. J. mar. Freshwat. Res.* **15**: 53–61.

Brooks, R. R. and D. Rumsey (1974). Heavy metals in some New Zealand commercial sea fishes. *N.Z. J. mar. Freshwat. Res.* **8**(1): 155–66.

Brown, B. E. (1978). Lead detoxification by a copper-tolerant isopod. *Nature, Lond.* **276**: 388–90.

Brown, D. A. (1977). Increases of Cd and the Cd:Zn ratio in the high molecular weight protein pool from apparently normal liver of tumor-bearing flounders (*Parophrys vetulus*). *Mar. Biol.* **44**: 203–9.

Brown, D. A. and T. R. Parsons (1978). Relationship between cytoplasmic distribution of mercury and toxic effects to zooplankton and chum salmon (*Oncorhynchus keta*) exposed to mercury in a controlled ecosystem. *J. Fish. Res. Bd. Canada.* **35**: 880–84.

Brown, D. A., C. A. Bawden, K. W. Chatel and T. R. Parsons (1977). The wildlife community of Iona Island Jetty, Vancouver, BC, and heavy metal pollution effects. *Environ. Conserv.* **4**(3): 213–16.

Bruce, J. R. (1926). The respiratory exchange of the mussel (*Mytilus edulis* L.). *Biochem. J.* **20**: 829–46.

Bruland, K. W., G. A. Knauer and J. H. Martin (1978). Cadmium in northeast Pacific waters. *Limnol. Oceanogr.* **23**: 618–25.

Brungs, W. A., E. N. Leonard and J. M. McKim (1973). Acute and long-term accumulation of copper by the brown bullhead, *Ictalurus nebulosus. J. Fish. Res. Bd. Canada.* **30**: 583–6.

Bryan, G. W. (1964). Zinc regulation in the lobster *Homarus vulgaris.* I. Tissue zinc and copper concentrations. *J. mar. biol. Ass. UK.* **44**: 549–63.

Bryan, G. W. (1966). The metabolism of zinc and Zn^{65} in crabs, lobsters and freshwater crayfish. In: *Radioecological concentration processes* (B. Åberg and F. P. Hungate (eds)) pp. 1005–16. (Proceedings of the International Symposium, Stockholm, 1966), Pergamon Press, Oxford.

Bryan, G. W. (1967). Zinc regulation in the freshwater crayfish (including some comparative copper analyses). *J. exp. Biol.* **46**: 281–96.

Bryan, G. W. (1968). Concentrations of zinc and copper in the tissues of decapod crustaceans. *J. mar. biol. Ass. UK.* **48**: 303–21.

Bryan, G. W. (1969). The absorption of zinc and other metals by the brown seaweed *Laminaria digitata. J. mar. biol. Ass. UK.* **49**: 225–43.

Bryan, G. W. (1971). The effects of heavy metals (other than mercury) on marine and estuarine organisms. *Proc. R. Soc. Lond., Series B.* **177**: 389–410.

Bryan, G. W. (1973). The occurrence and seasonal variation of trace metals in the scallops *Pecten maximus* (L.) and *Chlamys opercularis* (L.). *J. mar. biol. Ass. UK.* **53**: 145–66.

Bryan, G. W. (1976). Heavy metal contamination in the sea. In: *Marine pollution* (R. Johnston (ed.)), pp. 185–302, Academic Press, London and New York.

Bryan, G. W. and L. G. Hummerstone (1971). Adaptation of the polychaete *Nereis diversicolor* to estuarine sediments containing high concentrations of heavy metals. I. General observations and adaptation to copper. *J. mar. biol. Ass. UK.* **51**: 845–63.

Bryan, G. W. and L. G. Hummerstone (1973a). Brown seaweed as an indicator of heavy metals in estuaries in South-West England. *J. mar. biol. Ass. UK.* **53**: 705–20.

Bryan, G. W. and L. G. Hummerstone (1973b). Adaptation of the polychaete *Nereis diversicolor* to estuarine sediments containing high concentrations of zinc and cadmium. *J. mar. biol. Ass. UK.* **53**: 839–57.

Bryan, G. W. and L. G. Hummerstone (1973c). Adaptation of the polychaete *Nereis diversicolor* to manganese in estuarine sediments. *J. mar. biol. Ass. UK.* **53**: 859–72.

Bryan, G. W. and L. G. Hummerstone (1977). Indicators of heavy-metal contamination in the Looe Estuary (Cornwall) with particular regard to silver and lead. *J. mar. biol. Ass. UK.* **57**: 75–92.

Bryan, G. W. and L. G. Hummerstone (1978). Heavy metals in the burrowing bivalve *Scrobicularia plana* from contaminated and uncontaminated estuaries. *J. mar. biol. Ass. UK.* **58**: 401–19.

Bryan, G. W. and H. Uysal (1978). Heavy metals in the burrowing bivalve *Scrobicularia plana* from the Tamar Estuary in relation to environmental levels. *J. mar. biol. Ass. UK.* **58**: 89–108.

Bryan, G. W. and E. Ward (1965). The absorption and loss of radioactive and non-radioactive manganese by the lobster, *Homarus vulgaris. J. mar. biol. Ass. UK.* **45**: 65–95.

Bryan, G. W., G. W. Potts and G. R. Forster (1977). Heavy metals in the gastropod mollusc *Haliotis tuberculata* (L.). *J. mar. biol. Ass. UK.* **57**: 379–90.

Buchanan, D. V., R. E. Millemann and N. E. Stewart (1970). Effects of the insecticide Sevin on various stages of the Dungeness crab, *Cancer magister. J. Fish. Res. Bd. Canada.* **27**: 95–104.

Buhler, D. R. and W. E. Shanks (1970). Influence of body weight on chronic oral DDT toxicity in coho salmon. *J. Fish. Res. Bd. Canada.* **27**: 347–58.

Buhler, D. R., M. E. Rasmusson and W. E. Shanks (1969). Chronic oral DDT toxicity in juvenile coho and chinook salmon. *Toxicol. Appl. Pharmacol.* **14**: 535–55.

Buhler, D. R., R. R. Claeys and B. R. Mate (1975). Heavy metal and chlorinated hydrocarbon residues in California sea lions (*Zalophus californianus californianus*). *J.. Fish. Res. Bd. Canada.* **32**: 2391–7.

Buhler, D. R., R. M. Stokes and R. S. Caldwell (1977). Tissue accumulation and enzymatic effects of hexavalent chromium in rainbow trout (*Salmo gairdneri*). *J. Fish. Res. Bd. Canada.* **34**: 9–18.

Bulkley, R. V., R. L. Kellog and L. R. Shannon (1976). Size-related factors associated with dieldrin concentrations in muscle tissue of channel catfish *Ictalurus punctatus. Trans. Am. Fish. Soc.* **105**: 301–7.

Burdick, G. E., E. J. Harris, H. J. Dean, T. M. Walker, J. Skea and D. Colby (1964). The accumulation of DDT in lake trout and the effect on reproduction. *Trans. Amer. Fish. Soc.* **93**: 127–36.

Burnett, R. (1971). DDT residues: Distribution of concentrations in *Emerita analoga* (Stimpson) along coastal California. *Science.* **174**: 606–8.

Burrows, E. M. (1971). Assessment of pollution effects by the use of algae. *Proc. Roy. Soc. Lond. B.* **177**: 295–306.

Butler, P. A. (1966). The problem of pesticides in estuaries. In: *A symposium on estuarine fisheries*, Trans. Am. Fish. Soc. Spec. Publ., No. 3, 110–15.

Butler, P. A. (1969a). The significance of DDT residues in estuarine fauna. In: *Chemical Fallout* (M. W. Miller and G. G. Berg (eds)), pp. 205–20. Springfield, Illinois, Charles C. Thomas.

Butler, P. A. (1969b). Monitoring pesticide pollution. *BioScience.* **19**: 889–91.

Butler, P. A. (1970). The sub-lethal effects of pesticide pollution. In: *Symposium on the Biological Impact of Pesticides in the Environment* (J. W. Gillet (ed.)), pp. 87–96, Corvallis, Oregon, Oregon State University, 1970.

Butler, P. A. (1971). Influence of pesticides on marine ecosystems. *Proc. R. Soc. Lond. B.* **177**: 321–9.

Butler, P. A. (1973). Organochlorine residues in estuarine molluscs, 1965–1972—National Pesticides Monitoring Program. *Pestic. Monit. J.* **6**: 238–62.

Butler, P. A., L. Andrén, G. J. Bonde, A. Jernelöv and D. J. Reish (1971). Monitoring organisms. In: *FAO Technical Conference on Marine Pollution and its Effects on Living Resources and Fishing*, Rome, 1970. *Suppl. 1: Report of the Seminar on Methods of Detection, Measurement and Monitoring of Pollutants in the Marine Environment*, pp. 101–12. FAO Fisheries Reports No. 99, Suppl. 1.

Butler, P. A., R. Childress and A. J. Wilson (1972). The association of DDT residues with losses in marine productivity. In: *Marine pollution and sea life* (M. Ruivo (ed.)), pp. 262–6. London, Fishing News (Books) Ltd.

Butterworth, J., P. Lester and G. Nickless (1972). Distribution of heavy metals in the Severn Estuary. *Mar. Pollut. Bull.* **3**(5): 72–4.

Cairns, J., A. G. Heath and B. C. Parker (1975). Temperature influence on chemical toxicity to aquatic organisms. *J. Water Pollut. Control Fed.* **47**: 267–81.

Campbell, S. A. (1969). Seasonal cycles in the carotenoid content in *Mytilus edulis*. *Mar. Biol.* **4**: 227–32.

Carvajal, R. J. (1969). Fluctuación mensual de las larvas y crecimiento del mejillón *Perna perna* (L.) y las condiciones ambientales de la ensenada de Guatapanare, Edo, Sucre, Venezuela. *Boletin del Instituto Oceanografico de la Universidad de Oriente, Venezuala.* **8**: 13–20.

Cearley, J. E. and R. L. Coleman (1974). Cadmium toxicity and bioconcentration in largemouth bass and bluegill. *Bull. Environ. Contam. Toxicol.* **11**: 146–51.

CEGB (Central Electricity Generating Board) (1965). *Marchwood Power Station Marine Fouling Report*, pp. 1–13.

Cember, H., E. H. Curtis and B. G. Blaylock (1978). Mercury bioconcentration in fish: Temperature and concentration effects. *Environ. Pollut.* **17**: 311–19.

Chadwick, G. F. and R. W. Brocksen (1969). Accumulation of dieldrin by fish and selected fish-food organisms. *J. Wildl. Man.* **33**: 693–700.

Check, R. M. and M. T. Canario (1972). Residues of chlorinated hydrocarbon pesticides in the Northern quahog (hard-shell clam), *Mercenaria mercenaria*— 1968 and 1969. *Pestic. Monit. J.* **6**: 229–30.

Cherrington, A. D., U. Paim and O. T. Page (1969). *In vitro* degradation of DDT by intestinal contents of Atlantic salmon (*Salmo salar*). *J. Fish. Res. Bd. Canada.* **26**: 47–54.

Childs, E. A. and J. N. Gaffke (1973). Mercury content of Oregon ground-fish. *Fish. Bull., US Fish Wildl. Serv.* **71**: 713–17.

Chipperfield, P. N. J. (1953). Observations on the breeding and settlement of *Mytilus edulis* (L.) in British waters. *J. mar. biol. Ass. UK.* **32**: 449–76.

Choquet, M. (1970). Analyse des cycles sexuels naturels chez les mollusques hermaphrodites et gonochoriques. *Bull. Soc. zool. Fr.* **95**: 393–405.

Clegg, D. E. (1974). Chlorinated hydrocarbon pesticide residues in oysters (*Crassostrea commercialis*) in Moreton Bay, Queensland, Australia, 1970–1972. *Pestic. Monit. J.* **8**: 162–6.

Coe, W. R. (1932). Season of attachment and rate of growth of sedentary marine organisms at the pier of the Scripps Institute of Oceanography, La Jolla, California. *Bull. Scripps Inst. Oceanogr.*, Technical Series 3, 37–86.

Coe, W. R. (1946). A resurgent population of the Californian bay mussel *Mytilus edulis diegensis*. *J. Morphol.* **78**: 85–103.

Cole, H., D. Barry, D. E. H. Frear and A. Bradford (1967). DDT levels in fish, streams, stream sediments and soil before and after DDT aerial spray application for fall cankerworm in northern Pennsylvania. *Bull. Environ. Contam. Toxicol.* **2**: 127–46.

Conte, F. S. and J. C. Parker (1975). Effect of aerially-applied malathion on juvenile brown and white shrimp *Penaeus aztecus* and *P. setiferus*. *Trans. Amer. Fish. Soc.* **104**(4): 793–9.

Coombs, T. L. (1974). The nature of zinc and copper complexes in the oyster *Ostrea edulis. Mar. Biol.* **28**: 1–10.

Coombs, T. L. (1977). Uptake and storage mechanisms of heavy metals in marine organisms. Paper presented at a Meeting of the Scottish and North-East Regions Chemical Society, 25/03/77. *Proc. Analyt. Div. Chem. Soc.*, pp. 219–22, August, 1977.

Cottam, C. and E. Higgins (1946). DDT: Its effect on fish and wildlife. *US Dept. Int., Fish Wildl. Serv. Circ.* **11**: 14 pp.

Coulson, E. J., R. E. Remington and K. M. Lynch (1935). Metabolism in the rat of the naturally occurring arsenic of shrimp as compared with arsenic trioxide. *J. Nutr.* **10**: 255–70.

Courtney, W. A. M. and G. R. W. Denton (1976). Persistence of polychlorinated biphenyls in the hard-clam (*Mercenaria mercenaria*) and the effect upon the distribution of these pollutants in the estuarine environment. *Environ. Pollut.* **10**: 55–64.

Courtney, W. A. M. and W. J. Langston (1978). Uptake of polychlorinated biphenyl (Aroclor 1254) from sediment and from seawater in two intertidal polychaetes. *Environ. Pollut.* **15**: 303–9.

Cox, J. L. (1970). DDT residues in marine phytoplankton: Increase from 1955 to 1969. *Science.* **170**: 71–73.

Cox, J. L. (1971). DDT residues in sea water and particulate matter in the California current system. *Fishery Bull. US.* **69**: 443–50.

Crosby, D. G. and R. K. Tucker (1971). Accumulation of DDT by *Daphnia magna. Environ. Sci. Technol.* **5**: 714–16.

Cross, F. A., T. W. Duke and J. N. Willis (1970). Biogeochemistry of trace elements in a coastal plain estuary: Distribution of manganese, iron, and zinc in sediments, water, and polychaetous worms. *Chesapeake Sci.* **11**: 221–34.

Cross, F. A., L. H. Hardy, N. Y. Jones and R. T. Barber (1973). Relation between total body weight and concentrations of manganese, iron, copper, zinc, and mercury in white muscle of bluefish (*Pomatomus saltatrix*) and a bathyl-demersal fish *Antimora rostrata. J. Fish. Res. Bd. Canada.* **30**: 1287–91.

Crowley, M. (1970). The edible mussel—*Mytilus edulis*. Leaflet 15, Department of Agriculture and Fisheries, Fisheries Division, Dublin.

Cumont, G., G. Viallex, H. Lelievre and P. Bobenrieth (1972). Contamination des poissons de mer par le mercure. *Rev. Intern. Océanogr. Med.* **28**: 95–127.

Cunningham, P. A. and D. S. Grosch (1978). A comparative study of the effects of mercuric chloride and methylmercury chloride on reproductive performance in the brine shrimp, *Artemia salina. Environ. Pollut.* **15**: 83–99.

Cunningham, P. A. and M. R. Tripp (1973). Accumulation and depuration of mercury in the American oyster *Crassostrea virginica. Mar. Biol.* **20**: 14–19.

Cunningham, P. A. and M. R. Tripp (1975a). Factors affecting the accumulation and removal of mercury from tissues of the American oyster *Crassostrea virginica*. *Mar. Biol.* **31**: 311–19.

Cunningham, P. A. and M. R. Tripp (1975b). Accumulation, tissue distribution and elimination of ^{203}HgCl$_2$ and CH$_3$^{203}HgCl in the tissues of the American oyster *Crassostrea virginica*. *Mar. Biol.* **31**: 321–34.

Cutshall, N. H., J. R. Naidu and W. G. Pearcy (1977a). Zinc-65 specific activities in the migratory Pacific hake *Merluccius productus*. *Mar. Biol.* **40**: 75–80.

Cutshall, N. H., J. R. Naidu and W. G. Pearcy (1977b). Zinc and cadmium in the Pacific hake *Merluccius productus* off the Western US coast. *Mar. Biol.* **44**: 195–201.

Daniel, R. J. (1921). Seasonal changes in the chemical composition of the mussel (*Mytilus edulis*). *Report of the Lancashire Sea Fisheries Laboratory*. **30**: 74–84.

Dare, P. J. (1973). The stocks of young mussels in Morecambe Bay, Lancashire. *Min. Ag., Fish. Food, Shellfish Information Leaflet*. **28**: 1–14.

Davenport, J. (1977). A study of the effects of copper applied continuously and discontinuously to specimens of *Mytilus edulis* (L.) exposed to steady and fluctuating salinity levels. *J. mar. biol. Ass. UK*. **57**: 63–74.

Davenport, J. and A. Manley (1978). The detection of heightened sea-water copper concentrations by the mussel *Mytilus edulis*. *J. mar. biol. Ass. UK*. **58**: 843–50.

Davies, I. M. and J. M. Pirie (1978). The mussel *Mytilus edulis* as a bio-assay organism for mercury in seawater. *Mar. Pollut. Bull.* **9**(5): 128–32.

DeFilippis, L. F. and C. K. Pallaghy (1976). The effect of sub-lethal concentrations of mercury and zinc on *Chlorella*: III. Development and possible mechanisms of resistance to metals. *Z. Pflanzenphysiol.* **79**: 323–35.

Defoe, D. L., G. D. Veith and R. W. Carlson (1978). Effects of Aroclor 1248 and 1260 on the fathead minnow *Pimephales promelas*. *J. Fish. Res. Bd. Canada.* **35**: 997–1002.

Delong, R. L., W. G. Gilmartin and J. G. Simpson (1973). Premature births in California sea lions: Association with high organochlorine pollutant residue levels. *Science.* **181**: 1168–70.

Denton, G. R. W. (1974). *The uptake and elimination of polychlorinated biphenyls (PCBs) in the hard-shell clam* Mercenaria mercenaria. PhD thesis, London, 1974, 194 pp.

De Wolf, P. (1975). Mercury content of mussels from West European coasts. *Mar. Pollut. Bull.* **6**(4): 61–3.

Dix, T. G., A. Martin, G. M. Ayling, K. C. Wilson and D. A. Ratkowsky (1976). Sand flathead (*Platycephalus bassensis*), an indicator species for mercury pollution in Tasmanian waters. *Mar. Pollut. Bull.* **6**(9): 142–4.

Dorn, P. (1976). The feeding behaviour of *Mytilus edulis* in the presence of methylmercury acetate. *Bull. Environ. Contam. Toxicol.* **16**: 714–19.

Drescher, H. E., U. Harms and E. Huschenbeth (1977). Organochlorines and heavy metals in the harbour seal *Phoca vitulina* from the German North Sea Coast. *Mar. Biol.* **41**: 99–106.

Drummond, R. A., G. F. Olson and A. R. Batterman (1974). Cough response and uptake of mercury by brook trout, *Salvelinus fontinalis*, exposed to mercuric compounds at different hydrogen–ion concentrations. *Trans. Amer. Fish. Soc.* **103**: 244–9.

Dryssen, D., C. Patterson, J. Ui and G. F. Weichart (1971). Inorganic chemicals. In: *FAO Technical Conference on Marine Pollution and its Effects on Living Resources and Fishing, Rome, 1970.* Suppl. 1: *Report of the Seminar on Methods of Detection, Measurement and Monitoring of Pollutants in the Marine Environment*, pp. 37–52. FAO Fisheries Reports, No. 99, Suppl. 1.

Duffy, J. R. and D. O'Connell (1968). DDT residues and metabolites in Canadian Atlantic coast fish. *J. Fish. Res. Bd. Canada.* **25**: 189–95.

Duinker, J. C. and R. F. Nolting (1976). Distribution model for particulate trace metals in the Rhine Estuary, Southern Bight and Dutch Wadden Sea. *Neth. J. Sea Res.* **10**(1): 71–102.

Duinker, J. C. and R. F. Nolting (1977). Dissolved and particulate trace metals in the Rhine Estuary and the Southern Bight. *Mar. Pollut. Bull.* **8**(3): 65–71.

Duke, T. W., J. I. Lowe and A. J. Wilson (1970). A polychlorinated biphenyl (Aroclor 1254) in the water, sediment, and biota of Escambia Bay, Florida. *Bull. Environ. Contam. Toxicol.* **5**: 171–80.

Earnest, R. D. and P. E. Benville (1971). Correlation of DDT and lipid levels for certain San Francisco Bay fish. *Pestic. Monit. J.* **5**: 235–41.

Eaton, J. G. (1974). Chronic cadmium toxicity to the bluegill (*Lepomis macrochirus* Rafinesque). *Trans. Amer. Fish. Soc.* **103**: 729–35.

Eberhardt, L. L. (1975). Some methodology for appraising contaminants in aquatic systems. *J. Fish. Res. Bd. Canada.* **32**: 1852–9.

Eisler, R. (1967*a*). Tissue changes in puffers exposed to methoxychlor and methyl parathion. Technical Paper 17 of the Bureau of Sport Fisheries and Wildlife, US Dept. of the Interior Fish and Wildlife Service, 15 pp.

Eisler, R. (1967*b*). Variations in mineral content of sandbar shark vertebrae (*Carcharinus milberti*). *Naturaliste Can.* **94**: 321–6.

Eisler, R. (1967*c*). Acute toxicity of zinc to the killifish, *Fundulus heteroclitus. Chesapeake Sci.* **8**: 262–4.

Eisler, R. (1971). Cadmium poisoning in *Fundulus heteroclitus* (Pisces: Cyprinodontidae) and other marine organisms. *J. Fish. Res. Bd. Canada.* **28**: 1225–34.

Eisler, R. (1972). Pesticide-induced stress profiles. In: *Marine pollution and sea life.* (M. Ruivo (ed.)), pp. 229–33. London, Fishing News (Books) Ltd.

Eisler, R. (1974). Radiocadmium exchange with seawater by *Fundulus heteroclitus* (L.) (Pisces: Cyprinodontidae). *J. Fish. Biol.* **6**: 601–12.

Eisler, R. (1977). Toxicity evaluation of a complex metal mixture to the softshell clam *Mya arenaria. Mar. Biol.* **43**: 265–76.

Eisler, R. and P. H. Edmunds (1966). Effects of endrin on blood and tissue chemistry of a marine fish. *Trans. Amer. Fish. Soc.* **95**: 153–9.

Eisler, R. and G. R. Gardner (1973). Acute toxicology to an estuarine teleost of mixtures of cadmium, copper and zinc salts. *J. Fish Biol.* **5**: 131–42.

Eisler, R. and G. LaRoche (1972). Elemental composition of the estuarine teleost *Fundulus heteroclitus* (L.). *J. exp. mar. Biol. Ecol.* **9**: 29–42.

Eisler, R. and M. P. Weinstein (1967). Changes in metal composition of the quahaug clam, *Mercenaria mercenaria*, after exposure to insecticides. *Chesapeake Sci.* **8**: 253–8.

Elder, D. L., S. W. Fowler and G. G. Polikarpov (1979). Remobilisation of sediment-associated PCBs by the worm *Nereis diversicolor. Bull. Environ. Contam. Toxicol.* **21**: 448–52.

Elmhirst, R. (1923). *Notes on the breeding and growth of marine animals in the Clyde Sea area.* Report of the Scottish Marine Biological Station for 1922, 19–43.

Engle, J. B. and V. L. Loosanoff (1944). On season of attachment of larvae of *Mytilus edulis* L. *Ecology.* **25**: 433–40.

Epifanio, C. E. (1971). Effects of dieldrin in seawater on the development of two species of crab larvae, *Leptodius floridanus* and *Panopeus herbstii. Mar. Biol.* **11**: 356–62.

Epifanio, C. E. (1972). Effects of dieldrin-contaminated food on the development of *Leptodius floridanus* larvae. *Mar. Biol.* **13**: 292–7.

Epifanio, C. E. (1973). Dieldrin uptake by larvae of the crab *Leptodius floridanus. Mar. Biol.* **19**: 320–22.

Ernst, W. and H. Goerke (1974). Anreicherung, Verteilung, Umwandlung und Ausscheidung von DDT-C^{14} bei *Solea solea* (Pisces: Soleidae). *Mar. Biol.* **24**: 287–304.

Ernst, W., H. Goerke, G. Eder and R. G. Schaefer (1976). Residues of chlorinated hydrocarbons in marine organisms in relation to size and ecological parameters. I. PCB, DDT, DDE, and DDD in fishes and molluscs from the English Channel. *Bull. Environ. Contam. Toxicol.* **15**: 55–65.

Eschmeyer, P. H. and A. M. Phillips (1965). Fat content of the flesh of siscowets and lake trout from Lake Superior. *Trans. Amer. Fish. Soc.* **94**: 62–74.

Eustace, I. J. (1974). Zinc, cadmium, copper and manganese in species of finfish and shellfish caught in the Derwent Estuary, Tasmania. *Aust. J. mar. Freshwat. Res.* **25**: 209–20.

Fabacher, D. L. and H. Chambers (1971). Endrin resistance in a population of freshwater fish. *Bull. Environ. Contam. Toxicol.* **6**: 372–6.

Farkas, T. and S. Herodek (1964). The effect of environmental temperature on the fatty acid composition of crustacean plankton. *J. Lipid Res.* **5**: 369–73.

Farr, J. A. (1977). Impairment of antipredator behaviour in *Palaemonetes pugio* by exposure to sublethal doses of parathion. *Trans. Amer. Fish. Soc.* **106**(3): 287–90.

Favretto, L. (1968). Aspetti merceologici della mitilicoltura nel Golfo di Trieste. *Bollettino della Società Adriatica di Scienze naturali in Trieste.* **56**: 243–61.

Field, I. A. (1909). The food value of the sea mussel. *Bull. US Bureau Fish., Washington.* **29**: 85–128.

Field, I. A. (1922). Biology and economic value of the sea mussel *Mytilus edulis. Bull. US Bureau Fish., Washington.* **38**: 127–259.

Fingerman, S. W. and M. Fingerman (1978). Influence of the polychlorinated biphenyl preparation Aroclor 1242 on color changes of the fiddler crab *Uca pugilator. Mar. Biol.* **50**: 37–45.

Fisher, N. S. and C. F. Wurster (1973). Individual and combined effects of temperature and polychlorinated biphenyls on the growth of three species of phytoplankton. *Environ. Pollut.* **5**: 205–12.

Fisher, N. S., L. B. Graham, E. J. Carpenter and C. F. Wurster (1973). Geographic differences in phytoplankton sensitivity to PCBs. *Nature, Lond.* **241**: 548–9.

Foehrenbach, J. (1972). Chlorinated pesticides in estuarine organisms. *J. Wat. Pollut. Control Fed.* **44**: 619–24.

Folsom, T. R. and D. R. Young (1965). Silver-110 m and cobalt-60 in oceanic and coastal organisms. *Nature, Lond.* **206**: 803–6.

Folsom, T. R., D. R. Young, J. N. Johnson and K. C. Pillai (1963). Manganese-54 and zinc-65 in coastal organisms of California. *Nature, Lond.* **200**: 327–9.

Folsom, T. R., V. F. Hodge, K. M. Wong, R. Kishore and V. P. Guinn (1972). Some trace element concentration variations observed in marine organisms that suggest caution in sampling. In: *Report for the IDOE Workshop on Baseline Measurements*, Upton, New York, Brookhaven National Laboratory.

Forrester, C. R., K. S. Ketchen and C. C. Wong (1972). Mercury content of spiny dogfish (*Squalus acanthias*) in the Strait of Georgia, British Columbia. *J. Fish. Res. Bd. Canada.* **29**: 1487–90.

Foster, P. (1976). Concentrations and concentration factors of heavy metals in brown algae. *Environ. Pollut.* **10**: 45–53.

Foster, P. and A. W. Morris (1971). The seasonal variation of dissolved ionic and organically associated copper in the Menai Straits. *Deep-Sea Res.* **18**: 231–6.

Fowler, B. A., D. A. Wolfe and W. F. Hettler (1975). Mercury and iron uptake by cytosomes in mantle epithelial cells of quahog clams (*Mercenaria mercenaria*) exposed to mercury. *J. Fish. Res. Bd. Canada.* **32**: 1767–75.

Fowler, S. W. and G. Benayoun (1974). Experimental studies on cadmium flux through marine biota. In: *Comparative studies of food and environmental contamination*, pp. 159–78. International Atomic Energy Agency, Vienna, 1974.

Fowler, S. W. and G. Benayoun (1976a). Selenium kinetics in marine zooplankton. *Mar. Sci. Comm.* **2**(1): 43–67.

Fowler, S.W. and G. Benayoun (1976b). Accumulation and distribution of selenium in mussel and shrimp tissues. *Bull. Environ. Contam. Toxicol.* **16**: 339–46.

Fowler, S. W. and G. Benayoun (1976c). Influence of environmental factors on selenium flux in two marine invertebrates. *Mar. Biol.* **37**: 59–68.

Fowler, S. W. and D. L. Elder (1978). PCB and DDT residues in a Mediterranean pelagic food chain. *Bull. Environ. Contam. Toxicol.* **19**: 244–9.

Fowler, S. W. and J.-C. Guary (1977). High absorption efficiency for ingested plutonium in crabs. *Nature, Lond.* **266**: 827–8.

Fowler, S. W. and B. Oregioni (1976). Trace metals in mussels from the North-West Mediterranean. *Mar. Pollut. Bull.* **7**(2): 26–9.

Fowler, S. W., L. F. Small and J. M. Dean (1971). Experimental studies on elimination of zinc-65, cesium-137 and cerium-144 by euphausiids. *Mar. Biol.* **8**: 224–31.

Fowler, S. W., J. La Rosa, M. Heyraud and W. C. Renfro (1975a). Effect of different radiotracer labelling techniques on radionuclide excretion from marine organisms. *Mar. Biol.* **30**: 297–304.

Fowler, S. W., M. Heyraud and T. M. Beasley (1975b). Experimental studies on plutonium kinetics in marine biota. In: *Impacts of Nuclear Releases into the Aquatic Environment*, pp. 157–77. IAEA, Vienna, 1975.

Fowler, S. W., M. Heyraud and J. La Rosa (1978a). Factors affecting methyl and inorganic mercury dynamics in mussels and shrimp. *Mar. Biol.* **46**: 267–76.

Fowler, S. W., G. G. Polikarpov, D. L. Elder, P. Parsi and J. P. Villeneuve (1978b). Polychlorinated biphenyls: Accumulation from contaminated sediments and water by the polychaete *Nereis diversicolor*. *Mar. Biol.* **48**: 303–9.

Fox, H. M. (1924). Lunar periodicity in reproduction. *Proc. R. Soc. Lond., Series B.* **95**: 523–50.

Fox, D. L. and W. R. Coe (1943). Biology of the Californian sea mussel (*Mytilus californianus*). II. Nutrition, metabolism, growth and calcium deposition. *J. exp. Zool.* **93**: 205–49.

Fox, H. M. and H. Ramage (1930). Spectrographic analysis of animal tissues. *Nature, Lond.* **126**: 682–4.

Fox, H. M. and H. Ramage (1931). A spectrographic analysis of animal tissues. *Proc. R. Soc. Lond., Series B.* **108**: 157–73.

Frank, R., K. Ronald and H. E. Braun (1973). Organochlorine residues in harp seals (*Pagophilus groenlandicus*) caught in eastern Canadian waters. *J. Fish. Res. Bd. Canada.* **30**: 1053–63.

Frank, R., A. E. Armstrong, R. G. Boelens, H. E. Braun and C. W. Douglas (1974). Organochlorine insecticide residues in sediment and fish tissues, Ontario, Canada. *Pestic. Monit. J.* **7**: 165–80.

Frazier, J. M. (1975). The dynamics of metals in the American oyster, *Crassostrea virginica*. I. Seasonal effects. *Chesapeake Sci.* **16**: 162–71.

Frazier, J. M. (1976). The dynamics of metals in the American oyster, *Crassostrea virginica*. II. Environmental effects. *Chesapeake Sci.* **17**: 188–97.

Frederick, L. L. (1975). Comparative uptake of a polychlorinated biphenyl and dieldrin by the white sucker (*Catastomus commersoni*). *J. Fish. Res. Bd. Canada.* **32**: 1705–9.

Freeman, H. C., D. A. Horne, B. McTague and M. McMenemy (1974). Mercury in some Canadian Atlantic coast fish and shellfish. *J. Fish. Res. Bd. Canada.* **31**: 369–72.

Friberg, L., M. Piscator, G. F. Nordberg and T. Kjellström (1974). *Cadmium in the Environment.* (Second edition). 248 pp. CRC Press, Cleveland, Ohio.

Fuge, R. and K. H. James (1973). Trace metal concentrations in brown seaweeds, Cardigan Bay, Wales. *Mar. Chem.* **1**: 281–93.

Fuge, R. and K. H. James (1974). Trace metal concentrations in *Fucus* from the Bristol Channel. *Mar. Pollut. Bull.* **5**(1): 9–12.

Fukai, R. and L. Huynh-Ngoc (1968). Studies on the chemical behaviour of radionuclides in sea water. I. General considerations and study of precipitation of trace amounts of chromium, manganese, iron, cobalt, zinc and cerium. *Radioactivity in the sea* (22). Vienna, IAEA.

Fukai, R., C. N. Murray and L. Huynh-Ngoc (1975). Variations of soluble zinc in the Var River and its Estuary. *Estuar. cstl. mar. Sci.* **3**: 177–88.

Fukano, K. G. and F. F. Hooper (1958). Toxaphene as a selective fish poison. *Prog. Fish. Cult.* **20**: 189–90.

Gakstatter, J. H. (1968). Rates of accumulation of ^{14}C-dieldrin residues in tissues of goldfish exposed to a single sublethal dose of ^{14}C-aldrin. *J. Fish. Res. Bd. Canada.* **25**: 1797–801.

Gakstatter, J. H. and C. M. Weiss (1967). The elimination of DDT-C^{14}, dieldrin-C^{14} and lindane-C^{14} from fish following a single sublethal exposure in aquaria. *Trans. Amer. Fish. Soc.* **96**: 301–7.

Galley, R. A. E. (1974). The atmospheric distribution of organochlorine insecticides. *Chem. and Ind.* (2 March 1974), pp. 179–81.

Galtstoff, P. S. (1964). The American oyster *Crassostrea virginica* Gmelin. *Fish. Bull., US Fish Wildl. Serv.* **64**: 1–480.

García, A. P. and S. W. Fowler (1972). Análisis de microelementos en invertebrados marinos del Golfo de California. *Mem. IV Congr. Nac. Ocean (México)*, pp. 115–26.

Gardner, D. (1978). Mercury in fish and waters of the Irish Sea and other United Kingdom fishing grounds. *Nature, Lond.* **272**: 49–51.

Gaskin, D. E., M. Holdrinet and R. Frank (1971). Organochlorine pesticide residues in harbour porpoises from the Bay of Fundy. *Nature, Lond.* **233**: 499–500.

Gaskin, D. E., K. Ishida and R. Frank (1972). Mercury in harbour porpoises (*Phocoena phocoena*) from the Bay of Fundy region. *J. Fish. Res. Bd. Canada.* **29**: 1644–6.

Gaskin, D. E., R. Frank, M. Holdrinet, K. Ishida, C. J. Walton and M. Smith (1973). Mercury, DDT and PCB in harbour seals (*Phoca vitulina*) from the Bay of Fundy and the Gulf of Maine. *J. Fish. Res. Bd. Canada.* **30**: 471–5.

Gaskin, D. E., G. J. D. Smith, P. W. Arnold, M. V. Louisy, R. Frank, M. Holdrinet and J. W. McWade (1974). Mercury, DDT, dieldrin and PCB in two species of Odontoceti (Cetacea) from St Lucia, Lesser Antilles. *J. Fish. Res. Bd. Canada.* **31**: 1235–9.

George, S. G. and T. L. Coombs (1977*a*). Effects of high stability iron-complexes on the kinetics of iron accumulation and excretion in *Mytilus edulis* (L.). *J. exp. mar. Biol. Ecol.* **28**: 133–40.

George, S. G. and T. L. Coombs (1977*b*). The effects of chelating agents on the uptake and accumulation of cadmium by *Mytilus edulis. Mar. Biol.* **39**: 261–8.

George, S. G., B. J. S. Pirie and T. L. Coombs (1976). The kinetics of accumulation and excretion of ferric hydroxide in *Mytilus edulis* (L.) and its distribution in the tissues. *J. exp. mar. Biol. Ecol.* **23**: 71–84.

George, S. G., B. J. S. Pirie, A. R. Cheyne, T. L. Coombs and P. T. Grant (1978). Detoxification of metals by marine bivalves: An ultrastructural study of the compartmentation of copper and zinc in the oyster *Ostrea edulis. Mar. Biol.* **45**: 147–56.

Giam, C. S., R. L. Richardson, M. K. Wong and W. M. Sackett (1973). Polychlorinated biphenyls in Antarctic biota. *Antarct. J.U.S.* **8**: 303–5.

Giese, A. C. (1969). A new approach to the biochemical composition of the mollusc body. *Oceanogr. mar. Biol. Ann. Rev.* **7**: 175–229.

Giesy, J. P. and J. G. Wiener (1977). Frequency distributions of trace metal concentrations in five freshwater fishes. *Trans. Amer. Fish. Soc.* **106**(4): 393–403.

Godsil, P. J. and W. C. Johnson (1968). Pesticide monitoring of aquatic biota at the Tule Lake National Wildlife Refuge. *Pestic. Monit. J.* **1**: 21–6.

Goldberg, E. D. (1975*a*). Synthetic organohalides in the sea. *Proc. R. Soc. Lond. B.* **189**: 277–89.

Goldberg, E. D. (1975*b*). The mussel watch—A first step in global marine monitoring. *Mar. Pollut. Bull.* **6**(7): 111.

Goldberg, E. D., V. T. Bowen, J. W. Farrington, G. Harvey, J. H. Martin, P. L. Parker, R. W. Risebrough, W. Robertson, E. Schneider and E. Gamble (1978). The mussel watch. *Env. Conserv.* **5**: 101–25.

Goodbody, I. (1974). The physiology of ascidians. *Advances in Marine Biology.* (F. S. Russell and M. Yonge (eds)), Vol 12, pp. 1–49. Academic Press, London, New York, San Francisco.

Gordon, C. M., R. A. Carr and R. E. Larson (1970). The influence of environmental factors on the sodium and manganese content of barnacle shells. *Limnol. Oceanogr.* **15**: 461–6.

Gordon, M. *et al.* (1978). *Intertidal Study of the Southern California Bight*. Report of the Moss Landing Marine Laboratory, California (September 1978), 38 pp.

Graham, M. (1924). The annual cycle in the life of the mature cod in the North Sea. *Fishery Invest., Lond. Ser.* 2, *Sea Fisheries*. **6**(6): 77 pp.

Graham, G. M. (1956). *Sea fisheries. Their investigation in the United Kindgom*. Arnold, London.

Graham, W. F., M. L. Bender and G. P. Klinkhammer (1976). Manganese in Narragansett Bay. *Limnol. Oceanogr.* **21**: 665–73.

Grant, B. F. (1976). Endrin toxicity and distribution in freshwater: A review. *Bull. Environ. Contam. Toxicol.* **15**: 283–90.

Grant, B. F. and P. M. Mehrle (1970). Chronic endrin poisoning in goldfish, *Carassius auratus*. *J. Fish. Res. Bd. Canada*. **27**: 2225–32.

Grant, B. F. and P. M. Mehrle (1973). Endrin toxicosis in rainbow trout (*Salmo gairdneri*). *J. Fish. Res. Bd. Canada*. **30**: 31–40.

Greer, G. L. and U. Paim (1968). Degradation of DDT in Atlantic salmon (*Salmo salar*). *J. Fish. Res. Bd. Canada*. **25**: 2321–6.

Greig, R. A., B. A. Nelson and D. A. Nelson (1975). Trace metal content in the American oyster. *Mar. Pollut. Bull.* **6**(5): 72–3.

Greig, R. A., D. R. Wenzloff, A. Adams, B. Nelson and C. Shelpuk (1977). Trace metals in organisms from ocean disposal sites of the middle eastern United States. *Arch. Environ. Contam. Toxicol.* **6**: 395–409.

Greig, R. A., D. R. Wenzloff, C. L. MacKenzie, A. S. Merrill and V. S. Zdanowicz (1978). Trace metals in sea scallops, *Placopecten magellanicus*, from Eastern United States. *Bull. Environ. Contam. Toxicol.* **21**: 326–34.

Griffin, J. J., M. Koide, V. Hodge and E. D. Goldberg (1978). *Determining the ages of mussels by chemical and physical methods*. Unpublished MS from Scripps Institution of Oceanography, La Jolla, California.

Grimshaw, D. L., J. Lewin and R. Fuge (1976). Seasonal and short-term variations in the concentration and supply of dissolved zinc to polluted aquatic environments. *Environ. Pollut.* **11**: 1–7.

Gruger, E. H., R. W. Nelson and M. E. Stansby (1964). Fatty acid composition of oils from 21 species of marine fish, freshwater fish and shellfish. *J. Am. Oil Chem. Soc.* **41**: 662–7.

Grzenda, A. R., D. F. Paris and W. J. Taylor (1970). The uptake, metabolism and elimination of chlorinated residues by goldfish (*Carassius auratus*) fed a ^{14}C-DDT contaminated diet. *Trans. Amer. Fish. Soc.* **99**: 385–95.

Grzenda, A. R., W. J. Taylor and D. F. Paris (1971). The uptake and distribution of chlorinated residues by goldfish (*Carassius auratus*) fed a ^{14}C-dieldrin contaminated diet. *Trans. Amer. Fish. Soc.* **100**: 215–21.

Guary, J.-C. and S. W. Fowler (1978). Uptake from water and tissue distribution of neptunium-237 in crabs, shrimp and mussels. *Mar. Pollut. Bull.* **9**(12): 331–4.

Guary, J.-C. and A. Fraizier (1977). Etude comparée des teneurs en plutonium chez divers mollusques de quelques sites littoraux français. *Mar. Biol.* **41**: 263–7.

Guary, J.-C., M. Masson and A. Fraizier (1976). Etude préliminaire, *in situ*, de la distribution du plutonium dans différents tissus et organes de *Cancer pagurus* (*Crustacea: Decapoda*) et de *Pleuronectes platessa* (Pisces: Pleuronectidae). *Mar. Biol.* **36**: 13–17.

Guiseppe, C. (1964). Ciclo biologico reproduttivo di *Mytilus galloprovincialis* Lamark del lago di Ganzirri (Messina). *Atti della Società Peloritana di Scienze Fisiche, Matematiche, e Naturali, Messina*, **10**: 537–43.

Gunther, F. A. (1966). In: *Scientific aspects of pest control*. Nat. Acad. of Sci.-Nat. Res. Council Publ. **402**: 284.

Gunther, F. A., W. E. Westlake and P. S. Jaglan (1968). Reported solubilities of 738 pesticide chemicals in water. *Residue Rev.* **20**: 1–148.

Gutknecht, J. (1961). Mechanism of radioactive zinc uptake by *Ulva lactuca*. *Limnol. Oceanogr.* **6**: 426–31.

Gutknecht, J. (1963). Zn^{65} uptake by benthic marine algae. *Limnol. Oceanogr.* **8**: 31–8.

Gutknecht, J. (1965). Uptake and retention of cesium 137 and zinc 65 by seaweeds. *Limnol. Oceanogr.* **10**: 58–66.

Hamelink, J. L. and R. C. Waybrant (1976). DDE and lindane in a large-scale model lentic ecosystem. *Trans. Amer. Fish. Soc.* **105**: 124–34.

Hamelink, J. L., R. C. Waybrant and R. C. Ball (1971). A proposal: Exchange equilibria control the degree chlorinated hydrocarbons are biologically magnified in lentic environments. *Trans. Amer. Fish. Soc.* **100**: 207–14.

Hannerz, L. (1968). *Experimental investigations on the accumulation of mercury in water organisms*. Fishery Board of Sweden, Institute of Freshwater Research, Drottningholm. Report No. 48, pp. 120–76.

Hannon, M. R., Y. A. Greichus, R. L. Applegate and A. C. Fox (1970). Ecological distribution of pesticides in Lake Poinsett, South Dakota. *Trans. Amer. Fish. Soc.* **99**: 496–500.

Hansen, D. J. (1972). DDT and malathion: Effect on salinity selection by mosquitofish. *Trans. Amer. Fish. Soc.* **101**: 346–50.

Hansen, D. J. and A. J. Wilson (1970). Significance of DDT residues from the estuary near Pensacola, Fla. *Pestic. Monit. J.* **4**: 51–6.

Hansen, D. J., S. C. Schimmel and J. M. Keltner (1973). Avoidance of pesticides by grass shrimp (*Palaemonetes pugio*). *Bull. Environ. Contam. Toxicol.* **9**: 129–33.

Hansen, D. J., S. C. Schimmel and E. Matthews (1974). Avoidance of Aroclor 1254 by shrimp and fishes. *Bull. Environ. Contam. Toxicol.* **12**: 253–6.

Hardisty, M. W., S. Kartar and M. Sainsbury (1974*a*). Dietary habits and heavy metal concentrations in fish from the Severn Estuary and Bristol Channel. *Mar. Pollut. Bull.* **5**(4): 61–3.

Hardisty, M. W., R. J. Huggins, S. Kartar and M. Sainsbury (1974*b*). Ecological implications of heavy metal in fish from the Severn Estuary. *Mar. Pollut. Bull.* **5**(1): 12–15.

Hargrave, B. T. and G. A. Phillips (1976). DDT residues in benthic invertebrates and demersal fish in St. Margaret's Bay, Nova Scotia. *J. Fish. Res. Bd. Canada.* **33**: 1692–8.

Harrison, F. L. (1978). Effect of the physicochemical form of trace metals on their accumulation by bivalve molluscs. Paper submitted to American Chemical

Society Annual Meeting, 1978: Symposium on 'Chemical modeling—speciation, sorption, solubility and kinetics in aqueous systems'. Miami, Florida, Sept. 10–15, 1978, 25 pp.

Harrison, R. M. and D. P. H. Laxen (1978). Natural source of tetraalkyllead in air. *Nature, Lond.* **275**: 738–40.

Hartley, G. S. (1969). Evaporization of pesticides. In: *Pesticide formulations research* (R. F. Gould (ed.)), pp. 115–34. Washington DC, American Chemical Society.

Harvey, G. R. *et al.* (1973). Chlorinated hydrocarbons in open ocean Atlantic organisms. In: *The changing chemistry of the oceans* (D. Green and D. Jagner (eds)), pp. 177–86. New York, John Wiley.

Harvey, G. R., H. P. Miklas, V. T. Bowen and W. G. Steinhauer (1974). Observations on the distribution of chlorinated hydrocarbons in Atlantic Ocean organisms. *J. mar. Res.* **32**: 103–18.

Hattula, M. L., J. Janatuinen. J. Särkkä and J. Paasivirta (1978a). A five-year monitoring study of the chlorinated hydrocarbons in the fish of a Finnish lake ecosystem. *Environ. Pollut.* **15**: 121–39.

Hattula, M. L., J. Särkkä, J. Janatuinen, J. Paasivirta and A. Roos (1978b). Total mercury and methylmercury contents in fish from Lake Päijänne. *Environ. Pollut.* **17**: 19–29.

Haug, A. (1961). The affinity of some divalent metals to different types of alginates. *Acta chem. scand.* **15**: 1794–5.

Haug, A. and O. Smidsrød (1967). Strontium, calcium and magnesium in brown algae. *Nature, Lond.* **215**: 1167–8.

Haug, A., S. Melsom and S. Omang (1974). Estimation of heavy metal pollution in two Norwegian fjord areas by analysis of the brown alga *Ascophyllum nodosum. Environ. Pollut.* **7**: 179–92.

Havinga, B. (1929). Krebse und weichtiere. *Handbuch der Seefischerei Nordeuropas, Stuttgart,* **3**: 1–147.

Havinga, B. (1964). Mussel culture. *Sea Frontiers.* **10**: 155–61.

Havre, G. N., B. Underdal and C. Christiansen (1973). Cadmium concentrations in some fish species from a coastal area in Southern Norway. *Oikos.* **24**: 155–7.

Head, P. C. (1971). Observations on the concentration of iron in sea water, with particular reference to Southampton Water. *J. mar. biol. Ass. U.K.* **51**: 891–903.

Heesen, T. C. and D. J. McDermott (1974). *DDT and PCB in benthic crabs.* Southern California Coastal Water Research Project, Annual Report, 1974, pp. 109–11.

Heinonen, A. (1962). Reproduction of *Mytilus edulis* in the Finnish S.W. archipelago in summer 1960. *Suomalaisen eläin-ja kasvitieteelisen seuran vanomen julkaisuja,* **16**: 137–43.

Held, E. E. (1960). Land crabs and fission products at Eniwetok Atoll. *Pac. Sci.* **14**: 18–27.

Helle, E., M. Olsson and S. Jensen (1976a). DDT and PCB levels and reproduction in ringed seal from the Bothnian Bay. *Ambio.* **5**(4): 188–9.

Helle, E., M. Olsson and S. Jensen (1976b). PCB levels correlated with pathological changes in seal uteri. *Ambio.* **5**(5–6): 261–3.

Hemphill, J. E. (1954). Toxaphene as a fish toxin. *Prog. Fish. Cult.* **16**: 41–2.

Henderson, C., W. L. Johnson and I. Inglis (1969). Organochlorine insecticide residues in fish (National Pesticide Monitoring Program). *Pestic. Monit. J.* 3: 145–71.

Henderson, C., I. Inglis and W. L. Johnson (1971). Organochlorine insecticide residues in fish—Fall 1969 National Pesticide Monitoring Program. *Pestic. Monit. J.* 5: 1–11.

Henze, M. (1911). Untersuchungen über das Blut der Ascidien. I. Die Vanadiumbindung der Blutkörporchen. *Hoppe-Seyler's Zeitschrift für physiologishe Chemie.* 72: 494–501.

Heppleston, P. B. and M. C. French (1973). Mercury and other metals in British seals. *Nature, Lond.* 243: 302–4.

Herdman, W. A. (1893). Report upon the methods of oyster and mussel culture on the west coast of France. Report of the Lancashire Sea Fisheries Laboratory, 41–80.

Herdman, W. A. and A. Scott (1895). Report on the investigations carried on in 1894 in connection with the Lancashire Sea-Fisheries Laboratory (at University College Liverpool). *Proc. Transac. Liverpool Biol. Soc.* 9: 104–62.

Herman, S. G., R. L. Garrett and R. L. Rudd (1969). Pesticides and the western grebe. A study of pesticide survival and trophic concentration at Clear Lake, Lake County, California. In: *Chemical fallout. Current research on persistent pesticides.* (M. W. Miller and G. G. Berg (eds)), pp. 24–53. Charles C. Thomas, Springfield, Illinois.

Heyraud, M., S. W. Fowler, T. M. Beasley and R. D. Cherry (1976). Polonium-210 in euphausiids: A detailed study. *Mar. Biol.* 34: 127–36.

Hickling, C. F. (1934). Seasonal changes in the ovary of the immature hake, *Merluccius merluccius* L. *J. mar. biol. Ass. UK.* 20: 443–61.

Hirai, E. (1963). On the breeding seasons of invertebrates in the neighbourhood of the marine station of Asamushi. *Science Reports Tohoku University, Ser. 4, Biology.* 24: 369–75.

Hodge, V. F., T. R. Folsom and D. R. Young (1973). Retention of fall-out constituents in upper layers of the Pacific Ocean as estimated from studies of a tuna population. In: *Radioactive contamination of the marine environment*, pp. 263–76. IAEA, Vienna.

Hoggins, F. E. and R. R. Brooks (1973). Natural dispersion of mercury from Puhipuhi, Northland, New Zealand. *NZ J. mar. Freshwat. Res.* 7: 125–32.

Holcombe, G. W., D. A. Benoit, E. M. Leonard and J. M. McKim (1976). Long-term effects of lead exposure on three generations of brook trout (*Salvelinus fontinalis*). *J. Fish. Res. Bd. Canada.* 33: 1731–41.

Holden, A. V. (1962). A study of the absorption of C^{14} labelled DDT from water by fish. *Ann. appl. Biol.* 50: 467–77.

Holden, A. V. (1972a). Monitoring organochlorine contamination of the marine environment by the analysis of residues in seals. In: *Marine pollution and sea life* (M. Ruivo (ed.)), pp. 266–72. London, Fishing News (Books) Ltd.

Holden, A. V. (1972b). The effects of pesticides on life in fresh waters. *Proc. R. Soc. Lond. B.* 180: 383–94.

Holden, A. V. (1973). International cooperative study of organochlorine and mercury residues in wildlife, 1969–71. *Pest. Monit. J.* 7: 37–52.

Holden, A. V. and K. Marsden (1967). Organochlorine pesticides in seals and porpoises. *Nature, Lond.* 216: 1274–6.

Holliday, L. M. and P. S. Liss (1976). The behaviour of dissolved iron, manganese and zinc in the Beaulieu Estuary, S. England. *Est. cstl. mar. Sci.* **4**: 349–53.

Hornell, J. and M. R. Nayuda (1923). A contribution to the life-history of the Indian sardine, with notes on the plankton of the Malabar coast. *Madras Fish. Bull.* **17**: 129–97.

Hoss, D. E. (1964). Accumulation of zinc-65 by flounder of the genus *Paralichthys*. *Trans. Amer. Fish. Soc.*, **93**: 364–8.

Hoss, D. E. (1967). Marking post-larval Paralichthid flounders with radioactive elements. *Trans. Amer. Fish. Soc.* **96**: 151–6.

Hoss, D. E., D. S. Peters, W. F. Hettler and L. C. Clements (1978). Excretion rate of ^{65}Zn: Is it a useful tool for estimating metabolism of fish in the field? *J. exp. mar. Biol. Ecol.* **31**, 241–52.

Hrs-Brenko, M. (1971). Observations on the occurrence of planktonic larvae of several bivalves in the northern Adriatic Sea. In: *Fourth European Marine Biology Symposium*. (D. J. Crisp (ed.)), pp. 45–53. Cambridge University Press, London.

Hunt, E. G. and A. I. Bischoff (1960). Inimical effects on wildlife of periodic DDD application to Clear Lake. *Calif. Fish Game.* **46**: 91–106.

Hutcheson, M. S. (1974). The effect of temperature and salinity on cadmium uptake by the blue crab, *Callinectes sapidus*. *Chesapeake Sci.* **15**: 237–41.

Hutchinson, T. C. (1974). Comparative studies of the toxicity of heavy metals to phytoplankton and their synergistic interactions. *Wat. Pollut. Res. Can., Proc. 8th Can. Symp.*, pp. 68–75.

I.C.E.S. (1974). *Report of Working Group for the International Study of the Pollution of the North Sea and its Effects on Living Resources and their Exploitation.* Coop. Res. Report Series No. 39, pp. 191.

Ireland, M. P. (1973). Result of fluvial zinc pollution on the zinc content of littoral and sub-littoral organisms in Cardigan Bay, Wales. *Environ. Pollut.* **4**: 27–35.

Ireland, M. P. (1974). Variations in the zinc, copper, manganese and lead content of *Balanus balanoides* in Cardigan Bay, Wales. *Environ. Pollut.* **7**: 65–75.

Ireland, M. P. and R. J. Wootton (1977). Distribution of lead, zinc, copper and manganese in the marine gastropods, *Thais lapillus* and *Littorina littorea*, around the coast of Wales. *Environ. Pollut.* **12**: 27–41.

Ivanov, A. I. (1971). Preliminary results of breeding mussels (*Mytilus galloprovincialis*) in Kerch Bay and some other parts of the Black Sea. *Oceanology, Moscow.* **11**: 733–41.

Ivory Coast Fisheries Service (1972). *La contamination mercurielle des thons.* Ivory Coast Fish. Serv., Abidjan, 5 pp. (English translation by US Embassy, Abidjan, 7 pp.).

Jackim, E., G. Morrison and R. Steele (1977). Effects of environmental factors on radiocadmium uptake by four species of marine bivalves. *Mar. Biol.* **40**: 303–8.

Jan, T.-K., M. D. Moore and D. R. Young (1977). *Metals in Seafoods near Outfalls.* Southern California Coastal Water Research Project, Annual Report, 1977, pp. 153–7.

Jangaard, P. M., H. Brockerhoff, R. D. Burgher and R. J. Hoyle (1967a). Seasonal changes in general condition and lipid content of cod from inshore waters. *J. Fish. Res. Bd. Canada.* **24**. 607–12.

Jangaard, P. M., R. G. Ackman and J. C. Sipos (1967*b*). Seasonal changes in fatty acid composition of cod liver, flesh, roe, and milt lipids. *J. Fish. Res. Bd. Canada.* **24**: 613–27.

Jarvenpaa, T., M. Tillander and J. K. Miettinen (1970). Methylmercury: Half-time of elimination in flounder, pike and eel. *Suom. Kem. B.* **43**: 439–42.

Jarvie, A. W. P., R. N. Markall and H. R. Potter (1975). Chemical alkylation of lead. *Nature, Lond.* **255**: 217–18.

Jarvinen, A. W., M. J. Hoffman and T. W. Thorslund (1977). Long-term toxic effects of DDT food and water exposure on fathead minnows (*Pimephales promelas*). *J. Fish. Res. Bd. Canada.* **34**: 2089–103.

Jefferies, D. F. and C. J. Hewett (1971). The accumulation and excretion of radioactive caesium by the plaice (*Pleuronectes platessa*) and the thornback ray (*Raja clavata*). *J. mar. biol. Ass. UK.* **51**: 411–22.

Jennings, J. R. and P. S. Rainbow (1979). Studies on the uptake of cadmium by the crab *Carcinus maenas* in the laboratory. I. Accumulation from seawater and a food source. *Mar. Biol.* **50**: 131–9.

Jensen, A. and E. Sakshaug (1970). Producer-consumer relationships in the sea. 2. Correlation between *Mytilus* pigmentation and the density and composition of phytoplanktonic populations. *J. exp. mar. Biol. Ecol.* **5**: 246–53.

Jensen, A., B. Rystad and S. Melsom (1974). Heavy metal tolerance of marine phytoplankton. I. The tolerance of three algal species to zinc in coastal sea water. *J. exp. mar. Biol. Ecol.* **15**: 145–57.

Jensen, A., B. Rystad and S. Melsom (1976). Heavy metal tolerance of marine phytoplankton. II. The copper tolerance of three species in dialysis and batch bioassays. *J. exp. mar. Biol. Ecol.* **22**: 249–56.

Jensen, S. (1966). Report of a new chemical hazard. *New Scientist.* **32**: 612.

Jensen, S., A. G. Johnels, M. Olsson and G. Otterlind (1969). DDT and PCB in marine animals from Swedish waters. *Nature, Lond.* **224**: 247–50.

Jensen, S., A. G. Johnels, T. Odsjö, M. Olsson and G. Otterlind (1970). PCB— Occurrence in Swedish wildlife. In: *Proceedings of the PCB Conference, Wenner-Gren Centre, Stockholm,* 29 September 1970. Available from the Research Secretariat, Statens Naturvårdsverk, Fack, 171 20 Solna, Sweden.

Jensen, S., A. G. Johnels, M. Olsson and G. Otterlind (1972). *DDT and PCB in Herring and Cod from the Baltic, the Kattegat and the Skagerrak.* Ambio Spec. Rep., No. 1, 71–85.

Jensen, S., M. Olsson and R. Vaz (1975). Levels of DDT and PCB in littoral fishes along the Swedish coast. In: *Proceedings of Soviet-Swedish Symposium on the Baltic Pollution,* 3rd, Stockholm, Sweden, September 1975.

Johnels, A. G. and T. Westermark (1969). Mercury contamination of the environment in Sweden. In: *Chemical fallout* (M. W. Miller and G. G. Berg (eds)), pp. 221–41. C. C. Thomas, Springfield, Illinois.

Johnels, A. G., T. Westermark, W. Berg, P. I. Persson and B. Sjöstrand (1967). Pike (*Esox lucius* L.) and some other aquatic organisms in Sweden as indicators of mercury contamination in the environment. *Oikos.* **18**: 323–33.

Johnson, B. T., C. R. Saunders, H. O. Sanders and R. S. Campbell (1971). Biological magnification and degradation of DDT and aldrin by freshwater invertebrates. *J. Fish. Res. Bd. Canada.* **28**: 705–9.

Johnstone, J. (1898). The spawning of the mussel (*Mytilus edulis*). *Proc. Transac. Liverpool Biol. Soc.* **13**: 104–21.

Jørgensen, C. B. (1946). Referred to in Thorsen, G. Reproduction and larval development of Danish marine bottom invertebrates. *Meddelelser fra Danmarks Fiskeri- og Havundersøgelser, Serie Plankton.* **4**: 1–523, 1946.

Kameda, K., M. Shimizu and Y. Hiyama (1968). On the uptake of Zn^{65} and the concentration factor of Zn in marine organisms. I. Uptake of Zn^{65} in marine organisms. *J. Radiat. Res.* **9**: 50–62.

Kändler, R. (1926). Muschellarven aus dem Helgoländer Plankton. Wissenschaftliche Meeresuntersuchungen der Kommission sur Wissenschaftlichen Untersuchung der Deutschen Meere, Abt. *Helgoland.* **16**: 1–9.

Kania, H. J. and J. O'Hara (1974). Behavioural alterations in a simple predator–prey system due to sublethal exposure to mercury. *Trans. Amer. Fish. Soc.* **103**: 134–6.

Karbe, L., C. H. Schnier and H. O. Siewers (1977). Trace elements in mussels (*Mytilus edulis*) from coastal areas of the North Sea and the Baltic. Multielement analyses using instrumental neutron activation analysis. *J. Radioanal. Chem.* **37**: 927–43.

Keckes, S., B. Ozretic and M. Krajnovic (1968). Loss of Zn^{65} in the mussel *Mytilus galloprovincialis. Malacologia.* **7**: 1–6.

Kellog, R. L. and R. V. Bulkley (1976). Seasonal concentrations of dieldrin in water, channel catfish, and catfish-food organisms, Des Moines River, Iowa— 1971–73. *Pestic. Monit. J.* **9**: 186–94.

Kelly, P. B., R. Reiser and D. W. Hood (1958). The effect of diet on the fatty acid composition of several species of freshwater fish. *J. Am. Oil Chem. Soc.* **35**: 503–5.

Kelly, T. M., J. D. Jones and G. R. Smith (1975). Historical changes in mercury contamination in Michigan walleyes (*Stizostedion vitreum vitreum*). *J. Fish. Res. Bd. Canada.* **32**: 1745–54.

Kelso, J. R. M. and R. Frank (1974). Organochlorine residues, mercury, copper and cadmium in yellow perch, white bass and smallmouth bass, Long Point Bay, Lake Erie. *Trans. Amer. Fish. Soc.* **103**: 577–81.

Kelso, J. R. M., H. R. Maccrimmon and D. J. Ecobichon (1970). Seasonal insecticide residue changes in tissues of fish from the Grand River, Ontario. *Trans. Amer. Fish. Soc.* **99**: 423–6.

Kimura, K. and R. Ichikawa (1972). Accumulation and retention of ingested cobalt-60 by the common goby. *Bull. Jap. Soc. scient. Fish.* **38**: 1097–103.

Kiseleva, G. A. (1966). Some problems of the ecology of the larvae of Black Sea mussels. In: *Distribution of the benthos and biology of benthic organisms in the southern seas.* Akademiya Nauk Ukrainskoi, SSR. Seriya Biologiya Marya, Kiev, pp. 16–20.

Koeman, J. H., W. J. M. Peeters, C. J. Smit, P. S. Tjioe and J. J. M. De Goeij (1972). Persistent chemicals in marine mammals. *TNO Nieuws.* **27**: 570–8.

Koeman, J. H., W. H. M. Peeters, C. H. M. Koudstaal-Hol, P. S. Tjioe and J. J. M. De Goeij (1973). Mercury–selenium correlations in marine mammals. *Nature, Lond.* **245**: 385–6.

Koeman, J. H., W. S. M. Van de Ven, J. J. M. De Goeij, P. S. Tjioe and J. L. van Haaften (1975). Mercury and selenium in marine mammals and birds. *Sci. Total Environ.* **3**: 279–87.

Kopfler, F. (1974). The accumulation of organic and inorganic mercury compounds by the Eastern oyster (*Crassostrea virginica*). *Bull. Environ. Contam. Toxicol.* **11**: 275–80.

Krauskopf, K. B. (1956). Factors controlling the concentrations of thirteen rare metals in sea water. *Geochim. cosmochim. Acta.* **9**: 1–32B.

Krebs, C. T., I. Valiela, G. R. Harvey and J. M. Teal (1974). Reduction of field populations of fiddler crabs by uptake of chlorinated hydrocarbons. *Mar. Pollut. Bull.* **5**(9): 140–2.

Kriaris, N. (1967). La vie larvaire et la croissance de la moule en Bretagne. *Penn ar bed.* **6**: 25–30.

Krygier, E. E. and W. G. Pearcy (1977). The source of cobalt-60 and migrations of albacore off the west coast of North America. *Fishery Bull. US.* **75**(4): 867–70.

Kühl, H. (1972). Hydrography and biology of the Elbe estuary. *Oceanogr. mar. Biol. Ann. Rev.* **10**: 225–309.

Kuznetzov, V. V. and T. A. Mateeva (1948). Details of the bioecological features of marine invertebrates of eastern Murman. *Trudȳ Murmanskoi Biologicheskoi Stanstii.* **1**: 241–60.

Kynard, B. (1974). Avoidance behaviour of insecticide susceptible and resistant populations of mosquitofish to four insecticides. *Trans. Amer. Fish. Soc.* **103**: 557–61.

Laarman, P. W., W. A. Willford and J. R. Olson (1976). Retention of mercury in the muscle of yellow perch (*Perca flavescens*) and rock bass (*Ambloplites rupestris*). *Trans. Amer. Fish. Soc.* **105**(2): 296–300.

Lambert, L. (1935). La culture de la moule en Hollande. *Revue des Travaux de l'Office (scientifique et technologique) des Pêches Maritimes.* **8**: 431–80.

Lambert, L. (1950). Les coquillages comestibles, huîtres, moules, coquillages variés. *Que sais-je.* **416**. Presses Universitaires de France.

Langston, W. J. (1978a). Accumulation of polychlorinated biphenyls in the cockle *Cerastoderma edule* and the tellin *Macoma balthica*. *Mar. Biol.* **45**: 265–72.

Langston, W. J. (1978b). Persistence of polychlorinated biphenyls in marine bivalves. *Mar. Biol.* **46**: 35–40.

Laurs, R. M. and R. J. Lynn (1977). Seasonal migration of north Pacific albacore, *Thunnus alalunga*, into North American coastal waters: Distribution, relative abundance, and association with transition zone waters. *Fish. Bull., US.* **75**: 795–822.

Leatherland, J. F. and R. A. Sonstegard (1978). Lowering of serum thyroxine and triiodothyronine levels in yearling coho salmon, *Oncorhynchus kisutch*, by dietary mirex and PCBs. *J. Fish. Res. Bd. Canada.* **35**: 1285–9.

Lebour, M. V. (1906). *The mussel beds of Northumberland.* Northumberland Sea Fisheries Commission, Report No. 28.

Lebour, M. V. (1938). Notes on the breeding of some lamellibranchs from Plymouth, and their larvae. *J. mar. biol. Ass. UK.* **23**: 119–44.

Leffler, C. W. (1975). Effects of ingested mirex and DDT on juvenile *Callinectes sapidus* Rathbun. *Environ. Pollut.* **8**: 283–300.

Le Gall, P. (1970). Etude des moulières Normandes; renouvellement, croissance. *Vie et Milieu.* **21B**: 545–90.

Lenon, H. L. (1968). *Translocations and storage equilibria for minnows involving sublethal levels of dieldrin in aquatic ecosystems.* PhD thesis, Michigan State University, Michigan. 85 pp.

Linko, R. R. and K. Terho (1977). Occurrence of methyl mercury in pike and Baltic herring from the Turku archipelago. *Environ. Pollut.* **14**: 227–35.

Linko, R. R., J. Kaitaranta, P. Rantamäki and L. Eronen (1974). Occurrence of DDT and PCB compounds in Baltic herring and pike from the Turku Archipelago. *Environ. Pollut.* **7**: 193–207.

Livingston, R. J., M. P. Thompson and D. A. Meeter (1978). Long-term variation of organochlorine residues and assemblages of epibenthic organisms in a shallow north Florida (USA) estuary. *Mar. Biol.* **46**: 355–72.

Lloyd-Jones, C. P. (1971). The evaporization of DDT. *Nature, Lond.*, **229**: 65–6.

Lo Bianco, S. (1899). Notizie biologische reguardanti specialmente il periodo di maturità sessuale degli animali del Golfo di Napoli. *Mitteilungen aus der Zoologischen Station zu Neapel.* **13**: 448–573.

Lockhart, W. L., J. F. Uthe, A. R. Kenney and P. M. Mehrle (1972). Methylmercury in northern pike (*Esox lucius*): Distribution, elimination, and some biochemical characteristics of contaminated fish. *J. Fish. Res. Bd. Canada.* **29**: 1519–23.

Lockhart, W. L., D. A. Metner and J. Solomon (1977). Methoxychlor residue studies in caged and wild fish from the Athabasca River, Alberta, following a single application of blackfly larvicide. *J. Fish. Res. Bd. Canada.* **34**: 626–32.

Love, R. M. (1970). *The chemical biology of fishes.* Academic Press, London and New York, 1970, 547 pp.

Lovern, J. A. (1934*a*). Fat metabolism in fishes. IV. Mobilization of depôt fat in the salmon. *Biochem. J.* **28**: 1955–60.

Lovern, J. A. (1934*b*). Fat metabolism in fishes. V. The fat of the salmon in its young freshwater stages. *Biochem. J.* **28**: 1961–3.

Lovern, J. A. (1935). Fat metabolism in fishes. VII. The depôt fats of certain fish fed on known diets. *Biochem. J.* **29**: 1894–7.

Lovern, J. A. (1938). Fat metabolism in fishes. XIII. Factors influencing the composition of the depôt fat of fishes. *Biochem. J.* **32**: 1214–24.

Lovern, J. A. (1942). The composition of the depôt fats of aquatic animals. *Spec. Rep. Fd Invest. Bd D.S.I.R.* **51**, 72 pp.

Lovett, R. J., W. H. Gutenmann, I. S. Pakkala, W. D. Youngs and D. J. Lisk (1972). A survey of the total cadmium content of 406 fish from 49 New York State fresh waters. *J. Fish. Res. Bd. Canada.* **29**: 1283–90.

Lowe, J. I., P. D. Wilson, A. J. Rick and A. J. Wilson (1971). Chronic exposure of oysters to DDT, toxaphene and parathion. *Proc. natn. Shellfish. Ass.* **61**: 71–9.

Lowe, J. I., P. R. Parrish, J. M. Patrick and J. Forester (1972). Effects of the polychlorinated biphenyl Aroclor 1254 on the American oyster *Crassostrea virginica.* *Mar. Biol.* **17**: 209–14.

Lubet, P. (1957). Cycle sexuel de *Mytilus edulis* L. et de *Mytilus galloprovincialis* Lmk. dans le Bassin d' Arcachon (Gironde). *Année biologique.* **33**: 19–29.

Lubet, P. E. (1961). *Rapport au Gouvernement de la Yougoslavie sur l'Ostreiculture et la Mytiliculture, Programme elargi d' Assistance Technique.* Report 1334, FAO, Rome. 55 pp.

Lubet, P. and P. Le Gall (1967). Observations sur le cycle sexuel de *Mytilus edulis* L. à Luc-s-Mer. *Bulletin de la Société Linnéene de Normandie.* **10**: 303–7.

Lucas, H. F., D. N. Edgington and P. J. Colby (1970). Concentrations of trace elements in Great Lakes fishes. *J. Fish. Res. Bd. Canada.* **27**: 677–84.

Lunde, G. (1969). Water-soluble arseno–organic compounds in marine fishes. *Nature Lond.* **224**: 186–7.

Lunde, G. (1973a). Separation and analysis of organic-bound and inorganic arsenic in marine organisms. *J. Sci. Fd. Agric.* **24**: 1021–7.

Lunde, G. (1973b). The synthesis of fat and water soluble arseno–organic compounds in marine and limnetic algae. *Acta chem. Scand.* **27**: 1586–94.

Lunetta, J. E. (1969). Reproductive physiology of the mussel *Mytilus perna. Boletin da Faculdade de Filosofia, Ciências e Letras, Universidade de São Paulo. Zoologia e Biologia Marhina.* **26**: 33–111.

Luoma, S. N. (1977a). The dynamics of biologically available mercury in a small estuary. *Est. cstl. mar. Sci.* **5**: 643–52.

Luoma, S. N. (1977b). Physiological characteristics of mercury uptake by two estuarine species. *Mar. Biol.* **41**: 269–73.

Luoma, S. N. and G. W. Bryan (1978). Factors controlling the availability of sediment-bound lead to the estuarine bivalve *Scrobicularia plana. J. mar. biol. Ass. U.K.* **58**: 793–802.

Lyman, L. D., W. A. Tompkins and J. A. McCann (1968). Massachusetts pesticide monitoring study. *Pestic. Monit. J.* **2**: 109–22.

Macek, K. J. (1968a). Reproduction in brook trout (*Salvelinus fontinalis*) fed sublethal concentrations of DDT. *J. Fish. Res. Bd. Canada.* **25**: 1787–96.

Macek, K. J. (1968b). Growth and resistance to stress in brook trout fed sublethal levels of DDT. *J. Fish. Res. Bd. Canada.* **25**: 2443–51.

Macek, K. J. (1975). Acute toxicity of pesticide mixtures to bluegills. *Bull. Environ. Contam. Toxicol.* **14**: 648–52.

Macek, K. J. and S. Korn (1970). Significance of the food chain in DDT accumulation by fish. *J. Fish. Res. Bd. Canada.* **27**: 1496–8.

Macek, K. J., C. R. Rodgers, D. L. Stalling and S. Korn (1970). The uptake, distribution and elimination of dietary ^{14}C-DDT and ^{14}C-dieldrin in rainbow trout. *Trans. Amer. Fish. Soc.* **99**: 689–95.

MacGregor, J. S. (1974). Changes in the amount and proportions of DDT and its metabolites, DDE and DDD, in the marine environment off Southern California, 1949–1972. *Fishery Bull., US.* **72**(2): 275–93.

MacGregor, J. S. (1976). DDT and its metabolites in the sediments off Southern California. *Fishery Bull., US.* **74**(1): 27–35.

Mackay, N. J., R. J. Williams, J. L. Kacprzac, M. N. Kazacos, A. J. Collins and E. H. Auty (1975a). Heavy metals in cultivated oysters (*Crassostrea commercialis = Saccostrea cucullata*) from the estuaries of New South Wales. *Aust. J. mar. Freshwat. Res.* **26**: 31–46.

Mackay, N. J., M. N. Kazacos, R. J. Williams and M. I. Leedow (1975b). Selenium and heavy metals in black marlin. *Mar. Pollut. Bull.* **6**(4): 57–61.

MacLeod, J. C. and E. Pessah (1973). Temperature effects on mercury accumulation, toxicity, and metabolic rate in rainbow trout (*Salmo gairdneri*). *J. Fish. Res. Bd. Canada.* **30**: 485–92.

Madsen, H. (1940). A study of the littoral fauna of north west Greenland. *Meddelser om Grønland.* **124**: 1–24.

Majori, L., G. Nedoclan, G. B. Modonutti and F. Daris (1978). Study of the seasonal variations of some trace elements in the tissues of *Mytilus gallo-provincialis* taken in the Gulf of Trieste. *Rev. int. Océanogr. méd.* **49**: 37–40.

Manly, R. and W. O. George (1977). The occurrence of some heavy metals in populations of the freshwater mussel *Anodonta anatina* (L.) from the River Thames. *Environ. Pollut.* **14**: 139–54.

Mann, H. (1961). Fish cultivation in Europe. In: *Fish as food.* (G. Borgstrom (ed.)), Vol. 1, pp. 77–102. Academic Press, London.

Mantoura, R. F. C., A. Dickson and J. P. Riley (1978). The complexation of metals with humic materials in natural waters. *Est. cstl. mar. Sci.* **6**: 387–408.

Marafante, E. (1976). Binding of mercury and zinc to cadmium-binding protein in liver and kidney of goldfish (*Carassius auratus* L.). *Experentia.* **32**: 149–50.

Marafante, E., G. Pozzi and P. Scoppo (1972). Heavy metals detoxification in fish: Isolation of metallothionein from liver of *Carassius auratus*. *Bull. Soc. Ital. Biol. Sper.* **48**: 109–19.

Marchand, M., D. Vas and E. K. Duursma (1976). Levels of PCBs and DDTs in mussels from the N.W. Mediterranean. *Mar. Pollut. Bull.* **7**(4): 65–9.

Martin, H. (Editor) (1963). *Insecticide and fungicide handbook for crop protection.* Blackwell Scientific Publications, Oxford.

Martin, J. H. and A. R. Flegal (1975). High copper concentrations in squid livers in association with elevated levels of silver, cadmium and zinc. *Mar. Biol.* **30**: 51–5.

Martin, J.-L. M. (1974). Metals in *Cancer irroratus* (Crustacea: Decapoda): concentrations, concentration factors, discrimination factors, correlations. *Mar. Biol.* **28**: 245–51.

Mason, J. (1969). Mussel raft trials succeed in Scotland. *World Fishing.* **18**: 22–4.

Mateeva, T. A. (1948). The biology of *Mytilus edulis* L. in eastern Murman. *Trudȳ Murmanskogo biologicheskogo Instituta.* **1**: 215–41.

Matthews, A. (1913). Notes on the development of *Mytilus edulis* and *Alcyonium digitatum* in the Plymouth Laboratory. *J. mar. biol. Ass. UK.* **9**: 557–60.

Maugh, T. H. (1973). DDT: An unrecognised source of polychlorinated biphenyls. *Science.* **180**: 578–9.

Mayer, F. L., J. C. Street and J. M. Neuhold (1970). Organochlorine insecticide interactions affecting residue storage in rainbow trout. *Bull. Environ. Contam. Toxicol.* **5**: 300–10.

McBride, B. C. and R. S. Wolfe (1969). Abstract only: 'The methylation of arsenic by bacteria.' *Bacteriol. Proc.* **130**: 85.

McDermott, D. J. and D. R. Young (1974). *Trace metals in flatfish around outfalls.* Southern California Coastal Water Research Project, Annual Report, 1974. pp. 117–21.

McIntosh, W. C. (1885). On the British species of *Cyanea* and the reproduction of *Mytilus edulis* L. *Annals and Magazine of Natural History, London.* **5**: 148–52.

McIntosh, W. C. (1891). *Report on the mussel and cockle beds in the estuaries of the Tees, the Esk and the Humber.* pp. 1–87.

McKim, J. M. and D. A. Benoit (1971). Effects of long-term exposures to copper on survival, growth and reproduction of brook trout (*Salvelinus fontinalis*). *J. Fish. Res. Bd. Canada.* **28**: 655–62.

McKim, J. M. and D. A. Benoit (1974). Duration of toxicity tests for establishing 'no effect' concentrations for copper with brook trout (*Salvelinus fontinalis*). *J. Fish. Res. Bd. Canada.* **31**: 449–52.

McKim, J. M., G. F. Olson, G. W. Holcombe and E. P. Hunt (1976). Long-term effects of methylmercuric chloride on three generations of brook trout (*Salvelinus fontinalis*): Toxicity, accumulation, distribution, and elimination. *J. Fish. Res. Bd. Canada.* **33**: 2726–39.

Meaney, R. A. (1970). Investigations on the mussel (*Mytilus edulis* L.) resources in the River Boyne estuary, Ireland, during 1969. Fisheries Development Division, Resource Record Paper, Dublin, January, 1970. pp. 1–15.

Mears, H. C. and R. Eisler (1977). Trace metals in liver from bluefish, tautog and tilefish in relation to body length. *Chesapeake Sci.* **18**(3): 315–18.

Melhuus, A., K. L. Seip and H. M. Seip (1978). A preliminary study of the use of benthic algae as biological indicators of heavy metal pollution in Sørfjorden, Norway. *Environ. Pollut.* **15**: 101–7.

Menasveta, P. and R. Siriyong (1977). Mercury content of several predacious fish in the Andaman Sea. *Mar. Pollut. Bull.* **8**(9): 200–4.

Menzel, D. W., J. Anderson and A. Randtke (1970). Marine phytoplankton vary in their response to chlorinated hydrocarbons. *Science.* **167**: 1724–6.

Metcalf, R. L., G. K. Sangha and I. P. Kapoor (1971). Model ecosystem for the evaluation of pesticide biodegradability and ecological magnification. *Environ. Sci. Technol.* **5**: 709–13.

Miettinen, J. K., M. Tillander, K. Rissanen, V. Miettinen and Y. Ohmomo (1969). Distribution and excretion rate of phenyl- and methylmercury nitrate in fish, mussels, molluscs and crayfish. *Proc. 9th Japan Conf. Radioisotopes, Tokyo,* pp. 474–8.

Miettinen, J. K., M. Heyraud and S. Keckes (1972). Mercury as a hydrospheric pollutant. II. Biological half-time of methyl mercury in four Mediterranean species: A fish, a crab, and two molluscs. In: *Marine Pollution and Sea Life* (M. Ruivo (ed.)), pp. 295–8. Fishing News (Books) Ltd, London.

Mishima, J. and E. P. Odum (1963). Excretion rate of Zn[65] by *Littorina irrorata* in relation to temperature and body size. *Limnol. Oceanogr.* **8**: 39–44.

Miyazaki, I. (1935). On the development of some marine bivalves, with special reference to the shelled larvae. *J. Imp. Fish. Inst., Tokyo,* **31**: 1–10.

Modin, J. C. (1969). Chlorinated hydrocarbon pesticides in California bays and estuaries. *Pestic. Monit. J.* **3**: 1–7.

Moore, D. R. and D. J. Reish (1969). Studies on the *Mytilus edulis* community in Alimitos Bay, California. 4. Seasonal variation in gametes from different regions in the Bay. *Veliger.* **11**: 250–5.

Moore, S. A. and R. C. Harriss (1972). Effects of polychlorinated biphenyl on marine phytoplankton communities. *Nature, Lond.* **240**: 356–8.

Moore, S. A. and R. C. Harriss (1974). Differential sensitivity to PCB by phytoplankton. *Mar. Pollut. Bull.* **5**(11): 174–6.

Moreno, De A., V. J. Moreno and A. M. Malaspina (1971). Estudios sobre el mejillón (*Mytilus platensis* d'Orb) en explotación comercial del sector bonaerense Mar Argentino. 2. Ciclo anual en los principales componentes bioquimicos. *Contributions, Institute of Marine Biology, Mar de Planta.* **156**: 1–15.

Morris. A. W. (1971). Trace metal variations in sea water of the Menai Straits caused by a bloom of *Phaeocystis*. *Nature, Lond.* **233**: 427–8.

Morris, A. W. (1974). Seasonal variation of dissolved metals in inshore waters of the Menai Straits. *Mar. Pollut. Bull.* **5**(4): 54–9.

Morris, A. W. and A. J. Bale (1975). The accumulation of cadmium, copper, manganese and zinc by *Fucus vesiculosus* in the Bristol Channel. *Est. cstl. mar. Sci.* **3**: 153–63.

Morris. R. J. (1971). Seasonal and environmental effects on the lipid composition of *Neomysis integer. J. mar. biol. Ass. U.K.* **51**: 21–31.

Morris, R. J. and F. Culkin (1976). Marine lipids: Analytical techniques and fatty acid ester analyses. *Oceanogr. mar. Biol. Ann. Rev.* **14**: 391–433.

Morris, R. J. and F. Culkin (1977). Marine lipids: Sterols. *Oceanogr. mar. Biol. Ann. Rev.* **15**: 73–102.

Morris, R. L. and L. G. Johnson (1971). Dieldrin levels in fish from Iowa streams. *Pestic. Monit. J.* **5**: 12–16.

Morton, B. (1970). The tidal rhythm and rhythm of feeding and digestion in *Cardium edule. J. mar. Biol. Ass. U.K.* **50**: 499–512.

Morton, B. S. (1977). The tidal rhythm of feeding and digestion in the Pacific oyster, *Crassostrea gigas* (Thunberg). *J. exp. mar. Biol. Ecol.* **26**: 135–51.

Mosser, J. L., N. S. Fisher, T.-C. Teng and C. F. Wurster (1972a). Polychlorinated biphenyls: Toxicity to certain phytoplankters. *Science*. **175**: 191–2.

Mosser, J. L., N. S. Fisher and C. F. Wurster (1972b). Polychlorinated biphenyls and DDT alter species composition in mixed cultures of algae. *Science*. **176**: 533–35.

Mosser, J. L., T.-C. Teng, W. G. Walther and C. F. Wurster (1974). Interactions of PCBs, DDT and DDE in a marine diatom. *Bull. Environ. Contam. Toxicol.* **12**: 665–8.

Mount, D. I. (1962). Chronic effects of endrin on bluntnose minnows and guppies. *U.S. Fish. Wildl. Serv. Res. Rep.* **58**: 1–38.

Mount, D. I. (1968). *Report on insecticides in Lake Michigan*. Pesticides Committee of the Lake Michigan Enforcement Conf., Duluth, Minn., Federal Water Pollution Control Administration (Mimeographed).

Mullin, J. B. and J. P. Riley (1956). The occurrence of cadmium in sea water and in marine organisms and sediments. *J. mar. Res.* **15**(2): 103–22.

Murphy, B. R., G. J. Atchison and A. W. McIntosh (1978). Cadmium and zinc in muscle of bluegill (*Lepomis macrochirus*) and largemouth bass (*Micropterus salmoides*) from an industrially contaminated lake. *Environ. Pollut.* **17**: 253–7.

Murphy, P. G. (1970). Effects of salinity on uptake of DDT, DDE and DDD by fish. *Bull. Environ. Contam. Toxicol.* **5**: 404–7.

Murphy, P. G. (1971). The effect of size on the uptake of DDT from water by fish. *Bull. Environ. Contam. Toxicol.* **6**: 20–3.

Murphy, P. G. and J. V. Murphy (1971). Correlations between respiration and direct uptake of DDT in the mosquitofish *Gambusia affinis. Bull. Environ. Contam. Toxicol.* **6**: 144–55.

Myklestad, S., I. Eide and S. Melsom (1978). Exchange of heavy metals in *Ascophyllum nodosum* (L.). Le Jol. *in situ* by means of transplanting experiments. *Environ. Pollut.* **16**: 277–84.

N.A.S. (1971). Chlorinated hydrocarbons in the marine environment. Washington DC, National Academy of Sciences, USA.

Navrot, J., A. J. Amiel and J. Kronfeld (1974). *Patella vulgata:* A biological monitor of coastal metal pollution—A preliminary study. *Environ. Pollut.* **7**: 303–8.

Nelson, I. C. (Ed.) (1961). *Evaluation of radiological conditions in the vicinity of Hanford for 1960.* Hanford Atomic Operations Report No. HW-68435. 151 pp.

Nickless, G., R. Stenner and N. Terrile (1972). Distribution of cadmium, lead and zinc in the Bristol Channel. *Mar. Pollut. Bull.* **3**(12): 188–90.

Nielsen, S. A. (1974). Vertical concentration gradients of heavy metals in cultured mussels. *NZ J. mar. Freshwat. Res.* **8**(4): 631–6.

Nimmo, D. W. R. and L. H. Bahner (1976). Metals, pesticides and PCBs: Toxicities to shrimp singly and in combination. In: *Estuarine processes, Vol. 1; Uses, stresses, and adaptation to the estuary.* Academic Press, New York. pp. 523–32.

Nimmo, D. R., A. J. Wilson and R. R. Blackman (1970). Localization of DDT in the body organs of pink and white shrimp. *Bull. Environ. Contam. Toxicol.* **5**: 333–41.

Nimmo, D. R., R. R. Blackman, A. J. Wilson and J. Forester (1971*a*). Toxicity and distribution of Aroclor 1254 in the pink shrimp *Penaeus duorarum. Mar. Biol.* **11**: 191–7.

Nimmo, D. R., P. D. Wilson, R. R. Blackman and A. J. Wilson (1971*b*). Polychlorinated biphenyls absorbed from sediments by fiddler crabs and pink shrimp. *Nature, Lond.* **231**: 50–1.

Nimmo, D. R., J. Forester, P. T. Heitmuller and G. H. Cook (1974). Accumulation of Aroclor 1254 in grass shrimp (*Palaemonetes pugio*) in laboratory and field exposures. *Bull. Environ. Contam. Toxicol.* **2**: 303–8.

Nimmo, D. R., D. J. Hansen, J. A. Couch, N. R. Cooley, P. R. Parrish and J. I. Lowe (1975). Toxicity of Aroclor 1254 and its physiological activity in several estuarine organisms. *Arch. Environ. Contam. Toxicol.* **3**: 22–9.

Norstrom, R. J., A. E. McKinnon and A. S. W. deFreitas (1976). A bioenergetics-based model for pollutant accumulation by fish. Simulation of PCB and methylmercury residue levels in Ottowa River yellow perch (*Perca flavescens*). *J. Fish. Res. Bd. Canada.* **33**: 248–67.

Norstrom, R. J., D. J. Hallett and R. A. Sonstegard (1978). Coho salmon (*Oncorhynchus kisutch*) and herring gulls (*Larus argentatus*) as indicators of organochlorine contamination in Lake Ontario. *J. Fish. Res. Bd. Canada.* **35**: 1401–9.

Obusan, R. A. and E. E. Urbano (1968). Tahong—Food for the millions. Technical Paper of the Indo-Pacific Fisheries Council, No. 29, 25 pp.

Odum, W. E., G. M. Woodwell and C. F. Wurster (1969). DDT residues absorbed from organic detritus by fiddler crabs. *Science.* **164**: 576–7.

O'Hara, J. (1973*a*). The influence of temperature and salinity on the toxicity of cadmium to the fiddler crab, *Uca pugilator. Fish. Bull. U.S. Fish Wildl. Serv.* **71**: 149–53.

O'Hara, J. (1973*b*). Cadmium uptake by fiddler crabs exposed to temperature and salinity stress. *J. Fish. Res. Bd. Canada.* **30**: 846–8.

Olafson, R. W. and J. A. J. Thompson (1974). Isolation of heavy metal binding proteins from marine vertebrates. *Mar. Biol.* **28**: 83–6.

Olson, K. R., H. L. Bergman and P. O. Fromm (1973). Uptake of methyl mercuric chloride and mercuric chloride by trout: A study of uptake pathways into the whole animal and uptake by erythrocytes *in vitro*. *J. Fish. Res. Bd. Canada*. **30**: 1293–9.

Olson, K. R., K. S. Squibb and R. J. Cousins (1978). Tissue uptake, subcellular distribution, and metabolism of $^{14}CH_3HgCl$ and $CH_3^{203}HgCl$ by rainbow trout, *Salmo gairdneri*. *J. Fish. Res. Bd. Canada*. **35**: 381–90.

Olsson, M. (1974). Time and space dependence of pollutant levels in aquatic biota. Field studies. In: *Proceedings of the International Conference on Transport of Persistent Chemicals in Aquatic Ecosystems, Ottowa, Canada*, III49–III60.

Olsson, M. (1976). *Mercury levels in biota from Mörrum River during a 10 year clean-up period*. Fishery Board of Sweden: Institute of Freshwater Research, Drottningholm. Report No. 55, pp. 71–90.

Olsson, M. and S. Jensen (1975). *Pike as the test organism for mercury, DDT and PCB pollution. A study of the contamination in the Stockholm archipelago*. Fishery Board of Sweden: Institute of Freshwater Research, Drottningholm. Report No. 54, pp. 83–102.

Opuszýnski, K. (1971). Temperature preference of fathead minnow (*Pimephales promelas* Raf.) and its changes induced by copper salt $CuSO_4$. *Pol. Arch. Hydrobiol.* **18**: 401–8.

Oshida, P. S. (1976). *Effects of chromium on reproduction in polychaetes*. Southern California Coastal Water Research Project, Annual Report, 1976, pp. 161–7.

Oshida, P. S. (1977). *A safe level of hexavalent chromium for a marine polychaete*. Southern California Coastal Water Research Project, Annual Report, 1977, pp. 169–80.

Osterberg, C., J. Pattullo and W. Pearcy (1964). Zinc 65 in euphausiids as related to Columbia River water off the Oregon coast. *Limnol. Oceanogr.* **9**: 249–57.

Overnell, J. (1975). The effect of heavy metals on photosynthesis and loss of cell potassium in two species of marine algae, *Dunaliella tertiolecta* and *Phaeodactylum tricornutum*. *Mar. Biol.* **29**: 99–103.

Pagenkopf, G. K. and D. R. Neuman (1974). Lead concentrations in native brook trout. *Bull. Environ. Contam. Toxicol.* **12**: 70–5.

Pagenkopf, G. K., R. C. Russo and R. V. Thurston (1974). Effect of complexation on toxicity of copper to fishes. *J. Fish. Res. Bd. Canada*. **31**: 462–5.

Palichenko, Z. G. (1948). On the biology of *Mytilus edulis* in the White Sea. *Zoologicheskii Zhurnal*. **27**: 411–20.

Papadopoulou, C. and G. D. Kanias (1977). Tunicate species as marine pollution indicators. *Mar. Pollut. Bull.* **8**(10): 229–31.

Papadopoulou, C., G. D. Kanias and E. M. Kassimati (1978). Zinc content in otoliths of mackerel from the Aegean. *Mar. Pollut. Bull.* **9**(4): 106–8.

Parker, J. G. and F. Wilson (1975). Incidence of polychlorinated biphenyls in Clyde seaweed. *Mar. Pollut. Bull.* **6**(3): 46–7.

Patterson, C. and D. Settle (1977). Comparative distributions of alkalies, alkaline earths and lead among major tissues of the tuna *Thunnus alalunga*. *Mar. Biol.* **39**: 289–95.

442 *References*

Paul, M. D. (1942). Studies on the growth and breeding of certain sedentary organisms in Madras Harbour. *Proc. Ind. Acad. Sci. Sect. B.* **15**: 1–42.

Peakall, D. B. and J. L. Lincer (1970). Polychlorinated biphenyls: Another long-life widespread chemical in the environment. *Bioscience.* **20**: 958–64.

Pearcy, W. G. and C. L. Osterberg (1968). Zinc-65 and manganese-54 in albacore *Thunnus alalunga* from the west coast of North America. *Limnol. Oceanogr.* **13**: 490–8.

Peden, J. D., J. H. Crothers, C. E. Waterfall and J. Beasley (1973). Heavy metals in Somerset marine organisms. *Mar. Pollut. Bull.* **4**(1): 7–9.

Penrose, W. R., R. Black and M. J. Hayward (1975). Limited arsenic dispersion in sea water sediments, and biota near a continuous source. *J. Fish. Res. Bd. Canada.* **32**: 1275–81.

Pentreath, R. J. (1973*a*). The accumulation from water of ^{65}Zn, ^{54}Mn, ^{58}Co and ^{59}Fe by the mussel, *Mytilus edulis. J. mar. biol. Ass. U.K.* **53**: 127–43.

Pentreath, R. J. (1973*b*). The accumulation and retention of Zn^{65} and Mn^{54} by the plaice, *Pleuronectes platessa* L. *J. exp. mar. Biol. Ecol.* **12**: 1–18.

Pentreath, R. J. (1973*c*). The accumulation and retention of ^{59}Fe and ^{58}Co by the plaice, *Pleuronectes platessa* L. *J. exp. mar. Biol. Ecol.* **12**: 315–26.

Pentreath, R. J. (1973*d*). The accumulation from sea water of ^{65}Zn, ^{54}Mn, ^{58}Co and ^{59}Fe by the thornback ray, *Raja clavata* L. *J. exp. mar. Biol. Ecol.* **12**: 327–34.

Pentreath, R. J. (1976*a*). Some further studies on the accumulation and retention of ^{65}Zn and ^{54}Mn by the plaice, *Pleuronectes platessa* L. *J. exp. mar. Biol. Ecol.* **21**: 179–89.

Pentreath, R. J. (1976*b*). The accumulation of inorganic mercury from sea water by the plaice, *Pleuronectes platessa* L. *J. exp. mar. Biol. Ecol.* **24**: 103–19.

Pentreath, R. J. (1976*c*). The accumulation of organic mercury from sea water by the plaice, *Pleuronectes platessa* L. *J. exp. mar. Biol. Ecol.* **24**: 121–32.

Pentreath, R. J. (1976*d*). The accumulation of mercury from food by the plaice, *Pleuronectes platessa* L. *J. exp. mar. Biol. Ecol.* **25**: 51–65.

Pentreath, R. J. (1976*e*). The accumulation of mercury by the thornback ray, *Raja clavata* L. *J. exp. mar. Biol. Ecol.* **25**: 131–40.

Pentreath, R. J. (1977*a*). The accumulation of cadmium by the plaice, *Pleuronectes platessa* L. and the thornback ray, *Raja clavata* L. *J. exp. mar. Biol. Ecol.* **30**: 223–32.

Pentreath, R. J. (1977*b*). The accumulation of ^{110m}Ag by the plaice, *Pleuronectes platessa* L. and the thornback ray, *Raja clavata* L. *J. exp. mar. Biol. Ecol.* **29**: 315–25.

Pentreath, R. J. (1978*a*). ^{237}Pu experiments with the plaice *Pleuronectes platessa. Mar. Biol.* **48**: 327–35.

Pentreath, R. J. (1978*b*). ^{237}Pu experiments with the thornback ray *Raja clavata. Mar. Biol.* **48**: 337–42.

Pequegnat, J. E., S. W. Fowler and L. F. Small (1969). Estimates of the zinc requirements of marine organisms. *J. Fish. Res. Bd. Canada.* **26**: 145–50.

Perkins, E. J. (1974). *The biology of estuaries and coastal waters.* Academic Press, London.

Peterson, C. L., W. L. Klawe and G. D. Sharp (1973). Mercury in tunas: A review. *Fish. Bull. US Fish Wildl. Serv.* **71**: 603–13.

Peterson, R. H. (1976). Temperature selection of juvenile Atlantic salmon (*Salmo salar*) as influenced by various toxic substances. *J. Fish. Res. Bd. Canada.* **33**: 1722–30.

Petrocelli, S. R., J. W. Anderson and A. R. Hanks (1975*a*). Controlled food-chain transfer of dieldrin residues from phytoplankters to clams. *Mar. Biol.* **31**: 215–18.

Petrocelli, S. R., J. W. Anderson and A. R. Hanks (1975*b*). Biomagnification of dieldrin residues by food chain transfer from clams to blue crabs under controlled conditions. *Bull. Environ. Contam. Toxicol.* **13**: 108–16.

Phillips, D. J. H. (1976*a*). The common mussel *Mytilus edulis* as an indicator of pollution by zinc, cadmium, lead and copper. I. Effects of environmental variables on uptake of metals. *Mar. Biol.* **38**: 59–69.

Phillips, D. J. H. (1976*b*). The common mussel *Mytilus edulis* as an indicator of pollution by zinc, cadmium, lead and copper. II. Relationship of metals in the mussel to those discharged by industry. *Mar. Biol.* **38**: 71–80.

Phillips, D. J. H. (1977*a*). Effects of salinity on the net uptake of zinc by the common mussel *Mytilus edulis*. *Mar. Biol.* **41**: 79–88.

Phillips, D. J. H. (1977*b*). The use of biological indicator organisms to monitor trace metal pollution in marine and estuarine environments—A review. *Environ. Pollut.* **13**: 281–317.

Phillips, D. J. H. (1977*c*). The common mussel *Mytilus edulis* as an indicator of trace metals in Scandinavian waters. I. Zinc and cadmium. *Mar. Biol.* **43**: 283–91.

Phillips, D. J. H. (1978*a*). The common mussel *Mytilus edulis* as an indicator of trace metals in Scandinavian waters. II. Lead, iron and manganese. *Mar. Biol.* **46**: 147–56.

Phillips, D. J. H. (1978*b*). Use of biological indicator organisms to quantitate organochlorine pollutants in aquatic environments—A review. *Environ. Pollut.* **16**: 167–229.

Phillips, D. J. H. (1979*a*). Trace metals in the common mussel, *Mytilus edulis* (L.), and in the alga *Fucus vesiculosus* (L.) from the region of the Sound (Öresund). *Environ. Pollut.* **18**: 31–43.

Phillips, D. J. H. (1979*b*). Toxicity and accumulation of cadmium in marine and estuarine biota. In: *Biogeochemistry of cadmium* (J. O. Nriagu (ed.)), John Wiley, New York (in press).

Phillips, D. J. H. (1979*c*). The rock oyster *Saccostrea glomerata* as an indicator of trace metals in Hong Kong. *Mar. Biol.* (In press.)

Phillips, G. R. and D. R. Buhler (1979). Influences of dieldrin on the growth and body composition of fingerling rainbow trout (*Salmo gairdneri*) fed Oregon moist pellets or tubificid worms (*Tubifex* sp.). *J. Fish. Res. Bd. Canada.* **36**: 77–80.

Pickering, Q. H., C. Henderson and A. F. Lemke (1962). The toxicity of organic phosphorus insecticides to different species of warm water fishes. *Trans. Amer. Fish. Soc.* **91**: 175–84.

Pike, R. B. (1971). *Report on mussel farming and mussel biology for the fishing industry board.* Technical Report, New Zealand Fisheries Industry Board. **71**: 1–7.

Pilkley, O. H. and H. G. Goodell (1963). Trace elements in recent mollusk shells. *Limnol. Oceanogr.* **8**: 137–48.

Pilkley, O. H. and R. C. Harriss (1966). The effect of intertidal environment on the composition of calcareous skeletal material. *Limnol. Oceanogr.* **11**: 381–5.

Pillai, K. C., R. C. Smith and T. R. Folsom (1964). Plutonium in the marine environment. *Nature, Lond.* **203**: 568–71.

Piscator, M. (1964). On cadmium in normal human kidneys together with a report on the isolation of metallothionein from livers of cadmium-exposed rabbits. *Nord. Hyg. Tidskr.* **45**: 76–82.

Portmann, J. E. (1975). The bioaccumulation and effects of organochlorine pesticides in marine animals. *Proc. Roy. Soc. Lond. B.* **189**: 291–304.

Portmann, J. E. and P. Neall (1973). I.C.E.S. C.M. 1973/E: 12, Fish. Improv. Comm.

Preston, A., D. J. Jefferies, J. W. R. Dutton, B. R. Harvey and A. K. Steele (1972). British Isles coastal waters: The concentrations of selected heavy metals in sea water, suspended matter and biological indicators—A pilot survey. *Environ. Pollut.* **3**: 69–82.

Preston, E. M. (1971). The importance of ingestion in chromium-51 accumulation by *Crassostrea virginica* (Gmelin). *J. exp. mar. Biol. Ecol.* **6**: 47–54.

Pringle, B. H., D. E. Hissong, E. L. Katz and S. T. Mulawka (1968). Trace metal accumulation by estuarine molluscs. *J. Sanit. Engng Div. Am. Soc. civ. Engrs.* **94**: 455–75.

Pyefinch, K. A. (1950). Notes on the ecology of ship-fouling organisms. *J. Animal Ecol.* **19**: 29–35.

Pytkowicz, R. M. and D. R. Kester (1971). The physical chemistry of sea water. *Oceanogr. mar. Biol. Ann. Rev.* **9**: 11–60.

Rae, B. B. (1967*a*). The food of cod in the North Sea and on west of Scotland grounds. *Mar. Res.* (1), 68 pp.

Rae, B. B. (1967*b*). The food of cod on Faroese grounds. *Mar. Res.* (6), 23 pp.

Rafatjah, H. A. and A. R. Stiles (1972). *Summary review of use and offtake of DDT in anti-malaria control programs.* World Health Organisation VBC/72.5.

Ratkowsky, D. A., T. G. Dix and K. C. Wilson (1975). Mercury in fish in the Derwent Estuary, Tasmania, and its relation to the position of the fish in the food chain. *Aust. J. Mar. Freshwat. Res.* **26**: 223–31.

Raymont, J. E. G. (1963). *Plankton and productivity of the oceans.* Pergamon Press, Oxford.

Raymont, J. E. G. (1972). Some aspects of pollution in Southampton Water. *Proc. R. Soc. Lond., Series B.* **180**: 451–68.

Raymont, J. E. G. and B. G. A. Carrie (1964). The production of zooplankton in Southampton Water. *Internationale Revue der gesamten Hydrobiologie und Hydrographie,* **49**: 185–232.

Reed, R. J. (1966). Some effects of DDT on the ecology of salmon streams in southeastern Alaska. *U.S. Fish Wildl. Serv., Spec. Scient. Rep., Fisheries.* No. 542, 15 pp.

Reinert, R. E. (1967). *The accumulation of dieldrin in an alga* (Scenedesmus obliquus) *daphnia* (Daphnia magna), *guppy* (Lebistes reticulatus) *food chain.* PhD thesis, University of Michigan, Ann Arbor, Michigan. 76 pp.

Reinert, R. E. (1969). Insecticides and the Great Lakes. *Limnos Magazine (US).* **2**(3): 4–9.

Reinert, R. E. (1970). Pesticide concentrations in Great Lakes fish. *Pestic. Monit. J.* **3**: 233–40.

Reinert, R. E. (1972). Accumulation of dieldrin in an alga (*Scenedesmus obliquus*), *Daphnia magna*, and the guppy (*Poecilia reticulata*). *J. Fish. Res. Bd. Canada.* **29**: 1413–18.

Reinert, R. E. and H. L. Bergman (1974). Residues of DDT in lake trout (*Salvelinus namaycush*) and coho salmon (*Oncorhynchus kisutch*) from the Great Lakes. *J. Fish. Res. Bd. Canada.* **31**: 191–9.

Reinert, R. E., L. J. Stone and W. A. Willford (1974). Effect of temperature on accumulation of methylmercuric chloride and p,p' DDT by rainbow trout (*Salmo gairdneri*). *J. Fish. Res. Bd. Canada.* **31**: 1649–52.

Renfro, W. C., S. W. Fowler, M. Heyraud and J. La Rosa (1975). Relative importance of food and water in long term zinc[65] accumulation by marine biota. *J. Fish. Res. Bd. Canada.* **32**: 1339–45.

Renzoni, A. (1961). Variazione istologische stagionali dell gonadi di *Mytilus galloprovincialis* Lam. in rapporto al ciclo riproduttivo. *Rivista di Biologia (Perugia)*, Rome. **54**: 45–59.

Renzoni, A. (1962). Ulteriori dati sul ciclo biologico riproduttivo di *Mytilus galloprovincialis* Lam. *Rivista di Biologia (Perugia)*, Rome. **55**: 37–47.

Renzoni, A. (1963). Ricerche ecologiche e idrobiologiche su *Mytilus galloprovincialis* Lam. nel Golfo di Napoli. *Bolletino di Pesca, Piscicoltura e Idrobiologia*, Rome. **18**: 187–238.

Riisgård, H. U. (1979). Effect of copper on volume regulation in the marine flagellate *Dunaliella marina*. *Mar. Biol.* **50**: 189–93.

Riley, J. P. and I. Roth (1971). The distribution of trace elements in some species of phytoplankton grown in culture. *J. mar. biol. Ass. U.K.* **51**: 63–72.

Riley, J. P. and D. A. Segar (1970). The distribution of the major and some minor elements in marine animals. I. Echinoderms and coelenterates. *J. mar. biol. Ass. U.K.* **50**: 721–30.

Risebrough, R. W. (1969). Chlorinated hydrocarbons in marine ecosystems. In: *Chemical fallout* (M. W. Miller and G. G. Berg (eds)), Charles C. Thomas, Springfield, Illinois.

Risebrough, R. W., V. Vreeland, G. R. Harvey, H. P. Miklas and G. M. Carmignani (1972). PCB residues in Atlantic zooplankton. *Bull. Environ. Contam. Toxicol.* **8**: 345–55.

Risebrough, R. W., B. W. DeLappe and T. T. Schmidt (1976). Bioaccumulation factors of chlorinated hydrocarbons between mussels and seawater. *Mar. Pollut. Bull.* **7**(12): 225–8.

Roberts, D. (1972). The assimilation and chronic effects of sublethal concentrations of endosulfan on condition and spawning in the common mussel *Mytilus edulis*. *Mar. Biol.* **16**: 119–25.

Roberts, D. (1975). Sub-lethal effects of chlorinated hydrocarbons on bivalves. *Mar. Pollut. Bull.* **6**(2): 20–4.

Roberts, D. (1976). Mussels and pollution. In: *Marine mussels: Their ecology and physiology.* (B. L. Bayne (ed.)), pp. 67–80. Cambridge University Press, Cambridge.

Roberts, J. R., S. W. de Freitas and M. A. J. Gidney (1977). Influence of lipid pool size on bioaccumulation of the insecticide Chlordane by northern redhorse suckers (*Moxostoma macrolepidotum*). *J. Fish. Res. Bd. Canada.* **34**: 89–97.

Roberts, T. M., P. B. Heppleston and R. D. Roberts (1976). Distribution of heavy metals in tissues of the common seal. *Mar. Pollut. Bull.* **7**(10): 194–6.

Robertson, O. H. (1961). Prolongation of the life span of kokanee salmon (*Oncorhynchus nerka kennerlyi*) by castration before beginning of gonad development. *Proc. Natn. Acad. Sci. USA.* **47**: 609–21.

Robinson, J., A. Richardson, A. N. Crabtree, J. C. Coulson and G. R. Potts (1967). Organochlorine residues in marine organisms. *Nature, Lond.* **214**: 1307–11.

Roburn, J. (1965). A simple concentration-cell technique for determining small amounts of halide ions and its use in the determination of residues of organochlorine pesticides. *Analyst.* **90**: 467–75.

Romeril, M. G. (1971*a*). The uptake and distribution of Zn^{65} in oysters. *Mar. Biol.* **9**: 347–54.

Romeril, M. G. (1971*b*). C.E.R.L. Laboratory Note No. RD/L/N31/71, 1-8. (Referred to in Raymont, 1972—see above.)

Romeril, M. G. (1974). Trace metals in sediments and bivalve molluscs in Southampton Water and the Solent. *Revue Int. d'océan. méd.* **33**: 31–47.

Romeril, M. G. (1977). Heavy metal accumulation in the vicinity of a desalination plant. *Mar. Pollut. Bull.* **8**(4): 84–7.

Roubal, W. T. (1974). Spin-labelling of living tissue—A method for investigating pollutant–host interaction. In: *Pollution and physiology of marine organisms* (F. J. Vernberg and W. B. Vernberg (eds.)), pp. 367–79. Academic Press, New York.

Rucker, J. B. and J. W. Valentine (1961). Salinity response of trace element concentration in *Crassostrea virginica*. *Nature, Lond.* **190**: 1099–100.

Rummel, W., H. J. Bielig, W. Forth, K. Pfleger, W. Rudiger and E. Seifen (1966). Absorption and accumulation of vanadium by tunicates. *Protides of the Biological Fluids.* **14**: 205–10.

Runnström, S. (1929). Weitere studien über die Temperaturanpassung der Fortplanzung und Einwicklung mariner Tiere. *Bergens museums Årbog.* **10**: 1–46.

Ruohtula, M. and J. K. Miettinen (1975). Retention and excretion of [203]Hg-labelled methylmercury in rainbow trout. *Oikos.* **26**: 385–90.

Sadykhova, I. A. (1970). A contribution to the biology of *Crenomytilus grayanus*. (Dysodonta, Mytilidae). *Zoologicheskii Zhurnal.* **49**: 1408–10.

Sagiura, Y. (1959). Seasonal change in sexual maturity and sexuality of *Mytilus edulis* L. *Bull. Jap. Soc. Sci. Fish.* **25**: 1–6.

Saliba, L. J. and M. G. Vella (1977). Effects of mercury on the behaviour and oxygen consumption of *Monodonta articulata*. *Mar. Biol.* **43**: 277–82.

Sameoto, D. D., D. C. Darrow and S. Guildford (1975). DDT residues in euphausiids in the upper estuary of the Gulf of St. Lawrence. *J. Fish. Res. Bd. Canada.* **32**: 310–14.

Sanborn, J. R. and C. C. Yu (1973). The fate of dieldrin in a model ecosystem. *Bull. Environ. Contam. Toxicol.* **10**: 340–6.

Sanborn, J. R., W. F. Childers and R. L. Metcalf (1975). Uptake of three polychlorinated biphenyls, DDT, and DDE by the green sunfish, *Lepomis cyanellus* Raf. *Bull. Environ. Contam. Toxicol.* **13**: 209–17.

Sanders, H. O. and J. H. Chandler (1972). Biological magnification of a polychlorinated biphenyl (Aroclor 1254) from water by aquatic invertebrates. *Bull. Environ. Contam. Toxicol.* **7**: 257–63.

Sano, T. (1960). Haematological studies of the culture fishes in Japan. 3. Changes in blood constituents with growth of rainbow trout. *J. Tokyo Univ. Fish.* **46**: 77–87.

Savage, R. E. (1956). The great spatfall of mussels in the River Conway Estuary in Spring 1940. *Fish. Invest., Min. Ag. Fish. Food, London, Ser. II.* **20**: 1–21.

Savilov, I. A. (1953). The growth and variations in growth of the White Sea invertebrates *Mytilus edulis, Mya arenaria* and *Balanus balanoides. Trudy Instituta Okeanologii, Akademiya nauk SSR, Moscow.* **7**: 198–259.

Saward, D., A. Stirling and G. Topping (1975). Experimental studies on the effects of copper on a marine food chain. *Mar. Biol.* **29**: 351–61.

Schipp, R. and F. Hevert (1978). Distribution of copper and iron in some central organs of *Sepia officinalis* (Cephalopoda). A comparative study by flameless atomic absorption and electron microscopy. *Mar. Biol.* **47**: 391–9.

Schmidt, U. and F. Huber (1976). Methylation of organolead and lead (II) compounds to $(CH_3)_4Pb$ by microorganisms. *Nature, Lond.* **259**: 157–8.

Schoor, W. P. and S. M. Newman (1976). The effect of mirex on the burrowing activity of the lugworm (*Arenicola cristata*). *Trans. Amer. Fish. Soc.* **105**(6): 700–3.

Schroeder, H. A., A. P. Nason, I. H. Tipton and J. J. Balassa (1967). Essential trace elements in man: zinc. Relation to environmental cadmium. *J. chron. Dis.* **20**: 179–98.

Schulz-Baldes, M. (1972). Toxizität und Anreicherung von Blei bei der Miesmuschel *Mytilus edulis* im Laborexperiment. *Mar. Biol.* **16**: 226–9.

Schulz-Baldes, M. (1973). Die Miesmuschel *Mytilus edulis* als Indikator für die Bleikonzentration im Weserastuar und in der Deutschen Bucht. *Mar. Biol.* **21**: 98–102.

Schulz-Baldes, M. (1974). Lead uptake from sea water and food and lead loss in the common mussel *Mytilus edulis. Mar. Biol.* **25**: 177–93.

Scott, A. (1901). Note on the spawning of the mussel *Mytilus edulis. Proc. Transac. Liverpool Biol. Soc.* **15**: 161–4.

Scott, D. M. and C. W. Major (1972). The effect of copper-II on survival, respiration and heart rate in the common blue mussel, *Mytilus edulis. Biol. Bull. mar. biol. Lab., Woods Hole.* **143**: 679–88.

Scott, D. P. (1974). Mercury concentration of white muscle in relation to age, growth, and condition in four species of fishes from Clay Lake, Ontario. *J. Fish. Res. Bd. Canada.* **31**: 1723–9.

Scott, D. P. and F. A. J. Armstrong (1972). Mercury concentration in relation to size in several species of freshwater fishes from Manitoba and Northwest Ontario. *J. Fish. Res. Bd. Canada.* **29**: 1685–90.

Scott, J. S. (1977). Back-calculated fish lengths and Hg and Zn levels from recent and 100-year-old cleithrum bones from Atlantic cod (*Gadus morhua*). *J. Fish. Res. Bd. Canada.* **34**: 147–50.

Scura, E. D. and G. H. Theilacker (1977). Transfer of the chlorinated hydrocarbon PCB in a laboratory marine food chain. *Mar. Biol.* **40**: 317–25.

Seba, D. B. and E. F. Corcoran (1969). Surface slicks as concentrators of pesticides in the marine environment. *Pestic. Monit. J.* **3**: 190–3.

Seed, R. (1969). The ecology of *Mytilus edulis* L. (Lamellibranchiata) on exposed rocky shores. I. Breeding and settlement. *Oecologia.* **3**: 277–316.

Seed, R. (1971). A physiological and biochemical approach to the taxonomy of *Mytilus edulis* L. and *M. galloprovincialis* Lmk. from south-west England. *Cahiers Biol. marine, Roscoff.* **12**: 291–322.

Seed, R. (1975). Reproduction in Mytilus (*Mollusca: Bivalvia*) in European waters. Pubblicazioni della Stazione Zoologica di Napoli, Milan.

Seed, R. (1976). Ecology. In: *Marine mussels: Their ecology and physiology* (B. L. Bayne (ed.)), pp. 13–65. Cambridge University Press, Cambridge.

Seeliger, U. and P. Edwards (1977). Correlation coefficients and concentration factors of copper and lead in seawater and benthic algae. *Mar. Pollut. Bull.* **8**(1): 16–19.

Segar, D. A., J. D. Collins and J. P. Riley (1971). The distributions of the major and some minor elements in marine animals. II. Molluscs. *J. mar. biol. Ass. U.K.* **51**: 131–6.

Sergeant, D. E. (1965). Migrations of harp seals *Pagophilus groenlandicus* (Erxleben) in the northwest Atlantic. *J. Fish. Res. Bd. Canada.* **22**: 433–64.

Sergeant, D. E. and F. A. J. Armstrong (1973). Mercury in seals from Eastern Canada. *J. Fish. Res. Bd. Canada.* **30**: 843–6.

Seymour, A. H. (1966). Accumulation and loss of zinc-65 by oysters in a natural environment. In: *Disposal of radioactive wastes into seas, oceans and surface waters*, pp. 605–19. Vienna, International Atomic Energy Agency.

Seymour, A. H. and V. A. Nelson (1973). Decline of ^{65}Zn in marine mussels following the shutdown of Hanford reactors. In: *Radioactive contamination of the marine environment*, IAEA-SM-158/16. IAEA, Vienna.

Sharp, J. W., R. M. Sitts and A. W. Knight (1979). Effects of Kelthane on the estuarine shrimp *Crangon franciscorum. Mar. Biol.* **50**: 367–74.

Sheline, J. and B. Schmidt-Nielsen (1977). Methylmercury–selenium: Interaction in the killifish, *Fundulus heteroclitus*. In: *Physiological responses of marine biota to pollutants*. (F. J. Vernberg, A. Calabrese, F. P. Thurberg and W. B. Vernberg (eds)). pp. 119–30. Academic Press, New York, 1977.

Sheppard, C. R. C. (1977). Relationships between heavy metals and major cations along pollution gradients. *Mar. Pollut. Bull.* **8**(7): 163–4.

Sheridan, P. F. (1975). Uptake, metabolism, and distribution of DDT in organs of the blue crab, *Callinectes sapidus. Chesapeake Sci.* **16**: 20–6.

Shimizu, M., T. Kajihara, I. Suyama and Y. Hiyama (1971). Uptake of Co^{58} by mussel, *Mytilus edulis. J. Radiat. Res.* **12**(1): 17–28.

Shore, R., G. Carney and T. Stygall (1975). Cadmium levels and carbohydrate metabolism in limpets. *Mar. Pollut. Bull.* **6**(12): 187–9.

Shumway, S. E. (1977). Effect of salinity fluctuation on the osmotic pressure and Na$^+$, Ca^{2+} and Mg^{2+} ion concentrations in the hemolymph of bivalve molluscs. *Mar. Biol.* **4**: 153–77.

Silbergeld, E. K. (1973). Dieldrin. Effects of chronic sublethal exposure on adaptation to thermal stress in freshwater fish. *Environ. Sci. Technol.* **7**: 846–9.

Simpson, R. D. (1979). Uptake and loss of zinc and lead by mussels (*Mytilus edulis*) and relationships with body weight and reproductive cycle. *Mar. Pollut. Bull.* **10**(3): 74–8.

Sirota, G. R. and J. F. Uthe (1977). Determination of tetraalkyl lead compounds in biological materials. *Anal. Chem.* **49**: 823–5.

Skipnes, O., T. Roald and A. Haug (1975). Uptake of zinc and strontium by brown algae. *Physiologia Pl.* **34**: 314–20.

Small, L. F. (1969). Experimental studies on the transfer of Zn^{65} in high concentration by euphausiids. *J. exp. mar. Biol. Ecol.* **3**: 106–23.

Smith, R. M. and C. F. Cole (1970). Chlorinated hydrocarbon insecticide residues in winter flounder, *Pseudopleuronectes americanus*, from the Weweantic River estuary, Massachusetts. *J. Fish. Res. Bd. Canada.* **27**: 2374–80.

Smith, T. G. and F. A. J. Armstrong (1975). Mercury in seals, terrestrial carnivores, and principal food items of the Inuit, from Holman, N.W.T. *J. Fish. Res. Bd. Canada.* **32**: 795–801.

Södergren, A. (1968). Uptake and accumulation of C^{14}-DDT by *Chlorella* sp. (Chlorophyceae). *Oikos.* **19**: 126–38.

Södergren, A. (1973). Transport, distribution and degradation of chlorinated hydrocarbon residues in aquatic model ecosystems. *Oikos.* **24**: 30–41.

Södergren, A., B. Svensson and S. Ulfstrand (1972). DDT and PCB in south Swedish streams. *Environ. Pollut.* **3**: 25–36.

Spärck, R. (1920). Nogle bemaerkninger angående yngleforhold hos *Mytilus edulis* L. *Videnskabelige Meddelelser fra Dansk naturhistorisk Forening i Kjøbenhavn.* **71**: 161–4.

Spehar, R. L. (1974). *Cadmium and zinc toxicity to* Jordanella floridae (*Goode and Bean*)*: Effects on growth, reproduction, survival, and behaviour.* MS thesis, University of Minnesota, Duluth, 66 pp.

Spehar, R. L. (1976). Cadmium and zinc toxicity to flagfish, *Jordanella floridae. J. Fish. Res. Bd. Canada.* **33**: 1939–45.

Sprague, J. B. (1964). Lethal concentrations of copper and zinc for young Atlantic salmon. *J. Fish. Res. Bd. Canada.* **21**: 17–26.

Sprague, J. B. and J. R. Duffy (1971). DDT residues in Canadian Atlantic fishes and shellfishes in 1967. *J. Fish. Res. Bd. Canada.* **28**: 59–64.

Sprague, J. B., P. F. Elson and J. R. Duffy (1971). Decrease in DDT residues in young salmon after forest spraying in New Brunswick. *Environ. Pollut.* **1**: 191–202.

Stafford, J. (1912). On the recognition of bivalve larvae in plankton collections. *Contrib. Canadian Biol. Fish.* 1906–10.

Stansby, M. E. (1967). Fatty acid patterns in marine, freshwater, and anadromous fish. *J. Am. Oil Chem. Soc.* **44**: 64–72.

Stegeman, J. J. (1974). Hydrocarbons in shellfish chronically exposed to low levels of fuel oil. In: *Pollution and physiology of marine organisms* (F. J. Vernberg and W. B. Vernberg (eds)), pp. 329–47. Academic Press, New York.

Stenersen, J. and J. Kvalvag (1972). Residues of DDT and its degradation products in cod liver from two Norwegian fjords. *Bull. Environ. Contam. Toxicol.* **8**:120–1.

Stenner, R. D. and G. Nickless (1974). Distribution of some heavy metals in organisms in Hardangerfjord and Skjerstadfjord, Norway. *Wat. Air Soil Pollut.* **3**: 279–91.

Stenner, R. D. and G. Nickless (1975). Heavy metals in organisms of the Atlantic coast of South-West Spain and Portugal. *Mar. Pollut. Bull.* **6**(6): 89–92.

Stenzel, H. B. (1971). Oysters. In: *Treatise on invertebrate palaeontology* (K. C. Moore (ed.)), pp. N953–N1224. Part N, Vol. 3, *Mollusca 6.* Geological Society of America and the University of Kansas, Boulder, Colorado.

Stephenson, M. D., J. H. Martin and M. Martin (1978). *Trace metal concentrations in the California mussel at areas of special biological significance.* Annual Report for 1978 of the California State Mussel Watch.

Stevens, J. D. and B. E. Brown (1974). Occurrence of heavy metals in the blue shark *Prionace glauca* and selected pelagic fish in the North-East Atlantic ocean. *Mar. Biol.* **26**: 287–93.

Stirling, E. A. (1975). Some effects of pollutants on the behaviour of the bivalve *Tellina tenuis. Mar. Pollut. Bull.* **6**(8): 122–4.

Stohler, R. (1930). Beitrag zur Kenntnis des Geschlechtszyklus von *Mytilus californianus* Conrad. *Zoologischer Anzeiger.* **90**: 263–8.

Stout, V. F., F. L. Beezhold and C. R. Houle (1972). DDT residue levels in some US fishery products and some treatments in reducing them. In: *Marine pollution and sea life* (M. Ruivo (ed.)), pp. 550–3. London, Fishing News (Books) Ltd.

Strömgren, T. (1979). The effect of copper on length increase in *Ascophyllum nodosum* (L.) Le Jolis. *J. exp. mar. Biol. Ecol.* **37**: 153–9.

Stubbings, H. G. (1954). The biology of the common mussel in relation to fouling problems. *Research.* **7**: 222–9.

Sturesson, U. (1976). Lead enrichment in shells of *Mytilus edulis. Ambio.* **5**: 253–6.

Sturesson, U. (1978). Cadmium enrichment in shells of *Mytilus edulis. Ambio.* **7**: 122–5.

Suburo, S. and E. Sakamoto (1951). On the reproduction of *Mytilus grayanus* Dunker. *Bull. Jap. Soc. Sci. Fish.* **17**: 63–6.

Sullivan, J. F., G. J. Atchison, D. J. Kolar and A. W. McIntosh (1978). Changes in the predator–prey behaviour of fathead minnows (*Pimephales promelas*) and largemouth bass (*Micropterus salmoides*) caused by cadmium. *J. Fish. Res. Bd. Canada.* **35**: 446–51.

Tagatz, M. E. (1976). Effect of mirex on predator–prey interaction in an experimental estuarine ecosystem. *Trans. Amer. Fish. Soc.* **105**: 546–9.

Talbot, V., R. J. Magee and M. Hussain (1976). Lead in Port Phillip Bay mussels. *Mar. Pollut. Bull.* **7**(12): 234–7.

Ten Berge, W. F. and M. Hillebrand (1974). Organochlorine compounds in several marine organisms from the North Sea and the Dutch Wadden Sea. *Neth. J. Sea Res.* **8**: 361–8.

Thomas, W. H., O. Holm-Hansen, D. L. R. Seibert, F. Azam, R. Hodson and M. Takahashi (1977). Effects of copper on phytoplankton standing crop and productivity: Controlled Ecosystem Pollution Experiment. *Bull. mar. Sci.* **27**: 34–43.

Thorp, V. J. and P. S. Lake (1974). Toxicity bioassays of cadmium on selected freshwater invertebrates and the interaction of cadmium and zinc on the freshwater shrimp, *Paratya tasmaniensis* Riek. *Aust. J. mar. Freshwat. Res.* **25**: 97–104.

Tong, S. S. C., W. D. Youngs, W. H. Gutenmann and D. J. Lisk (1974). Trace metals in Lake Cayuga Lake Trout (*Salvelinus namaycush*) in relation to age. *J. Fish. Res. Bd. Canada.* **31**: 238–9.

Tooby, T. E. and F. J. Durbin (1975). Lindane residue accumulation and elimination in rainbow trout (*Salmo gairdneri* Richardson) and roach (*Rutilus rutilus* Linnaeus). *Environ. Pollut.* **8**: 79–89.

Topping, G. (1973). Heavy metals in shellfish from Scottish waters. *Aquaculture.* **1**: 379–84.

Topping, G. (1974). *Fish Improvement Comm., I.C.E.S.* (Mimeographed). CM 1974/E:32.

Ünlü, M. Y. and S. W. Fowler (1979). Factors affecting the flux of arsenic through the mussel *Mytilus galloprovincialis*. *Mar. Biol.* **51**: 209–19.

Ünlü, M. Y., M. Heyraud and S. Keckes (1972). Mercury as a hydrospheric pollutant. I. Accumulation and excretion of $^{203}HgCl_2$ in *Tapes decussatus* L. In: *Marine pollution and sea life* (M. Ruivo (ed.)), pp. 292–5. Fishing News (Books) Ltd, London.

Uthe, J. F. and E. G. Bligh (1971). Preliminary survey of heavy metal contamination of Canadian freshwater fish. *J. Fish. Res. Bd. Canada*. **28**: 786–8.

Vallee, B. L. and D. D. Ulmer (1972). Biochemical effects of mercury, cadmium and lead. *Ann. Rev. Biochem.* **41**: 91–128.

Valli, G. (1971). Ciclo di maturita sessuale in *Mytilus galloprovincialis* Lmk. di Duino (Trieste). *Bolletino di Pesca, Piscicoltura e Idrobiologia, Rome*. **26**: 259–65.

Vernberg, F. J., M. S. Guram and A. M. Savory (1978). Metabolic response to thermal changes of the adult fiddler crab *Uca pugilator* and the effect of PCBs. *Mar. Biol.* **48**: 135–41.

Vernberg, W. B. and J. O'Hara (1972). Temperature–salinity stress and mercury uptake in the fiddler crab, *Uca pugilator*. *J. Fish. Res. Bd. Canada*. **29**: 1491–4.

Vernberg, W. B. and J. Vernberg (1972). The synergistic effects of temperature, salinity, and mercury on survival and metabolism of the adult fiddler crab, *Uca pugilator*. *Fishery Bull. U.S.* **70**: 415–20.

Vernberg, W. B., P. J. De Coursey and J. O'Hara (1974). Multiple environmental factor effects on physiology and behaviour of the fiddler crab, *Uca pugilator*. In: *Pollution and physiology of marine organisms* (F. J. Vernberg and W. B. Vernberg (eds)), pp. 381–425. Academic Press, New York.

Vernberg, W. B., P. J. De Coursey, M. Kelly and D. M. Johns (1977). Effects of sublethal concentrations of cadmium on adult *Palaemonetes pugio* under static and flow-through conditions. *Bull. Environ. Contam. Toxicol.* **17**: 16–24.

Vreeland, V. (1974). Uptake of chlorobiphenyls by oysters. *Environ. Pollut.* **6**:135–40.

Walker, G. (1977). 'Copper' granules in the barnacle *Balanus balanoides*. *Mar. Biol.* **39**: 343–9.

Walker, G., P. S. Rainbow, P. Foster and D. J. Crisp (1975a). Barnacles: Possible indicators of zinc pollution? *Mar. Biol.* **30**: 57–65.

Walker, G., P. S. Rainbow, P. Foster and D. L. Holland (1975b). Zinc phosphate granules in tissue surrounding the midgut of the barnacle *Balanus balanoides*. *Mar. Biol.* **33**: 161–6.

Walker, T. I. (1976). Effects of species, sex, length and locality on the mercury content of school shark *Galeorhinus australis* (Macleay) and gummy shark *Mustelus antarcticus* Guenther from south-eastern Australian waters. *Aust. J. mar. Freshwat. Res.* **27**: 603–16.

Ward, D. V. and D. A. Busch (1976). Effects of temefos, an organophosphorous insecticide, on survival and escape behaviour of the marsh fiddler crab *Uca pugnax*. *Oikos*. **27**: 331–5.

Ward, D. V., B. L. Howes and D. F. Ludwig (1976). Interactive effects of predation pressure and insecticide (temefos) toxicity on populations of the marsh fiddler crab *Uca pugnax*. *Mar. Biol.* **35**: 119–26.

Ward, E. E. (1966). Uptake of plutonium by the lobster *Homarus vulgaris*. *Nature, Lond.* **209**: 625–6.

Ward, J. V. (1973). Molybdenum concentrations in tissues of rainbow trout (*Salmo gairdneri*) and kokanee salmon (*Oncorhynchus nerka*) from waters differing widely in molybdenum content. *J. Fish. Res. Bd. Canada*, **30**: 841–2.

Warlen, S. M., D. A. Wolfe, C. W. Lewis and D. R. Colby (1977). Accumulation and retention of dietary C^{14}-DDT by Atlantic menhaden. *Trans. Amer. Fish. Soc.* **106**(1): 95–104.

Waslenchuk, D. G. and H. L. Windom (1978). Factors controlling the estuarine chemistry of arsenic. *Est. cstl. mar. Sci.* **7**: 455–64.

Watkins, J. and J. D. Yarbrough (1975). Aldrin and dieldrin uptake in insecticide-resistant and susceptible mosquitofish (*Gambusia affinis*). *Bull. Environ. Contam. Toxicol.* **14**: 731–7.

Watling, H. R. (1978). *Selected molluscs as monitors of metal pollution in coastal marine environments*. PhD thesis, University of Cape Town, South Africa.

Watling, H. R. and R. J. Watling (1976a). Trace metals in oysters from the Knysna Estuary. *Mar. Pollut. Bull.* **7**(3): 45–8.

Watling, H. R. and R. J. Watling (1976b). Trace metals in *Choromytilus meridionalis*. *Mar. Pollut. Bull.* **7**(5): 91–4.

Webb, D. A. (1939). Observations on the blood of certain ascidians, with special reference to the biology of vanadium. *J. exp. Biol.* **16**: 499–523.

Webb, D. A. (1956). The blood of tunicates and the biochemistry of vanadium. *Publicazzioni della Stazione zoologica di Napoli.* **28**: 273–88.

Weis, J. S. (1976). Effects of mercury, cadmium, and lead salts on regeneration and ecdysis in the fiddler crab, *Uca pugilator*. *Fishery Bull.*, *U.S.* **74**(2): 464–7.

Weis, J. S. (1978). Interactions of methylmercury, cadmium, and salinity on regeneration in the fiddler crabs *Uca pugilator*, *U. pugnax* and *U. minax*. *Mar. Biol.* **49**: 119–24.

Weis, J. S. and L. H. Mantel (1976). DDT as an accelerator of limb regeneration and molting in fiddler crabs. *Est. cstl. mar. Sci.* **4**: 461–6.

Weis, J. S. and P. Weis (1975). Retardation of fin regeneration in *Fundulus* by several insecticides. *Trans. Amer. Fish. Soc.* **104**: 135–7.

Weis, P. and J. S. Weis (1974a). DDT causes changes in activity and schooling behaviour in goldfish. *Environ. Res.* **7**: 68–74.

Weis, P. and J. S. Weis (1974b). Schooling behaviour of *Menidia menidia* in the presence of the insecticide sevin (carbaryl). *Mar. Biol.* **28**: 261–3.

Weis, P. and J. S. Weis (1978). Methylmercury inhibition of fin regeneration in fishes and its interaction with salinity and cadmium. *Est. cstl. mar. Sci.* **6**: 327–34.

Weiss, C. M. (1965). Use of fish to detect organic insecticides in water. *J. Wat. Pollut. Control Fed.* **37**: 647–58.

Werner, B. (1939). Uber die Entwicklung und Artuntersscheidung von Muschellarven des Norseeplanktons, unter Gesonderer Beruchsichtigung der Scholenentwicklung. *Zoologische Jahrbücher (Anatomie).* **66**: 237–70.

Westermark, T. (1965). Kvicksilver hos vattenlevande organismer. *Kvicksilverfrågan i Sverige*, Royal Swedish Ministry of Agriculture, pp. 25–42.

Westernhagen, H. Von and V. Dethlefsen (1975). Combined effects of cadmium and salinity on development and survival of flounder eggs. *J. mar. biol. Ass. U.K.* **55**: 945–57.

Westernhagen, H. Von, H. Rosenthal and K. R. Sperling (1974). Combined effects of cadmium and salinity on development and survival of herring eggs. *Helg. wiss. Meeres.* **26**: 416–33.

Whedon, W. F. (1936). Spawning habits of the mussel *Mytilus californianus* with notes on the possible relation to mussel poison. *Univ. Calif. Publ. Zool.* **41**: 35–44.

Wheeler, W. B. (1970). Experimental absorption of dieldrin by *Chlorella*. *J. agric. Fd Chem.* **18**: 416–19.

White, K. M. (1937). *Mytilus*. Liverpool Marine Biology Committee Memoirs, No. 31. University of Liverpool Press, Liverpool. 177 pp.

Whittemore (1973). Personal communication to E. D. Goldberg, cited by Goldberg (1975a). All data used in present work derived from latter authority.

Whyte, J. N. C. and R. J. Englar (1974). *Elemental composition of the marine alga* Nereocystis luetkeana *over the growing season*. Fish Mar. Service, Environ. Canada, Technical Report No. 509. 29 pp.

Wiener, J. G. and J. P. Giesy (1978). Concentrations of Cd, Cu, Mn, Pb, and Zn in fishes in a highly organic softwater pond. *J. Fish. Res. Bd. Canada.* **36**: 270–9.

Wiese, C. S. and D. A. Griffin (1978). The solubility of Aroclor 1254 in seawater. *Bull. Environ. Contam. Toxicol.* **19**: 403–11.

Wilbur, K. M. and G. Owen (1964). Growth. In: *Physiology of Mollusca*, Vol. 1 (K. M. Wilbur and C. M. Yonge (eds)), pp. 211–42. Academic Press, New York.

Wildish, D. J. and V. Zitko (1971). Uptake of polychlorinated biphenyls from sea water by *Gammarus oceanicus*. *Mar. Biol.* **9**: 213–18.

Wilkins, N. P. (1967). Starvation of the herring, *Clupea harengus* L.: Survival and some gross biochemical changes. *Comp. Biochem. Physiol.* **23**: 503–18.

Williams, R. and A. V. Holden (1973). Organochlorine residues from plankton. *Mar. Pollut. Bull.* **4**(7): 109–11.

Williams, P. M. and H. V. Weiss (1973). Mercury in the marine environment: Concentration in sea water and in a pelagic food chain. *J. Fish. Res. Bd. Canada.* **30**: 293–5.

Williamson, H. C. (1907). *The spawning, growth and movement of the mussel* (Mytilus edulis), *horse mussel* (Modiolus modiolus) *and the spoutfish* (Solen siliqua). Scientific Investigations, Fishery Board, Scotland. 25th Annual Report, 221–55.

Wilson, J. (1886). *On the development of the common mussel* (Mytilus edulis). Scientific Investigations, Fishery Board, Scotland. 5th Annual Report, 247–56.

Wilson, B. R. and E. P. Hodgkin (1967). A comparative account of the reproductive cycles of five species of marine mussels (Bivalvia; Mytilidae) in the vicinity of Freemantle, W. Australia. *Aust. J. mar. Freshwat. Res.* **18**: 175–203.

Wilson, J. H. and R. Seed (1975). Reproduction in *Mytilus edulis* L. (Mollusca; Bivalvia) in Carlingford Lough, Northern Ireland. *Irish Fish. Invest., Dublin, Ser. B, Marine.*

Windom, H. L. and R. G. Smith (1972). Distribution of iron, magnesium, copper, zinc, and silver in oysters along the Georgia coast. *J. Fish. Res. Bd. Canada.* **29**: 450–2.

Windom, H., R. Stickney, R. Smith, D. White and F. Taylor (1973). Arsenic, cadmium, copper, mercury and zinc in some species of North Atlantic fishes. *J. Fish. Res. Bd. Canada.* **30**: 275–9.

Wisely, B. (1964). Aspects of reproduction, settling and growth in the mussel *Mytilus edulis planulatus*. *J. Malacol. Soc. Aust.* **8**: 25–30.

Wolfe, D. A. (1970a). Levels of stable Zn and ^{65}Zn in *Crassostrea virginica* from North Carolina. *J. Fish. Res. Bd. Canada.* **27**: 47–57.

Wolfe, D. A. (1970b). Zinc enzymes in *Crassostrea virginica. J. Fish. Res. Bd. Canada.* **27**: 59–69.

Wolfe, D. A. and C. B. Coburn (1970). Influence of salinity and temperature on the accumulation of cesium-137 by an estuarine clam under laboratory conditions. *Hlth. Phys.* **18**: 499–505.

Wong, P. T. S., Y. K. Chau and P. L. Luxon (1975). Methylation of lead in the environment. *Nature, Lond.* **253**: 263–4.

Wong, P. T. S., Y. K. Chau and P. L. Luxon (1978). Toxicity of a mixture of metals on freshwater algae. *J. Fish. Res. Bd. Canada.* **35**: 479–81.

Wood, J. M. (1974). Biological cycles for toxic elements in the environment. *Science.* **183**: 1049–52.

Woodwell, G. M., C. F. Wurster and P. A. Isaacson (1967). DDT residues in an east coast estuary: A case of biological concentration of a persistent insecticide. *Science.* **156**: 821–4.

Woodwell, G. M., P. P. Craig and H. A. Johnson (1971). DDT in the biosphere: Where does it go? *Science.* **174**: 1101–7.

Wrench, J. J. (1978). Biochemical correlates of dissolved mercury uptake by the oyster *Ostrea edulis. Mar. Biol.* **47**: 79–86.

Wrench, J., S. W. Fowler and M. Y. Ünlü (1979). Arsenic metabolism in a marine food chain. *Mar. Pollut. Bull.* **10**(1): 18–20.

Wright, D. A. (1976). Heavy metals in animals from the North East coast. *Mar. Pollut. Bull.* **7**(2): 36–8.

Wright, D. A. (1977a). The effect of salinity on cadmium uptake by the tissues of the shore crab *Carcinus maenas. J. exp. Biol.* **67**: 137–46.

Wright, D. A. (1977b). The uptake of cadmium into the haemolymph of the shore crab *Carcinus maenas*: The relationship with copper and other divalent ions. *J. exp. Biol.* **67**: 147–61.

Wright, D. A. (1977c). The effect of calcium on cadmium uptake by the shore crab *Carcinus maenas. J. exp. Biol.* **67**: 163–73.

Wright, D. A. and C. C. Brewer (1979). Cadmium turnover in the shore crab *Carcinus maenas. Mar. Biol.* **50**: 151–6.

Wright, F. (1917). Mussel beds, their reproduction and maintenance. *Ann. Appl. Biol.* **4**: 123–5.

Wurster, C. F. (1968). DDT reduces photosynthesis by marine phytoplankton. *Science.* **159**: 1474–5.

Yoshida, T., F. Takashima and T. Watanabe (1973). Distribution of (C^{14}) PCBs in carp. *Ambio.* **2**: 111–13.

Young, D. R. and T. R. Folsom (1967). Loss of Zn^{65} from the California sea-mussel *Mytilus californianus. Biol. Bull. mar. biol. Lab. Woods Hole.* **133**: 438–47.

Young, D. R. and T.-K. Jan (1976). *Metals in scallops.* Southern California Coastal Water Research Project, Annual Report, 1976. pp. 117–21.

Young, D. R. and T.-K. Jan (1977). Fire fallout of metals off California. *Mar. Pollut. Bull.* **8**(5): 109–12.

Young, D. R., T. C. Heesen and D. J. McDermott (1976). An offshore biomonitoring system for chlorinated hydrocarbons. *Mar. Pollut. Bull.* **7**(8): 156–9.

Young, D. R., D. McDermott-Ehrlich and T. C. Heesen (1977). Sediments as sources of DDT and PCB. *Mar. Pollut. Bull.* **8**(11): 254–7.

Young, M. L. (1975). The transfer of Zn^{65} and Fe^{59} along a *Fucus serratus* (L.) → *Littorina obtusata* (L.) food chain. *J. mar. biol. Ass. U.K.* **55**: 583–610.

Young, R. T. (1942). Spawning season of the Californian mussel *Mytilus californianus. Ecology.* **23**: 490–2.

Young, R. T. (1946). Spawning and setting season of the mussel *Mytilus californianus. Ecology.* **27**: 354–63.

Youngs, W. D., W. H. Gutenmann and D. J. Lisk (1972). Residues of DDT in lake trout as a function of age. *Environ. Sci. Technol.* **6**: 451–2.

Zinck, M. E. and R. F. Addison (1975). The effect of temperature on the rate of conversion of p,p'-DDT to p,p'-DDE in brook trout (*Salvelinus fontinalis*). *Can. J. Biochem.* **53**: 636–9.

Zingmark, R. G. and T. G. Miller (1975). The effects of mercury on photosynthesis and growth of estuarine and oceanic phytoplankton. In: *Physiological ecology of estuarine organisms* (F. J. Vernberg (ed.)), University of South Carolina Press, Columbia, S.C., pp. 45–57.

Zitko, V. (1971). Polychlorinated biphenyls and organochlorine pesticides in some freshwater and marine fishes. *Bull. Environ. Contam. Toxicol.* **6**: 464–70.

Zitko, V., P. M. K. Choi, D. J. Wildish, L. F. Monaghan and N. A. Lister (1974). Distribution of PCB and p,p'-DDE residues in Atlantic herring (*Clupea harengus harengus*) and yellow perch (*Perca flavescens*) in eastern Canada— 1972. *Pestic. Monit. J.* **8**(2): 105–9.

Zuckerkandl, E. (1960). Hémocyanine et cuivre chez un crustacé décapode, dans leurs rapports avec le cycle d'intermue. *Annls. Inst. Océanogr. Monaco.* **38**: 1–122.

Author Index

Roman type denotes references to authors within the text; italic type denotes references to authors within tables; and an asterisk denotes references to authors within figure captions.

Species Index

Roman type denotes references to species within the text; italic type denotes references to species within tables; and an asterisk denotes references to species within figure captions.

467

Subject Index

Roman type denotes references to topics within the text; italic type denotes references to topics within tables; and an asterisk denotes references to topics within figure captions.